IN ARDUIS FIDELIS

Her Majesty Queen Elizabeth the Queen Mother, our Colonel-in-Chief

IN ARDUIS FIDELIS

by

Dr John S.G. Blair

CENTENARY HISTORY OF THE
ROYAL ARMY MEDICAL CORPS

iynx publishing

Second Edition published by iynx publishing 2001

First published by
Scottish Academic Press Ltd.
56 Hanover Street, Edinburgh EH2 2DX

ISBN 0–9540583–2–1

British Library Cataloguing in Publication Data

A catalogue record for this book is available from
the British Library

Typeset by Trinity Typesetting
Printed in Great Britain by Antony Rowe Ltd, Eastbourne

Dedication

This history is dedicated to Her Majesty Queen Elizabeth the Queen Mother, with her gracious permission. This wonderful lady was our incomparable Colonel-in-Chief for fifty years.

Three subsidiary dedications are made, with our Colonel-in-Chief's agreement:

Lieutenant Arthur Martin-Leake,
in the urgency of battles awarded the first double Victoria Cross;

Private Clarence Whittaker,
who carried a stretcher at Gallipoli and in France;

Captain George Blair,
doctor in a Japanese prison camp.

Contents

Introduction

This book tells the story of the Royal Army Medical Corps throughout its first century as a Corps of the British Army.

It was not written as a complete and detailed history; the Official Histories already serve this purpose, and can be consulted if a reader wishes to know what happened when and where. It was written to coincide with the centenary celebrations of 1998, and according to the remit given me in 1991 by the Director General who asked me to undertake the work, Major General A.J. Shaw. The other senior officer who knew me well as a National Service Regular and later Territorial officer, and who gave my name to General Shaw, was Lieutenant General Sir James Baird. I am grateful to them for the trust they had, and I hope very sincerely that this centenary history fulfills their aims.

The remit was to write a work suitable for academic reference which was to include the history of professional achievement — the ethos and development of military medicine as a speciality; the history of military achievement; and the socio-political progress during the century — the place of the Corps within the Army.

The account has had to be representative of the many units and individuals who served in the Corps over the century. The amount of information was vast; in the 1914–18 War the war diaries of the field units alone fill box upon box in the Imperial War and other museums. So there had to be selection, and I have tried to select units and individuals from all parts of the United Kingdom of Great Britain and Northern Ireland. I realise that many others gave as great a service and contribution, but the final choice in this account has been mine.

Since this was an objective work for academic reference, as indeed laid down by Generals Baird and Shaw, it has had to contain fact and not be a "club history", without mention of flaw or failure or discord.

To complement this written history of the century is a separate picture-book, "The Royal Army Medical Corps, Reflections on 100 years of Service." General A. C. Ticehurst and I worked together to produce this book. It was a pleasure to have him as a colleague, and since he has not been publicly thanked otherwise, I do so now.

Our Corps has had its achievements but, like all human institutions, has had its shortcomings. There is no human institution which does not have its failures as well as its successes. But the failures of our Corps were remarkably few and when they occurred, they were not infrequently the result of external failings over which we had no control. We are immensely proud of our Corps, those of us who have served in it — life career as Regular or Territorial, and war engagement colleagues. As the Director General of the Second War, Sir Alexander Hood, wrote in setting up the War Memorial Appeal in 1947: "Who was it, then, who made up this team? We had, of course, the incalculable help of some of the finest intellects in our profession, but most of our officers came to us from their practices or fresh from junior hospital appointments."

"Among our men we profited enormously from the large number of technicians; pharmacists, physiotherapists, laboratory workers, male nurses and many others who came into our ranks, but the vast majority were drawn, quite untrained, from bench or counter, workshop or lathe, from the study or the farm. They came up with no grandiose ideas of heroism or glory; all became inspired with our traditions of service, and over 2,000 of them paid the supreme sacrifice."

"These were the men who waded ashore with our commandos and assault troops, carrying their equipment over their heads in watertight containers, the teams who did incredible feats of surgery in Japanese prison camps with carpenters' saws, old bits of thread, old safety razor blades and bent up table spoons, and who nursed their comrades through dysentery, malaria, and beri-beri with the skill and tenderness of a trained nurse."

No Regiment of Armoured Corps, Household Brigade, Regiment of the Line, Artillery, or the Corps large and smaller, can be prouder than we. For we are the preservers of life, of foe as well as friend, and in a longer war, the conservers of manpower for a tiny country whose manpower over many centuries has been a critical commodity.

Our men and our officers have as their motto "In Arduis Fidelis." Perhaps the best and shortest expression of the ethos of the Royal Army Medical Corps, which is the true hero of this history, is in two verses of A Hymn for the Fallen of the Army Medical Corps:

> They faced the worst that cruel war meant,
> Brought mercy to the ruthless strife,
> Relieved the wounds, assuaged the torment,
> And dying, gave their comrades life.
>
> Unarmed they bore an equal burden,
> Shared each adventure undismayed;
> Not less they earned the Victor's guerdon,
> Not least were these in the crusade.

Dr John S.G. Blair

Acknowledgements

I wish to thank a number of friends who gave their time and interest in reading special parts of the account and advising on content and clinical and scientific detail: my life-long friend Alastair Simmons, who did his service in Kaduna, and has advised on especially bacteriology and basic science; Major General John Matheson, who after a distinguished Service career went on to become Post-Graduate Dean in Edinburgh University — who provided so much background general and detailed information; Professor Kenneth Lowe and Professor Ronald Girdwood, for clinical advice and confirmation of my conclusions out of their huge ability and war-time experience; Colonel Geoffrey Banks, Regimental Secretary of the Corps, who so gladly and promptly sent me so much information not obtainable elsewhere, and who was my great and continuing support over the six years of researching and writing; Dr Nicholas Burgess, for his knowledge about the College in Millbank and for making it easy for me to gain access to material in the Imperial War Museum.

I had to go through so much primary material in the Poynter room in the Wellcome Institute that the staff must have often tired of seemingly endless requests; they for the most part were extremely patient and helpful. I wish to thank Lieutenant Colonel Roy Eyions and Captain Peter Starling for their help in obtaining material from the Corps Museum.

I have to thank the Carnegie and Wellcome trusts, and the Guthrie trust, for granting me research grants towards carrying out the work. I am indebted to them all.

A large number of medical officers and soldiers gave their recollections willingly; they are referred to in the text unless they did not wish their names given — these are referred to in general terms only. To them I give my thanks and that of our Corps.

One person I would like particularly to thank is WOI K. Sumner, the last clerk serving in the RAMC following the formation of the Adjutant General's Corps, the Administrative Warrant Officer at the Royal Army Medical College. As the book neared completion he did a great deal of work in processing and correcting text, and became a colleague I was happy to work with. Mrs J. Martin proof-read the entire work and her contribution was invaluable.

The committees which oversaw the work at its outset and until 1996 were most helpful. By agreeing the principles on which the history was to be developed, and by advising upon the factual content as it was written, they helped enormously.

It was a pleasure to work regularly with such friendly and courteous people, who were always happy to communicate with me directly.

I wish to thank the British Medical Association and the large number of leading medical historians who supported me in getting the first edition published. It would have been tragic if the former Corps members who wrote and spoke to me – including General Mayes and all the earlier Directors General before him, giving their verbal personal history and comments – had had their contributions lost to posterity.

Air Marshal Sir John Baird has my special thanks for reading and confirming new material in the last chapter of this second edition.

I would like to thank the remarkably large number who have written, e-mailed, and spoken to me, from all over the world, with kind comment on the first edition. I am grateful too for those who have corrected errors in the text.

Members of both Houses of Parliament have expressed their thanks for the recent detailed historical account, for the usefulness of its criticism, and for the necessity for it to be recorded in the manner it was.

Thanks are due to the Scottish Society of the History of Medicine and to St Andrews University, for most recent financial support.

Because the first edition sold so well, it has engendered a second edition. General Sir James Baird has agreed I may quote his thanks, which I received on 9th January 1999.

"I have just finished reading it carefully and in great detail and have found it fascinating. But then I have been closely concerned in and with the RAMC for 60 years of its 100 years. You have undertaken what is virtually an impossible task and have done a marvellously good job at it. It is so readable and brings alive people and events and yet it has obviously been carefully researched, requiring so much detailed work, with historical accuracy.

I must congratulate you upon it and thank you on behalf of the Corps. I was glad to see the good reviews especially that of John (Lord) Walton, another, like yourself a life long staunch Corps supporter."

John S.G. Blair.

Prologue

The nineteenth century had been the century of the British. Britain had begun to be a significant power over the second half of the eighteenth century, since her world-wide victories over the French. But it was following the victories over post-revolutionary France and her mighty Emperor that Great Britain became a super-power indeed, unrivalled in naval technology and with an industrial base which seemed stronger as the century progressed. By 1860, Great Britain with 2 per cent of the world's population, alone was responsible for 20 per cent of world commerce, 40 per cent of the world's trade in manufactured goods, and one-third of the world's commercial shipping. As well as administering more and more of the world's surface, Britain produced sensible and forward-looking legislation for New Zealand Canada and Australia to lay the earliest foundation of the idea of the Commonwealth, a unique grouping which encompasses a truly world-wide spread of differing peoples.

The Empire extended over the Far East and over more and more of Africa — not by conquest primarily, but by the continuing expansion of trade. India remained the most important area strategically; as long as India and the British garrison there was secure, the world-wide power of Great Britain would surely remain. European rivals, notably Germany, united late into a large land power, were ready to contest Britain's position. And yet farther behind, the United States of America was a whole new continent with huge untapped resources and an apparently endless capacity to satisfy its immigrants, steadily becoming an industrial power. But over this nineteenth century it had been Great Britain who had interests everywhere, intervening to try to maintain stability if she thought there was a need or if she saw her trade threatened. And because of her power and wealth, Great

Britain was as unpopular at the beginning of the twentieth century as the United States would be at the end, and for the same reasons.

This was the British world scene. Within it, among a multitude of others, were the local changes in the status and organisation of the Medical Services to the British Army which resulted in the formation of the Royal Army Medical Corps in 1898. This history will tell of its achievements, its disappointments and its difficulties over the 20th century to its centenary year in 1998.

It was not the army medical officers who won the changes. It was the British Medical Association (BMA) which, as ill reports continued to come back to Britain from the parts of the Empire where local wars were taking place, or garrisons suffering disease, increased the pressure on the military hierarchy in the last decade of the 19th century.

On 17th December, 1897, the BMA sent a memorandum to Lord Lansdowne, then Secretary of State for War, pressing for reforms. On January 20th, 1898, the BMA brought together a deputation of prominent medical men to meet him. The letter they took with them stated plainly: "the only effective remedy for the present low status of the Army Medical Staff ... should be a Medical Corps in which the officers should have substantive army rank...."[1]

Negotiations went on over the spring; the "Big Army", as the Medicals always called the fighting troops and their General Staff, refused to allow any rank above that of Colonel in such a new Corps, declaring that medical officers could not be allowed to hold rank which they might use to order the conduct of the battle. They also said they would abolish the rank of Major General for medical officers. Letters passed to the Secretary of State from the BMA hierarchy and from the Senatus Academicus of Edinburgh University, then still the pre-eminent British Medical School.

On May 4th the City of London extended its hospitality for the first time to the medical profession at the Lord Mayor's banquet. On May 7th, the British Medical Journal reported Lord Lansdowne's speech: "Lord Lansdowne gave a frank and friendly speech which will mark the end of the controversy into which the profession was forced on behalf of its members who entered the military services of the State." The Queen had agreed to the new Corps being called "Royal Army Medical Corps" — the difficulty with officers holding General rank "requiring to be fit to command in the field" had been overcome — the BMA had negotiated the rank of "Surgeon General" (S.G.) which had been accepted by the War office.

Sir William MacCormac spoke for the BMA. Lord Lister said Lord Lansdowne's statement "had removed a terrible cloud from the medical profession and a terrible evil from the nation".[2]

The popular press claimed: "The War Office has given way."

The Royal Warrant Army Order 93 of 1898 confirmed the formation of the Royal Army Medical Corps:

"Whereas We have deemed it expedient to alter in certain respects...it is Our Further Will and Pleasure that the designation "Medical Staff Corps " shall be abolished, and that the corps formed as above mentioned shall be styled "The Royal Army Medical Corps."...

The twentieth century began, as it would end, with Britain's involvement in war. Wars were nothing new for the British, who had fought a succession of wars in parts of the world where tropical diseases were a hazard greater than the weapons of the enemy. The medical services had considerable experience of the infections of war, but since the Crimea, they had had no direct experience of European small arms whose effectiveness was now increasing with accelerating speed. There had been the war surgery experience of the American Civil War, and later of other smaller wars in Central America, which the British Army Medical Services could read about and study. But there had been no direct experience. So the main unknown for those Medical Services at the start of the Boer War was the effect and the tactical use of the weapons the enemy would use, the first enemy for many years who had worn shoes.[3]

The Boer War was to be the first test of the newest Corps of the British Army, the Royal Army Medical Corps. The conflict it was to engage in seemed at first to be a limited one, another small colonial action happening in Southern Africa. But it turned out to be a war of the greatest importance, not just for this Corps formed only a year before its outbreak, but for the whole army and for the whole nation. Before its end Britain would have placed nearly half a million men in the field, the biggest force she had hitherto sent overseas in her history.[4]

There were five main factors which determined the effectiveness of the RAMC as a professional body, set to deliver medical and health care to the army it was to serve in Southern Africa in 1899. These factors came and went in varying degrees throughout the remainder of the twentieth century.

The first was the uncertainty amongst members of the very new Corps about the amount of support it could expect from its masters in the War Office. A near half-century of resentment had built up following the cynical whittling down of the promised reforms of the Pay Warrant of 1858 by both officers of the General Staff and politicians. The obstinate refusal of the Horse Guards to grant a military rank structure for medical officers, to encourage them to serve in adequate numbers for a full career, had been opposed by no less a person than Miss Florence Nightingale herself in the 1860's, and to no avail. The continuing disappointment about rank led to an immediate drop in the total numbers volunteering to serve in the Army Medical Services, and also dissuaded the more able, who inevitably left to seek careers in civil life.

With this uncertainty about their status — for medical officers then as now realised in their first few weeks of service that from the point of view of the Regular Army mind, rank meant all — went an uncertainty about how well any professional medical advice they offered might be accepted. The opposition of senior military officers to the termination of the Regimental system and its replacement by one Department of medical officers, having their own professional training in medicine, surgery, and especially in army health, and even being allowed to have their own uniforms, was still so recent as to be angrily remembered.

The second factor was the nature of the terrain and the nature of the enemy. The British Army had unique experience of fighting in bad stations in the tropics, where the local infectious diseases were the main destroyers of armies. In this war they knew the prevalent diseases in Southern Africa, and had some knowledge, from earlier encounters, of the nature of the enemy.

The third factor was the ability of their own generals, their own non-medical commanders. In all their history, the Royal Army Medical Corps doctors were called upon to serve as members of a learned profession assisting fighting troops. But no

matter how skilled their professional status, how experienced
their physicians and surgeons, how diligent their hygiene
standards, how brave and physically durable their bearer company
soldiers, they were all still totally dependent upon the professional
skill as soldiers of their generals who commanded generally.

The fourth was the presence of a volunteer reserve of medical
officers as an organised back-up to the permanent cadre of
officers and men. The Volunteer Medical Staff Corps was at this
time another recently formed element, whose formation in the
1880's by the entrepreneurial efforts of Mr James Cantlie
deserves re-reading.[5] In due course it would become part of the
Territorial Force, but the Boer War was its first effective
contribution.

And the fifth was the presence of the news media. News
reports had made a real contribution to public awareness in the
Crimean War of the deficiencies in medical services. From this
new war onwards they would play an increasing part in the
history of all subsequent campaigns.

Notes and references

PROLOGUE

[1]*BMJ* 1898; **1** :39. "The only effective remedy for the present low esteem among young medical men would be the consolidation of the Army Medical Staff and the Medical Staff Corps into an army medical corps in which the officers should have substantive rank with limited command, and with that rank the military titles which alone are appreciated in the army. The report refrains from asking that the proposed corps should receive the title of the Royal Army Medical Corps, since this is a privilege that can only be accorded by the Crown; but it will be known to the Queen and to her advisers that such a mark of Her Majesty's favour would be most highly appreciated both by the medical officers of her army and by the profession of which they form a part."

[2]*BMJ* 1898; **1** : 329–332.

BMA Parliamentary Bill Committee. STRICTLY PRIVATE AND CONFIDENTIAL.

Report of Sub-Committee to consider the question of Advancing Army Medical Reform. May 11th, 1897.

The report was 9 pages long. It had 4 sources of information, from it quoted freely:

"What has perhaps struck us most forcibly in reviewing the above evidence has been the apparent indifference manifested through a long series of years by the War office, not merely to claims of admitted justice, but even to the serious necessities of the Medical Service." (Lord Herbert's Commission of 1858 p ixv (sic)).

"It is not, however, by money alone that the ablest and most accomplished medical men will be attracted to the Army Medical Service; the rank, the position, and the honours which can be obtained constitute perhaps the strongest inducements to the highest class of minds." (Sir Ralph Thompson's Committee, 1878 p 35).

The B.M.A. thesis went on: "It can scarcely be hoped that the pecuniary attractions of the public service will rival, except perhaps quite at the commencement of the career, those of civil life. Honours and distinctions must strike the balance." It is interesting what stress the BMA laid upon rank. Many of their points were still being argued over by their successors in the BMA Armed Forces Committee a hundred years later.

At this time, before the army doctors were granted proper military rank, they were called "surgeons", with the relative rank of captain. They wore two stars. After 12 years of service, they became majors, wearing a crown. After 20, a star was added — equivalent to the present Lieutnant Colonel, but they were still called "surgeon-major." There were many compound titles, such as brigade-surgeon-Lieutenant Colonel. Medical officers were called "sergeant-major" or "sergeant-captain" by some.

[3]W.S. Churchill, A History of The English-speaking Peoples, *IV*, Chapter *VII*. Cassell, 1958.

[4]Lieutenant General Sir Neil Cantlie, A History of the Army Medical Department, 2, 360–364. Churchill Livingstone, 1974.

[5]For a useful short assessment of weaponry and the technical background to European war at the end of the 19th. Century, see Michael Howard, The Franco-Prussian War, *1*, 1. Granada, 1979.

Foreword by
Sir A. W. Macara,
Chairman of Council, British Medical Association

The British Medical Association was delighted to take the opportunity to support the publication of John Blair's masterly history of the Royal Army Medical Corps, in whose establishment over a century ago it was largely instrumental. To quote from the British Medical Journal of 7th May 1898: "We congratulate the nation as well as the Army Medical Department and the profession on this happy termination of a victory which ought not to have arisen." This somewhat ambiguous encomium continued: "We think also that the British Medical Association has reason to be proud of a victory in which it may justly claim for itself a considerable share."

The nation has good reason to be proud of the service rendered by the RAMC throughout a turbulent century in which not all the battles which have been fought and won have been waged against the enemy without. Successive governments and their servants today have proved no more responsible in their provision of care for those who are prepared to sacrifice their lives for the nation than in the past. The reward for valiant and sacrificial achievement on the battlefield has sadly been one of "downsizing" — in the deplorable contemporary jargon. In the best tradition of the Defence Medical Services, John Blair persisted – against apathy at best and hostility at worst – to bring his perspective and revealing chronicle into the public domain. He, and those whose contributions to the nation's integrity he has so faithfully recorded, have been rewarded by a warm response to the 1st Edition, which Colonel Blair has brought up-to-date.

July 2001

Foreword by
Professor Struther Arnott, Principal,
St Andrews University

John Blair is an alumnus of St Andrews, Scotland's first university founded 1410–1413 with the motto 'Always Strive To Be The Best'. The apparent imprecision of the founding date takes account of the curious historical fact that Scotland's new years began not on January 1st but on March 1st until the 17th century and many important St Andrews' anniversaries are in February. There is the question of whether to credit the founding date to Bishop Wardlaw's teaching licence, or to King James' charter or to the papal bull of Pedro di Luna, Pope Benedict XIII. John Blair is the man who could explain all this more deftly and interestingly from the perspective of one who has been a devoted historian from his schooldays at William Wallace's ancient alma mater, Dundee High School.

This devotion to History has never had the character of a passive bystander but has been pursued with the same productiveness and professionalism that John Blair has brought to his medical and military careers. His top first in the 1955 London Bachelor of Arts examinations, taken after he had graduated MB, ChB at St Andrews, formally announced that he was not only willing but prepared to continue with a serious commitment to history no matter what other career paths he would follow also no matter what conflict might arose.

In fact he has resolved any potential conflict by combining his career strands. Among the products have been his *History of the St Andrews Officer Training Corps* (1982) followed by his *magnum opus* the *History of Medicine in the University of St Andrews* (1987) which traces the teaching of medicine at St Andrews from its mediaeval beginnings up to modern times with exemplary proficiency. The work prompted the award, rare to a scientist, of an honorary D.Litt. from St Andrews. His new Centenary History of the Royal Army Medical Corps is another synthesis of John Blair's diverse professional interests and will be perceived like his earlier historical works to be well-above the genre, keeping the faith with his alma mater's exhortation ever to strive to be the best.

June 1998

Foreword by
Lord Walton, Kt, TD, MA, MD,
FRCP, DCL

*Former Professor of Neurology and Dean of Medicine, University
of Newcastle upon Tyne and Warden, Green College, Oxford.
Past-President, BMA, RSM and GMC. Former Col. (late
RAMC) and OC no. 1 (N) General Hospital (TA) 1963–66,
and Hon. Col. no. 201 (N) General Hospital (TAVR) 1968–73*

I have always had a deep affection for the RAMC. I suppose that
my interest in matters military was first fired by my service in the
infantry and medical units of the war-time Senior Training Corps
when I was a medical student in Newcastle. After graduating, I
spent over two years in the RAMC, eventually becoming Major
and 2 I/C of two hospital ships, in one of which we covered the
final evacuation of Palestine in 1948. On demobilisation and on
becoming a medical registrar in Newcastle, I soon joined the TA
and my 16 years of service with the no. 1 (N) General Hospital
were in every way memorable. I have often said that if I had not
become a doctor, my second choice would have been to be a
barrister and my third to be a regular Army officer. But with
research, teaching and practice in neurology, combined with TA
service, I believe I enjoyed the best of both worlds. I have described
in detail the many pleasures (and occasional problems) which I
encountered during my RAMC service and later in the TA, in my
autobiography *The Spice of Life* (Heinemann-Royal Society of
Medicine, 1993). Not only did my military experience teach me
much about the Services and their role and organisation, but I am
sure that the administrative experience I acquired stood me in very
good stead in my subsequent career.

It has been a privilege to have been invited to contribute a foreword to this outstanding work by Colonel Blair. It describes in loving, even intimate, detail the formation and subsequent achievements (as well as a few tribulations) of the Corps, and each chapter concludes with detailed references to original sources. It is not only easy and enjoyable to read, but I believe that it is a considerable work of scholarship. Past, present and future members of the Army Medical Services will undoubtedly enjoy it and profit from reading it, but in addition it will surely prove to be an invaluable reference source for future medical and military historians. Well done, Colonel Blair!

June 1998

Foreword to the Second Edition by Lord Walton of Detchant, Kt, TD, MA, MD, FRCP, FMedSci

Former Professor of Neurology and Dean of Medicine, University of Newcastle upon Tyne; former Warden, Green College, Oxford. Past-President, BMA, RSM and GMC. Former Col. (late RAMC) and OC no. 1 (N) General Hospital (TA) 1963–66, and Hon. Col. no. 201 (N) General Hospital (TAVR) 1968–73

As I said in my foreword to the first edition of this excellent book, I have always had a deep affection for the RAMC and I found Colonel Blair's centenary history fascinating and compelling. It seems to me to give a faithful and detailed analysis of the role of the Royal Army Medical Corps, and indeed of the Army and other defence medical services to some extent, over the century before it was written. The triumphs, as well as some of the tribulations, of the medical services were faithfully recorded in that volume and much of the turmoil arising over reorganisation in the 1990s was, I believe, handled appropriately. It is good to know that the book was so well reviewed and was such a success that a second edition has been called for, and I have read with interest and edification the amendments and supplementary material which Colonel Blair has included in this new and revised edition. As he said in the first edition and reiterates in this one, no army of any size can take the field or undertake a peace-keeping requirement without well-trained and well-equipped medical support. The Royal Army Medical Corps, in his view, must be capable of fulfilling this role, and this is a sentiment with which I entirely concur.

As with the first edition, I am sure that past, present and future members of the Army Medical Services will enjoy this book and will profit from reading it, but in addition, I am in no doubt that it will prove to be an invaluable reference source for future medical and military historians.

John Walton
Oxford
June 2001

Chapter 1

The outbreak of the Boer War. The South African political scene. Preparation and mobilization.

"A great nation can have no such thing as a little war" (The Duke of Wellington).

When the Boer War broke out, the establishment of the RAMC, the arrangement of units, their size and function, and the number of officers and soldiers required to man them — all to enable it to carry out its war role, had been greatly reduced. The war role had been stated in the *Medical Staff Corps Manual* of 1885 and had not been changed with the transformation of the Medical Department into a Corps of the Active Army:

> "On taking the Field, the Medical Department with an army corps will include an organisation designed expressly for the purpose of speedily collecting the wounded during and after an engagement, and removing them from the battlefield to the field hospitals in the rear."[1]

The organisation designed for the purpose of carrying out this role had been created following the report in 1876 of a special committee chaired by the then Director General, Sir William Muir. For an army corps of 36,805 all ranks, there were to be 6 types of field medical units — first a bearer company , which was the short title of a stretcher bearer unit, to carry wounded from the regimental aid post (RAP) to the second-line unit, called a "movable field hospital." From there the wounded would be carried by waggons to the smaller "stationary" and larger "general" hospitals. As well as these treatment elements, there was to be a depot of medical stores, a hospital ship or ships, and a sanitary

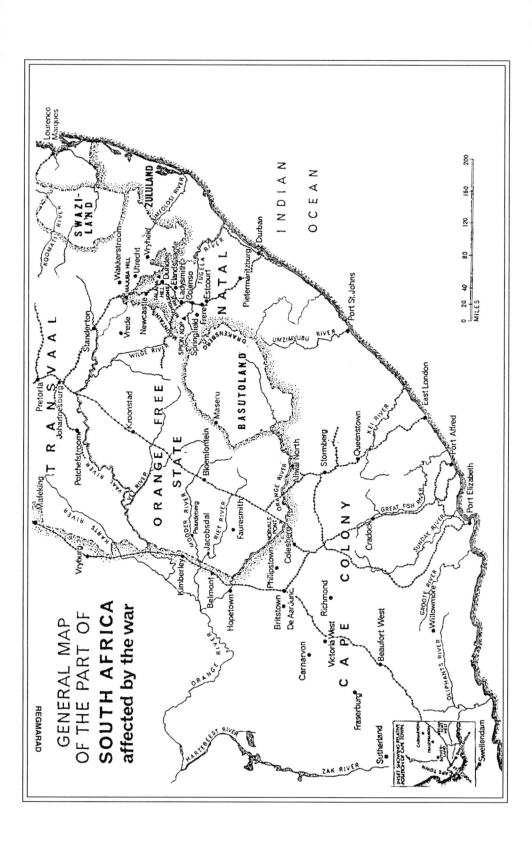

GENERAL MAP
OF THE PART OF
SOUTH AFRICA
affected by the war

REGMARAD

INDIAN OCEAN

TRANSVAAL

ORANGE FREE STATE

NATAL

ZULULAND

SWAZI-LAND

BASUTOLAND

CAPE COLONY

Lourenço Marques
Koomati River
Wakkerstroom
Utrecht
Vryheid
Umfolosi River
Majuba Hill
Newcastle
Standerton
Vrede
Wilge River
Dundee
Glencoe
Elandslaagte
Talana Hill
Biggarsberg
Ladysmith
Colenso
Tugela River
Estcourt
Frere
Spion Kop
Springfield
Drakensberg
Durban
Pietermaritzburg
Pretoria
Johannesburg
Potchefstroom
Kroonstad
Maseru
Umzimvubu River
Port St.Johns
Vaal River
Harts River
Mafeking
Vryburg
Kimberley
Belmont
Bloemfontein
Modder River
Paardeberg
Jacobsdal
Riet River
Fauresmith
Orange River
Norvals Pont
Philipstown
Colesberg
Stormberg
Queenstown
Kei River
East London
Fort Alfred
Port Elizabeth
Cradock
Great Fish River
Sunday River
Grootte River
Willowmore
Oliphants River
Hopetown
Britstown
De Aar Junc
Victoria West
Richmond
Beaufort West
Carnarvon
Fraserburg
Sutherland
Orange River
Hartebeest River
Zak River
Swellendam

INSET SHOWING RELATIVE
POSITION OF CAPE TOWN
CAPE TOWN
CARNARVON
PAARL
CALVINIA
WORCESTER

MILES
0 20 40   80   120   160   200

department. The last should be noted carefully; a sanitary department was included in the medical order of battle.

The first professional the wounded or sick soldier would meet was the successor to the regimental surgeon — the regimental medical officer (RMO). He was a doctor. The change of title was significant; there was the implication that this new officer was a doctor with responsibility for health as well as for bandaging wounds. He had 16 regimental stretcher bearers to help him. He also had his own laid-down scale of doctor's professional equipment — two medical panniers, a field medical companion (a smaller container with professional necessities), a box of splints, a canteen of utensils to go along with his tent and marquee, 14 stretchers, mules, pack horse, storage cart, ambulance cart, and — again significantly because it was his responsibility — a water barrel. Last of all, he had an operating table -soon to disappear as anaesthesia was now available at hospital level for the first time and operating done there — and a medical comforts box, containing rum or spirits — long to remain. It was very different from the days of the Crimea.

After skilled first-aid at the RAP, the wounded man's journey back to definitive treatment was to the movable field hospital. The medical unit responsible for this stage of the carry, the bearer company, (BC) was a large unit of 95 stretcher bearers (SBs), increased by a further 11 reservists to act as batmen and helpers. It had a medical commanding officer — a Major RAMC, 7 other medical officers some of whom were to be surgeons, 3 quartermasters, and 36 non-commissioned officers (NCOs) and men to continue treatment initiated at the RAP. All these were RAMC personnel. The Army Transport Corps, formed in 1888, provided the drivers of the ambulance carts and supply vehicles. There were 4 equipment and 33 ambulance waggons. The Transport Corps establishment was 1 officer, 9 NCOs, and 46 drivers. It had its own tentage and medical supplies which included enough to re-supply the RMO in his RAP when his own stores ran out. The bearer company had no treatment element; its tentage was domestic and storage only.

The second-line treatment was done in the field hospitals. "Movable field" hospitals received sick and wounded brought by the bearer company, held them for a day or two if their wound or illness was slight and they could soon return to duty, or sent them farther back along the line to the "stationary" field or "general" hospitals.

The movable and stationary field hospitals had the same establishment: 200 beds divided into 4 sections, with 7 MOs, 1 quartermaster, and 37 other ranks RAMC and Transport Corps. They also had their waggons — 6 of these — with bell tents and palliasse mattresses. The general hospitals were at the rear of the line of communication (LofC), as the line from base to front was called. Marquees replaced bell tents. There were usually 500 beds in these general hospitals, plus a complement of now specialist medical staff. This was the first level at which nursing sisters were employed. Definitive surgery — surgery with the aim of cure as distinct from first aid — took place at both these hospital levels.

The post-1876 establishment of all these was generous: one bearer company was allocated to each of the three divisions of the army corps, with a fourth divided between the cavalry brigade and the assortment of important re-supply troops who worked in the background of the corps area, called the corps troops. There were 12 movable field hospitals to each corps. 13 stationary hospitals of 200 beds each were to be available, and 2 general hospitals, for the corps as a whole. The sanitary officers had their own supporting NCOs, all to be specially trained.

The reduction in establishment referred to had occurred in the 1880's following the 1882 Egyptian War where the new organisation was first tested in battle. There was criticism of the medicals in this war for various reasons, and although the Director General (D.G.) Sir Thomas Crawford had good professional answers for the criticism, it was concluded by the War Office that a much lower establishment was adequate. So by the outbreak of the South African War, the establishment of personnel in bearer companies had been reduced by 50 per cent and their number reduced by 1, the size of the movable hospitals halved to 100 beds, and their number reduced to 14 in total. The stationary field hospitals were reduced in number to 8, but still with 200 beds in each. The two hospital ships remained, each of 200 beds, plus 2 "sick transport ships." Medical store depots — forward and base — remained the same, as did the base general hospitals. Each division of troops retained its sanitary detachment. Further reductions in the number of ambulance waggons, bearer companies, and field hospitals occurred in 1888.

This list of levels of medical care, of details of organisation and numbers of medical, RAMC soldier, nursing, and transport personnel may seem tediously long, but is necessary to record as the pattern established at this time continued throughout the century and remains to the present. It will be referred to many times and the medical professional and nursing care carried out at the various steps on "the way back", as the RAMC training expression has it, is hugely informative of the development of medicine, surgery, and nursing, and mirrors the enormous scientific advances of the last hundred years.

The pattern established then recognised the need for prompt basic care in the front line by a medical establishment of a doctor — and in recent years a fully trained male nurse — plus RAMC NCOs, together with some soldiers skilled too in primary care but belonging to the regiment. The medical members wear the RAMC cap badge but they share the comradeship of the unit they are attached to. Over the years, many regiments have honoured attached personnel — padres as well as medical — by allowing them the real honour of wearing their very own headgear or other peculiar item of uniform.[2]

From this very first entry into the medical care system, a procedure of the highest importance is initiated. This is the recording of the injured or sick man's clinical state. Medical documentation, from which all subsequent assessment of the success or failure of what the medical and nursing staff are setting out to do, was from this time and still is, another of their responsibilities.

Once the sick or injured man left the RAP, with his dressings in place and his first clinical notes attached to his person, he was carried by the safe drivers of the Transport Corps — later Royal Army Service Corps, recently Royal Corps of Transport, and, in the reductions imposed by the 1990s Conservative Government, Royal Logistic Corps. His next stop was for reassessment of his clinical progress at a field unit — where as a rule only life saving procedures were carried out. He was then carried, again by "waggoners", to one or other of the locations where his definitive treatment began. Finally, he was, if his clinical condition demanded, evacuated from the war theatre to what has always been called the Home or U.K. Base. During his time at all these levels he remained in the continuing care of the men of the medical corps and the women of the nursing corps, today helped by dentists and a whole range of skilled para-medical persons, other professional helpers — padres — and members of voluntary organisations.

Our account of the Army Medical Department during the 20th century is not concerned with the politics of the various wars, nor with their military details, except insofar as these have a bearing on professional medical and nursing matters. In the Boer War the nature of the enemy involved, and the general and local political background, are very relevant to an understanding of the medical problems which these medical officers, nursing sisters, and RAMC soldiers had to face.

The Boer War has often been described as an imperialist war where the major power underestimated the strength of the enemy. It has been described as a colonial war which was "the first indication to the colonial powers of the end of their easy dominance over backward peoples."[3] But such standard descriptions often seem to miss the fact that the Boer War was not, at its date in history, a minor colonial war. In the context of the 20th century, and especially in the terms of the later part of that century, it is perhaps better described as an OUT-OF-AREA conflict. For if it is taken that the standard location for European powers to fight one another in the 19th century was in the continent of Europe, then the South African Boer War was a war between representatives of two European nations — Britain and Holland — fought in Southern Africa.

The Boer War has also been described as a transition war, between the closely arrayed colourful armies shooting with slow-firing, short range and relatively inaccurate small arms of the 19th century and the lethal conflicts of a totally new level of intensity, range, and accuracy of small arms fire, and the first automatic weapons, high explosive artillery, barbed-wire entanglements, observation balloons, and fifth column terrorist tactics of the 20th. This is certainly true. Finally it is also true that in this South African OUT-OF-AREA conflict, the Royal Army Medical Corps made its own transition from an irregularly organised, civilian-orientated service of the 19th century to the fully organised professional Corps of the Army of the 20th. So for our Corps it was an important War.

The enemy in this conflict were not primitives; they were Europeans who had become in their own eyes the First White tribe of Africa. The strong unyielding Calvinism they had brought with them from Holland in the mid-sixteenth century had remained within their closed community. They had intensified it, in the way such close brethren do. But they remained European. They retained links with other European nations, particularly Germany.

And then the British had begun to arrive and settle the southernmost part of South Africa — where the Afrikaners would insist they had found no other humans on their own first arrival. In 1814, Great Britain acquired Cape Colony from Holland for 6 million pounds. In 1834 by the Emancipation Act the Boers were forced to free their black slaves, and sought to escape from the British whom they despised. They trekked north, between the Orange River and the Vaal, and northwards again towards the Limpopo. They set up the Orange Free State and the Transvaal, and by 1852 had forced the British to concede their independence.

In these more northerly regions the Boer farmers pursued their solitary lives, their luxury-free homesteads, their mode of life which developed the need to ride, shoot, and farm for survival. The supply problem which so limited British strategy did not exist for them. They were suspicious of strangers. Their reading matter was limited to the Bible, and they held Old Testament severity in higher esteem than New Testament grace. But this nation of individuals still regarded the white man as deserving respect; for the black sons of Ham they had none. It is easier for us at the end of the 20th century to understand the Boer mentality better than Britons did at the beginning; the Afrikaner mentality which produced the apartheid system after 1948 was the same as that which wished the departure of the English 50 years earlier.

The qualities which made the Boers the finest mounted infantry in the world made them ineffectual citizens of a community. The local disagreements and hot jealousies of the Transvaal, its hopeless government, when allied to the barbarities constantly carried out on rebellious Zulus, made the British fear a major black incursion into the southern regions, and in 1877 the Transvaal was annexed. But the effort at reconciliation which followed failed. The Boers rebelled, won several minor actions, and after defeating the British at Majuba, intensified their movement to push the British out. They showed neither respect nor gratitude for Gladstone's liberal attitude. A decade later gold was discovered at Witwatersrand. Immigrants flowed in. The Calvinistic Boers believed God had by concealing the gold from the British declared that they were the chosen elect to rule all of Southern Africa. Demands for civic rights by the immigrants, the *uitlanders*, were denied by a series of impossible conditions, so that there was no possibility of the impure being able to outvote those of pure Boer stock. The foolish Jamieson raid of 1895 inevitably failed, the confidence of President Kruger rose, and he saw himself as the saviour of his race and his religion. Further, as he struck at the infidel English, he was sure that thousands of Boers living in Cape Province would rise as one man, to support his holy war.

By 1899, a petition to Queen Victoria resulted in her High Commissioner in Cape Town, Sir Frederick Milner, going to Bloemfontein in late May, to discuss the Boer demands with President Kruger. Though Milner was perhaps also not entirely averse to war, agreement was always possible, for like the succession of dictators we will see in due course over the 20th century, Kruger was always ready to talk peace on his own terms. Papers later recovered at Pretoria, after the war, showed that he was merely playing for time while he continued to buy the most modern weapons from Germany, France — and Britain — and while the hot summer unhelpful to the warfare he envisaged, passed. His advocate who ensured the talks did not succeed was J.C.Smuts.

It will be seen repeatedly over this history that British governments of different persuasions over a hundred years would go to any length never to be the aggressor, never to break off negotiations while there appeared to them, and to their press and public if to no other nation, the slightest chance of a peaceful solution. This gentlemanly policy undoubtedly allowed Great Britain to enter major wars with the government party but perhaps more importantly the opposition party of the day conscious of the rightness of its action, in agreement with voices calling for peace, and ensuring parliamentary approval, but it allowed less scrupulous enemies the time to stock their armouries from roof to floor.

In spite of the failure of the Bloemfontein Conference and the certainty of war, no reinforcements were sent to South

Africa, new signalling equipment purchase was cancelled; nothing was to be done which the prospective enemy and the outside world would see as provocation. It is not surprising that all major wars Great Britain was involved in during the 20th century opened with a series of setbacks for that country. When war did eventually come, it was only the unbelievable failure of the warlike enemy to capitalise its four to one numerical superiority in fighting men which allowed the British time to rush a force from the U.K. base and, especially important as will be seen from the medical point of view, reinforcements from the India base.

Although there was a succession of initial defeats, the war proper was over quite quickly once the earlier generals had been replaced by more competent ones and the resources of the home country mobilized. That the conflict dragged on for another full year was because of the refusal of individual Boers to accept defeat, making necessary the anti-terrorist measures some of which earned Britain a name for unnecessary cruelty in the wider world, and continuing hatred by the defeated within Southern Africa.[4,5]

At the date of declaration of war, at 5 o'clock on the afternoon of 11th October, 1899, the garrison in South Africa had been considerably strengthened by 3 cavalry and 4 infantry regiments, plus 3 batteries of field artillery, numbering in all some 5,600 officers and men. These had arrived a few days before from India. The total Force in Cape Colony was now 11,262, including 6,000 local and Rhodesian Forces, and 16,009 in Natal, including 6,000 local volunteers and 317 police.

The medical support of the Cape Colony Force was 15 medical officers RAMC and 6 medical officers from the Cape Medical Staff Corps. The other ranks totalled 99 RAMC and 140 from the Cape Corps. There were only 2 quartermasters. In the Natal Force of 16,000, there were 39 RAMC officers, 1 quartermaster and 99 RAMC other ranks. The Natal Volunteer Contingent had produced another 18 medical officers and 60 other ranks. With this Natal Force were 3 Army Nursing Sisters, who had been in Cape Colony previously, and 2 Indian Medical Service (IMS) officers. It was not a large number and well below the theoretical establishment already quoted. The number of quartermasters was particularly low.

The hospital support for the entire Field Force (permanent hospitals were in Cape Colony where Wynberg was the best equipped, and at Maritzburg and Ladysmith in Natal) came entirely from the Indian Army reinforcement. A great deal needed to be done, both in Africa and at home. With the rest of the Army, the Army Medical Services had to be mobilized.

Medical preparations in South Africa itself had been hampered by the small size of the permanent hospitals — only sufficient for the resident garrison, and with medical stores of a correspondingly small amount. Shortages were real and serious. In Cape Town apart from Wynberg there was an old hospital at Woodstock. There was some hospital accommodation in barracks at King Williamstown and Grahamstown but no separate hospital building. As well as Maritzburg in Natal there were some barrack rooms suitable for conversion but nothing else. In Ladysmith there was a hutted hospital within the army camp.

Medical planning of routes of evacuation depended on the likelihood that the main Boer attack would be in Natal. The only available ports in Cape Colony — Cape Town, Port Elizabeth and East London, and the railway lines from them to De Aar, Middleburg, and Naauwpoort, and on to Sterkstroom, Stromberg, and Burgersdorp, would be required for the landing of troops and their concentration prior to an advance to the North.

Preparations were also hampered "for reasons which need not be discussed here", as the official report *Medical Arrangements for the South African War* tactfully put it. But the local medical planners sensibly and quietly increased stocks of medical equipment, sent a medical officer to De Aar, Sterkstroom, Stromberg and other sites on the trunk railway lines to find accommodation suitable for hospital use and initiate conversions and acquisitions where necessary. They also prepared two trains for casualty evacuation, and obtained vehicles for ambulance between trains and docks by local purchase. Medical equipment of all kinds was placed in stores in De Aar, Kimberley, and Mafeking. But the essential extra equipment for Natal did not arrive from the U.K. base until November, a full month after the Indian contingent with its three-and-a-half British and one

Indian Field Hospitals had disembarked in Natal. The reinforcements from the India base were vital.

The Expeditionary Force detailed on 5th October, 1899 to proceed from Southern England to South Africa consisted of 1 cavalry division, 1 army corps, and Lines of Communication (LofC) troops. This had a strength of 39,741 for the Field Force and 12,217 for the LofC. For this strength hospital accommodation was calculated on a possible sick rate of 10 per cent of the Force, which meant, if agreed establishments were to be met, 12 Field Hospitals each of 100 beds, 4 General Hospitals each of 520 beds, 2 Stationary Hospitals each of 100 beds, 2 hospital trains and 2 hospital ships. In turn this required 278 RAMC officers (but since 24 were quartermasters only 254 were MOs) and 1890 other RAMC personnel, a total of 2168. These MOs were for the RAMC field units only; they did not include base staff or LofC staff. And at the beginning of the war, the allowed establishment of soldiers RAMC — apart from MOs — was 2106. This number was increased, after mobilization of the Regular Reserves, to 2866. Simple arithmetic made it not surprising that with the departure of the Regular RAMC to South Africa, there was nothing left to service the home base military hospitals, let alone provide medical support for a second Army Corps should this be needed. On October 7th an advertisement appeared in the quality newspapers in Britain for "a limited number of civilian medical practitioners (CMPs) for temporary service with the troops in the U.K. It was signed by the D.G., "J. Jameson."[6]

Although the large deficiency was of non-doctors, the deficiency of doctors was much more serious. Because of the disparaging refusal by the Horse Guards General Staff to give medical officers the status and conditions of service they and their Director General had begged for, both numbers and, even more important, quality of professional ability and skill, were lacking. The shortfall was made up in the only way it could be, by employment of civilian surgeons. And the salaries which had to be offered to induce men of high quality to serve were very much higher, *pro rata*, than the cost of a more equitable career structure for permanent RAMC physicians and surgeons would ever have been. By cutting costs before the war, the Treasury was forced to over-spend after it began. The role of these civilian surgeons and physicians, and their role in the professional development of the Medical Services of the nation, will be seen as the story unfolds.[7]

The Regular elements of the RAMC mobilized smoothly. The earliest major RAMC units to sail left in fact on 30th September, before the main force on 20th October. They were No 1 Stationary Hospital and No 12 Field Hospital, and they arrived in Natal on October 26th. No 1 General Hospital sailed on October 6th, arriving at Cape Town on October 27th. As with the rest of the army, the Regular units had the lowest numbers. No 1 General Hospital proceeded at once to Wynberg, which had by now been converted into a large hospital.

The rest of the medical support for the various formations followed in sequence; field units and Numbers 2,3, and 4 General Hospitals, store depots, hospital train staff and hospital ships. The field units, with two exceptions — one due to the loss of the transport ship *Ismore* — arrived with the troops of the brigades to which they belonged. This was a sensible arrangement. The medical personnel were glad of the chance to meet their comrades in the teeth arms (the expression for the active fighting soldiers, infantry, artillery, sappers, and, much later in the century, armoured corps) of the day whose medical support they were to provide, and the month-long voyages made the establishment of such good relations possible.

This happy relationship between the brigades and their medical support was upset when General Sir Redvers Buller, V.C., arrived on October 31st. He found Kimberley, Mafeking, and Ladysmith beleaguered and the Boers in possession of all Natal north of the Tugela River. They were only 120 miles (190Km) from Durban. There were fears that the Dutch in Cape Colony were only waiting for some success by their brother Boers in the north to rise in large numbers. But the three besieged towns had every expectancy of holding out, and the Orange Free State Boers were known not to be wholeheartedly for the war. Like the Transvaal Boers, they were also known to be fearful of any threat to their rear. The Regular British Army was in transit on the high seas. The plan already decided on at home in Britain was that Buller should make a powerful thrust towards the centre, using the British-held railways as his supply lines, towards Bloemfontein. "The capture of Bloemfontein must, it was felt, knock the Orange Free State out of the war as the next objective, Pretoria, must knock out the Transvaal." Such was the plan Buller was expected to execute.[8]

But General Buller, as expert military writers at the time and ever since agreed, was not an able general. Within a few days he had split his army into three unequal parts and had lost his advantage of concentrated power. Part of the Army Corps was diverted to Natal, with elements of 2 Division and 1 Division, and a reconstituted 1st Division under Lord Methuen, a remnant of the 3rd Division under General Gatacre plus a small force of cavalry under General French in Cape Colony. *The Official Medical History* of the Boer War recorded: "it will be seen that the division of so large a proportion of the Army Corps to Natal and its inevitable replacement by troops not previously brigaded and provided with medical units, introduced considerable confusion into the medical arrangements, owing to the unavoidable re-distribution of the existing field units. There was also the necessity of providing others from the resources of the country (South Africa) in addition to those sent from England, for at this time only the actual number of units allowed by scale for field army had arrived." The medical services followed their orders; in the event the Force under Lord Methuen had the medical units with it that they had already got to know.

Throughout November 1899 the medical infrastructure was systematically set *in situ*. No 1 General Hospital under Colonel A.H. Anthoniz opened on 30th October. It was reinforced by No 4 Stationary Hospital under Major R. Kirkpatrick by November 20th. A depot camp for troops disembarking was set up nearby with its small hospital and convalescent section to take care of those ill while at sea. Extra buildings already planned were quickly erected by late November, also at Wynberg Camp, for No 2 General Hospital (Colonel A.W. Duke). Further small hospitals were set up at Port Elizabeth and East London, and the hospital ship *Trojan* moored nearby. No 3 General Hospital was set up under Lieutenant Colonel O. Wood close to Cape Town at Rondenbosch in late November, but was not ready to receive patients until the New Year. It was joined by the Portland Hospital, the first of the civilian hospitals to arrive.

Hospital trains, which were to prove of such great importance in the South African campaign, were also set up. No 1 hospital train made its first trip from Ladysmith just before hostilities began. It could carry 70 casualties. No 2 hospital train, under command of Captain C.C. Fleming DSO,(Distinguished Service Order) had had its rolling stock prepared in South Africa but could not leave for the front until 22nd November, as its staff had to be sent from the U.K. base. As will be seen very soon, it arrived just in time to bring down wounded from the Battle of Belmont. No 3 train, under command of Major M.W.H. Russell, followed 3 days later, after a different sequence of events during its mobilization. Its RAMC staff came to it on transfer from No 3 Stationary Hospital. This train brought wounded from the Modder River Battle back to Cape Town.

At home, all units had been standing by in readiness to embark. The doctors hurried to buy special uniform and kit. "The army tailors must be making a fortune", Lieutenant Matthew Fell wrote to his mother. Brown boots had to be taken to blend with the colour of the khaki clothing. Each medical officer had, in order of importance, a water bottle, instrument case, revolver, ammunition pouch, haversack and lastly sword and belt. "I look like a walking pedlar", said Matthew Fell. Dress belts — in gold, with steel scabbards — were sent home with instructions for safe keeping. Lieutenant Fell also found himself being given a bunch of printed instructions and notes by his senior officer as part of his mobilization kit.

Most units had a week's notice of their embarkation date. Captain Maurice Holt was telegraphed by his Principal Medical Officer (PMO) to say he was to take command of one-half of 26 British Field Hospital on 8th September; next day he was telegraphed to say it was No 24 Field Hospital. While they were waiting, many officers bought personal supplies of fruit, vegetables, tinned meats and other items to eat on the 4 week voyage.

Captain Hugh Morton, who sailed on December 11th on the *S.S. Avondale Castle* with 10 Brigade (Bde) Bearer Company and Field Hospital — the two units travelled together — was inoculated with typhoid vaccine while at sea. "I was only slightly out of sorts with some fever for a day or so" he remembers. "But several of the men had to be admitted to hospital with fever." As far as we know, Captain Morton did not develop typhoid fever. Lieutenant J.M. Blair, a Volunteer officer of 1st. Hampshire Bn.

was inoculated in the flank and described the pain spreading up his arm, along with "terrible headache." He improved in 48 hours. While he developed malaria later, he never had typhoid.

Routine on board was much less regimental than 8 years previously, when Surgeon-Major W. Johnston left Southampton in February 1881 with his Bearer Company for the 1881–82 Boer War. Then the daily orders were strict, with frequent inspections by orderly officers and orderly sergeants, checks of hammocks, latrines, and prisoners. There was no evidence of recreation or training on voyage. But now things seemed much more relaxed.

Colonel Brisbane Sommerville-Large, who commanded No 6 General Hospital, was perhaps fortunate in having an O.C. ship — a Royal Artillery Colonel — who was ahead of his time in allowing all ranks a day or two after leaving Southampton to do very little except settle down into the sea routine. And Colonel Large co-operated enthusiastically with the gunner colonel in arrangements for physical training, health and sanitary drills, and marching practice to keep the mens' feet in good condition. Colonel Large arranged first-aid classes for all ranks, when he allowed the soldiers and officers to wear any comfortable dress, and to smoke if they liked. "This established a good feeling between officers and men", he said, "which never died out." The account of the voyage and all that was organised for the soldiers "who otherwise just loafed about, playing cards and 'house'(bingo)" has a late 20th century ring about it. He even set up a tented hospital on the free part of the main deck when the weather became hot. Pte W. Sykes of 2nd. West Yorks, recently enlisted, had taken a course in first-aid and had a certificate to prove it. He found himself volunteered, while sailing out on the *Rosslyn Castle*, as a regimental stretcher bearer and was taught bandaging by his RMO This did not excuse him from firing practice at barrels trailed behind the ship, daily runs and exercises, and duty on watch. Not only did the medical officers carry out this first-aid training, but the Medical Services had actually produced a booklet "HEALTH MEMORANDA FOR SOLDIERS", written by Lieutenant Colonel H.K. Allport RAMC, and issued as Army Form B51. Soldiers were encouraged to study this.

Coaling stops at Las Palmas or St Vincent in the Cape Verde Islands were exciting breaks in the sea routine. On occasion

African workers were so ineffectual at coaling that sailors from a Royal Naval vessel took over and filled bunkers overnight, to speed the military transports on their way. Ships' bands, or the pipes and drums when the Highland Brigade were passing, played to encourage them. As the troops sailed out after refuelling, the naval squadron invariably present in those days of British naval supremacy would cheer the soldiers away, "singing Rule Britannia and yelling and waving." Everyone who wrote a diary recorded this, and the flying fish when these began to appear.

Medical officers, as well as lecturing in first-aid, were on normal professional call both for routine sick parades and emergencies on voyage. Captain Holt recorded 11 deaths on the *Dunera*, in which he sailed, 9 from dysentery, 1 from sunstroke, and 1, apparently a suicide, from drowning. Much of his own time was spent managing an officer called Purcell, who became maniacal and remained so for most of the voyage. In one of his spare moments, he excised a big sebaceous cyst from a Lieutenant Colonel's scalp.

How ready were these RAMC personnel for the surgery and medicine of war they were about to meet? There is no doubt from the records, official, but much more especially personal, that they had a sense of occasion — this was their first baptism as a Corps of the Army.

Medical officers had not failed to notice that their new Corps had been made responsible for much more than nursing sick and dispensing medicines. Their manual of 1889 had made them also responsible for:

"charge of equipment, and to make timely requisition for fuel, light, provisions, and all requisite supplies and repairs; for the cooking and expenditure of diets, the custody of patients' kits, the cleanliness of the hospital and its surroundings, the exchange of soiled for clean linen, bedding and clothing; and the preparation of the necessary accounts, abstracts, and vouchers of expenditure."

Their basic training had included systematic instruction on tropical disease — especially of the India base — malaria, and a range of non-malarial fevers important to troops — Mediterranean (Malta) fever, plague, sunstroke, various forms of diarrhoea with dysentery and Asiatic cholera in particular, but also diarrhoea of infants; tropical diseases of the liver, beri-beri (from vitamin deficiency, though the cause was then unknown), and all the oriental sores, yaws, fungus infections of feet, and finally the range of parasites — bilharzia, guinea worm, hookworm, threadworm, and so on.

Military surgery comprised 16 lectures, and "lunacy", what we now call psychiatry, a full 6 lectures. This was a significant number and showed that mental afflictions of the military were by no means overlooked. Finally, military hygiene was taught in detail, both in theory and practice. For this war, special booklets giving details of diseases prevalent in the theatre — especially enteric fever — were prepared for doctors on posting.[9]

The manual of instruction for RAMC soldiers was also entirely up-to-date, with anatomy and physiology to a standard comparable to that of the end of the 20th century. Bandaging, basic nursing care, and the concept of sterility and practice of antiseptic dressings, were taught. Then there were all the details of the physical methods of casualty collection, transport, and handling, as well as first-aid including the control of haemorrhage, splinting of fractures, and resuscitation. As well as hand carry stretcher drills, there were railway waggons and pack saddle drills, and tent pitching drills.

The kit provided was comprehensive and yet basic enough for the requirements of the battlefield. The officers' "medical companion", weighing 13 lbs(6kg.) and 14x7x9 inches (32x17x23cm) in size, contained Tincture of Opium, Chloroform, Iodine, diarrhoea mixture, Spirit of Ammonia, Paraffin and Boric ointment, plus a supply of pills of Morphine, Mercury, Antimony, Ipecacuanha, Quinine, Strychnine, Camphor, Iron, Rhubarb (as aperient), and tablets of Podophylline resin (for warts), Oil of Menthol, Potassium Permanganate, and others. It also included bandages, scissors, pins and thread, splints, tourniquets, catheters, and a hypodermic syringe. There was, lastly, a water bottle.

Much bigger "No 1 and No 2 panniers", weighing 91 lbs (41kg.) and 72 lbs(37kg.) respectively, contained the same but in larger amounts. A separate "antiseptic case" — really a dressing case — was a new item. "Light surgical haversacks" were for first-aid, having bandages, splints, instruments, needles, and ligature thread plus a hypodermic syringe. "The No 1 pannier" was for "medical diseases" primarily, the "No 2" was for "surgical."

It was also called the "material" pannier and as well as having splints, gauze and plasters, had dental instruments. It had a supply of meat extract with its own food warmer. It even had a tiny anvil, for making or mending metal splints.

Because the carrier was often a pack horse, the medical services were supplied with cacolets or folding chairs, to carry patients sitting on a pack horse. Each pair weighed 56 lbs(25 kg.).

Construction and care of field kitchens and latrines were important parts of the hygiene training, as was water purification by filtration. A great deal of thought and care had gone into the preparation, extent, and method of teaching these important skills and lessons. The inclusion of "special-to-theatre" notes was clear evidence of careful planning. The Regular RAMC was considered by its senior officers as well prepared, in training material and methods, as possible. Time and experience would soon reveal how correct this belief might be.

Notes and references

CHAPTER 1

[1]Manual for the Army Medical Services (Medical Staff Corps) 1885.

[2]Different headgear was especially favoured over the years by the Scottish Regiments, though the King's Regiment was an English Regiment which also allowed its medical officer to wear its headgear. Major General R.E. Barnsley, as curator of the RAMC museum at Mytchett was very strongly against the wearing of a non-medical hat by RMOs. Taking an intake of officers around the museum in late 1952, he derided the "wearing of these hats — like monkeys." He was unaware that behind him, as he spoke, was a photograph of Noel Chavasse V.C. and bar, wearing the glengarry of the Liverpool Scottish!

[3]Kenneth Macksey, The Guinness History of Land Warfare, 134–135, London, 1976. This is probably the best shortest history of the war: 42 lines long.

[4]For a recent dramatised account of the Boer War, not written from the British point of view, see James A. Mitchener, "The Covenant", Corgi Books, 1987.

[5]R.C.K. Ensor, Oxford History of England, 344–348, Oxford, Clarendon Press, 1960.

[6]Director General James Jamieson was in post at the creation of the RAMC as a Corps of the Army, but was the only D.G. not to be knighted. This failure to award him the usual KCB was often commented on by later Corps members. A loyal view was that his repeated requests for additional men, officers, and services angered the senior general staff. A perusal of the record of his evidence to the post-war Royal Commission, however, suggests that he may have been passed over simply because he was not good enough. The evidence he gave before The Royal Commission on the War in South Africa in 1903 showed just how insultingly his requests were answered; he was asked the direct question whether it was the military opinion that was

against him, and he replied "Quite so." See also below, Chapter 3, Reference 4.

The personality of not only the Commander-in-Chief, Lord Wolseley, whose aversion to medical men holding substantive rank was well known, but also of General Sir Evelyn Wood, V.C., GCB, the Adjutant General, make this view about Jameson probably correct. Buller had previously been Quarter-Master General. If this was indeed the reason, it reflects no credit on the individuals concerned.

[7]In 1899 the RAMC had no Regular serving consultants of experience or ability. Further, the shortage of surgeons as distinct from physicians was very great. So serious was the shortfall that Sir William MacCormac, then President of the Royal College of Surgeons of England, offered to go to South Africa with Sir Redvers Buller's Field Force, and recommended that other senior consultants go also. These were in addition to the large number of civilian surgeons who volunteered. As a result, Mr Fredrick Treves of the London Hospital and Mr George Makins of Guy's were contracted to serve as surgical consultants, at the salary of £5,000 *per annum*. They and Sir William took with them their own theatre staff nurses, their own personal kit and surgical instruments, supplemented by many other gifted items. Treves left first, on 4th November, 1899, arriving in Capetown on 22nd November. Makins went to Natal and MacCormac to Durban. Other senior consultants followed later; Sir William Stokes and Sir Kendal Franks (Ireland), Mr Watson Cheyne and Mr G.L. Cheatle (London); later again went Sir T. Fitzgerald (Melbourne) and Sir Victor Horsley. Some senior surgeons like Mr A. Fripp, later Sir Alfred Fripp, and Mr David Wallace, FRCSEd., went with their own civil hospitals. Professor Ogston of Aberdeen was an important senior academic; his views are referred to below.

[8] W. Baring Pemberton, Battles of the Boer War, 1, 33. Pan Books Ltd., 1964.

[9]At this time, exact diagnosis of the enteric group of fevers was not possible, as bacteriological testing was not developed enough to distinguish infection by Bacillus Typhosus from infection by the related Bacillus Paratyphosus A and B organisms. "Continued Fever" was a blanket diagnosis which not only covered infection by these micro-organisms, but certainly others, and was a vague unscientific description.

Chapter 2

Into battle.

As the RMOs advanced north with their units, they looked in wonder with all the others at the country they saw before them. The variety of Europe — or even of India — was wanting in Southern Africa, once the columns had left the towns for the country. The scale was almost frightening — endless plains, while "a gloomy grandeur and death-like silence of the wilderness overpowered the spectator."[1] If this silence was broken, it was by thunderstorms. The mountains of the veldt were bare and rugged; as the land rose to 4000 feet (1200 metres) it seemed to become even more dry "and covered with a sort of stunted heathery stuff which feeds thousands of sheep. Every 2 miles (3km) or so you come to a range of hills or *kopjes* which we seem unable to dislodge them from." So said Matthew Fell on his march to contact at Belmont and Modder River, the first battles his division were to fight. Lieutenant Fell had previously noted in his diary that his Bearer Company's being posted to the Highland Brigade assured that "if there is any fighting you may be sure we will be in the thick of it." The Scottish Regiments were long since known to find themselves surprisingly often where the fiercest fighting took place. His own Commanding Officer, Major R.G. Hanley, who had given him a hard time on several occasions already when his work was not satisfactory, had served with The Scottish Rifles (Cameronians) in the past and was even more certain there was hard fighting to come.

Captain Alick Russell, a slightly older-than-usual RMO with the Royal Scots Greys, rode on his mare Peggy, whom he had brought with him from Britain. He soon found, while on the march, that his medical panniers on mules were left farther and farther behind the main unit, and wondered anxiously how he would cope when the fighting began. He feared for the horses in the heat.

In the shortest of time provided him by General Redvers Buller, Lord Methuen, at 54 years of age the youngest Lieutenant-General in the British Army, practised his troops in route marching, advancing in extended order and the use of cover; the doctors watched and learned also. Like medical officers since, they were wholly unused to watching large bodies of soldiers training. They soon made the sort of observations their professional and Corps training had taught them. First came the obvious lack of water and its implications. Next came the pattern of behaviour of troops — the many who fell out in the first days of marching reduced in number as their feet became hardened. (Being one of the very few junior officers mounted — the others being adjutants — the doctors were spared this embarrassment). Also came the whole range of accidental injuries the soldier was liable to — the scalds of the cooks, the falls from horses, the kicks from mules, the crushed fingers when a packing case of stores fell — and the whole range of minor sick parade complaints. Stretcher drill was practised, even the loading of hospital trains, by the medical personnel. Acquaintances were made, friendships deepened. The SB (Stretcher Bearer) brassard was worn.

But what the medical officers commented upon most of all was the climate and its effects. The burning heat of the days, with the dust storms which blinded men's and horses' eyes, contrasted with the freezing cold of the nights. Everything and everyone shared in the uniform brown discoloration — officers now wearing no badges of rank, wearing soldiers' belts and not the officers' leather Sam Browne, and carrying men's rifles. Slouch hats replaced Regimental ones. All buttons were dulled, all brass removed. Soon shortage of water would mean that shaving ceased to be obligatory for all ranks. Captain T.B.Beach, who was with the Guards' BC in the 1st. Division, and clearly liked his comforts (he had served in Bombay), described with pleasure the trapping and shooting of livestock for the mess table. But before long he, too, and his fellows were dusty and dirty, and longed for a bath.

Medical officers of slightly higher rank noted some items with disquiet: the Berkerfeld filters for water were not proving as successful as had been hoped, the readings on the commanding officers' compasses were seriously affected by the metallic rock, and most worrying of all, there were no maps of the area they were advancing into as traditional Treasury restrictions on expenditure had refused to fund adequate survey. At Principal Medical Officer (PMO) level they were also aware of the shortage of cavalry and that this restricted their division's patrolling capacity.

On the night of 20th November, 1899, Lieutenant-General Methuen's 10,000 struck tents and slept in their bivouacs. The next day the march towards Kimberly would begin. By that evening the column bivouacked at Witteputs, and the day after 2 miles (3km) south of Belmont, at a farm just to the west of their railway lifeline. The very next day the battle of Belmont was over in three-and-a-half hours. Though the Boer bullets flew, they were aimed too high to be effective, and the British troops advanced into dead ground — the hidden ground before a convex-shaped hillside where soldiers could advance unseen by the defenders — and with such speed that they almost reached the Boers as they rushed to withdraw. 4 officers and 71 men were killed and 21 officers and 199 men wounded. The Boers lost perhaps 100 killed. Captain Beach, already recording his respect for the Boers, described passing his BC casualties back to the field hospital. No 2 hospital Train, with Captain Fleming in its charge, chugged up the line in time to collect the wounded and return them to the rear, needing only 2 journeys. It was the very day its establishment of RAMC personnel was complete that it made its first casualty collection. For them, it seemed almost like a training exercise.

The RMOs were surprised, as they had been "expecting a big fight at Belmont." Like all the other British, they were amazed at the invisibility of their enemy. Matthew Fell from his point of view in the Bearer Company underestimated the number of Boers, assessing it at no more than 50–100. "This figure will be magnified into thousands in the English press", he joked. His main concern at this time was the pony he rode, which was almost unbroken and difficult to control. "Water was bad, food good, ale bad", was the soldiers' comment; "we hope to be in Kimberly in about 8 days" was the officers'.

But by December 2nd Methuen's force had fought the battles of Graspan and Modder River, and the tale was a very different one. At Modder River "we nearly got a buster ourselves" was an MOs comment: "they had ...strong artillery and a large force entrenched across the open plain ...not even knowing the place was occupied till we got to it ...but for our artillery we should have been beaten ...it all looks like something wrong in high places."

The 300 odd wounded had proved a heavy load to clear. Doctors in the Bearer Companies of this 1st Division recalled the burning sun, the sweating, unshaven, dehydrated men, "the poor fellows lying about yelling for water and covered with blood." The BC of 9 Bde collected most of the wounded after Graspan, but could not evacuate them till next day because the mules were so exhausted they could go no farther. Their 50 wounded were held overnight on the battlefield, they and their RAMC attendants all terrified they might be taken prisoner. 9 Bde stretcher unit were later extremely angry that the Guards BC were mentioned in despatches while they were not — a sometimes unfairness of war — "I was so done I could hardly stand" said one of their doctors next day. Another said "I forgot the day of the week."

In spite of their discomfort and their fear ("I was in plenty of funk" wrote Fell in his diary, "no worse than many and not as bad as some"), the RAMC staff recorded their clinical impressions as they saw them. They were now clearly aware of the intensity of the Mauser small-arms fire, and equally aware that the Boers with their smokeless powder were impossible to see. The nature of the very first casualties at Belmont rather took them by surprise, especially the fact that many of the men were wounded in three or four places. After the Modder River battle, a high incidence of body hits and bullet wounds through the thigh — two known serious regions to treat — was noted, and the severity of the wounds was also worrying. The individual regiments' casualty figures were recorded — the 91st had heavy losses, in spite of being pinned down and unable to move for several hours. Their kilts were a visible target. The first blister burns of the knees of the Scottish kilted regiments, as they lay face down for hours in the burning sun, were a further new comment.

Matthew Fell's diary is especially valuable for the human asides and remarks he made. "The Loyal N. Lancs look as fit as fiddles", he wrote. (He was from North Lancashire himself).

Like soldiers before and after, he liked a (rather unfair) dig at the Household Brigade: "Guards look absolutely worn out wrecks but they will get fit soon I expect ...a sudden come down from luxury to bully beef, biscuits, and bad water does not suit them ..."

The RAMC officers, too, recorded their observations on the morale of their troops, the effect of rumours, the shortage of mail from home, the appearance of diarrhoea in others and in themselves, and the disappointment at what they were beginning to see as failures on the part of their commanders. While military accounts of the war at this particular time do not report incursions by the Boers to cut the railway line, RAMC ones mention the line being "constantly cut" — for them the railway track was the evacuation route and not the supply line.

At this time, too, the RAMC doctors at BC and RMO level were caught in the traditional fog of war. On their small canvasses they tell of their exhaustion as they strove to clear the wounded, give them their initial clinical care — as far as the soldier in the fighting arm is concerned, the medical service is a professional one from the moment the first field dressing is applied, the splint adjusted, and the pain-relieving injection given. Their anxieties were immediate; they had little to say about the medical chain behind them. But for them, the disappointment at military mistakes was reflected in what they saw as needless casualties. The Infantry RMOs had uniform admiration for the efficiency and cool bravery of the Gunners, and this will be seen again as we record the RAMC view of the larger battle of Magersfontein, and look at the working of the next parts of the medical evacuation system.

There are many accounts of the battles of Magersfontein, Colenso, and Spion Kop, those three sad defeats of British Arms, the two latter the result of the ineptitude of the commanding General, but these have been by teeth arm soldiers, politicians, and general historical commentators. For perhaps the very first time, the account of these battles as seen by the doctors and surgeons of the RAMC and their soldiers deserves to be told.

Lieutenant J.C. Rutherford, one of the junior medical officers of the Divisional Field hospital, watched the column march out from base camp at Modder River. Already ahead were the 9th and 12th Lancers, then separate regiments, their RMOs Captain J.V.

Forrest and Major T.J. O'Donnell respectively. The 9th Lancers preceded the Guards brigade. The Infantry Brigades left in the early afternoon — the Highland Brigade, which had been given the honour of taking Magersfontein by their General Officer Commanding, (G.O.C.) Lord Methuen, but having Major General Wauchope as their own commander, set off at 3 p.m.(1500 hrs).

Rutherford was a young recently commissioned officer in the RAMC, far from his village of Glencar in Donegal. The RMOs of the Highland Regiments he knew — they were young officers too. He knew them all well. Lieutenant H.E.M. Douglas was attached to the 2nd Black Watch. He had split up his regimental stretcher bearers into teams accompanying individual rifle companies. He had had the idea of making up what he called "a concentrated solution of morphia" which he was going to use for seriously injured men. Lieutenant H. Ensor was RMO to the 2nd Seaforth. He had decided to keep his 16 regimental SBs — all bandsmen as ever — together, with Band Sergeant Hoare and an RAMC L/Cpl. He had removed some of the heavier medical items out of his haversack, filling it with dressings instead. Each man had one of the new style "first field dressings" and Ensor had checked particularly that no one was without one in the battalion. 1st Argyll and Sutherland Highlanders had Captain J.E. Carter RAMC as its RMO and 1st Highland Light Infantry Lieutenant T.C. Mackenzie, both riding in rear of their respective battalions. With 1st Gordons was Captain P.J. Probyn, who was keen to make good records of the engagement, intending to tally diligently all the wounded he treated.[2] He had as his regimental first-aid L/Cpl J.F. Mackay, who was a medical student. Lastly, in support was G Battery, Royal Horse Artillery (RHA), with Lieutenant G.G. Delap as their MO.

Lieutenant Rutherford also watched No 3 Highland Bde. BC form up with its ambulance carts and mules — the former No 1 Coy RAMC from Aldershot, home of the Corps, and having as its junior officer, Lieutenant Matthew Fell. Senior to Fell were Captain C.W.R. Healy, and the Officer Commanding, Major R.G. Hanley.

But there were many more in the RAMC order of battle — the Guards Bde had its RMOs — C.W. Parfeit of 3rd Grenadiers, A.W. Hooper of 1st Coldstream and A.F. Heaton (who was a

Volunteer officer and in later years remained in the Territorial Force) of 2nd Coldstream, S.G. Moore of 1st Scots Guards. All were Captains RAMC

Nor were all the medicals British Regulars. Civilian Surgeon J.G. Groghan served with No 1 Bearer Company. No 1 Field Hospital had on its staff *Stabsarzt* Dr Schmidt of the Royal Prussian Guarde-Fusilier Regiment and *Stabsarzt* Dr Krummacher of the Kaiser Wilhelm Academie. Not all Germans served with the Boers.

It was not the turn of the Divisional Field Hospital to set off until midnight. A hospital was then as now a unit whose place was to the rear of the teeth arm troops.

A most miserable night it was, pitch dark and raining heavily. The distance actually traversed was 3 miles(4km) but the Hospital took 6 hours to do it! Rutherford's main recollection of that dismal night was of falling asleep on his pony at intervals and being wakened up by a cold rivulet of rain flowing down the back of his neck. There were long halts while they were finding their way. When carts stuck there were other long delays while excited Cape boys, cracking whips and shouting at mules till the wheels began to turn again, overcame the stoppage.

At dawn Rutherford heard the tremendous crash of a naval gun on the left of the British position. This was "Joe Chamberlain", a 4.7 inch (110mm) gun, and the time was 0430 hrs. But Lieutenant Fell, much further forward, was wakened from sleep half an hour earlier by heavy infantry firing. By 0530 the whole of Magersfontein ridge was a mass of bursting shells. Rutherford from his vantage point saw "the koppe (sic) of Magersfontein where the enemy were — whistle of shell — its burst with a cloud of greenish-yellow smoke. They were firing Lyddite. Our field guns were on our right." But while he heard no Boer fire apart from "our old friend the maxim-norderfeldt with its bang-bang-bang", the medical officers nearer the front of the battle were already aware that something was wrong. When Major Henley came forward to tell Lieutenant Fell at 0600 that he would be relieved in an hour's time, they were both afraid that all was not well with the Highland Brigade. Captain Beach, too, with the Guards Division, realised that something was far wrong.

In no time later, the BC heard that "the Highland Brigade had stumbled on the Boers with unfixed bayonets and were badly cut up." The tea break was forgotten. Without delay, Major Henley and his officers and stretcher bearers had to rush forward with half their ambulances to collect the wounded.

Now all was confused, from RAP to BC level and beyond. The Highland Brigade RMOs were overwhelmed, not so much by the rush of casualties but by the retreat and demoralisation of the soldiers. Lieutenant Ensor with the Seaforths lost all his SBs in the confusion. "It was quite hopeless", he said later, "to try to remove seriously wounded under such hot fire." But he kept his head, and re-supplied his haversack from his Scotch cart,[3] and his large water bottles from his water cart.

Captain Carter with the Argylls saw the red light flash as the signal for the Boers to open fire. He could only stand and watch the "mix-up", as he called it; "many men lost their rifles thro' no fault of their own. They had to lie and take the shelling."

Pte Fred Bly of 2nd. Seaforths, who had fought at Omdurman, and like Pte Sykes of the West Yorks was a regimental first-aider, saw the red light flash too. He described vividly the death of his Company Commander and the deaths or wounding of one after another of his friends. "I put a field dressing on poor old Dudley Miller's thigh wound", he remembered. He could see no SBs, nor his RMO. As he carried back a wounded Black Watch soldier, he kept marvelling that he was not hit. For as they retreated "the Boers dropped our fellows in dozens." But there was no panic."

The 1st. H.L.I. retreated in disarray, and their RMO, Lieutenant Mackenzie, was actually trampled on. Later he became unconscious with heat exhaustion — having lost his helmet — and had to be evacuated himself.

As Lieutenant Fell and his bearers tried to move forwards they saw "dozens of 91st (Argylls) men skulking in the bushes." He and his men worked with the Volunteer Bearer Company (the equivalent of a Territorial Unit) in clearing casualties. "Every bush had men skulking behind it and there was no doubt that the 91st, Highland Light Infantry, were demoralised, the Black Watch cut to pieces, the Seaforths and Gordons behaving very well. The BW were leading, suffered terribly — retirement became a panic — first wounded could not be brought back." Captain A.R. Cameron of the Black Watch, already demoralised after the Modder River battle, spoke later while recovering from his wound of "horrible Magersfontein."

When the extent of the reverse was becoming clear, Rutherford's Field Hospital was ordered "to get in front with the others" — all four were advanced — his own Divisional, the Guards, Highland Brigade, and 9th Bde Field Hospitals. What was required so urgently was not beds, but additional doctors and surgeons.

As the medicals were moving forwards, Rutherford saw a highlander riding on in front of him. He caught up and asked eagerly for news. "Terrible bad news, sir", was the reply. "The Highland Brigade was cut up this morning. They marched up in close quarter column right up to within 200 yards of the Boer trenches. The enemy poured in a sudden fearful fire and half of them were shot, the remainder retreated."

"I came back with this startling news which was received with scorn and I did not pay much attention to it myself" was Lieutenant Rutherford's first response. But as the stretcher teams moved closer to the front, it became clear that the news was all too true. The RAMC unit found "here and there among the bushes groups of Jocks sitting, many of them without their rifles, not knowing where their regiments were, hungry and thirsty and completely demoralised." They spoke to a young Black Watch soldier and a medical officer asked why he was sitting there and where his regiment was. "I don't know where the regiment is, sir", he replied. "We all ran away this morning and I haven't seen them since."

The hospital staff found a dressing station (DS) which had been set up and joined in to help. Wounded were coming in slowly, "each suffering Jock was borne along carefully by some half dozen of his fellow-countrymen, who seemed all too happy to get away from the firing line and seized every opportunity of doing so." No regimental officers were to be seen, but later some did appear and tried to collect the soldiers together and "get them formed up for their grub." Later again a Provost Martial (military policeman) appeared and threatened the men.

After helping for about an hour at the DS, the hospital medical officers went about a mile(1500km) farther forward to a Clearing Station of one of the Bearer Companies where there were a number of ambulances. Clearing Stations were collecting points on "the way back"; as the wounded were brought in the medical officers and RAMC soldiers checked their dressings and sent them back via the DS to the hospital at Modder River. The medical evacuation chain was working. The training had not been wasted.

As they worked at the Clearing Station (CS), the RAMC watched with respect and admiration the battery "break out in fire." "It was fine to see the cool way the officers behaved, tho' every one of them was liable to be hit by the Boer riflemen. They calmly surveyed the enemy trenches thro' their glasses and gave the orders for their guns." Being professional men themselves, they admired professionalism in others.

It soon became evident that there were still wounded in the field who needed urgent surgery. So the MOs from the field hospitals — much fresher than the now exhausted Regimental Medical Officers — collected SB squads and moved right up to the firing line. There they met yet more highlanders bringing in their own wounded. The soldiers directed the doctors to a wire fence on the right of one of the field batteries. It was here that many of the troops had been hit as they tried to get through in the early morning semi-darkness. Lieutenant Rutherford found six wounded highlanders here, some wounded in both thighs and both arms, but none seriously, and no dead.

Later again the medical officers watched another phase of the battle. The Gordon Highlanders came through the silent guns and advanced steadily. Lieutenant Rutherford commented: "the futility of it struck me — nearly 5000 men, a whole *brigade*, had attempted to take those trenches and failed, and now half a battalion was sent out to try and do. Their poor colonel was wounded and died next day in hospital."

The doctors continued to look for wounded, using a field glass to search the bushes. One officer of the HLI was spotted this way, sitting in a pit he had dug for himself with his bare hands to get shelter from the Mauser bullets. He had been wounded in the thigh and could not move.

The Boers began to shell the forward areas again, and as it was now getting dark, the medical officers returned to their headquarters. Rutherford found in disgust that his pony, which he had left in safe keeping with a half company of Black Watch, had gone, together with the half company, when he returned. So he made his way back on foot, had a meal, and slept soundly.

The next morning a further casualty sweep was carried out, helped by the flag of truce which had been agreed with the enemy being flown. Fortunately there were few casualties left, because the British Naval guns kept on firing and the Boers recommenced in retaliation. But some wounded from the other side were brought in. These were from the Scandinavian Brigade, who were fighting with the Boers. Their fine physical condition and bearing impressed the RAMC. "We had a great talk with them and liked them very much — tough, straightforward fellows, not like most Boer wounded, who whine about their families and tell you they were forced to fight" was the verdict. "They said boldly they hoped they'd be exchanged when they'd come and fight again."

The next task was collection and burial of the dead. This was unpleasant, owing to the heat. A story told was of the Church of Scotland padre who found the body of General Wauchope close to the trenches. He was about to put it in an ambulance but the Boers refused, saying ambulances were for wounded. So the padre suggested tying it outside with rope, and this was done.

The work of the padres — a kindred profession to the doctors — deserves recognition. Their bravery was evident to foe as well as friend, and Boer despatches complained that their own clergy had hung back from the fighting, while the British of all denominations had been in the thick of it. The Presbyterian padres were fortified with large doses of whisky by their fellow Scots, especially when they had to go out to collect the decaying corpses of their dead comrades. On one occasion a Presbyterian padre who had "drink taken" was involved in an angry argument with a Roman Catholic colleague and had to be separated by Jocks of his unit!

Sgt Brammer of the King's Own Yorkshire Light Infantry was also part of 9 Bde. He watched the highland casualties being brought back from the battle from his battalion position, where his regiment was preventing the Boers from outflanking the highlanders. He saw his C.O., Colonel Baxter, being overcome by heat exhaustion and evacuated. Sgt. Brammer was yet another immediate eye-witness full of praise for the medicals. He described a stretcher party being near a shell burst: "a lot of them was knocked down but got on their feet again and walked along as if nothing had happened."

Finally, the medical officers heard with the others that the whole Force was to retire. "It was a dismal procession", recorded Rutherford in his diary written on the day, "and 300 highlanders volunteered to carry back dead and remaining wounded." Criticism of the command began. There was talk of the "deplorable mistake which led the highlanders into such a trap…naturally it has had a bad effect as Lord Methuen had done better than anyone up to that…but for that mistake we should not have lost half the men and might even have taken some part of the Boer position…we are now stuck fast"; were some of the MOs comments.

In the aftermath, a few memories stand out. Pte Fred Bly, after digging graves on the 13th, told of how thrilled all his fellows were at a special telegram from Queen Victoria on the 14th. He also remembers being spoken to by a war correspondent, and telling this man "what an awful thing war is." Captain Beach RAMC praised the Artillery but criticised Generals Methuen and Buller. Later again, he looked forward to a dining invitation to the Coldstream Guards Officers' mess, saying "will probably taste good wine for the first time in South Africa." Highland officers were angered by Methuen's address, which they regarded as unfair and patronising. News of the arrival of "Bobs" (Lord Roberts) was greeted with relief.

Out of some 14,000 men who took part in the battle, 22 officers and 198 men were killed, of whom 7 officers and 86 soldiers belonged to one unit, the Black Watch, and 45 officers and 645 men were wounded. 190 were missing. The Boers lost about 300, of whom 87 were killed. While subsequent commentators would say that by the standards of Sadowa in 1866 and Sedan in 1870 the casualties were not enormous, such thoughts did not occur to the men who had been working so hard in the burning sun of Magersfontein. And the medical evacuation from front line to hospital had been, in the circumstances, prompt and efficient. The RMOs had shown great personal bravery — Lieutenant Douglas, seriously wounded in the face later in the action, was awarded the V.C., and several of his medical orderlies from the battalion DCMs (Distinguished Conduct Medal). Lieutenant Ensor and Lieutenant Mackenzie with the Highland Brigade, Major O'Donnell with 12th Lancers and Captain Hooper with 1st Coldstream Guards were all awarded the DSO. And Captain Probyn and Cpl J.F. Mackay, with the Gordons, were awarded the DSO and V.C. respectively. Captain Probyn told afterwards of how he had set out to "put the regulation tally on the wounded but finding this impracticable, I threw the book away." "Between you and me and the post", wrote Matthew Fell to his parents in February of 1900, after the relief of Kimberley, "the much blackguarded Army Medical Corps has done d…d well — sacrificed themselves nobly and worked like blacks — for non-combatants our list of killed and wounded shows up very well considering the number of fellows actually in the firing line are very small, as the majority of Army doctors are in field lines of communication and base hospitals in absolute safety and never hear a bullet whiz over their heads."

In an earlier letter Fell wrote home: "You must have been terribly disheartened by the news of Redvers Buller's reverse at the Tugela." For while Magersfontein was a reverse but not a disaster, the same could not be said for the defeats suffered in Natal by the nominal Commander-in-Chief. On the continent of Europe Britain's name was ridiculed; the French, always ready to release their deep hatred of the English, showed some sharp cartoons including one of Queen Victoria having her naked buttocks beaten with a shovel by a grinning Boer farmer.

The military account of the disasters of Colenso and Spion Kop make dismal reading and reflect all too clearly the ineptitude of the senior British commanders. Worse still were the post-war enquiries where senior generals were evasive and dismissive in the way senior military persons sometimes are when asked a straightforward question to which they have no answer. At Colenso other regiments of the line were in action; the Irish Brigade under Hart — Dublin Fusiliers and Connaught Rangers plus the Border Regiment; 5 Field Batteries and 14 naval guns including 2 4.7s. The other brigades were commanded by Barton, Hillyard, and Lyttelton, whose contributions were as good as could be given the impossibility of Buller's orders, even before he may have become mentally upset after a shell had burst very near him. The cavalry element at Colenso was three times that of Methuen's; there were also locally raised South African Light horse and Natal Police. At Spion Kop regiments from Lancashire and the Middlesex Regiment suffered severely as they reaped the result of their commanding generals' limitations.[4]

We have had accounts of the war as seen through the eyes of RAMC officers and men at the front line, and the BCs who worked so closely with them. Now by contrast we can tell the tale of those who worked in the field, stationary and general Hospitals of the Army Medical Services.

The medical plan for Colenso (there was a similar one later for Spion Kop) can be briefly stated. The PMO, Colonel Galwey, had organised a Volunteer Ambulance Corps of 2000 men — 12 to a stretcher — to spare wounded the jogging in the ambulance waggons they would otherwise have suffered, and bring them in "one lift" to hospital level. This he considered particularly necessary in view of the rugged and hilly nature of the ground. Casualty Collecting Posts(CCPs) were placed by Colenso, and a Field Hospital at Chievely, 7 miles(4.8 km) in rear. There were Stationary hospitals at Estcourt and Pietermaritzburg: the Base (General) Hospital at Capetown; a hospital ship at Durban was tasked to convey wounded for Capetown also.

Galwey's plan was tested to the utmost and stood up. Within 40 hours of the fighting, 700 casualties were at stationary hospital level or at Durban. 16 surgeons — mostly civilian but some RAMC — had passed that number through the Field hospitals open to receive. Sir Fredrick Treves, reporting in February of 1900 to the press said: "Those who have hastily criticised the Army Medical Department should have seen the work done on that memorable Friday on the Naval Hill before COLENSO. The MOs worked hour after hour."[5]

Pte Sykes described the loss of the 10 guns at Colenso. He saw Buller pass near where he was: "he looked in a bad way." With his fellow bearers he was exhausted. "During the retreat our bearers waited till the last minute to pick up anybody that fell out. Water was short." At the end he went to the field hospital to replenish his battalion's medical supplies. Total British casualties were about 1000, plus the notorious loss of 10 guns; the Boers lost 6 killed and 21 wounded.

The dead on the top of Spion Kop, the morning after, when Lieutenant Blake Knox MD, RAMC, climbed up with his SBs, lay two and three deep in the trench system. Some Boers too had tears in their eyes. The 243 dead the British buried there and then; the medicals and others brought down 500 wounded, many of whom died quickly.

Hospital staffs know a different war from their colleagues in the front line and field collecting units. But, for all hospital ranks, the move to contact was as for any other British Army unit. On the way to Eastcourt, Captain H.M. Morton (who had been inoculated against enteric fever on the voyage from the U.K. base) remembered the "pouring rain as we struck tents *en route*, the floods up to your waist as you crossed rivers — up to your knees in mud — but the happy knowledge that the ox-drawn transport had dry clothes."

Hospitals followed their brigades and were set up then as now at sites directed by the General Staff. The Colonel of the Somerset Light Infantry told the 10th Brigade Field Hospital to move its tents closer to a hillside and less in the possible line of fire. But such advice was sometimes modified at the discretion of the medical officers — as at Elandslaagte where Surgeon-Captain M.P.C. Holt (who had lunched with Major and Mrs David Bruce when his unit disembarked having known them previously) recalled how after two of the MOs were killed by shell fire and a Volunteer Officer Dr Balfour wounded, the "Volunteer MOs were keen to move the location of the hospital — and their views prevailed." It was an amusing incident where the reservists told the regulars what to do!

Hospitals farther away from the fighting, as it continued over November and December 1899, seemed short of accurate information. Rumours — hard to understand by later 20th century soldiers when information is immediate — abounded. During November there were rumours that General Buller was, first, in Pretoria gaol, later in gaol in Magersfontein. Captain Holt wrote in his diary on November 24th: "Rumour that there was a big battle at Colenso today." Harder information was that a Boer 6 inch (150mm) gun which was called "Bulwana" was in place and that their tents were again in range. Any doubts of what was happening disappeared as the casualties from the major battles began to arrive.

The field hospitals were in constant movement. 10 Field received casualties "during (Major General) Lord Dundonald's and (General) Sir Charles Warren's actions and sent some back to 4 Stationary." On the evening of the next day they "were ordered to move so all their patients were transferred to 5 Divisional Hospital as No 4 Stationary was so full of wounded." "Next morning ready to move — moved to rear of the DORSET regiment. Overnighted ? only 4 miles (6.4 km) away. Found Sir C.Warren's Force held up by the Boers." The next day:

> "Pitched H again under cover of kopjes & behind the Artillery lines. 11 Bde FH pitched quite close and 2 Div Hosp 1000yds (1 Km) off. No wounded brought in till midnight. Had to treat a col. hit in the right temple by a shell fragment — became v. confused and noisy later — portions of brain extruded — at last he became quiet with morphia." The next day:

> "Had 300 cases. Many cases of haemorrhage to watch. packed out."

The day after this, their PMO told them they were to stop receiving and had to clear their hospital and be ready to move by 5 pm. The subsequent account told the story:

> "can put more serious on ambulance waggons. PMO said a retirement had been decided upon; the hill previously captured had been re-taken by the Boers....Boers refused to let any more cas be evacuated till General Botha had had a talk with the PMO...hospital cleared by 5 pm. Rain till that evening."

At the height of the casualty flow, surgeons worked "0830 till 2215" — i.e. all day. "I could not get round the wards till 0045 next morning" was a typical comment. The surgical accounts told of the "slight bullet wounds" and the myth of the "kindly wounds" by the Mauser — because they seemed to heal well — began to appear. Major wounds were excised, and major fractures set, under general anaesthesia. Ether was used as well as chloroform. Haemorrhage was a frightening event; there was no blood available; blood transfusion had not arrived.

Within their own Corps, the doctors heard of the loss of personal friends. "Louis Hughes killed at Colenso" wrote Fell. "He was a marked man in our corps. v. sorry." How often did death remove an outstanding man, and how often did promotion, sometimes unexpected, follow a contemporary's death. Deaths were from enemy action at the front, but as time passed, from the enteric fever which began to appear from December onwards. Some surgeons and some soldiers recall vividly their own initial symptoms and how they tried to keep working and hope they would improve. The RAMC soldiers recounted little of their clinical experience on the wards, but supply essential facts such as that there was a constant supply of good food and drink, the drudgery of having to strike and re-pitch tents, the rush to cut drains as the thunderstorms beat down, the rotting of canvas from constant soakings. Not all soldiers could, of course, keep records in English: *all* other ranks in 24 British Field hospital were Indian. In the hospital photograph, one of the medical officers was an Indian, working alongside his fellow RAMC from England.

The arrival of Field Marshal Lord Roberts altered the military situation at once, as he was a first-rate commander. The pettiness and snobbery of the home-based Senior Staff towards "Indian Officers" might have prevented his appointment at the beginning of the war, but not now: Lord Roberts was appointed as C.in C. in South Africa by the Cabinet 24 hours after the debacle of Colenso without their even consulting Lord Wolseley, the C.in C. at home. Roberts was 68 years old; he had spent 40 years abroad.

After Buller had shown himself even more incompetent at Spion Kop than at Colenso, his status with the officers, if not with the soldiers, was lost for good. The medical officers shared this contempt, and their personal accounts during the engagements at Tabanyama, Val Krantz (where Buller called a retreat after Brigadier Lyttelton's Brigade had captured it and retired in 48 hours with nothing to show except 34 killed and 335 wounded), Hlangwhame, and finally Pieter's Hill, are full of criticism. The story of 10 Field Hospital's doings over this short period have just been told in Captain Martin's account when he referred to "Sir C. Warren's actions", and show well the frantic settings up, the moves, the re-settings up, all evidence of the confusion and vacillations of the Directing Staff.

During January, Morton's Division (5th) was "resting in camp", and he describes "Buller appearing, inspecting the Division, expressing himself well satisfied with what had been done." He "declared to the men that he had found the key to Ladysmith" which, said Captain Martin sarcastically, "was an expression much commented on by everyone." Later, on February 4th when he was posted away to the 2nd East Surreys as RMO, he wrote: "we were going to have another try to get into Ladysmith with General Buller's new found key." The MOs were clearly angered by the heavy fighting in February 1900 with so little progress, but Morton made a comment echoed elsewhere about Buller even before he lost his nerve, that he was not prepared to sacrifice men unnecessarily.

For General Buller did seem to have the welfare of his troops very much at heart. Perhaps this was why his soldiers retained respect and affection for him even after his earlier reverses. All personal records refer to the constant supply of excellent food — and drink — he insisted must be provided, and there seems no doubt also that he did consult the medical support regularly and showed a real concern for them and for their various medical units, from bearer section to general hospital.

But the Boers *did* withdraw, and Captain Morton, RMO to the 2nd East Surreys, wrote in his diary on 2nd March, 1900: "I rode into Ladysmith today along with Richards, RMO Scottish Rifles." He noted how thin the inhabitants were and that "there is enterica here."

Captain Russell's account of his time as a "cavalry doctor" gives a fascinating picture of a mode of warfare now gone for ever. His regiment, the Greys, were part of General French's division. He had his earlier fears, about the medical panniers being too far behind the cavalry to be of use, confirmed. Like other RMOs in action for the first time, he was unaware of being under fire, and at the Riet river in February of 1900 had to be told to take cover by his C.O. His description of chatting with Mr Ross, the R.S.M., of seeing the cavalry charge from afar off, of the Boers' counter-attack, and of bravely dressing the wounded under fire and carrying them back to the SBs, are told with the matter-of-factness of all the doctors' accounts. Very obvious, too, was his concern for the wounded, for their lack of water and "dreadful bumping over stones and rocks." Exhaustion and death of horses saddened him. Most vivid of all is his account of carrying a wounded officer on his own horse through a fire storm started by the Boers, blackened with dust, and passing "3 horses scorched to death."

The largest independent medical units, the general hospitals, at this stage in the campaign shared the lot of the smaller in being pitched into action the moment they were disembarked. No 6 British General Hospital (BGH) arrived at Capetown on 17th February, 1900 and were ordered on the evening of the next day (a Sunday) to move to the rail junction of Naauwport and set up there. It took three tedious days to move to their location, because the engines were not powerful enough to pull the heavy loads of general hospital equipment up the incline and because of the large amount of rail traffic, much of higher priority. Their first site outside the village was chosen by the PMO, but the G.O.C. refused to sanction this as the fighting was taking place only 8 miles(12km) away. So they had to use the only other available site, inside the lines, which unfortunately had had troops encamped on it for a considerable period. This was the 21st, and they began to set up the hospital at once. In his report the C.O, said: "By 26th we had 520 beds fully equipped and 350 pts(patients) including officers, mostly wounded from Paaderburg. We had a local cottage hospital opened and used for officers. Lady O'Hagan superintended its administration. We also had a convalescent camp set up to take 500 pts — transfers from the main hospital." A late 20th century British General Hospital would have been proud to report as well.

On 1st March, the hospital extended to 600 beds. Convoys of about 600 arrived that week from Modder River, wounded and other sick but also enterica cases. By April 13th they had 830 patients under treatment and accommodation for 920. They had 3–400 in the convalescent camp, coming daily to the main hospital for treatment and checks of progress.

All the various elements of a large hospital were in place over March, thanks as ever to those wonderful men in the Royal Engineers and Ordnance. They were duly thanked by the medical and nursing officers. There were constructed a railway siding, a wooden operating theatre ("the tent on the home scale was useless and dangerous"), an incinerator ("which had to be changed as its construction was faulty"), disinfecting sheds for the enteric division of the hospital, other sanitary arrangements, water supply laid on, wash houses, kitchens, latrines, and all manner of stores. The construction of the hospital was "greatly expedited by the G.O.C., Major General A.B. Wavell" the RAMC colonel remembered.[6]

The details of the BGHs of this war are fascinating. They show how far improvements had come since the days of the Crimea, and how professional the doctors of the day really were.

The hospitals had traditional medical and surgical divisions as did all hospitals, but also an entirely separate enterica division. There was also an officers' wing. As well as the main kitchen, with its specially constructed hotplate, there was a cookhouse solely for milk ("frequently 1500 pints(900litres) of milk had to be sterilised *per diem*"). There was a special steriliser for enteric excreta — a Kaffir pot built into a brick surround.

Each marquee had 25 candle power electric lights, as had the hospital paths. Hospital tents had stronger lighting — 50 candlepower. Each ward had food boxes and dust bins; there was the complete range of departments, offices, guard tents, Q.M., steward's, linen and pack stores, and so on. But two departments of a late 20th century BGH were lacking. There was no pharmacy — though there were "compounders" of medicines on the RAMC soldier establishment — and there was no hospital laboratory.

Operating theatres were 20 or 30 feet(6–9metres) square, built of corrugated zinc externally, and had large windows fitted with roller blinds, and a skylight. The lower windows had dulled glass. Later in the war theatres had wood linings inside. There were 150 candlepower electric lights on wheeled bases. Instruments were kept in glass cases, with cupboards for the theatre sisters' necessaries. Instruments were listed and catalogued.

The heavy operating table was surrounded by tables of various sorts, from the heavy table for the steriliser to the movable tables for dressings, ligatures, sponges, gauze, drainage tubes; one or two for instruments, and one for the anaesthetist. The "administrator of anaesthetics", as he was called in the RAMC notes, had his own stool!

Sterile water was kept in large earthenware tanks. These had taps "as there was always a constant supply." Large irrigators — rather like reservoirs of fluid used with modern endoscopy procedures on the urinary tract — were, like some of the trolleys, on roller castors.

Beside every operating theatre was the new piece of diagnostic apparatus — the X-ray. This was either detached or in an annex to the theatre. The standard machine was a Mackenzie-Davidson worked with an APP's induction coil and Crooke's tube. It was regarded as satisfactory by the surgeons, but was not powerful enough to produce films at a level deep in the body. It also had batteries which needed recharging very frequently, especially if there was no dynamo available.[7]

Recreation facilities were also made available very quickly. There were reading rooms, party facilities — with Christmas in the bright summer sunshine — money raised for widows and children by raffles and fêtes. One hospital had a cycling track where convalescents could undergo rehabilitation in the most modern of atmospheres.

Hospitals varied in their efficiency and atmosphere. Captain Cameron of the Black Watch, in later life a General, was evacuated by train from Maggersfontein to Wynberg with a gunshot wound of his arm. Though critical of the organisation and food there, he was impressed by his treatment: "We have an excellent civilian doctor looking after this ward; all the doctoring is done by civilians, the soldiers doing the organisation...the soldier-doctors have done magnificently in action; our regimental one Douglas is having his behaviour brought to official notice." His wound was dressed weekly. By January 8th. it was all but healed and he was told it could now go into plaster-of-paris. Captain Cameron refused to go to a convalescent home "as the Surgeon-Major there is a good-natured old thing but not much of a doctor — I want to stay under my good civilian till my arm is in working order again."

The Imperial Yeomanry Hospital at Deelfontein had 19 doctors, including an eye surgeon and a dentist, 10 surgeon dressers, 40 nurses, 10 ward maids, and 76 St. John men. Colonel D.G. Sloggett was the C.O.

In November, 1900, Captain Russell wrote from Pretoria: "The Yeomanry Hospital here is a wonder. Officers say it is by far the best hotel in town. Officers get as much champagne as they can safely take, (convalescent soldiers were also given champagne) and tobacco and cigarettes are provided in the same way — all free of course. They have so much money that they don't know how to spend it."

Hospitals had interdenominational chapels, and Army padres' reports showed just how much work they did, both in leading worship and in looking after welfare problems of men and officers. They recognised stress and treated it; cases of acute panic attack in young officers and more chronic anxiety of NCOs and soldiers were correctly diagnosed and dealt with. "Stress" was by no means an invention of later wars.

The Entrance Of The News Media.

Many news reporters flocked to South Africa during the Boer War: it was not the first time this had happened. The excellent reports of the work of the Royal Army Medical Corps soon came back to the senior medical generals waiting a little anxiously at home, and to the medical profession themselves. The British Medical Association took a special interest in the new medical service it had had so much influence in helping to create, and whose conditions of service it had been so anxious to improve.

For anxiety at home over the new Corps had been very real. Reduction in establishments and in medical officer numbers had, as seen, reached a level where doctors and surgeons of real ability saw no benefit in a life career in the RAMC. Pleas over rank structure and status had gone on for 10 years; the Horse Guards had repeatedly ignored them. The audible remarks of the Commander-in-Chief, Lord Wolseley at the Review in Phoenix Park, Dublin: "Go to the left and tell those medical people to return swords. Inform them that they are only civilian attendants upon sick soldiers" had been widely reported in the medical press and still rankled in the medical profession at large and in the Army Medical Corps in particular.

At the outbreak of the war Director General Jameson had naturally to make the best public case he could. Speaking at the dinner of the Gynaecological Society in London, he made three points of significance. First he referred to the medical equipment being provided for the medical support, insisting that this had been brought fully up to date. (It was known that medical stores throughout the country had been cleared out to make up the amounts necessary; some had been scoured from other parts of Africa). So he praised the Berkefeld water filter tested at Netley military hospital — capable of sterilising 40 gallons(182 litres) of water every hour — and also the surgical instruments. Next he referred to the civilian surgeons who had been enlisted, and quoted approval of the surgical instruments not by one of his own medical officers, but by Mr G. Makins, "whose only comment had been that all that was needed was a few more nail brushes." Thirdly, he stated that "In this war there are two powerful enemy to contend with — the Boers and Enteric fever. The admission rate in Natal last year was $5^{1/2}$ per cent. Extraordinary precautions are, therefore, urgently required." There were question marks over all of these three points of which he must have been well aware.

But the *British Medical Journal* was not impressed. "The undermanned condition, as regards officers, of the AMS, long continued and notorious", said its leader, "has resulted, under pressure of war, in a condition of things, which it is impossible to blink, and is causing no little anxiety to those who choose to look below the surface." The *BMJ* quoted the *distribution* of officers in the Army List for November 1899, showing how blanket numbers of medical officers were used by the Authorities to hide shortages in clinical specialties.[8]

However, from the very beginning of the Boer War, appreciative comments began to be made about the RAMC and its personnel. A Regimental Field officer wrote in the *Army and Navy Gazette* on November 25th: "It is so usual for a narrow-minded section of military society to speak slightingly of the army doctor that I should like to bear testimony to the professional worth of those I have come in contact with. My regiment suffered at Elands Laagte, and I am able from personal observation to speak of the devotion and gallantry of the MOs on that dreadful night. No language would express adequately the debt the wounded owe them…upholding the credit and honour of their profession…they seemed, all of them, equally solicitous for friend and foe …wounded Boers very grateful…if the doctors go on as they have begun in this campaign their traducers in military clubland will have to hide their heads in shame."

After the Modder River battle *The Times* said: "The work of the medical staff was beyond praise. Their promptness in relieving and in removing the wounded under hot fire was extraordinary." After the Magersfontein battle, the RMOs, "walking up and down the firing line attending to the wounded under a hail of bullets…all the doctors and SBs showed the greatest coolness."…individual RMOs were mentioned, "showing conspicuous gallantry in attending the wounded under fire." The Boer general Cronje praised the casualty removal arrangements by the British in his despatch to President Kruger.

Nursing staff were also praised. At this early stage of the war there were only 20 superintendents and 60 sisters mobilized, though a further 4 and 40 would soon arrive, plus 12 trained sisters from the Army Nursing Reserve.

After Colenso, too, there was the highest praise, this time with a slightly different emphasis: "At a time when criticisms of everything and everybody are flying about, the admirable organisation of the Medical Department and the perfect smoothness of its working deserve the fullest recognition. It is usually that part of an army which breaks down first and is least adequate; in the present campaign it has so far proved entirely equal to all requirements."[9]

In the BMJ of December 23rd a clinical article described the various gunshot wounds (GSWs) of the campaign to date. Wounds of abdomen, groin, chest and head were detailed. There was high praise from the BMA's correspondent for the BGH at Wynberg, where "not even the most critical civilian could find anything to find fault with." Serving surgeons Colonel Supple and Major Stevenson were individually mentioned, along with the Hospital C.O. Lieutenant Colonel Hodson, and Colonel Stevenson who was in charge of the LofC.

In the same edition of the *Journal* its correspondent quoted Kruger. The Boer leader was believed to have made up his mind to eventual defeat, but "they are bent on its coming about at a cost which, to quote President Kruger, 'will stagger humanity'." "It is as well" the article went on, "to recognise this beforehand, and see that the medical *personnel* is sufficient for the future heavy demand."

Surgeon C. Marsh Breadnell, a Royal Navy surgeon with the Naval unit taking part in the Magersfontein battle, added praise from another Service. Speaking of the excellence of the Boers' defensive position, he wrote: "not a man of us knew what a veritable hornets' nest we had got into…we had anticipated a brief and easy victory and in consequence the men were not rationed…water was terribly scarce…every water cart had to beat a hasty retreat." He noticed the failings of the kilt as uniform for the climate, and made other sensible criticisms. Of the medical officers he said "The medical men have had a terrible time of it — working incessantly for 36 hours — rows and rows of dead — it is a sight, I think, would cure once and for all those worthy individuals who talk of 'the glories of war'."

An especially significant contribution came, after the Colenso battle, from Sir William MacCormac, President of the Royal College of Surgeons of England.

As well as commenting favourably on the casualty collection by the SBs and their initial application of first field dressings and splints on the soldiers, together with the swift evacuation by hospital train, he mentioned the value of sorting casualties into clinical categories of varying severity, and of labelling each casualty with a ticket giving details of wounding and clinical notes. In this battle the medical service was anticipating the future in these two now basic requirements of war surgery. An interesting omission was the work of the anaesthetists, which he did not mention. Sir William himself did not seem to have done any operating on this occasion. The opinion of Treves about this battle has already been heard; it was then that he apparently said for the first time that "The Mauser bullet is a very merciful one."

By contrast to Sir William, Treves worked hard in the theatre, often carrying out secondary procedures; he acted as a true consultant surgeon.

The loudest praise came between January and April of 1900. At a dinner at the Metropole Hotel in London on the 13th January by members of King's College, Mr Watson Cheyne, one of four more civilian surgeons appointed to go to South Africa, spoke in glowing terms. "The methods of moving sick and wounded in South Africa", he said, "are the most perfect that have yet been applied in war." Like Sir William MacCormac, he applauded the RAMC as a "regiment", stressing its efficiency as an organised Corps. The Army Nursing Reserve was also warmly praised. And as far as civilian surgeons were concerned, Mr Cheyne added tactfully that the Army surgeons were not resentful of their appointments.[10]

One Mr Jonathan Hutchison, writing the same month in the *Polyclinic*, went farther. "Never before in the history of the world were wounded soldiers more rapidly restored to the combatant ranks. The term 'wounded'", he went on, "will soon cease to have the fearful significance it once had, and all those coming under it will hardly be counted as losses, when we realise that 2/3 will probably be back in the ranks within a fortnight...the only fatal part is the heart, and this will soon be protected by a breastplate. Even head wounds are not invariably fatal."

Just as it was already being discovered that the many civilian doctors serving with the Regular Army were not at all frightened to speak their minds when the senior non-medical officers were clearly in the wrong or unjust, so the British Medical Association refused to take the official line that all was wonderful. While agreeing that the RAMC had, unlike other Arms, earned unstinted praise, its leader of February 10th attacked what it saw as the attitude of the highest ranks. Referring to the contempt shown by the Commander-in Chief at Phoenix Park, it continued:

> "It may perhaps be difficult to define what special qualifications or employments make a man a soldier; but if entire self-abnegation in the cause of duty, if patient endurance of fatigue and hardship in the course of military operations, if the profoundest disregard of danger on the battlefield, if the fact of their officers and men being large sharers in the death and injury that smite the *personnel* of an army, are any of the conditions that mark a true soldier, the Royal Army Medical Corps can say 'No men are more soldiers than we'. This must be reiterated again and again; for, in the face of these very palpable facts, there can be no doubt that in certain military quarters — and those, so far, very influential quarters — there is still a very deep-rooted feeling of animosity towards the Medical Service. Or is it possible that the feeling is rather one of jealousy, when the purely combatant administration has, to say the least, not been too successful? Specific army status has been granted to the medical department, but this has not always carried with it the recognition that is due."

On the 24th of March *The Times* joined in:

> "The case may be stated in a nutshell. A single Army Corps — in round numbers, with a LofC, 50,000 men — sent to South Africa exhausted the whole available Army Medical Directorate of England. There was not a man left at home. The source was dried up. We shall shortly have 194,000 men in this country. This leaves a balance of 144,000 men for whose medical services Parliament has made no organised provision."

On 7th April *The Times* continued:

> "The critics stated that officers only asked for rank and titles so that they might sink their profession and strut in borrowed plumes. An overwhelming answer is now forthcoming; since the commencement of the war, the Corps has steadily come to the front until at the present moment it stands acknowledged by the verdict of every officer in South Africa whose opinion is worthy

of notice as the only really efficient branch of the Service, excepting the Army Service Corps. The bestowal of substantive rank has been more than justified. The opinions of MOs are now listened to with respect, and carry a weight which was formerly unknown."

Adulation reached its highest peak at the dinner in the Reform Club on April 30th, given in honour of Sir William MacCormac and Mr Frederick Treves. The Toast to them and to the medicals was given by Lord Rosebery in which he said: "Our medical and hospital service has been practically perfect."

And then, almost overnight as it seemed, everything changed. A special correspondent wrote in *The Times* in mid May attacking the "administrative load, unnecessary forms, regulations, etc, of the Medical Services." The paper work associated with the return of wounded soldiers' kits was also criticised. The BMA at once defended the RAMC, suggesting that this was a calculated attack on the ability of the medical officers to administrate efficiently.

It was a fortnight later that the major explosion occurred. A long and dramatic letter on 29th May was to put the future of the new Corps in jeopardy. And it was the clinical competence of the medicals that was called in question.

"The time has come to speak out" was the headline — thin by popular press standards, but this was *The Times*. The report referred to the events of almost a month before; there was not the immediacy of the late 20th century.

"On Saturday 28/4 hundreds of men to my knowledge were lying in the worst stages of typhoid, with only a blanket and a thin waterproof sheet (not even that for many of them) between their aching bodies and the hard ground, with no milk and hardly any medicines, without a single nurse amongst them, only 'orderlies' rough and utterly untrained in nursing. There were 3 doctors to 350 patients."

"Nameless torture for want of any ambulance transport or simple comforts" — the account went into excruciating detail and did not forget the heavy rain. "By what incredible ignorance of then current facts, by what bankruptcy of insurance against patent dangers, were such funeral bakemeats permitted to furnish forth that ill-fated feast at the Reform Club."

"Up till now things had been fairly, but not wholly, satisfactory…in that quality (bravery) the RAMC shows no flaw; but it can no more provide a proper medical service in war than the bravery of our troops can supply tactics and strategy.

So far as the sick are concerned there have been two plagues in South Africa — the plague of blindness and the plague of whitewash."

The writer quoted the estimate of an initial limit of casualties to 5000. "Yet the lesson of every war that ever occurred is writ large in history and carved on a million tombstones — 3 sick at least for 1 wounded. They should have allowed 10 per cent of the Force — 20,000 beds."

"Was it fair to the British Public to go on thumping the tub of perfection…before the real trial had begun? It was no longer even a matter of speculation; already typhoid had opened her deadly wings, and spread them, like some monstrous vulture over march and camp and field and town, from front to base. But typhoid is known as the 'scourge of South Africa'. The danger was always patent. Was it not one's duty to think, to warn, to prepare?"

Further, the special correspondent went on, the outbreak occurred 2 months after the occupation of Bloemfontein by the Army. Bloemfontein would remain our advanced base. The innuendoes were very obvious.

The letter was signed W. BURDETT-COUTTS, M.P. for WESTMINSTER.

This letter would colour the whole of the rest of the campaign for the Medical Services, and have a great effect in further lowering the already shaken confidence of the whole nation. It was typical of the sort of media intervention which would become an increasing hazard in all future wars in the 20th century. It was mainly as a result of the letter that there would be a Royal Commission after the war was over to examine the role and adequacy of the Army Medical Services.

The inevitable sequence of happenings followed. The Under Secretary for War, Mr Wyndham, answered questions in the House. He revealed that a letter had been received from Lord Roberts on June 6th, explaining that railway bridges had all been blown by the enemy (confirming what Lieutenant Matthew Fell had said several times in his diary, that the railway behind the

British front was blown more times by the Boers than the news reporters ever were aware). This had meant delay in getting supplies up which were a high priority. He and Lord Methuen had repeatedly visited the town and the sick. Suffering would have been much worse had the medical arrangements not been so good.

Bloemfontein was not a large town, the Field Marshal continued in his courteous reply, but all suitable buildings had been converted to hospitals. He had sent up as soon as possible tents, equipment, nurses. "I can quite understand", he went on, "that people who have no practical experience in such matters are much concerned to hear the hardships which sick and wounded soldiers have to undergo in time of war, especially when they are not aware of the many difficulties involved. Mr Cheyne and Mr Cheadle the civilian surgeons would be returning soon and could give an up-to-date account." Finally Lord Roberts, whose only son had been killed while serving under the command of Buller, stated that if any men "of sound and common sense be sent to South Africa to investigate, he will guarantee all assistance and if any recommendations are made, he will be the most pleased of all." The reply should have been enough to satisfy any reasonable person.

At Dorchester Town Hall, Mr Treves spoke of the Bloemfontein hospital controversy. "A terrible bomb had burst in London with the report in *The Times* of Mr Burdett-Coutts", he told his audience. "I could not imagine anything more likely to give rise to a greater panic — it sounded like the Crimea", he continued. He went on to explain the real nature of military medicine and military surgery. A huge strain had been placed on the surgeons, especially at Colenso. They had coped well with higher-than-expected casualties. As far as lying on the ground was concerned, he himself had lain on the ground for three weeks on end. The nature of mobile military hospitals was such that they could not take beds. But why no huts? Men were a thousand times better off in tents, was the answer. Mr Burdett-Coutts had spoken of brutality and neglect; this was hard and untrue. The Medical Corps were glad of his firm support, for they knew this was an issue that would not go away.

Mr Burdett-Coutts' outburst may have been the result of the first impression he had of military medicine when he visited

No 3 BGH many miles distant from the front line. In April he wrote a despatch extolling the clean sheets, flowerbeds, help from ladies which he found there. He wrote of personally tasting the excellent range of food offered by the excellent cooks. He thought it very strange that food was supplied by the Army Service Corps and beds by the Ordnance.

Conditions at the front he found very different, and he seemed to have forgotten all he had previously said. "The only thing the Army Medical Department possesses are medical stores." In another emotionally charged despatch, he wrote fiercely against men nursing: "A glaring blot on our present Army system...it is a violation of nature — for this is women's work, not men's." Men being found to nurse at the front he called "an antediluvian prejudice. Since the Crimea, we have fought no war where nurses were possible; they can rarely go to savage countries." He gave a long list of answers to his own list of supposed reasons why women could not be employed.

Counter-reports appeared at once. A typical one was from the *Daily Telegraph* correspondent: "It is well known that the outbreak of typhoid from Modder River to Paaderberg was of such a character as no human foresight could have anticipated. There is a modicum of truth in Mr Burdett-Coutts' charges, plus gross exaggeration. Deficiency of clothing is admitted, but it was impossible to meet the sudden demand."

The emergency debate in the House of Commons showed party behaviour following the usual lines — the opposition refusing to see any good in the Government's policy and vice versa. The Ministerial statement agreed the sick were in terrible hardship, but emphasised that re-supply was entirely adequate. It was pointed out that typhoid patients could not be moved as Mr Coutts had demanded without killing them.

In the later debate Burdett-Coutts was cheered by the Opposition. Mr David Lloyd George spoke, nastily criticising arrangements made for the Welsh Volunteer hospital. (Welsh Nationalists were strongly pro-Boer at this time). It was admitted that for the number of troops in South Africa, the medical cover was numerically inadequate. Many letters were quoted, attacking the War Office and senior generals for their condescension to the RAMC and its officers. Summing up for the Opposition, Sir Henry Campbell-Bannerman made sensible points of criticism and spoke positively; the Prime Minister, Lord Balfour, made the standard reply for the Government, saying all was well. But it was made clear that as most of the RAMC orderlies had themselves fallen sick with typhoid, regimental orderlies had to be used instead. It was also made clear that had Burdett-Coutts waited a day or two longer before writing his letter, he would have found that much extra medical help had arrived; earlier, military supplies had to have precedence.

A Hospitals Commission began to investigate what had happened immediately upon arriving in Capetown on 21st August. Its Blue Book was issued on 22nd January, 1901. It had three findings:

1) There had been a deplorable want of foresight by the War Office,

2) The Army Medical Services were exonerated. But the RAMC were deficient in strength, training and organisation,

3) There was no convincing evidence for Mr Burdett-Coutts' extreme allegations.[11]

The M.P. who had started the whole affair wrote six columns of reply in *The Times* on February 11th, again full of rhetoric. He did not desist until March 23rd, 1901, ending his last communication: "Come another war, Thomas Atkins will have a better time."

Mr Burdett-Coutts does not emerge with credit from the affair. He reported wildly, without any knowledge of the nature of the disease involved, or of the particular difficulties the Medical Corps had to overcome. His subsequent refusal to admit this, or retract any of his most extreme remarks, even when reasoned replies were given, show his limitations. They also showed how dangerous such an intervention could be.

Later Phases Of The War.
The autumn of 1900 saw a surer control of the activities of the troops as they followed Field Marshal Roberts' advance from Graspan from February 10th onwards (being in the Southern hemisphere, the seasons were reversed). General Cronje had to withdraw from his defensive system of trenches at Magersfontein, and at Paaderberg on the Modder River he was

surrounded. He eventually surrendered with 4000 men on the nineteenth anniversary of Majuba Hill, the 27th of February, 1900. Ladysmith and Kimberley were relieved; the doctors who went in with the Army noted the contrast between the inhabitants' nutrition and general medical state — those in Kimberley looked well-nourished while those in Ladysmith were thin and ill.

The epidemic of enteric fever, so sensationally described by Mr Burdett-Coutts, plus the need to repair the blown rail lines between Bloemfontein and Capetown, delayed the next advance of Lord Roberts for seven weeks. His force of now 100,000 moved on Pretoria. Mafeking was relieved on the 17th of May. After the Diamond Hill and Belfast battles, plus the capture of Koomati Port, the war should have been over. Sadly, a further nearly 2 years of angry warfare followed. The Boer leaders tried to regain the initiative in early 1901. Botha raided Natal, while De Wet, Hertzog and Kritzinger separately invaded Cape Colony and tried to raise the Dutch there. These daring offensives failed. Very few Cape Dutch rose. The Dutch asked for peace, but negotiations broke down. The last phase involved the sweeping up of the enemy, the phase of the lines of blockhouses and of the concentration camps.

The Medical Corps over these second and third phases of the war — the military victory followed by the eventual overcoming of the guerrilla resistance — were closely involved. In the military phase Field Marshal Roberts set out to deceive the enemy over his tactics and therefore moved forces about rapidly. Later, brigade-sized units had to march and counter-march equally rapidly, seeking out groups of enemy still offering fierce resistance or counter-attacks. Significant casualties and sick continued till the very end of the war.[12]

As in the first phase — of defeats when General Buller was in command — it was the BCs, the field hospitals, and the RMOs, who bore the brunt of this often exhausting moving. 15 Bearer Company, whose C.O. was Colonel Rawlinson, were ordered by Lord Roberts himself on February 23rd, only two days after their arrival following a hectic period, to collect wounded at Cronje's laager. During an overnight camp *en route* Cpl Dyer RAMC was excited to find the unit visited by no less than 3 senior officers — Roberts, Kitchener, and French. 15 BC returned over March 1st,

2nd, 4th and 5th to the Modder River base. This unit was in constant movement over the next several months.

But by now the better organisation of the Army was evident. Water supplies though variable were always adequate. Food was never short, though it had never been, although half rations were often ordered to save weight on the march. At this time, the ration boxes were labelled "Senior Catering Officer, Field Force, from which came the soldiers' expression 'SCOFF'." Rest camps as long as 2–3 days — 15 BC had a rest on March 3rd on their way back to Modder -with the opportunity for a good wash — were used sensibly, although they produced some medical problems.

Ration reductions to save weight were important when a day's march might be 30 miles(48km) — but the soldiers were encouraged to buy provisions locally, apparently in sterling. Bread cost 1 shilling and 6 pence for a 2 lb loaf(7p per kg), tea 3 shillings per kg(15p), jam 2 shillings a tin(10p), Quaker oats, which provided roughage, 2 shillings a tin(10p).

Bearer Companies necessarily accompanied their "flying columns", but at times were kept at a stationary hospital to reinforce its staff — especially if typhoid was prevalent. They were also used to assist hospital train staff.

The role of the senior RAMC NCOs merits mention and recognition. There is no doubt that these NCOs established themselves in the Boer War as entirely comparable with their opposite numbers in the teeth arms, though performing a different task. They had responsibility for ordering stores and medicines, making weekly returns not only of their own men's state but also of the physical state of the mules and horses in their units to the Veterinary Corps. They were responsible for the issue of clothing to their soldiers, and for the issue of mail and the rum ration. They did not, from their own accounts, regard the paper work they had to do as excessive.[13]

Discipline, too, was in their remit. S/Sgt J.H. Gibbon, a moustachioed veteran with a row of medals, disagreed with his section officer whose punishments he regarded as too lenient, especially to native drivers. He considered a good flogging would do much more good than a 10 shilling(50p) fine!

Quartermasters, as they always have, made a vital contribution. Their work of re-supply was extra hard in South Africa, because of the distances, the terrain, and the uncertainty of the horses and bullocks which drew the waggons. While every other RAMC category seemed to find time to write a diary, no Quartermaster ever did. They were just too busy.

The Royal Army Medical Corps saw and could comment upon the whole range of happenings in a way that few others in the South African Army could do. They followed all branches of the Field Force. They took part in the battles. Edward Hewitt, commissioned in August 1899, collected 40 wounded near Kimberley; rifle bullets "passed by but I was too busy to notice." They kept trying to ensure hygiene was good. They wrote letters of commiseration. They had trouble with their C.O.s: "getting on better with my boss now", wrote one. "It must be because he's fed better in a standing camp."

They were sometimes captured by the enemy and released after their officer had parleyed, often with a Boer general. At Bothasville on 20th October, 1900, they came on a gaol where they found, as well as "47 loyal Boers", "a British MO, nursing sister and orderly, who were left behind with Lord Methuen's force with sick and wounded." At Nooitgedacht the doctors were appalled to find British prisoners of the Boers released by General French "half-starved and toothless."

Sometimes a disaster occurred. On some occasions a Bearer Company moving with part of a battle group became involved in an action and lost both MOs and men. Doctors nursing sisters and medical orderlies died of typhoid. During the enterica epidemic at Bloemfontein especially, doctors and nurses watched with the sorrow of the best members of caring professions: "and so the little cortege moved off", wrote a doctor in his diary, "insignificant, unnoticed, with its unsung hero, who, to some one, somewhere, was, perhaps, the one man in all the world." Sister D.L. Harris, of the New Zealand Contingent, left Wynberg on 30th April and arrived with two other sisters at Bloemfontein on May 7th. On May 14th she wrote: "This hospital is terribly over-crowded. It is equipped for 500, and once had nearly 1700 cases — almost all are enteric, and nearly all are very bad. The orderlies are terribly over-worked, and have only about one night a week in bed, so they are often found asleep on duty. The men are wonderfully cheerful and are the nicest patients, and take all their troubles in a most philosophical manner." Sister Harris comes through her diary as a most kind and gentle person. She speaks of her fellow sisters who became ill, of New Zealand and Canadian doctors she worked with, and, amusingly, of how the sisters "went into town for tea" on their afternoons off. There was the humorous side, as always. It is amusing, in view of the Member of Parliament for Westminster's remarks, to read the report of No 3 BGH — at one time commanded by Lieutenant Colonel A. Keogh — later re-numbered No 12, and find it was for some reason a small hospital with between 360 and 580 beds. The photograph of the medical officers shows them to look very fat — the result of the excellent diet enjoyed also by Mr Burdett-Coutts! One of its interesting photographs is of the snowstorm in May 1902, when the Nursing Sisters wore long cloaks in the snow.

One medical officer laughingly recalled how a new C.O. (Colonel Joynt) had objected to one of his MOs wearing a white coat on the wards, saying "We are officers." Another tells of an officious Colonel checking a soldier for not recognising his rank who replied "I didn't think you were a proper doctor!"

The attitude of the medical officers to the Boer non-combatants was equivocal. Most were rather disinterested and rather looked down on what they saw as the gross lack of hygiene the farms and settlements showed. One doctor commented that he had gone into a Kaffir kraal and found it much fresher and less smelly than the Boer ones; he judged this to be because it was a Christian community, whose medical missionary had taught the natives basic hygiene which they had not forgotten. Several commented on the ugliness of the Boer women, with "their huge dirty coal-scuttle bonnets." There was concern at the bad conditions in the Boer camps, and one MO warned that the bitterness he found amongst the Boer women would last more than a generation.[14]

Lieutenant F.J. Palmer RAMC, who had been at Trinity College Dublin as a student, was posted to the 1st Leicesters on 2nd May, 1900. His writing adds a poetry to the majority of more mundane diaries. His accounts of the hot days and frosty nights, when he awoke to find his hair and eyebrows sparkling with frost, he strengthened with accompanying photos: "Must take a photo of the frosty veldt or you will think I am exaggerating." He gives a picture of the life of an RMO which could be used as a training booklet: the early start, the patrols going ahead to make sure the railway line was clear of mines, the pilot engine then going ahead, the visits he made on his pony to all the companies of the battalion, his concern with men's kit, food, accidents through carelessness or mishap, his disappointment at being told by his C.O. that he would have to stay back while 4 companies of the battalion advanced with a reinforcement group, and the periods when his professional skill was needed.

Lieutenant Palmer was a good regimental officer. He had access to the battalion Intelligence maps, and knew the names of all the farms, features, and hazards as well as his infantry fellow-officers. He used to light his pipe by unscrewing the lens of his field glasses, and using it as a burning glass. He enjoyed "a good dinner" after a busy day in action. He knew all about the tactical problems: "Snipers all round. 2 men killed as they slept — head wounds…we could never see anything to fire at and could do little to keep down the sniping." He had a clear knowledge of the general political background of the war, too. He respected the enemy: "one cannot help admiring these doppers for the stubborn way in which they continue to resist, when all hope of ultimate success must be over….when the prejudices of war have been removed by time, we shall ungrudgingly yield them the credit they deserve."

But he saw the need for hard decision. "We shall have to start farm burning etc to stop the guerrilla warfare. Leniency having proved unavailing, we are now burning all deserted farms to stop the guerrilla warfare into which this war is fast degenerating."

Age-long grouses of the military he expressed as soldiers always will: "Rear-guard again. I am quite sick of it. Of course K's bde (General Kitchener's brigade) is the favoured one in this Division, where from the general down everyone of importance seems to be a rifleman."

He kept in touch with his fellow medical officers: "Got leave from the Colonel and rode to Volksgust today to visit Major Hinde of ours, whom I knew so well in the BC. Had tea with 18th Hussars." After Pretoria was taken, he went along to the BGH when it was set up, to chat as doctors always do about medicine and interesting patients. After all his hard months in the front line, he recalled he "wished he too could become an inmate, but with something not too serious"! But after the victory parade, at which every officer and man was dressed in new uniforms asked for by Lord Roberts, and obtained by return in those days when Great Britain was the richest country on earth, he became a member of the officers' club. There was no bar on RAMC officers now; they were accepted as officers like all the others. "The club is quite neat, with a billiard table, and it is a pleasure to spend an afternoon there after my wandering life."

Captain Beach, too, wrote in striking, almost poetic terms of the scenery — the veldt, the sunrises and sunsets.

Like all doctors, they enjoyed to laugh at things. Food: "Biscuits blow you out. Bully is awful in hot weather." Marching and counter-marching: "I can sympathise with the Wandering Jew." "Boers (prisoners) boasted that 10,000 Russians had invaded India." Of the newly appointed Intelligence Officers: "a worthy gentleman appointed by the WO (War Office) to collect lies and rumours and circulate them by means of daily bulletins...uses an army of Kaffirs who say whatever they think will please." "We call the Kaffirs 'The Black Watch'."

And, like all RAMC officers before and since, they were conscious of the differences between regiments and corps: "We get on very well indeed with the swells in the cavalry. How on earth army men can treat us as half civilians after this I don't know. We share all the dangers and have already had many officers killed and wounded."

These immediate personal accounts of officers and soldiers of the Royal Army Medical Corps give as good a picture, or a better one, than any third person narrative. The first achievement of the members of that Corps in their first major test was to win a status they were never to lose, and like Lieutenant Palmer, they were justifiably proud. They were members of a caring profession who had chosen to serve in the harsh world of war as soldiers of the Queen. Though non-combatant, their bravery — perhaps the first virtue of the soldier[15] — was now established and recognized. Medical officers had certainly won the Victoria Cross in previous local engagements and major wars, but they were regimental and not RAMC. In the first Boer War of 1881, Lance Corporal John Farmer was awarded the V.C. at Majuba.

In this War, Lieutenant Henry Douglas won the V.C. at Magersfontein on December 11th, 1899 and Major Babtie at Colenso on December 15th. Later Lieutenant Edgar Inkson, William Nickerson, Regular officers, and Captain Thomas Crean, a Reserve officer of The Imperial Light Horse, won the award.

Arthur Martin-Leake was another who left his civilian appointment to serve. From Hemel Hempstead he joined the Hertfordshire Company of The Imperial Yeomanry as a trooper. He then joined the South African Constabulary as Surgeon Captain under General Baden-Powell. On 8th February, 1902 Captain Martin-leake was awarded the Victoria Cross:

> "For great devotion to duty and self-sacrifice at Vlakfontein, 8 Feb 1902, when he went out into the firing-line to dress a wounded man under very heavy fire from about 40 Boers only 100 yards off. When he had done all he could for him, he went over to a badly wounded officer, and while trying to place him in a more comfortable position he was shot three times. He only gave up when thoroughly exhausted, and then he refused water until other wounded men had been served."

Captain Martin-Leake was operated on by Sir Victor Horsley, and while he was convalescing, he studied for and passed the FRCS of England in 1903. After the War he left the Corps. In 1914 he would become the first man to be awarded a bar to his V.C.[16]

Peace.

The Boer War eventually ended in 1902 with the Peace of Vereenigning. By common consent, the settlement was a very fair one, which gave the defeated Boers a considerable degree of safeguard for their own areas of the country and a considerable degree of political independence. Sadly, the extreme Boer element destroyed the settlement 40 years later; their apartheid and republicanism brought them isolation and a hatred in the wider world which would never have come about had they maintained the British link and the tolerance which went with it.

The fairness of the settlement in no way reduced the dislike of the other European Powers for Great Britain, and the risk of further conflict soon became evident. During the war itself, the sending of a squadron of the British Navy through the English Channel had served as a reminder to those other powers of Britain's might at sea and as a warning to them not to interfere. At the beginning of this century, Britain could act militarily as the USA would be capable of doing at the end of it.

Notes and references

CHAPTER 2

[1]The German Account of the War in South Africa, translated by Colonel W.H.H. Waters, CVO, RA, John Henry, London, 1904. This very professional account is recommended for further study. Of interest is its support for British Strategy in the later phases of the war. The diary of Captain A.F. Russell, RMO to the Royal Scots Greys for much of the war (later Colonel Russell, CMG) contains a great deal of interesting detail and comment on the policy of removing Boer civilians to isolated camps. The Greys' padre, posted in in November 1900, had worked for four years in South Africa and was a great friend of the Dutch, yet approved of destroying small towns. Russell describes going to Boer farms and taking away families to camps, and how they all hated it. The padre was taken also, as many young women were amongst those removed. "We ought", said Captain Russell, "to have a brigade of sturdy matrons for this job !"

[2]The "tally" was the casualty ticket tied to the wounded man with details of his time and place of wounding, diagnoses, and initial treatment. It was the ancestor of the contemporary field medical card and envelope.

[3]The Scotch cart was the name of the box-shaped waggon used to carry all the RMO's medical kit and large enough to transport casualties if required.

[4]For the account of Colenso by the successful Boer General, see "General Botha at the battle of Colenso, 15 December, 1899" by C.J. Barnard, South African Mil. History Journal, *1*, 7, p 1, Dec. 1970. This gives Botha's report and comment in Afrikaans with English translation. It is also of interest in giving descriptions of alleged misuse of the Red Cross by the British.

[5]The German Account of the War in South Africa, as well as giving detailed information about the small arms and artillery used in this battle and elsewhere, gives clear praise for the medical services. Noting

first the medical plan to cover the battle of Colenso (as recorded above) it goes on:

"The medical service was hampered less by the number of wounded than by the extent of the battlefield. A volunteer bearer corps of 2400 men undertook the task of bringing the wounded to the DS and to the Field Hospitals. By 5pm all the wounded had been bandaged and were in the hands of the doctors; they were then sent to Estcourt in the ambulance train, which did the journey from Chievely to Estcourt and back 5 times between 2pm on December 15th. and 8am on December 18th. Some of the casualities were sent to Pietermaritzburg and Durban, but as there was not sufficient hospital equipment in those places, it was decided to send the sufferers to Cape Town, to take advantage of the favourable climate and local conditions there. No proper hospital ships were available, but a transport was fitted up in 4 1/2 days for the accomodation of 250 invalids."

[6]The father of Field Marshal Lord Wavell, who was a major allied commander in the Second World War, ending his service as Viceroy of India.

[7]"Shadows on the move — mobile radiological services up to 1918", Jean Guy, 1994. This excellent account, with a full set of references, of the use of radiography on the battlefield in the British Army from its first use in India in 1897, in the North West Frontier in the Tirah campaign that year. At his own expense Surgeon-Major Beevor equipped himself with X-ray apparatus which was carried successfully over difficult terrain and in appalling weather. He was photographed using the apparatus to examine a patient outside his tent — one of 200 such examinations. On his return he demonstrated his radoigraphs to admiring lay, medical, and military audiences.

[8]80 years later, the M.O.D. used the same device with respect to the Sponsored (Specialist) units of the Territorial Army.

[9]*The Times*, 26th December, 1899.

[10]Mr Cheyne's denial covered the fact that there were undoubtly tensions — resentment being felt by some Regulars against the "civil gentlemen", as some RAMC officers called their new colleagues, and vice versa. See diaries of Lieut. Blair, 1st. Vol. Hampshires and Captain Cameron, Black Watch, in RAMC archives, Wellcome Institute.

[11]Minutes of Evidence taken before the Royal Commission appointed to consider and report on the Care and Transport of the Sick and Wounded during the South African Campaign, HMSO, London, 1901. Price 5 shillings and 2 pence (25p). Witnesses were examined in London and Netley in July, 1900, in South Africa in August, 1900, and in Bloemfontein in September, 1900. Other witnesses were questioned in Pretoria in September, when Lord Roberts gave evidence,

and in Johannesburg. It may be thought that at this time soldiers would be too scared to criticise freely, and that frank criticism is a product of the so-called liberal late 20th century. Reading what soldiers actually said in 1900 quickly destroys the notion. Their criticisms were for the most part directed at the Regular RAMC, and some were very fair indeed. But overall the evidence was supportive.

[12]See "The Activity of General Pieter Hendrick Kritzninger's Boer Commando, 15 Dec 1900 – 6 Dec 1901", Military Hist. J. Johannesberg, Dec. 1970, *1*,7, p 30–32.

[13]See the diaries of Major David Bruce, while O.C. 1/2 No 18 British Field Hospital, 4/5/1900 – 28/8/1900, Lieut. F.J. Palmer, RAMC, RMO 1st. Leicesters, 1900, Lieut. Hugh M. Morton, RAMC, especially relating to ration scales, S/Sgt. J.H. Gibbons, RAMC, and Cpl. R. Dyer, 19 B.C. RAMC, later 15 B.C., papers and letters of Colonel T.B. Beach, RAMC, "Cavalry Doctor", letters written from the field 1900–1911 by Colonel A.F. Russell, CMG, Colonel J.C. Rutherford, Major General Sir Maurice Holt, Lieutnant General Sir Matthew Fell, Lieut- Colonel C.H. Butchell, Pte. W. Furniss, RAMC, Pte. W. Sykes, Pte. Fred Bly, Sister D.L. Harris, R.N.Z. Nursing Corps, and others.

[14]Diaries of Boer combatants in English are not easy to obtain. A comprehensive one is "Diary of a Boer", by G.S. Preller, Archives, National Army Museum, Ac No 8012–77, which has a good deal to say about the British medical support, including conversations with RAMC officers. His style is flowery by British standards, full of Biblical quotations to support the Boer cause, and with an inflexible determination to see no good in the "English".

The Boer antagonism to the African is also very evident. Letters quoted from President Steyn (Sept. 1901, vol 3, p196) and from Vice-President S.W. Burger (p197–204) in Preller's diary are particularly interesting.

[15]"Defeat into Victory", Field Marshal Viscount Slim, Cassell, London, 1956.

[16]Despatches from Lieut-General Lord Methuen, *London Gazette*, 26th January, 1899, give details of medical arrangements for the battles of Belmont, Enslin, Modder River, and of 16th March, 1900, of those for the battle of Maggersfontein, including citations for bravery.

Chapter 3

After the Boer War. The Royal Commission. The clinical achievements and problems of the Medical Services. New professionalism.

Perspective
The first military specification for an aeroplane was drawn up in 1908 by the U.S. Navy Department. The next year the U.S. purchased a Wright machine. In 1910 came the first firing of a rifle and dropping of lead darts from an aircraft.

THE ROYAL COMMISSION of 1903.
The Boer War had exposed grave deficiencies in the British Army, in training but especially in the organisation and competence of the Senior Staff at the War Office. Deficiencies in Government were not reviewed,[1] but Government alarm plus public concern demanded a thorough review of all aspects of the Army. The Medical Services were not exempt from this close scrutiny, in spite of their undoubted successes and emergence as one of the most dedicated and effective elements within the Field Force in South Africa.

The term "Medical Services" is a more strictly correct one than "RAMC", as the services providing medical care in the Boer War were as much civilian as military. While the most shrill criticism during hostilities had been by Mr Burdett-Coutts of the medical management of the enteric fever epidemic at Bloemfontein, others had undoubtedly emerged after the war was over, and many were made by what were described as "the civilian surgeons."

The Report of the Royal Commission, and especially the Minutes of Evidence, showed clearly the differences in emphasis and priority which the Regular Medical Staff and their civilian colleagues had. By and large the Regular Army witnesses had justifiable complaints about their treatment by the "Big Army", but otherwise thought in terms of numbers of medical officers and men on establishment, scales of equipment and the collection and general care of the sick and wounded. The civilian contribution was of two kinds; the first was criticism of equipment and clinical ability they found amongst their Regular officer colleagues. The second will be discussed later.

The Commission's Report amply confirmed how short the General Staff were on foresight as far as the RAMC was concerned. The warnings of the British Medical Journal of December 23rd, 1899, when its leader quoted President Kruger's admission that the war would end for the Boers in eventual defeat, followed at once by his assertion that the Boers were "bent on its coming about at a cost which will stagger humanity", were proved correct. The BMJ leader had gone on to insist "it is well to recognise this (shortage) beforehand, and see that the medical personnel is sufficient for the future heavy demand." The even more forthright leader in *The Times* of 24th March, 1900, already quoted, but worth repeating, was also confirmed: "The case may be stated in a nutshell. A single Army Corps — in round numbers, with line of communication, 50,000 men — sent to South Africa exhausted the whole available Army Medical Department of England. There was not a man left at home; the source dried up...we shall shortly have 194,000 men in this country. This leaves a balance of 144,000 for whose medical services parliament has made no organised provision": Surgeon General Jameson's evidence showed that the establishment was not even *equal to peace time* requirements. Had it not been for the influx of civilian volunteers, it would not have been possible to provide medical support for the Army in Southern Africa.

The War Office had considered that 99 civilian surgeons would have to be recruited to make good the deficiency in the Army Medical Service on outbreak of a war. In the Boer War there had been 9 senior consulting surgeons — and 385 civilian surgeons. This was against a grand total of 476 RAMC MOs. Colonel W. Johnston, in giving evidence to the commission, stated that this meant 75 per cent of the medical officers were civilians.[2] In fact, since a large proportion of the Regulars were either senior officers in administrative posts or junior as RMOs, the number of civilians at hospital levels greatly outnumbered the army officers. In a few hospitals, even the Officer Commanding was civilian. Mr Charles Stonham, CMG, FRCSEng., senior surgeon and senior lecturer at Westminster Hospital, commanded the Imperial Yeomanry Field hospital with distinction. When pressed by the Royal Commission examiners about "a certain feeling of distrust among military officers of the skill and professional experience of doctors of the RAMC as compared with civil doctors" Colonel Johnston could only reply, lamely, "An Army doctor is a general practitioner in the fullest sense of the word. It is unfair to compare us to these specialists."

This inevitable distinction between "civilians" and "regulars" with respect to their clinical professional ability came out again and again in the evidence. Colonel Johnston's remark, "This distrust is very painful to every member of the Medical Service",[3] showed the still-existing anxiety Corps doctors had of the reality of their support by their non-medical Service seniors. The suggestion made in the British Medical Journal of 4th. October, 1902 by Surgeon General J.B. Hamilton, that civil doctors should have been commissioned as local or acting Lieutenants, would not have helped; many of the civilians were much too mature to have worked holding such a junior rank.

Questions about how the difficulty in gaining post-graduate experience of Regular RAMC specialists could be overcome formed another important part of the Report. They raised important issues for the medical professional training of full-time members of the Corps, and what was written in 1902 could have been written 90 years later. The senior AMS officers accepted without question the necessity for post-graduate experience having to be gained in a civilian hospital, and indeed pressed for it.[4] Unfortunately the London Medical Schools they had approached usually refused.[5] The further plea the AMS made to the Commission was for medical officers returning from a tour in India or elsewhere overseas to have the right to attend refresher courses on their return. The problem then as now was that such leave would require a larger staff, or the employment of civilians in their places, and so would cost money. Some who had applied had been unable to take a place offered, as there was no-one to do their work in the military hospital or unit.[6]

The Senior Medical Officers naturally defended their Corps against criticism by the Commission, and this was particularly noticeable when the professional standard of their MOs was called in question. Asked if he considered the officers entering the RAMC were equal to those in civil life, the D.G. replied "Not only that; I think they were much superior. I do not think, perhaps, they were the very cream of the profession, but I think the average is high."

General Jameson was questioned closely:

"A few years ago there was a difficulty in getting the class of men you wished to have; and that was before you took up the position?"

D.G. "Yes, and my time, too, there was difficulty."

"That was owing to their status, in great measure, in the Army, and insufficiency of pay, was it not?"

D.G. "Exactly. They found, or they thought, they could do better in civil life; and there were certain conditions that the medical profession itself did not approve of with regard to social standing and army rank."

"So that at times it was almost impossible to get the men that were wanted"?

D.G. "Nobody came up. There were no examinations held at all for some time, because there were no candidates."

"In short, the Service may be said to have been boycotted?"

D.G. "Public opinion, of course, exercises a great influence on young doctors as upon anybody else, and the feeling throughout the (medical) schools was antagonistic to the medical department."

"We have evidence that in the Continental Armies, in Germany and Austria, and in Russia, the position of the medical officer is better. He is recognised as being equal, socially and every respect, to any of the military officers?"

D.G. "I think it is a great pity it should not exist here."

This part of the Report makes it even more clear that the RAMC medical officers had still, in spite of their recent excellent record, a long way to go to achieve the full recognition they deserved, from civilians also.

But there was another group of "civilians, yet not quite civilians" whose appearance in the Boer War was of great historical importance. Their contribution was in historical terms much more significant than that of the "civilian surgeons." These were the Volunteer Medical Staff Corps; it is surprising that they were never mentioned by the D.G. when he gave evidence to the Royal Commission, although the young MOs in the field had been well aware of their contribution.[7] Colonel Johnston referred to them in his examination. 100 all ranks of the London Company who had volunteered for the war were divided amongst the Regular RAMC, the Imperial Yeomanry Hospital at Deilfontein, and the Imperial Yeomanry Bearer Company. There were many others.

The Imperial Yeomanry Bearer Company shares with the Australian Medical Contingent in South Africa the credit of being the first medical units to work on the lines of the present Field Ambulance, in effect the Bearer Company and the Field Hospital combined. The bright, forward-thinking Australians had had the same idea; both groups, unhindered by fear of regulations, found it worked and went on using it.

As far as equipment was concerned, the Regular officers defended it, but the senior civilian consultants remained critical. While surgical instruments were adequate, many were out of date. They also criticised the amount of administration so many RAMC had to do, in relation to equipment. Both Treves and Ogston agreed; they saw senior clinical men in the Regular RAMC "having all their time taken up with accounting for every stretcher and blanket, so that they had no time for anything else." "In a civil hospital", said Treves, "it would be preposterous to suggest that the senior surgeon should be answerable for blankets and all these things. At the great hospital of Maritzburg at Fort Napier, one of the best medical officers as a medical man never saw a patient, he was entirely engaged in office work...then as to the Field Hospital, its equipment is based upon certain tabulated forms, and is supposed to be quite complete in itself; and the result is that in the many journeys we had to make in Natal up to the Tugela and back again, we were dragging with us what amounted to tons of useless material....I suppose I would not be using any exaggeration if I said we could have thrown away quite half our outfit, and not missed it...there was a very large number of boxes of drugs which could never be required and were never opened, but had to be dragged about...."

While conceding that there is no more common accusation against a government department than that something is deficient which ought to have been there, Sir Frederick made the suggestion that as well as a depot of medical stores at the base, there should be an advanced depot of medical stores, from which only essential and locally necessary items were drawn.

Treves further noted that the practice of wounded being brought to a collecting point and subsequently to a first dressing station was wasteful; he also emphasised the absolute necessity for clear clinical notes on the casualty label. He was another observer who saw the need to combine the BC and field hospital: "It would be much better if the bearer company were a part of the field hospital, and could work under the instructions of the officer in charge of that hospital...who will be a man with the rank of colonel."

Treves' next point was that there should be a large mobile field hospital with each column. He had seen at once, in Natal, the number of lives lost by wounded, especially with large compound fractures or intra-abdominal injuries, having to be " lifted into an ambulance and jolted 10 or 12 miles"(16–20km). He went on: "There is no doubt that the mortality of war is very largely increased by inefficient transport. The experiment was tried in Natal of having at the head of the column a large field hospital, to which I was attached, and it was an unqualified success. That was the first time it was ever employed...practically the whole of the wounded in Natal came through the field hospital and therefore had first class treatment as soon as it could be got...bad cases must, of course, be left but if you had a big F.H. you could keep them...we kept our very badly wounded after Spion Kop...it is the dragging of the man about that kills him...." He noted too the failure of the "rigid English ambulances, compared to the light carts such as the Indian two-wheeled Tonga." When told that the Service evidence was that the Mark V ambulance (the standard British model) "stood the work across country" he replied, "Yes, but the patients did not." Regular officers questioned, however, rejected criticism of the Mark V.

The bulk of the medical officers in the field hospital where Treves worked were civil surgeons. He was full of praise for them, calling them "splendid." He also, when asked if he would say that the medical work in the war had been done well, replied "Admirably done, and Mr Brodrick's Committee had rectified most of the faults that were apparent to us".[8]

Sir Frederick Treves' evidence to the Royal Commission deserves study. But it was very obvious that, as a senior medical person he obtained both staff and equipment which a low-ranking MO could not have even hoped for. His was the only field hospital that had nursing sisters — he obtained General Buller's authority to employ two, and they served at Colenso. Later in the war, others were employed forward. "The idea was that a wounded man should have as good attention on the veldt as he would have in London, and the War Office for that purpose gave me an exceedingly elaborate outfit."

Treves demanded, and got, the best facilities available. His authority made this possible. He was quick to praise and not in the least afraid of the senior generals.

The second senior figure who was not afraid to criticise constructively was Professor Alexander Ogston of Aberdeen University. Unlike Treves, he went to South Africa under his own private arrangements. Already well acquainted with foreign systems of military surgery from his visits to the Continent, he arrived in Africa in December 1899. His comments were as forthright as an Aberdonian's could be; his opinion "that England had not an Army Medical Service adequate for a European war, or such a war as this in South Africa proved to be", was formed from what he saw for himself between January and July, 1900. He visited General Gateacre's column before Stormberg, French's column at Rensberg; he served with Lord Methuen's Modder River column from Kimberley to Kronstad; he was with it immediately after Magersfontein.

His two most severe strictures were against the lack of elementary hygiene of the RAMC soldiers with the failure of the system to instruct them, and for the lack of laboratory facilities. He was also concerned at the lack of X-ray apparatus available. His contribution towards the controversy over the enteric epidemic will be seen later.

Ogston like Treves saw the Regular Army surgeon as deficient not in potential ability, but in training and experience: "They are not equal simply from want of practice."

The third senior civilian who gave evidence to the Royal Commission was Sir Alfred Fripp. His evidence was more amusing and apparently light-hearted than either Treves' or Ogston's, but was no less important. He had gone to Africa in February 1900 with the Imperial Yeomanry Hospital of 520 beds, later enlarged to 1000. He visited many military hospitals, but saw the war very much more from the aspect of the civilian — more so than the other two.

Fripp was aware of the advantage the civil hospitals had of being able to obtain extras which the military had difficulty in requisitioning through official channels. He was quite scathing in his criticism of the relationship between the RAMC and the senior Generals: "all the senior officers, from the PMO (Sir William Wilson) downwards are impressed with a sort of feeling first of all, that they are looked at askance — that their branch is secondary; and next, that they must not approach any commanding officer...without their knees chattering together with alarm and fright; they must not think of advising him that it really would be good for the Army if a camp was not pitched on a certain proposed site because it is covered by stinking horses in various degrees of decomposition. My impression is that Lord Roberts would have been only too delighted if somebody had warned him by saying to him...that a site was already fouled."

Fripp too, though feeling at first that it would be better if doctors had no rank, had come round to the view that it was essential to give them status and credibility when dealing with the non-medical staff. His comments are of interest in being so thoroughly "civilian" in outlook.

Like Ogsten, his most serious criticism was of the lack of sanitary measures to prevent disease. Unlike the other surgeons, he had asked to take a physician with him (a Dr Washbourne); and in spite of being laughed at, had won his point. He spoke very strongly:

> "Tommy (the ordinary soldier) does not understand it (sanitation) because his officer regards it as just a fad. If only the combatant officer can be interested in the elements of hygiene and sanitation, then he will see that his men obey the laws of personal health, as to boiling the water and so on, when it can be done. What we cannot get the authorities to see is the strategic importance of it, which comes out very prominently if

the figures are examined. How much sooner Lord Roberts hands would have been free to move from Bloemfontein, and dash after the Boers to Johannesburg, if it had not been for that heavy epidemic. It would have saved the nation a considerable number of men and a correspondingly large amount of money."[9]

Overall the criticisms were constructive, and added weight and support to many of the pleas the AMS Headquarter staff had been making without avail for nearly ten years. At the time of the Commission's Report, the Advisory Board to the Medical Department set up under the chairmanship of The Rt. Hon. St. John Brodrick, M.P., was not only correcting several of the outstanding problems, but creating a new climate of co-operation with the universities.

But the last word from the Report of the Royal Commission on the War should perhaps be left to the Commander-in-Chief, who had not so very long written in his instruction manual for regimental officers that a hygiene man should be sent as far away from the scene of operations as possible, there to indulge his fad. When asked: "And the Service (Medical) did well in the war?" Field Marshal The Rt. Hon. Viscount Wolseley replied: "So far as I know they have done very well indeed."[10]

Clinical Achievements And Problems.
The second contribution made by the civilians attached to the Army Medical Services during the Boer War was their clinical one. Civilian physicians contributed, especially in the civilian hospitals, but civilian surgeons carried out the greater proportion of definitive surgery, both in military and in volunteer hospitals.

This contribution is seen in the detail of case reporting of surgical patients and in the number of papers written by the civilians and published in medical journals. The suggestion that it would be advisable to recruit eminent surgeons selected from the profession in the U.K. was actually made by the Secretary of State for War, Lord Lansdowne, and accepted by Surgeon-General Jameson. The formal *Report on the Surgical Cases noted in the South African War 1899–1902*, and edited by Surgeon-General W.F.Stevenson, CB, KHS,[11] paid special tribute to them. They were very valuable in giving a second opinion, and in carrying out revision surgical procedures and the most major operations. After the capture of Pretoria in June 1900 they returned to Britain, Ireland, and Australia; only Sir Kendal Franks remained. Sir Victor Horsley served later.

Case reporting is at present date very anonymous, with numbers graphs and charts. In 1902 it was much more personal — lists of individual case histories, with initials of every single patient — are included in the report. Different, too, from recent wars was the fact that the Boers carried mainly small arms — their rifles and repeating machine guns, so the blast and burn injuries of later warfare are found less frequently. They had of course field guns, using them to deadly effect at Spion Kop. The only burns, apart from the inevitable accidental ones, were to the backs of the knees of the highlanders at Magersfontein. But the accuracy of the rifle fire, and the fact that many men suffered multiple hits, meant that many casualties which occurred could be serious and demand skilled courageous surgery.

Although experimentation with the missiles of the day had been carried on since the Battle of Crecy in 1346, it had reached a high degree of science by 1899. Surgeon Captain Breadnell, RN, who was with the Naval Brigade at Magersfontein, had researched the effects of both Mauser and Lee-Metford rifles. He had fired over 1000 rounds of Remington brass-coated bullets and nickel-coated Lee-Metford at a wide range of animate and inanimate objects. Of his animal experiments, he concluded that the wounds which gave least trouble and healed most rapidly were made by : 1) very high velocity bullets 2) a flat trajectory 3) a hard smooth bullet sheath with a smooth rounded apex, and 4) (surprisingly) close range. Experiments with the new high velocity Mauser rifles fired at skulls of corpses appeared to show serious fragmenting of skull bones.

The work of this Naval officer showed that some serving MOs were carrying out research. But the major paper on the subject was that of Victor Horsley, whose work was among the most brilliant in the history of military surgery.[12]

In practice, the surgeons discovered that the degree of comminution of the cranial bones and the degree of destruction of bone substance was much less when living skulls were wounded. 133 were listed in the Official Report, and 18 described in detail. Of these, 16 were treated by civilian surgeons and 2 by RAMC officers. The trephine was used regularly and without hesitation.

Gutter wounds of the scalp and outer bony layer (table) of the cranium were freely opened, pieces of bone removed, and abscess tracks along the line of the projectile drained. Some cases showed remarkable recovery. The thick outer fibrous covering of the brain proper just within the skull bone, the dura mater, surgeons learned to leave intact unless there was an underlying abscess in the brain substance. Mr L.G. Irvine, a civil surgeon, sent a special report on skull fractures to the War Office during the campaign.

Surgery of cranial gunshot wounds showed a distinct advance over what had been available in previous European wars. The use of chloroform as a general anaesthetic was a further aid. The Boer War (except for the Spanish-American War which had just ended) was the first European War where surgery of GSWs of the skull became not only more often justified but more often followed by success. Whereas in the US Civil War only 13 per cent of skull GSWs had been operated on, in the Boer War the British operated on 75 per cent, with a death rate of 34 per cent as against 60 per cent in the USA.

GSWs of the spine had formerly been usually fatal. Mr G.L. Cheatle's and Mr Irvine's paper in the RAMC Journal of October 1903 not only showed an improved outlook, but demonstrated the surgical pathology of a high-velocity small arms trajectile well: "concussion of the spinal cord" — even pulping — was observed at autopsy even where there was no direct injury and no fracture. The surgeons concluded: "the changes must have been due to the vibratory concussion communicated to it (the spinal cord) by the passage of the bullet at a high rate of velocity."

This close and accurate observation of the changes following injury to the cord by a high velocity missile was repeated for wounds in general by Lieutenant Colonel S. Hickson, RAMC. He recorded that, for short ranges (under 200 yards-180 m) "so great is the force of impact that the fragments (of bone), receiving a certain amount of energy from the bullet, are forced into the surrounding tissues, or even completely out on the exit side, or they may be thrust through the skin and so make secondary apertures of exit. A large, somewhat conical cavity is formed in the limb (the apex being at the point of entry) containing blood, fragments, and débris of bone, and torn shreds of soft tissue. In bones not well covered with muscle, such as those in the lower

1/3 of the forearm or the tibia, this type of wound is generally known as the 'explosive' and is characterised by a very large irregular aperture of exit, from which protrudes jagged ends of muscles or tendons. In a deeply covered bone such as the femur, although the destruction of the bone itself may be just as great, the strong muscles surrounding it prevent any great increase in the size of the wound, or protrusion of muscles and other tissues. Sepsis is the rule in this type in consequence of the size of the wound and its lacerated condition."

As an example of a typical case report was that of Captain M.S. wounded at Pieter's Hill on 22/2/00:

"Probably Mauser. Estimated range 300 yds. Admitted base hospital Pietermaritzburg, two days later. Entrance wound: normal Mauser in right fold of buttock 1 inch(2.5cm) below ischial tuberosity. Exit large, 1 inch by 1/2 inch, in front of thigh, in middle line. Severe 1/2 (fracture) of femur. Enormous swelling of thigh. Antiseptic dressings; Liston's long splint, with internal (medial) and posterior splints; weight extension. Aseptic union in six weeks, but some tilting of upper fragment. On ninth week, plaster case to thigh, with waistband. Invalided to England in May. (Civilian surgeon Irvine)."

Although the Listerian antiseptic method was now routinely practised, the surgeons then as still today knew the ravage of sepsis and feared its appearance. "It is the occurrence of suppuration that threatens the life of the patient and necessitates amputation in the vast majority of cases requiring that operation…Everything else sinks into insignificance beside it…" said Lieutenant Colonel Hickson. They recognised, too, factors in the field leading to sepsis — apart from compound fractures; failure to apply the first field dressing properly, much soft-tissue damage, and long journeys by ambulance waggons.

In all previous wars, GSW of the abdomen were fatal (in the American Civil War, for example, over 90 per cent) unless by chance the large bowel injury produced a path to the outside — a faecal fistula — through which bowel contents and sepsis could escape. It was well known, from post-mortem studies, that bullets going through the abdominal cavity produced holes in the bowel — with leakage of contents and peritonitis — and injury to organs which bled. Injuries to the urinary bladder allowed leakage of urine, also with inevitable infection.

In this war, the surgeons were in a position to open the abdominal cavity, look inside, and repair what damage they found; in medical terminology, to carry out a laparotomy. Surgeons who went to South Africa held the traditional view that immediate laparotomy was essential. The civilian surgeons were aware that this thinking was in the context of civilian hospitals, where good staff, assistance, asepsis, were taken for granted.

In South Africa conditions were very different. Surgeons in field hospitals — and it must be stressed, at field hospital level in the chain of evacuation — found no unlimited supply of water suitable for making antiseptic solutions. What water was available was always contaminated, especially muddy at the Modder River areas of the front, and would not pass through the Berkefeld filter. Boiling was not possible because of lack of fuel. Thus laparotomies in field hospitals at this level failed to save 70 per cent of patients; of 15 patients where bullet holes in the intestine were sutured, three quarters died.

But conditions were different again at the stationary hospitals or general hospitals. (The so-called "movable hospitals" in the original establishment never functioned in practice). Here successful resections of lengths of damaged bowel, or segments devitalised by haemorrhage, were carried out especially by Dr Neale at Eastcourt, and Mr Luke at Kronstadt, as well as by MacCormac and Treves.[13,14] Both operated on men wounded between 6 and 12 hours previously, by which time peritonitis would certainly have been present.

And then it began to be observed that a significant number of patients who had had a bullet wound of the abdomen and were left unoperated on recovered without operation. Treves at Colenso, as already mentioned, described the Mauser bullet as "a very merciful one", saying "at some longer ranges it passed through like a needle." Further, Sir Frederick went on to say he was "certain that the hole in the gut is closed almost directly by the apposition of other coils of intestine."[15]

So there arose a dilemma for the surgeon. Because of the great mortality which followed operations on the abdomen in field hospitals, and the many soldiers with obviously penetrating wounds who were found to recover with little or no indication of damage to an internal abdominal viscus, it began to be accepted that no abdominal case required operation, certainly not as a primary laparotomy and only at a later period "if the symptoms showed that recovery was hopeless without it. But by that time they were usually hopeless in either case, with or without operation. Thus the assumption for immediate laparotomy requires modification."[16] This assumption continued to be held fourteen years later, with results to be described in the account of that war.

Yet, to give favourable results, surgeons knew that with certain signs present laparotomies had to be performed *early*, and under full antisepsis. The cardinal signs were of haemorrhage, when then as now the surgeon must operate and risk infection; the surgeon of 1900 was just as aware of the type of patient where there is only a *suspected* lesion to hollow viscera (i.e. bowel or bladder) by contrast with haemorrhage, as his successor is today. Favourable results could not be guaranteed at field hospitals. The dilemma remains. And, as Treves said of his otherwise successful forward-placed field hospital at Colenso, where he worked and superintended others, "abdominal wounds were hopeless, from the surgical point of view, when they were carried by hand and waggons over the difficult road between the top of the road and the hospital." This point was made again and again. The other factor was the range — it has to be remembered that the favourable results recorded by all the civilian surgeons referred to long range small-arms fire, the Boers' specialty — of 500yds(460m) up to 3000yds(2700m).

Wounds of the lower large bowel and rectum, and of the urinary bladder, had a poorer outlook, again from the advent of sepsis. But bladder wounds were treated actively; surgical drainage was done, with a catheter inserted through the perineum or active suction via a tube put into the site of the injury and mechanical suction carried out. This was now technically possible.

Wounds of the spleen, kidney, and liver, previously always fatal, were now treated successfully by both conservative management and intervention. Mr Makins reported successfully packing wounds of the liver with surgical gauze, and removing the pack at a later date. Again, antisepsis made this possible.

Chest wounds often caused amazingly little disability. Full case records show that blood was aspirated, often repeatedly, from the thoracic cavity. The prognosis was regarded as "decidedly good" unless there was extensive bleeding. Thoracotomies were occasionally carried out; Major Holt, an RAMC officer, had a successful outcome. Detailed accounts of management of GSW of head and neck, larynx, and of injuries to the peripheral nerves, show just how far war surgery had advanced and how scientifically it was carried out.

Primary amputations were not common. The chief indication was wounds with much tissue destruction. Amputation patients did not do particularly well. One soldier was given saline by intravenous infusion after a secondary amputation; this was very unusual. Intravenous therapy had not yet arrived as a procedure. Saline was given by the subcutaneous route, and this was a new technique now available to the soldier in the general hospital.

Tetanus was a rare complication in this war. In the Official Report only 3 cases are reported, all of whom died. They followed Martini-Henry wounds, not Mauser, and one a bomb fragment. One patient was taken to theatre; a septic GSW of his right thigh was dressed. He was then trephined over both the frontal lobes of his brain and 5cc of tetanus antitoxin injected in front of the motor areas (sections of the brain responsible for the initiation of voluntary movements) in an effort to stop the muscle spasms characteristic of the disease. Spasms ceased for 15 hours then recurred . He was then given large doses of Potassium Bromide, a sedative, again with temporary improvement. His case was treated by Mr Sydney Hulke and Major S.F. Freyer.

Overall the surgeons could be reasonably satisfied with their performance. All agreed the views of military surgeons would need considerable modification. The use of the hard-mantled bullet of small diameter and great energy and the use of modern methods of surgical procedure were two factors affecting their clinical results. The lethal effects of small-arms fire had varied enormously over the previous 200 years, but these variations had depended on the nature of the ground where they occurred and the kind of operation available. The final conclusion on the so-called "humanity of the modern bullet" was that it was perhaps less unpleasant than older missiles, but only a very little.[17]

The use of antiseptics had yet again showed its worth.[18] While a few surgeons believed the reason why only 20 per cent of GSW suppurated was climate, sunshine and fresh air, the majority agreed that modern antiseptic technique, including the provision of an antiseptic first field dressing, was the real reason. Carbolic 1:40 was the most commonly used antiseptic, but turpentine was also employed. The most important limitation of antiseptic procedures was of course the absence of suitable water.

Mortality was undoubtedly less than in any previous war. 8.7 per cent of wounded died; i.e. deaths of wounded were reduced by 50 per cent when compared to previous wars. Chest wounds had a mortality rate of only 27 per cent — it had been at least 50 per cent before.

Post-operative cases needed then as now rehabilitation before invaliding back to the U.K. base. What was available varied with the enthusiasm of the hospital C.O., but some rehabilitation units were undoubtedly very good. Embarkation and disembarkation of troops from the medical point of view was well reported by Major C.J.W. Tatham, RAMC,[19] who made the point that no nation had previously transported 400,000 men, with horses, arms and baggage over 6000 miles by sea and back.

Troop transports were of two kinds — infantry, and cavalry. The troopships *Assaye*, *Plassey*, and *Dilwara* were permanently in use. Large liners were also employed. Those travelling on the "infantry" ships were better off than those on the "horse ships" as the "horses had the first consideration." The troop decks were below the horse decks. The ships' crews were less good. The food was less good. There were no refrigerators. The "troop-freight" ships, which also had some civilian passengers, were much better in every way.

All ships had hospital accommodation on board, for 3 per cent of the force going out, 6 per cent on homeward voyages. The hospital ships were very out-of-date initially, but were improved. "Invalids' ships took half as many troops as those for fit troops, as invalids required twice as much space as fit." There were three categories of patient: a) fit for discharge to the depot, b) convalescents fit for Aldershot or Woolwich, c) serious cases and insane, who went to Netley.

Clothing and food were also commented upon by the Medical Services, and advice was given. Food was good, apart from the march to Bloemfontein when there were some shortages. Biscuits, flour, bacon, cheese, pickles and jam were supplied in regular amounts; though some of these may have seemed hardly suitable for such a hot climate, it may well have been that the troops, as continues to happen, would eat only well-accustomed food. Lime juice and meat were particularly supplied. The doctors noticed that the colonial contingents drank tea instead of unboiled water,and had less enteric fever. So they recommended that the tea allowance be increased. Scales were increased for all hospitals; all milk was sterilised. Wines and spirits were supplied liberally; men recovering from enteric had ample champagne — wine was given to all ranks. There was ample money to pay, as Captain Russell wrote in his diary. Difficulties arose over the Geneva Convention. The Red Cross on stretcher bearers and ambulances was not always obvious at the longer ranges now commonplace. There were suspicions on both sides about the honest use of the Red Cross when casualties were being collected. The question of arms being found on ambulance waggons made difficulties — genuine difficulties led to recriminations. It was concluded that much more precise wording was essential, and that the MOs themselves were often ignorant of the Convention details, and should know them by heart. The basic principle was that arms were only to be used by RAMC, whether officers or soldiers, in defence of their patients.

The war had exposed deficiencies in medical stores — not so much the stores themselves, as their distribution. The absolute necessity of having a very experienced medical officer in charge became apparent, and the need for having enough capable subordinates. But practically everything asked for was supplied.

Especially in Natal and where Volunteer and Colonial doctors were working, the many original unhelpful rules about indenting for re-supply, the remnant of the attitude that medicals could not be trusted with administration, were broken. The Volunteers and Colonials did their Regular colleagues a service by their sensible attitude to all this. The doctors got permission to sign themselves for things like rail warrants and requisitions formerly denied them. It was concluded that much larger quantities of medical stores would be needed in another war.

The field surgical panniers were found to have been seldom required. The wooden cases were heavy and unwieldy, and the later durable basket and leather containers replaced them. Items like X-ray plates, chemicals, and plaster of paris were used increasingly; one depot issued 1,500 X-ray plates up till May 1902.

Medical Disease.

In the Boer War as in all wars, medical disease was more important than surgical. Both civilian and military doctors would share the load, and some of the lessons learned would pass into the annals of British military medicine.

It is often believed that the incidence of "medical" disease, as distinct from "surgical" disease, is always necessarily higher in time of war. But *excluding enteric fever and dysentery* the incidence of general medical diseases was actually 126 per 1,000 less during the period of active hostilities than in the garrison before war broke out. New cases of gonorrhoea and syphilis were substantially reduced. There was also a decrease in pulmonary tuberculosis, probably because diagnosed cases were rapidly evacuated. Diseases due to infection by parasites, and alcoholism, were also somewhat less common.[20]

The physicians were pressed from the outset. Some civilian hospitals, expecting nothing else than casualties, were surprised to find they had to re-orientate their thinking.[21] Active war service produced many men sick with exhaustion (then called "debility"), rheumatism, circulatory disease, and nervous disease. Yet the incidence of "nervous disease" increased only slightly over peace-time rates, at least initially. Pneumonia appeared in variable amount; in some hospitals there were local epidemics with high case mortality. There was influenza in small epidemics, and there were the standard infectious diseases such as measles and chickenpox. There were many, many "small" ailments, which in civil life would not have required hospital admission, but in field conditions could be treated nowhere else. Eye diseases were important. Conjunctivitis caused by dust produced 2,363 hospital cases. Nearly 1,000 men lost their power of focussing — these were long-sighted in whom the persistent strain of looking into the distant horizon had broken their ability to constrict their pupils. As a result, they could no longer see to shoot. Nine men out of every 1,000 suffered from infection in the ear — either the middle ear, giving them otitis media, or the external ear.

Heart disease doubled. This was largely due to rheumatic disease of the heart valves, and some to aneurysm in older men, the result of syphilis of long standing. Varicose veins, then a "medical disease", produced enough disability to need hospital admission in 1,000 soldiers.

Of great interest was the diagnosis of disordered action of the heart. Rare in officers, it was equally common amongst Regulars, Volunteers, and Imperial Yeomanry soldiers. Of 3,631 patients admitted to hospital, 3 died, 1470 were invalided out of the Army (40.5 per cent), but 2,158 (59.5 per cent) returned to duty. The physicians believed there were three causes of the condition, of rapid pulse (tachycardia) with sometimes palpitations and irregularity which they labelled "disorderly action." These were first, the belief that enlistment medical examinations became less stringent, allowing young men who had "weak hearts" to join up; second, the unavoidable mental and physical strain of war, mental more severe on officers, physical more severe on soldiers — this they associated with increased blood pressure and anxiety. The third cause was considered to be malnutrition and this is of great interest as the records concerning it are the main reference to dental disease — there was no Dental Corps then. Colonel R.J.S. Simpson wrote: "The field ration was good and ample. But the very general prevalence of dental caries, the loss of teeth, and the associated oral sepsis, made it impossible for many of the men to chew the bully beef and biscuit, or to digest the lumpy mass which they swallowed. The officers were better off in this respect; their teeth were, as a rule, in better condition, and they had more opportunity of adding to the ration than the men".[22]

Were any of these officers and men thought to be suffering from psychiatric illness? The doctors noted that "functional nervous affections" were more prominent among officers — the reverse of disordered heart action. There was certainly the conclusion that both types of disorder were basically the result of "stress": "the whole experience of the incidence of disease (other than epidemic) in war shows that it is those systems of the body which are especially overworked that break down."[23] It was everywhere recognised that the increased responsibility of the officers was a factor in producing the symptoms of anxiety; "panic attacks" talked through and out of by the padres were diagnosed exactly as they would be today.

One form of psychiatric illness which appeared in this war and added to the medical officers' range of clinical knowledge was cordite eating. It was described as a new disease by Major J.W. Jennings and our friend Captain H.M. Morton, who "wrote it up" for the RAMC Journal.[24]

"Such a trifling matter as a dearth of matches led to a knowledge of the drug. For men extracted the cords from the Lee-Metford cartridges to light their pipes and cigarettes with, and found that it affected their heads. Thus it may be supposed the fatal knowledge would arise and spread. The craving for drink, which could not be had in the field, would conduce to the use of the narcotic, once it had become known."

"The drug is taken in two to three ways e.g. eaten solid, boiled down in water or tea, or mixed with beer."

"In small doses to those unaccustomed to its use, or to other narcotics, cordite, like some other drugs, has a by no means pleasing effect", as Major Jennings found to his cost on eating a quarter-stick by way of experiment. The stuff was sweet in the mouth, but it gave him a most racking, splitting headache. "The habitué is able to take the contents of a cartridge or more. His face flushes, head throbs, and seems to swell, and then in about fifteen minutes comes long deep sleep. On awakening he has an intense headache, thirst, etc. Taken with beer or hot tea, the first effects are wild delirious intoxication, and this is followed by sleep. Morphia, opium, and alcohol in *small* quantities are 'pick-me-ups' after cordite; and apparently some men have used cordite as a reviver after alcohol. Optical, and mental delusions, timidity, weakness, and general breakdown, moral and physical, result from prolonged use of cordite as a drug."

Chest diseases — bronchitis, "catarrh", tuberculosis, and pleurisy, were not different from those seen at home. Of those who developed pneumonia, 17 per cent died; there was no difference in mortality rate between men and officers. Pneumonia as expected increased very greatly in the months of greatest cold — June, July, and August.

Diseases of the digestive system — tonsillitis (then placed in this category!) gastritis, dyspepsia, constipation, incidental diarrhoea — were said to account for 86 per cent of admissions, but only 13 per cent of deaths. Then as now in the general practitioner's surgery, "simple" diseases occurred most commonly. Though "jaundice" as a diagnosis was a rarity, viral hepatitis must surely have occurred; "enteritis", "typhlitis" (possibly appendicitis), peritonitis, cirrhosis of the liver, all had significant death rates. But cholecystitis was rare with only one recorded fatality.

So-called "veldt sore" was common — an itching, flat papule with a moist centre. It had a red spreading margin, and increased in size if not treated. Carbolic with antiseptic dressings seemed to be the treatment of choice. These occurred on the backs of the hands of cavalry soldiers — where anthrax was a differential diagnosis — but on the legs, faces and ears of infantry, of all ranks. Veldt sore is now known to be cutaneous diphtheria.

Venereal disease included soft chancre (now called "chancroid"), epididymitis, and urethral stricture, as well as syphilis ("hard chancre") and gonorrhoea. There were 100 cases in total of chancre, syphilis and gonorrhoea in officers in South Africa as against 15,078 in men; Regular soldiers presented more often with secondary syphilis than Volunteers, who presented themselves to the doctor much earlier.

One small group of interest is lightning strikes. Severe storms of lightning and thunder were very frequent in the South African War. Lightning strikes caused 206 hospital admissions and 16 deaths out of hospital. Considering the frequency and severity of the storms and the total want of protection, this incidence was perhaps remarkably low.

The effect of heat and its lethal effects was well known to all doctors, both civilian and serving. No ice being available in the field — ice *per rectum* was a recommended treatment by Professor McLean of Netley — it was treatable only at this date by giving the dehydrated soldier water to drink. And this water being so often infected, its swallowing led to the infections which dwarfed all the others just described.

"Enterica" or enteric fever, with dysentery, were the devastating diseases of the South African War. Their potential for producing morbidity and mortality made them well known to the public, and their appearance led to the public outcry against the Medical Corps, the accusations of lack of foresight, neglect, ignorance, and many more. And as their eventual elimination was to be one of the major problems of the new Corps in the next decade and longer, they will now be examined in some historical detail.

Infectious disease had been the destroyer of populations since history began to be recorded. The characteristic symptom was fever, which was accompanied by a wide variety of clinical features and wide variations in severity. The concept of microbes as causal agents was very new at the end of the nineteenth century.

Malaria ("by far the greatest disease in the world" as Professor W.J. Tulloch used to teach his students)[25] was well known from ancient times; but it was not a serious problem in South Africa. Though found in the coastal parts of Natal and Zululand, it was only of significance for troops stationed in Koomati Poort, at the lower end of the Krokodil Valley and on the frontier between the Transvaal and Portuguese East Africa. But soldiers who had served in India had the usual recurrences.

The diseases of enteric (typhoid) fever and dysentery were those of the greatest importance. They were both endemic and epidemic. Detailed accounts of their incidence, spread, and management are many, and their conclusions often reflect the attitude and experience of the observer — highly critical by visiting civilian doctors and by the dreaded Burdett-Coutts, supportive and conciliatory by serving RAMC physicians.

Enteric Fever — it was not understood that its symptoms were produced by more than one micro-organism at the date of the Boer War — was well known to be a serious problem amongst all races in Southern Africa. The disease is now known to be characterised by an initial essential phase of septicaemia followed by gastro-enteritis and is a consequence of infection with one of the "enteric group" namely Salmonella typhi, S.paratyphi A, B, or C, or S.sendai. It is now also known that several other salmonellae can cause septicaemia from time to time but this is a complication rather than an essential precursor of the gastro-enteritis that is commonly associated with all these organisms. "Enterica" was however a problem in all armies and in every sort of climate — not only in Continental Europe, but in South America and in the Japanese Army in the Manchurian War. It was by no means peculiar to the British Army, as many lay critics believed. Nor was the mortality as bad as in other armies.

There were two phases in the history of the British Army in the South African War in relation to enteric fever and dysentery. The first was that of the invasion, development, and dissemination of the two diseases; the second was that when both diseases were generally prevalent, varying in incidence according to seasonal change and local conditions. The first period was characterised by severe epidemics, especially in Ladysmith, Kroonstadt, and above all Bloemfontein. Assessment of the natural history of the diseases and of effectiveness of management is complicated by the fact that there were essentially different bodies of troops involved, one static in the beleaguered towns of Ladysmith, Kimberley, and Mafeking, and the other moving in the field or on the LofC. Geography was also important; enteric fever developed differently in Natal from in the so-called "western line", where Lord Methuen's and Lord Roberts' Forces were fighting. The explosive epidemic at Bloemfontein in the autumn of 1900 (April–May) was once again the epidemic of most historical importance to the professional history of the RAMC, because it was the most devastating, and was the epidemic which led to the most serious and angry criticism of the Medical Services.[26]

The other disease was dysentery. Dysentery is an infectious disease of the bowel which produces blood, pus, and mucus in the stools, with diarrhoea. It is highly infective, and leads to death by dehydration and exhaustion. Unlike enteric, it is not a systemic disease, although this was also not understood at the time. The reason enteric was called "enterica" was because of the ulcers found in patches of lymphoid tissue in the small bowel or *enteron*, shown regularly at post-mortem. Skin spots also appeared in enterica, with changes in other organs, notably the myocardium of the heart.

Dr Francis Boyd, FRCP Edinburgh, gave a description of the disease as he saw it; all experienced medical officers knew the symptoms and signs in the same precise detail:

> "The onset was in most cases identical. There was pain in the head, the pain was very severe in the back of the head and in the neck, and was usually accompanied by pains in the limbs. The headache was usually accompanied by constipation. In only a few cases was the commencement of the disease characterised by the presence of diarrhoea as a symptom. When diarrhoea was present at the start it was frequently succeeded by constipation. Foulness of the mouth was a marked early sign — thought to be due to the dust and dryness of the climate.

> Skin. The rash well marked in most of the cases.

> Cardiovascular system. Rapid pulse. Gradual cardiac failure in a number of cases.

Lungs. Pneumonia, broncho-pneumonia, pleurisy with effusion, hiccup associated with peritonitis affecting the diaphragm, etc.

Genito-urinary. Nephritis, cystitis.

Central Nervous system. Delirium noted in a fair number, associated with fever."

The patient severely ill with typhoid fever could lie, little better than helpless, for weeks on end. Even today, his skin and mouth need meticulous and constant attention and every resource known to a trained nurse to prevent bedsores. Urinary or faecal incontinence, or both, could occur at any time, often when least expected; then the soiled bedclothes need changing. The patient's appetite is poor and capricious. Distension of the abdomen with tenderness and guarding were danger signs of haemorrhage or perforation of the gut, and even today, surgery for these complications is fraught with danger, and requires an experienced operator. It was an illness to horrify the ignorant lay person and to concern the experienced nurse and doctor. It is hardly surprising that semi-trained orderlies were out of their depth, and that the beds once filled at Bloemfontein remained so.

At Bloemfontein, there can be no doubt that the concentration of large numbers of men, many of whom were incubating the disease and some of whom were symptomless carriers of the typhoid organism, plus the lack of adequate hygiene discipline ("We were a considerable time there…with a number of cases of diarrhoea and typhoid fever…for three days and two nights there were no latrines dug there, and the men went out into the veldt, and what with heat, and dust storms, and floods, all this was washed about, and of course it disseminated disease. Some of the officers had the duty of being sanitary officers attached to them; but what can one man do? In a camp where he has no men to carry out his instructions whom he can trust, who are trained to do it, the name is nothing…In our Army we would camp where a previous expedition had passed, and there was nothing to mark where their slaughterhouse or latrines had been….").[27]

Service MOs of the time did their best to contain the epidemic. They were hampered by the numbers of doctors themselves becoming ill, and of trained orderlies as well; their replacement by untrained regimental helpers was unsatisfactory, as these men had no ideas of nursing seriously ill patients or of how to dispose of their excreta and fomites. There were no hospital pyjamas for the sick — a major omission in medical planning.

Service doctors were aware of the possible modes of origin of these epidemics. One was the idea of infection from without, a mass infection, another was that of infection from within, auto-infection. The first implied a general source outside of and unconnected with the body of soldiers. Such would have a definite date of onset, and with best investigation carried out, that date could be correlated to known exposure from a known source of infection.

Auto-infection implied gradual and in time general infection of a body of men by a comparatively small number of already infected carriers, or by men already infected from elsewhere. In this type the first few cases produced fresh foci, with multiplication of cases by geometric progression. Successive drafts of soldiers into the Bloemfontein location provided both the seed and the soil for such an epidemic. The military factor, not understandable by civilian doctors, was the priority requirement for ammunition and logistic supplies over medical; forty-four years later, the same would happen in Normandy. On both occasions patients who would otherwise have been evacuated had to be held. This principle applied at Bloemfontein. So some surgical patients had to stay, and blocked medical beds. Lord Roberts was quite firm in his remarks to the Royal Commission of 1901 and in military terms quite correct.

Criticism about lack of trained medical personnel was criticism of the highest ranks to provide. Criticism of clothing facilities provided by the AMS was criticism of their own failure. Other criticism, of patients not being evacuated who were clinically too ill to be moved, was due to ignorance. But there was another criticism which was given high priority especially in the 1903 Commission; that was of failure to provide bacteriological services and inoculation.

Professor Alexander Ogston deserves particular mention in this connection. Unlike Treves, whose amazement at operating in field conditions was just what any trained Service medical officer would expect — and due to Treves' total ignorance of the horrors of war, Ogston had made it his business to travel abroad to see what Continental surgeons did, and had gone to the

Egyptian War of 1884–85. Also unlike Treves, he had accepted totally Lister's concept of bacterial infection. He had a particularly good reason for being angry at what he saw as lack of laboratory support; he had studied the discharge from septic wounds under his microscope, and noted the constant appearance of rounded microbes. These were the staphylococci, the pus-formers. His papers describing his finding, and suggesting that these microbes were a specific infector of wounds or injuries, were (like Lister's) rubbished by the powerful *Lancet* and their publication refused. The same findings were published abroad soon afterwards, and his finding no longer denied the recognition it deserved.

Ogston was already a strong supporter of the Medical Corps of the army. When the medical delegation had been received by Lord Lansdowne, the Secretary of State in 1898, it was Ogston's strong advocacy which had helped him to accept substantive rank for medical officers. It was Ogston's speech at the British Medical Association meeting in 1899 at Portsmouth, where he said he was appalled to find from his visits to Germany, France and Russia how far ahead of Britain their Army Medical Services were, which made such an impact. In particular, the professor instanced the advanced procedures already standard in the German Medical Services for bacteriological testing of water, soil, and human excreta, and the searching examinations required before sites were declared safe for troops to set up camp. Not unnaturally, he was disliked by the seniors of the British Army for the truth of his remarks, for which some of them never forgave him. Now he was at Bloemfontein again, "when the truth of all he had said was being revealed".[28] Ogston himself nearly died of enteric fever while there.

Ogston's criticism of the failure to use the Widal Test, and of failure to inoculate troops, was the result of his bacteriological training and bias. But in any assessment of the reasons for failure of the AMS to inoculate troops against enterica, we have to remember the state of knowledge of the time.

Bacteriology was in 1900 a very new subject — only twenty years old. In 1880 Eberth observed the typhoid bacillus (now called the *Salmonella typhi*); it was in 1881 that Ogston had observed and later isolated staphylococci, the round microbes, from septic, purulent, discharges. In 1884 Gaffky isolated the typhoid bacillus and grew it in the laboratory. It had only been in 1880 that Pasteur had discovered that animals "vaccinated" (he used the term as an act of homage to Jenner) with germs treated to reduce their virulence became immune to the same germs even if virulent. It was only in 1888 that Chantemesse and Widal had proved that even a vaccine composed of *dead* germs could develop in the blood the strength necessary to overcome the microbe of typhoid fever. And it was as recently as 1891 that Almroth Wright returned from Sydney to England and in 1892 was appointed Chief Pathologist in the far away Army Medical School at Netley.

Typhoid was not, as had long been thought, a disease which affected the intestine only. It therefore required, for its prevention, an agent to be provided which would make the patient's blood, and hence his whole system, resist the microbe. Towards this end, Wright developed a technique by which the power of the blood to kill bacteria could be measured. He was then able to show that the blood of an immunised person would kill from ten to fifty times more bacteria than before, and retained this formidable ability for several months. He also showed that after inoculation there was often a short period of discomfort and fever when the bactericidal activity of the blood was lower than normal. However, its antibacterial activity always increased markedly as the inoculated person's symptoms disappeared. Sure of his facts, he advised the War Office to have all men going overseas immunised against enteric fever.

The very first officer who volunteered to receive the first inoculation from Almroth Wright was Surgeon-Lieutenant Maxwell Dick (later Lieutenant Colonel) of the Indian Medical Service. The second was Surgeon-Lieutenant George Bushman Riddick of the AMS, (later Lieutenant Colonel RAMC,) who "volunteered to be next, if Dick was still alive in a few days." Lieutenant Colonel David Riddick, a Regular Officer and Consultant anaesthetist at Millbank Hospital 50 years later, recalled his father telling him that "Dick was very ill, but did survive, and I was very ill too — but survived." Both officers were on the same Basic Training course at Netley. They were both brave men, whom the Corps should remember and honour.

There were some good results in troops in India. At the start of the Boer War Wright wanted immunisation made compulsory in the army. The General Staff and the Senior Medicals declined, saying it was to be done only on volunteers. In the event, only 16,000 out of 350,000 volunteered. It was not possible to follow up those inoculated and those not, and only sporadic results were published. Though Wright was angry and resigned in 1902, the AMS were probably right to confine the inoculation to volunteers in the first instance. From the published results, there was definite advantage in inoculation against typhoid, and many doctors and nurses took advantage of the offer.

The "Widal" test, which was used to diagnose previous infection by the typhoid bacillus, was not as specific or as useful as Ogston believed, but at this time he was not to know this. In retrospect, it seems almost certain that its use would have had very limited success in diagnosing and isolating carriers of the disease in the conditions of the Boer War. It was too early in the history of bacteriology for precise methods of isolation, culture, and immunity responses to be available even in Teaching Hospitals. But by 1902, laboratories *had* appeared in British base hospitals. The Medical Authorities had taken the first steps to develop a laboratory service, and they had done it promptly.

The new RAMC had had its share of criticism. Yet it had developed a professional and medical ethos in a remarkably short time. Aware that the majority of failures so harshly catalogued were not of their own making, the serving officers would now look forward to developments they hoped would increase their professionalism further: the first priority a medical college of their own, the second improvements in their permanent hospitals,[29] and lastly a solution to the problem of shortage of trained professional reinforcements if a subsequent major war occurred.

Little change was required at front-line level. RMOs had performed extremely well. The bearer company and field hospital would need to be replaced by a joint unit, which would be styled the "Field Ambulance." The RAMC had taken note of the good new ideas of their welcome colleagues from Australia, New Zealand, and Canada, and were ready and happy to praise especially several features of the Australian Medical Corps — from its ambulance carts to its excellent horses.

At hospital level there was much to consider, but this related to shortage of specialists and changes in equipment — both hopefully rectifiable. A forward-placed surgical unit looked essential. Medical records was another source of concern. The greatest single problem remained hygiene discipline: in the South African War, the British Army employed 557,653 men, with an average strength of 208,226. There were 57,684 cases of enterica with 8,022 deaths. In the Bloemfontein epidemic alone, there were 6,379 cases, and 953 deaths(29)

This detailed account emphasises the enormous importance in which military infectious disease — with typhoid the specimen variety — was held at the beginning of the century.

Notes and references

CHAPTER 3

[1]"Generals have often been reproached with preparing for the last war instead of for the next — an easy jibe when their fellow-countrymen and their political leaders, too frequently, have prepared for no war at all." Field Marshall Lord Slim, Defeat into Victory, Cassell, 1956, Chapter XX111, p35.

[2]Report on the Royal Commission on the War in South Africa, 1903, Question 4054.

[3]ibid, Q 4051.

[4]ibid, 1903, D.G.'s evidence, Qs 11587–11599.

[5]J. Johnstone Abraham qualified in 1901 and was keen to go to South Africa. Dissuading him, one of his surgical teachers said: "a year ago, all right, but not now... you want to be a real surgeon, don't you?...it's all typhoid now..The Medical Service is a disgrace to this country. It's the fault of the War Office. It has always treated its doctors like dirt, and as a consequence it has got the doctors it deserves — a lot of incompetent asses. We do not want any of our good men to go into the Medical Services. We're going to boycott it until we get proper recognition of our value." He did not volunteer. Abraham, J. Johnston, "A Surgeon's Journey", London, Heinemann, 1958.

[6]Report of the Royal Commission on the War in South Africa, 1903, Q 11791. "While they were away on courses, the work would have to be done in some way."

[7]At the start of the Boer War, the Army General Reserve of 1000 men were called up first. Militia Medical Corps were also available at once. But a Special Army Order had to be invoked, so that the Volunteer Army Medical Corps could be enlisted. The parallel with the present TA is evident. Later again, "old soldiers of the AMS" were called up for hospital duties in UK, and later again the St. John Ambulance Brigade. but *none* of this process had been thought out before the war began (Q 11315), apart from a suggestion to use the St.John Brigade.

[8]This committee, chaired by The Rt. Hon. St. John Brodrick, M.P., set up an Advisory Board to overlook the Army Medical Department. It included senior consultants, academic staff from universities, and senior army officers.

[9]Report of the Royal Commission on the War in South Africa, 1903, Qs 11864–11879.

[10]ibid, Q 9188. The grandfather of General Sir Philip Christison, whose XV Corps re-entered Rangoon in 1945, performed the first operation to be carried out in the field under general anaesthesia on a member of the British Armed Forces. The patient was a young ensign called Wolseley. See "Slim, the Standardbearer", by Ronald Lewin, Leo Cooper, London, 1976, p.249.

[11]Report on the Surgical Cases noted in the South African War, 1899–1902, edited by Surgeon-General W.F. Stevenson, CB, KHS (King's Honorary Surgeon) London, HMSO, 1905. An analysis of casualties can be found in Mr G.H. Makins' book, "Surgical Experiences in South Africa, 1899–1900", and other analyses in the reports of the various civil hospitals.

[12]V. Horsley, The Destructive Effects of Projectiles. Proceedings of the Royal Institution of Great Britain, Vol XIV 1893–95, 228–238.

[13]Sir William MacCormac, The War in South Africa — Case Notes. *Lancet* 1900; **1**: 59.

[14]Sir Frederick Treves, The wounded in the present war, *BMJ* 1900; **1**: 1156–1162.

[15]Med-Chirurgical Transactions, 83, May, 1900.

[16]Report on the Surgical Cases noted in the South African War, 1899–1902, HMSO, 1905.

[17]C.T. Dent, Small-bore rifle bullet wounds and the "humanity" of the present war. *BMJ*: **1**: 1209–1213.

[18]Treves had in the past ridiculed continental surgeons (who had accepted the ideas of Lister earlier and more whole-heartedly than the London ones) for their insistence on meticulous technique: "In this practical country (London) we have been fortunately spared the extravagances which have brought certain Continental operating theatres into ridicule......the exquisite ceremonial on the part of the operator, the surgeon in his robes of white mackintosh and his india-rubber fishing boots...this exhibition may be scientific, but it is no part of surgery..the surgical ritualists appeal to the infallible tests of the bacteriological laboratory." A review of the surgery of the peritoneum, *BMJ* 1896; **2**: 1305–1308.

[19]Report on the Surgical Cases note in the South African War, Part XI, p 239, Major C.J.W. Tatham, RAMC

[20]Medical History of the South African War, Lieutenant Colonel

R.J.S. Simpson, RAMC, J R Army Med Corps, Vol XV, 552ff. (ISSN 0035–8665).

[21]Report of the Edinburgh and East of Scotland South African Hospital, Oliver and Boyd, 1901.

[22]Medical History of the South African War, J R Army Med Corps, Vol XVI, 24.

[23]ibid, p 25, Major Smith, DSO, RAMC

[24]J R Army Med Corps, Vol I, 271.

[25]Professor W.J. Tulloch, OBE, MD, University of St Andrews, discoverer of "Tulloch Types." See p 116.

[26]Report of the Royal Commission on the Boer War, 1903, Q 11090.

[27]For an excellent account of Sir Alexander Ogston and the Royal Army Medical Corps, see the paper by Lieutenant General Sir James Baird, D.G. 1973–77, in "The Staphylococci" — Proceedings of the Alexander Ogston Centennial Conference, ed. Alexander Macdonald and George Smith, Aberdeen University Press, 1981.

[28]This was one of the pressing post-war needs. Report of the Royal Commission on the Boer War, 1903, Q 12111 ff.

[29]History of the Great War. Medical Services. Diseases of the War, *1*, Chapter II. Major J.A. Torrens, RAMC(T), MD, FRCP.

Chapter 4

The new College and professional education.
Sir Alfred Keogh, D.G. Control of infectious disease.
The new Nursing Corps. The new Reserve Army.

Several important questions posed by the Royal Commission
Report of 1903 now had to be answered and action taken.
Contrary to many rather facile reports of the time and indeed
ever since, the Medical Corps had not had a poor record in the
recent out-of- area conflict. It had been the Bloemfontein
epidemic alone which had beaten them, and that only for a
short time. "Enteric fever" and "bad sanitation" were the words
everyone thought of when Boer War casualties were mentioned.
The other complaints, of lack of professional experience and
skill, coupled with the sad shortage of medical staff and
consequent need to call on hundreds of civilian doctors with
medical but no military knowledge, were minor, as far as the
public were concerned, in comparison to the giant spectre of
Enteric fever.

One of the many benefits of the involvement of so many
civilian doctors was their determination to have discovered faults
rectified, and rectified without delay. The British Medical
Association continued to give solid support in the background.
The major figures, though critical, were very willing to use all
their considerable authority to put things right. Mr Brodrick's
Reorganisation Committee, along with the Advisory Board
chaired by the already famous David Bruce, FRS, discoverer of
the causative organism of Mediterranean Fever and the
Trypanosome of Sleeping Sickness, had begun to function even
before the armistice was signed.[1]

In 1902 their *primary* aim was in their own words "to establish a centre for post-commissioning study and post-graduate professional training in central London." They stated: "We look for a closer union of civil and military members of the medical profession, including the auxiliary (reserve) medical services. It should be possible to adapt the school to the requirements of the profession generally, and of the auxiliary forces, by means of lectures, exhibitions, i.e. by the formation of a military medical institute."

There was no argument that the new College should not be in London, in the nation's capital. For some years Netley had been seen as too far from the London Teaching Hospitals, Medical Schools and Learned Societies, as well as inconvenient for foreign visitors. Some had wished the College to go to Woolwich, near the Herbert Hospital. But the new hospital already building north of the recently opened Tate Gallery, on the riverside, was the determining factor. The new Queen Alexandra Military Hospital was the obvious complement of the new Royal Army Medical College. Further, there was space available on Crown land, immediately south of the Tate. So this was where the prestigious new College would be built.

The existing Army Medical School at Netley closed on July 29th, 1902. The prizes that day were presented by Lord Roberts. The opening of that College in 1860 (there had been a short-lived older one at Fort Pitt in Chatham) had been at the instigation of Miss Florence Nightingale herself. She had badgered the Secretary of State Mr Sydney Herbert over a period of three long years before he confirmed its building and location. The huge correspondence between her and the often evasive and dilatory politicians makes interesting reading.[2]

There were, then, staff already in post to move to London. The department of highest quality at Netley was that of Military Hygiene. Edmund Alexander Parkes laid the foundation of systematic teaching of hygiene — military hygiene, of course — there being more important civilian departments in major British cities — and deserves his high place in the professional history of the British Armed Forces Medical Services. A serious recent loss was Professor Almroth Wright, appealing as he waited to take up his post at St Mary's Hospital to the Minister for War for an impartial investigation into the merits of inoculation against typhoid fever.

On the transition to London the new Professor was Lieutenant Colonel R.H. Firth. He had written widely on the pathology of dysentery and the influence of soil and flies on the spread of enteric. Major Horrocks had already co-operated with Firth in some of this work, but was also an expert on the bacteriological examination of water. Now Assistant Professor, he would in due course reach highest fame in the history of Army Health.

The next year was full of activity. The new College had no buildings, but accommodation for officers on courses was found in the Belgravia Hotel, Victoria Street, and the "Royal Army Medical College" was publicly announced by the Secretary of State from the temporary officers' mess there on October 8th. It had in fact been open since August. In his speech, he asked serving medical officers not to take media criticisms too seriously, and to be assured that new building in London was really going to take place.

Mr Brodrick also referred to the new *Regulations for the RAMC* issued by Royal Warrant of 24/3/02, emphasising the determination of the government to improve all aspects of their Service. It was known, too, that in the background the King and Queen were in strong support and lending their weight to speed the changes. They were supporting all measures to improve the general standards in military hospitals, which they had found so wanting on their many visits during the recent war.

The D.G., Sir William Taylor had in July sent a circular to all officers asking their views on a Corps Journal, and whether they would be prepared to support it by a subscription of £1 *per annum*. By October, he could report enthusiastic agreement.

On 31st July the RAMC Fund was started "to perpetuate the memory of distinguished officers of the RAMC." First brevet ranks — another new departure — were announced on October 31st. Majors C. Birt, M.W. Russell, and S. Hickson were to be brevet Lieutenant Colonels; Captains D.D. Shahan and A.F. Tyrrell brevet Majors. The BMA warmly approved this recognition of ability by rank status.

On 1st October new Regulations for Queen Alexandra's Imperial Military Nursing Service were published. Amongst them were details of dress — the grey cloak/dress with scarlet collar (following the original choice of colour and design made by Florence Nightingale), tropical dress, duties and responsibilities. RAMC soldiers were not forgotten in the improvements. Male NCOs if judged of high enough quality were to be trained to State standards as women were; State Registered Nursing Training within the QAIMNS began, for practical purposes, from this time onwards.

Nor were the Volunteer Medical Services forgotten. In late October a memorial to members who had died in South Africa was unveiled in the Church of St Bartholomew the Great.

A completely new Manual of Sanitation was published and this was specifically "for the use of all army officers." It was not the first so directed — Sir John Pringle's of 1752 had the same aim — but was to reinforce the need to shake out for ever the previous dismissive attitude of regimental comrades. It was "all happening."

For teaching purposes, laboratories were needed, and these were found in the Examination Hall of the Conjoint Board of the London Royal Colleges on the Victoria Embankment. Library space and a reading room were also needed. Room 8, 3rd. floor, at 68 Victoria Street, became the home of the library. Mr Rowden, the second clerk in the Commandant Colonel H.E.R. James' office, issued the books. There had been a library since Fort Pitt days, but what was asked for now by students of 1903 were modern text-books and contemporary journals. The first small collection was subdivided into:

Pathology and Bacteriology, Hygiene, Surgery, Medicine, Special Subjects (Paediatrics, Gynaecology, Obstetrics, Ear Nose and Throat Diseases, Eye Diseases, Anaesthetics and their administration). All were standard civilian text-books, including some in German and French.

There was also a miscellaneous group:

German Official Account of the War in South Africa.
The Nature of Man (Metchnikoff).
BMJ 1887–1903. (35 vols).
Lancet. 1889–1903. (23 vols).
Local Govt. Board Reports. 1880–1903.
Report on the medico-military arrangements
of the Japanese Army in the Field. 1894–5.
Manhattan Eye and Ear Hospital Reports.
Report on the Commission on the Nature, Pathology, and
Prevention of Dysentery and its relationship to Enteric Fever, 1900.

This list grew rapidly over the next few years, while teaching became more firmly established.

As well as books by civilian authors, there next appeared in the library from 1903 the *Journal of the Royal Army Medical Corps.* There was obvious delight that the doctors had at last a Journal of their very own.[3] In no time this professional Journal flourished, with leaders by the first editor, Colonel Firth, reports of the Royal Commission applicable to doctors, but most impressive of all, an explosion of case reports, laboratory research, new procedures, and articles of historical and cultural interest. The Journals of these years were fatter than at any time subsequently, and the range of material mirrors the world-wide spread of the British Colonial Empire — from all over India and Africa, Egypt, Malta, Cyprus, Hong Kong, China, the West Indies.

Transport of troops by train was criticised, especially the sanitary arrangements. A hole in the floor or a bucket were considered inadequate. Conditions on ships returning from India were also revealed by Colonel R.H. Forman, and improvements demanded. The doctors were the conscience of the army, and their writings disturbed the often careless and uncaring General Staff. There were the standard reports of wounds and diseases. There were many comments on the Russo-Japanese War — the apparent low incidence of typhoid amongst Japanese troops, the results of early abdominal surgery from Russia. All stressed that the small calibre of the bullets (Russian 7.62mm and Japanese Ariska 6.5mm) resulted in straightforward quick healing. No reports of the medical side of the U.S. Civil War were available — perhaps because that war was thought to be too long in the past. This was unfortunate, as the material would have been of such value in the War that was to come. "Treatment of Sweating Feet by Formaldehyde ointment" was the title of one article. Others included: Fever in Sierra Leone by Major F. Smith, DSO, Trypanosomiasis in West African troops by Captains H.W. Grattan and E.W. Cochrane, Enterica in Bermuda by Major J.W. Cockerill, the 1903 expedition to Abyssinia, Arrow poisoning in Accra on the Gold Coast by A.J. Chalmers, with his account of testing on laboratory animals, and his conclusion that the effect was due to poisoning of the respiratory/cardiac centre in the medulla of the brain, anti-malarial operations at Mian Mir in India by Captain E.P. Sewell, the use of X-ray apparatus by Lieutenant(Q.M.) F. Bruce, "Notes on Health of Europeans in Peking" by Captain F.E. Gunter, with the Tibet Mission Force of 1903–04, treatment of syphilis, pneumonia, meningitis, and of "a new disease called, for want of a better name, paratyphoid", and "the falling birthrate in 1905."

Surgical articles were almost always individual case reports — for example, of the new disease appendicitis, and they revealed all too clearly the extremely limited surgical operations RAMC surgeons had to do now the war was over. Captain Gunter, returned to the Irish Command from China, reported on his operations at the Curragh -38 in all and all very minor, the most major being hernia repair. He did not appear to have his Fellowship. The largest series of those years was of 212 cases operated on at Colchester over a year by Major Porter. He had done them all under local anaesthesia, and strongly recommended this instead of chloroform, saying that although he could not "claim there was *never* any discomfort", this was "not more than a soldier can bear." His 110 adult circumcisions, his commonest operation, were perhaps not entirely pain-free procedures, nor his few "excisions of external piles"!

An interesting trend was the appearance of articles on soldiers' teeth. The majority were reports of small series, or suggestions for issuing dentures, but perhaps the most striking was one on "The teeth of the Soldier" by Lieutenant Colonel S. Westcott, CMG, in Vol. VIII. He collected dental statistics from the recent war, and found that of 627 hospital admissions for caries, 225 were actually invalided. "It was of the nature of an epidemic", was his conclusion, and was due to the climate and the diet. His results confirmed earlier shorter reports.

Many technical failures from the South African War had been investigated and attempts made at correction. A new Field Service Filter, described in 1906 by the man of many parts Colonel Firth, weighed 68lbs(14kg) and sounded (almost) soldier-proof!

A few articles were contributed later in the decade by Reserve MOs. One which will strike a chord in every Resident Surgical Officer's memory was the one by Lieutenant Colonel F.J. Greig, RAMC(T), who described "A case of ulcer of the duodenum with perforation" in a Stirlingshire miner. The clinical picture sounded to later ears all too typical, but the diagnosis was missed, and a lower abdominal incision for appendicitis with perforation used. The surgeon, not thinking of another source of perforation, merely drained the wound. The patient died, and the diagnosis was made *post-mortem*.

All these articles quoted show the pent-up desire of many years by RAMC officers for a professional Journal of their own now being satisfied. They are full of clinical interest, and the best ones are, as might be expected, about tropical infectious disease in all its forms, with the corresponding army health problems. Review articles, apart altogether from those of the giants of tropical disease, Bruce, Leishman, and Sir Ronald Ross (who although of the Indian Medical Service published in the *RAMC Journal*),[4] were often noteworthy for their careful preparation and exposition. Though rather wordy by later century fashion, they were full of confidence that what was being written had the chance of being read and listened to. From the criticism of the early forms of identification tagging came the definitive identity disc which continues to this day. A few suggestions, such as that in 1905 that senior NCOs be taught to administer anaesthetics under supervision, as had been done in the Japanese Medical Services, were much ahead of their time.

These articles were by trained army doctors. The new candidates in this new period from 1902 onwards had become all of a sudden too many for the vacancies available. This was unprecedented for peace-time, and yet more evidence of the new status of the Corps. In the first entrance examination under the new regulations, there were 80 candidates for 30 commissions offered. On August 2nd, 1902, the examination marks totalled 800, divided equally between medicine and surgery. A.B. Smallman was first with 626, and P. Davidson second with 623. The lowest to pass was W.C. Rivers with 493. The BMJ praised Mr Brodrick for accepting their suggestions and advice: ."...the result is that the Medical Services of the Army, which...owing to the prejudices of a military caste had become a by-word and a reproach...has been rehabilitated."[5]

Once selected, the Lieutenants on probation began their Junior Course in the temporary class-rooms and laboratories. A few had served as war-time officers in South Africa — such as J.G.Bell, remembered as being posted around until finding his niche with the Royal Northumberland Fusiliers, who sat his examination for a permanent commission on 31/1/03. After his Junior Course at Victoria Street he left for Aldershot on 1st July, completing his field course there on 1st August. His next spell had a modern ring: Bordon, Longmoor Camp for manoeuvres with 19 Bde Royal Field Artillery, but then followed a tour no longer possible; he left for India on February 4th, 1904. While there his tour seemed to include no clinical work, but he made up for this by taking a trip as ship's surgeon to Colombo, the Far East, New Zealand and Australia!

Time for promotion was made much quicker. Lieutenant to Captain was $3^{1/2}$ years, Captain to Major 12, and Major to Lieutenant Colonel by selection at 20 years. Distinction in professional examination results or in field service brought accelerated promotion.

The first staff of the College included Colonel H.E.R. James, who for some inexplicable reason was described as "temporary", as Commandant and Director of Studies. A distinguished-looking man with the smart moustache of the times, he could surely have been granted substantive rank in view of his considerable responsibilities. Major C.G. Spencer, MB, FRCS Eng., otherwise unknown, was Professor of Clinical and Military Surgery. Lieutenant Colonel R.J.S. Simpson, CMG, who wrote an excellent account of medical diseases in the Boer War, was Professor of Tropical Medicine, and the omnipresent R.H. Firth listed as Professor of Military Medicine. Leishman was Professor of Pathology. Later more were added.

The first class was addressed by the D.G., Sir William Taylor: "You will sometimes hear it said that the Army doctor has little to do. Let not that disturb you; you will find from experience that it is otherwise. Work on unceasingly, work earnestly with might and main at prevention, which is better than cure; strive unremittingly to teach every soldier under your care how to avoid the little ailments of daily life, as well as how to safeguard himself, as far as it is possible to do so, against those more serious and dangerous diseases to which he is specially exposed. It is also said that his practical experience is confined to the diseases of early manhood, and that this limitation of practice leads to stagnation of effort, and to blunting of mental acuteness and judgment. Believe me, there is nothing farther from the truth. No Army MO need let his knowledge rust; his opportunities for keeping himself abreast of the knowledge of the times are as good, and I think even better, than those of the doctor in civil practice. There is abundance and variety of clinical work to be found in our Army hospitals. The field of the Army surgeon is world-wide, and in the domain of tropical medicine he will find a field for observation and research that affords opportunities for practice and progress that no other section of our profession possesses."[6]

The next step was the appointment to the College of clinical teachers, and in February of 1903 these were: Dr Sharkey at St Thomas's, Dr Hale White at Guy's, Mr Pearce Gould at the Middlesex, Mr Stanley Boyd at St George's. For Dental Surgery, Mr Badcock at Guy's, for Midwifery and Gynaecology, Dr Dakins of St George's, for Ophthalmology, Mr Teacher Collins of the Royal London Ophthalmic Hospital, and for Otology, Mr A. Cheatle of King's College, were appointed. Dr Garrard of Great Ormond Hospital was appointed in Pediatrics(sic), and in Psychological Medicine, Dr Craig of the Bethlehem Royal.

By now the College, still in cramped and very temporary accommodation, was firmly in the business of teaching. The Junior Course for the newly-joined Lieutenants lasted 5 months, and included 2 months at the depot at Aldershot, and the senior course, for Captains working for promotion to Major, lasted 6 months. There were 2 of each of these every year, so the staff were kept as busy as any of their civilian medical school counterparts.

The only lecture notes remaining from these first years are those of Professor Leishman, written in Army Book 130 in his small, clear handwriting. From the beginning, students wore civilian clothes, as did their teachers, and a photograph of brevet-Lieutenant Colonel Leishman shows him at his desk, already very bald, preparing a lecture. The syllabus included the appearance of normal blood under the microscope, the examination, staining, and counting of the various cells, use of the haemocytometer and haemoglobinometer, examination of the bone marrow, estimation of the alkalinity and coagulability of the blood, and the use of the erythrocyte sedimentation tube. It also taught changes in the blood in disease, a large amount of bacteriology, and descriptions of infectious diseases.

Typhoid inoculation and a summary of the latest statistics concluded the course. In late 20th century terms, this was a haematology-bacteriology course. It did not include the systematic study of disease processes, nor what has come to be called histopathology. It was for these reasons limited, but the limitation was to the diseases likely to be met by a newly-posted RAMC officer; it was, like all the other instruction, applicable to military medical conditions and not civilian ones.[7]

As part of the aim of giving the College the highest possible status in the world of University Medicine, formal applications were made for recognition by various Medical Schools — whose acceptance would be proof of the Corps' new standing.

Another formal request was made for the Professor of Hygiene to be recognized as a teacher of the subject by London University. This had in the first instance to be sent for War Office approval, as it implied inspection by the University of London. It was coupled with the request for admission as a School of the University. The schedule of correspondence "requesting the Professor of Hygiene to be recognized as a teacher of Hygiene in London University" fills a War Office file. The file was passed around 28 desks and referrals within the War Office! In October, 1908 the College was recognized as "one of the Medical Schools of the University of London", an honour it retained until it was lost in the 1930s. It was also accepted as a teaching institute in Pathology by Cambridge University for its Degree of Bachelor of Medicine in 1910, and for instruction in operative Surgery by the Royal College of Surgeons of England.

This College, called before it actually moved into its new building the Medical Staff College, functioned remarkably well from the beginning. It had a Board of Studies consisting of the D.G., the Commandant, and one civilian and one military member of the Advisory Board, plus the professors of Military Hygiene and Pathology, together with an officer of the Indian Medical Service nominated by the India Office. As well as the Belgravia Hotel, the St Ermin's Hotel was used as living accommodation for the officer students, until the permanent Royal College was open.

In 1908 the Inspector General of the Forces, a new post created by the major changes brought about by Lord Esher's Committee when the old Army Board was abolished and the

Army Council set up in its place in 1904, suggested that training in staff duties in the field begin at the College. The inevitable committee was set up to study the implications of this, under the chairmanship of the Assistant Director of Staff Duties, Colonel Kiggell. The programme worked out was an extensive one. It proposed medical officers be given lectures by senior staff officers, attend war games and what were then used for tactical exercises, staff rides; have their own medical staff rides, and undergo a full course in all the duties and responsibilities a non-medical staff officer of equivalent seniority would have. These included transportation of casualties from the front, discipline and maintenance of combatants, re-supply of food, military stores and clothing, siting of camps, fitting their units into the line of march — the same functions as officers of other units with the sole exception of combatant work. It was as different from the days of Lord Wolseley as could be imagined. Accepted at once, it was added to the courses and a special Field Training Manual written for the RAMC

While not medical training, this was as much professional training for the new-style medical officer as was the new hygiene training now obligatory for the teeth arms. The new recruits to the Corps were being taught to think towards the next possible war, a major European one, by the publication of a range of books on the medical sections of the Directorates of military operations of the armies of all the European powers in a way that had not been done before. By the same attitude of mind, medical manoeuvres were sanctioned by the General Staff for the first time. This was after a medical officer had attended such specialist manoeuvres in France, and had come back as people do, full of a good new idea. The first of these took place on Salisbury Plain in 1910; others took place in 1912 in Rawalpindi, the RAMC Headquarters in Northern India, and in 1913–14 in the Southern Command in Poona. Some medical officers from the Independent Dominions, notably Canada, came to London to go through these new staff training courses.

As all this was going on, the walls of the College building were rising. The Queen Alexandra Hospital was opened in 1905, and the College on 15th May, 1907. Woodd and Ainslie were the architects, and their plaque can still be seen on the left-hand side above the reception desk in the back hall. Taken over for use in

September, it had cost the not inconsiderable sum of £80,000 to build. The BMA criticised the "red brick and stone facing", which was an absurd criticism, but could find no fault with the laboratories, which it called "excellent." BMA visitors must surely never have seen the magnificent woodwork in the public rooms in the officers' mess.[8] Press reports of the day described the "free classic architecture…the roof of the magnificent Grosvenor Road facade is supported by Ionic columns, with the Royal monogram above the granite portico…the fine brick and Portland stone…the handsome rooms (classrooms) with mosaic pavement." The Royal Army Medical Corps — not yet ten years old — had now a Post-Graduate Teaching Hospital, a Post-Graduate College, and a Headquarter Mess, which last was then and has remained the envy of the military in London.

Although the reports of the day talk of the military men involved in the setting up of these new and outstanding facilities for professional training, it must not be forgotten that it was the evidence of the civilians who had gone to the recent war, and their background influence and authority afterwards, which had caused the revolution. "The RAMC was unlikely to have been reformed from within after the Boer War, and a lay surgeon without the implicit backing of the monarch would have had a difficult time steering measures through the War Office."[9] The General Staff were happy with the decision of Lord Esher to remove the Medical Director from the new Army Council of 1904 and place him under the Adjutant General's office. The BMA were naturally most unhappy.[10] From then till the present the Adjutant General has spoken in the Defence Council on medical matters. Fortunately the impetus for change began before this happened, as certain Adjutants General then as later could well have been unhelpful.

Equally, it was not a coincidence that so many of the changes of the post-Boer War years were during the Director Generalship of Sir Alfred Keogh. This remarkable man — in a different league from his predecessor and successor — was from a Roman Catholic family of Roscommon near Galway. His father, Henry Keogh, was Resident Magistrate there and a member of the Irish bar. Alfred Keogh graduated from Queen's College, Galway in 1878 aged 21, as a Peel Prizeman. He left to do his house jobs in London, at the Royal Westminster Ophthalmic Hospital as clinical assistant, the Royal Arsenal at Woolwich as house surgeon and the Consumptive Hospital Brompton as house physician. As a young RAMC doctor he was Herbert Prizeman and Martin Memorial Gold Medallist in Medicine. The remainder of his life was spent outside Ireland.

During the Boer War he served first at the rear near Capetown at Rondebosch with No.3 BGH. He was probably hospital Registrar initially as Major, but later in command as Lieutenant Colonel. In May of 1900 he was posted with the local rank of Colonel to Springfontein (he was briefly PMO of the LofC); he escaped the Bloemfontein epidemic. But it was at No.2 BGH in Pretoria from June onwards that he made his name as what would today be called a troubleshooter. He was invalided to England the next February convalescing from typhoid, but in the meantime he had had an outstanding confidential report in Pretoria in September 1900: "a man of the most conspicuous ability", a mention in despatches, and finally a CB after being notified to the Commander-in-Chief. Decorations were so much more sensible in those days; there was not the sad tying of them to ranks as occured later. It was not so very unusual for a Lieutenant Colonel or even Major to be appointed at Commander level if he deserved it.

Sick leave continued from April 1901 till 26th July, and was followed by a "home establishment" posting. In fact, he joined Mr Brodrick's Committee. And then on 1st January 1902 he was appointed a Deputy Director General with the temporary rank of Surgeon General, substantive Colonel on 2nd December 1904 and Surgeon General Army Medical Services (AMS) on 3rd December 1904. He took over as Director General from the tall, handsome Sir William Taylor on January 1st 1905. It was surely the fastest promotion in the history of the RAMC.

During his first term as Director General, Keogh had five great achievements. He was as important for the 20th century as McGrigor had been for the 19th. They were:

1) Recognition of the QA Military Hospital and the RAM College for Post-Graduate Training and Research.

2) Appointment of civilian consultants of merit to the Army.

3) Establishment of the Army School of Health as a centre of excellence whose directions were heeded by the non-medical army in the taking of measures to control major infectious disease.

4) Establishment of medical and nursing services in the Territorial Force (Territorial Army).

5) Re-constitution of field medical units to deal with major casualty loads; development of new units.

Of other possible contenders, all of whom had been senior to General Keogh in Africa, Major General Sir Thomas Galwey was now PMO India at Simla, Surgeon General W.L. Gubbins was PMO Eastern Command India at Naini Tal, and Colonel A.T. Sloggett, CMG, was PMO London District.[11]

General Keogh's leap in promotion did not pass without comment. After scotching a rumour that Sir Fredrick Treves was to be the next Director General, the British Medical Journal of December 31st 1904, was as suspicious of the Army Establishment as it had ever been (it had good cause to be; the War Office were trying to get rid of the civilian members of the Advisory Committee):

"It could be safely taken for granted that the delay in appointing a D.G. in succession to Sir William Taylor meant that the military authorities were striving to do by craft what, fortunately, they are no longer able to do by force. It is no secret that this is precisely what is taking place. A comparatively junior officer had been recommended for the appointment because his previous services marked him out as pre-eminently fitted for the post. On the other hand the military authorities, though they could find no objection to the appointment, could not bring themselves to depart from the routine method. Every influence that could be brought to bear on the Secretary of State for War was made use of to prevent an appointment which was looked upon by the Sir Leycaster Deadlocks of Pall Mall as an opening of the flood-gates of revolution. His appointment will be particularly welcomed as an indication that the spirit of arrogant hostility towards the medical service which has proved so disastrous to the best interests of the army has passed away. Keogh has inherited none of the traditions and prejudices of the older militarism."

This last remark was true. The last Surgeon General of the old order, James Jameson, had died at his home at Newlands, Eltham, on 13th September 1904. His service in the field was 19th century. The new Director General had started his first war in the 20th century — the war, as already seen, of 20th century characteristics if not 20th century dimensions. Jameson had learned medicine without knowledge of bacteriology or biochemistry; Keogh had graduated as Koch and Wohler were opening the first volumes of these new sciences. In this very year, Landsteiner was discovering the blood groups. But this was the future. Control of infectious disease was the present problem.

Keogh's major Boer War experience had been Enteric fever. Not only had he seen the casualty figures and heard the tales of 40 burials a day at the height of the Bloemfontein epidemic, with bodies wrapped in blankets because there were not enough coffins, but he had treated the disease at Pretoria and had had it himself badly enough to require invaliding home. He was keenly aware of the deficiencies in sanitary and hygiene measures. He had assessed the attitude of non-medical staff officers. As happens with such depressing regularity, the non-medical staff were quickly forgetting the agonies of infectious disease. In 1902 the Advisory Board, still containing its quota of civilian members in spite of rumblings against their inclusion from War Office, had pressed for lectures on sanitation to be given not only to officer cadets at Woolwich and Sandhurst, but also to senior teeth arm officers attending the new courses at the Staff College Camberley. In 1903, the War Office for no clear reason and without consulting their medical advisors, reduced these lectures to such a ridiculously small number that their value became insignificant.[12]

Co-incident with General Keogh's appointment, reports began to appear in the civilian medical press of the apparently tiny incidence of typhoid and dysentery in General Oki's Army compared with the incidence in the Russian.[13] Though these were afterwards found to be false, they created a great deal of media excitement; the popular press were full of letters from every sort of expert and well-wisher giving advice on what had to be done. General Keogh asked for and obtained agreement to set up an entirely new School of Hygiene at Aldershot, at the Army Medical Service Training Depot. He was actively supported by General Baden-Powell, whose South African experience had also made him insistent that "sanitation must go into the domain of the soldier." During 1905 and 1906 Keogh said, and continued to say, "enteric and dysentery are easily preventable." At the time, this seemed a daring thing to declare. By the beginning of

November, 1906, the Aldershot School of Hygiene was open. This in itself was an achievement. It had 4 instructors: Lieutenant Colonel T.J.R. Lucas CB as Commandant, Instructors Lieutenant Colonel R.H. Firth (whose authority as a hygiene expert was increasing) and Major J.D. Ferguson, and Assistant Instructor Captain H.C.R. Hine. In cricketing parlance the new D.G. had not only got runs but scored them quickly.

Perhaps Sir Alfred Keogh seemed to the General Staff to be taking a great risk with his public statements about the dread typhoid fever. But he had a staff at Millbank of the highest calibre who were working all hours at the College there on the new inoculation measures. The credit for the basic research was Almroth Wright's, but perseverance and application honours must go to Leishman, Captain W.S. Harrison, Lieutenant A.B. Smallman (who had got top marks in the first entrance examination at Victoria Street), and Lieutenant F.M.G. Tulloch, later to die tragically in a tropical disease project.

In 1905[14] these researchers studied the changes in the blood following typhoid inoculation. In September of 1904 the Commanding Officer of the 2nd Royal Fusiliers had agreed that his battalion be inoculated. Bacillus Typhosus Vaccine, prepared by Professor Wright's method, was used. The medical officers inoculated themselves with differing doses. But the evidence that there was still real prejudice against the new procedure was shown by the fact that of 358 Warrant Officers, NCOs and soldiers, only 106 volunteered. They remembered that 1 officer and several well-known NCOs had died of typhoid after being inoculated prior to embarkation for South Africa. The trial was to estimate the development of (what were then called) protective substances in the blood of the inoculated men.

Clinical trials then as now take time to plan, organize, set up, and follow through. But by 1907, Leishman wrote an "Original Communication" in the Corps Journal.[15] This described the progress of anti-typhoid inoculation since the previous communication from the College.

Colonel Leishman recalled the use of vaccine (he continued to use the word "vaccine" as Wright had done, in deference to Pasteur and Jenner) on a large scale at the end of the last century in India and Egypt, the apparently encouraging results, the adoption of the procedure for troops leaving for the Boer War.

But the requirement that inoculation be voluntary, the failure to get information of statistical significance, and differing opinions of medical officers themselves had meant that no definite opinion could be reached.

Because of this, and following the concern by Bruce's Advisory Scientific Committee at the possible dangers of a "negative phase" after inoculation when natural resistance is in fact lowered, the procedure had been stopped after the war. Almroth Wright "with his customary candour" as Professor Leishman said, had been the first to point out the dangers to those inoculated before they had reached the "positive phase" of resistance. The new Army Council had set up a committee under Dr C.J. Martin, FRS, Director of the Lister Institute; this committee decided after a year and a half's break that typhoid inoculation be resumed.

The earlier report of 1905 had been concerned with the antibody response (showing the degree of active resistance the person had developed to the disease as the result of the inoculation) following different doses of vaccine. The aim had been to "discover the dose of vaccine (as they called it) which promised to produce the greatest quantity of protective substances without undue severity of local or general reaction, and without the danger of inducing a negative phase of resistance." The aim had been achieved, and the dose fixed. It had been adhered to since in the vaccine prepared in the College.

Now there was new information. The new clinical trial had been in progress over the past three years. Dr Martin's committee had asked that a medical officer be given a special course at the College and then remain overseas with a regiment for three years, to collect information on the progress of those inoculated. 8 doctors had been employed in the trial. They had done agglutination tests on the soldiers' blood, to determine the antibody response. The communication quoted the experience of the 17th Lancers, who had suffered a severe epidemic soon after arriving at Meerut in 1905, and the report of the attached MO, Lieutenant Luxmore. As well as checking the bloods of the soldiers, he had carried out post-mortem examinations after deaths from typhoid. "The uninoculated portion of the Regiment served, unintentionally, as controls", he said. "Of the 63 cases, 61 were amongst these controls, and only 2 among those inoculated. Further, of those 2 who got enteric, both had refused the second inoculation. This was the first result from a regiment using the new standard vaccine. "The result", concluded Dr Luxmore, "is one of significance which it is hard to minimise." Lieutenant E.J.H. Luxmore deserves his name in this history as much as any senior General. His own account is published alongside Professor Leishman's(15).

So now 15,000 doses had been sent to the PMO India from the Royal Army Medical College. Leishman noted the "keen personal interest shown by the Commander-in-Chief, Lord Kitchener", and the background support of the King. Along with the doses of typhoid antigen, "all necessary kit was being sent out."

Professor Leishman had not failed to notice that few men were being inoculated at home. He thought this had been because the medicals themselves had not been convinced of the advantages of the procedure, and now recommended that senior officers should lecture and supervise inoculation. Second inoculations were being done on board ship, on the way out overseas, the first being done just before embarkation. This overcame difficulties over late arrivals.

Preparation and the more difficult standardisation of the antigen to be injected had made the procedure less alarming now that experience and confidence had been gained. The antigen was no longer injected into the flank as the local reaction was less severe; the arm was used instead. It was vital to do a second injection. The dosage was 500 million treated bacteria in the first inoculation and 1000 million in the second, contained in 0.5cc and 1 cc respectively of the "vaccine." The conclusion, blessed also by the authority of the Pasteur Institute, was "We can now recommend anti-typhoid inoculation in every case where necessary."

At the end of the 20th century, where inoculation against virtually every sort of infectious disease is the norm, the magnitude of this work in 1907 and its conclusion is easy to forget. It had not yet had the opportunity of application; this would come all too soon. Other armies were of course working along similar lines, but the Royal Army Medical Corps had made its contribution with the best of them and better than many. In 1908, when Queen Alexandra visited the College, she was shown in pride of place the bacteriology department, the Commandant explaining to her that "the terrible ravages of fever during the South African War, as indeed in nearly all wars, makes it of first importance that the army doctors should understand bacteriology."

Once again, there seems little doubt from the accounts of the day that the interest and support the King and Queen continued to show to the new College and its Teaching Hospital gave it a status it would not have otherwise had; civilian consultants of real distinction were happy to be associated with it. Consulting physicians who were on the staff of the hospital were Dr J. Mitchell Bruce of Charing Cross, Dr J. Kingston Fowler of the Middlesex, and Professor W. Osler, FRS, of the University of Oxford. Surgeons were Messrs. A.E. Barker the Professor from University College Hospital, A.A. Bowlby of St Bartholomew's and G.H. Makins of St Thomas'.

General Keogh had not failed to observe the vital contribution the civilian surgeons had made in South Africa. But unlike most Regular senior officers since, he said plainly that the Regular RAMC specialists could never compete with civilian specialists in experience nor, apart from a few notable exceptions, in skill. He also realised that the influx of men with no military training, however able they were as clinicians, created considerable problems. This could only be overcome by the creation of a large, in fact a very large, reserve of medical men who had enough military training to fit in quickly to the Active Army in the event of a major war. Civilians like those who had rushed to Africa just would not do; in any event, changes in the Geneva Convention meant their safety could not be guaranteed.[16] And by the middle of the decade there was no doubt that the next war, if it occurred, would be in Europe and would involve large numbers of combatants and large numbers of casualties. The current Russo-Japanese War had given an inkling of just how large those casualty numbers would be. The apparently low incidence of typhoid fever in that war, which had produced sensational reports in the media and even misleading conclusions in the British Medical Journal, was now known, after more results had become available, to be because the battle casualties were significantly heavier in total and relatively greater in number than those due to the standard infectious diseases. This was "new", newer than the recollection of the casualties in the Franco-Prussian War of 1870; the weapons had now greater killing power.

The concept of an autonomous body of medical reserves was "new" also. On 31st January, 1883 the class of Metropolitan Volunteers had completed their course of training under Surgeon Cantlie of the London Scottish, assisted by Lieutenant Maclure, and were mustered for their inspection in their individual uniforms. Said Surgeon General Mackinnon soon afterwards: "I had often been struck by the very great advantage such a body of men would be with an army in the field, and looked forward to their being a great support to their brethren in the Regular Army."

Later, in May of 1883 Surgeon George Evatt of the Royal Military Academy Woolwich gave a formal address to a meeting of Volunteer surgeons and representatives of the London Medical Schools. He made several points, but the most apposite to the concept of this new force were first that it had only been the autonomy of the Army Medical Services gained first 10 years previously which had made possible the appearance of a similar autonomous reserve medical force, and second that military costs were now so high that it was unlikely a Regular Army Service large enough to support a major army in a "large foreign war", as he put it, could be afforded: "the results would be gloomy indeed were it not for the 'volunteer spirit' which would make good the deficiency." He pressed for a "Volunteer Medical Service" which would have personnel on the Army List, and for the D.G. to have power to commission directly suitably trained professional medical men, who after suitable training at Aldershot could provide an organised unit "able to stand on its own feet."[17]

General Evatt, as he became, was in these as in other of his ideas ahead of his time. But the recent war had, like a similar out-of-area war would do a hundred years later, changed things. There could then as later have been a dangerous reduction. Fortunately, by 1905 the "Territorial Principle" was accepted, together with the concept of short term enlistments in the full-time army.

Director General Keogh was undoubtedly aided by the change of government of December 1905, when the Liberals were returned, to rule for 10 years and for the last time in British history. Many of its former anti-war members now in office found responsibility made them have to change policy. Behind and senior to individual committees like the medical ones, was the Committee of Imperial Defence, its creation Mr Balfour's last great reform before leaving office. All aspects of military tactics and training — the best-known being that of musketry — but also "fire and movement" — were being improved to a very much higher level of performance than ever before. In the new cabinet of the shrewd Scot Mr Campbell-Bannerman was Mr Richard Haldane. It was Haldane who conceived and carried through the series of military reforms of the very highest importance over the 6 years from 1906. These included joint planning with the French — a new-found ally — for the immediate transport of a British Expeditionary Force of 150,000 men to France, along pre-arranged routes and to pre-arranged locations, in the event of war. The first element in his reforms was the creation and training of such a Regular Force, with a General Staff to run it, the second was the creation of a Territorial Force, replacing the previous Volunteers and Yeomanry, and the third was the formation of the Officers' Training Corps in schools and universities. This last had a medical component, the first being in Edinburgh, Oxford and Cambridge, and later in Dublin, Belfast, London, and Aberdeen. All these are important in the next period in the professional history of the Royal Army Medical Corps.

But no less important were the plans for Regular and Reserve Nursing Services. Queen Alexandra's Imperial Military Nursing Service had its numbers increased from 230 in 1901 to 382. As these numbers increased, so the numbers of the Army Nursing Reserve in military hospitals decreased. Some individual volunteer nurses in South Africa had been hopelessly bad and had been thought to be part of the official Nursing Reserve; its reputation had suffered unfairly in consequence. Irregularities were overcome when a Regular QA Reserve was formed, of high calibre Sisters.[18]

A Territorial Force Nursing Service was next organised, with its own Matron-in-Chief, in 1906. This was Miss S. Browne, who had just given up the appointment of Matron-in-Chief of the QAIMNS. Members enrolled in this new Force were matrons and nursing staff in the large civil hospitals connected with the medical schools where the Territorial Force Hospitals were to be formed. The TF Nursing Service had an establishment of 112 members in each of the proposed 23 TF General Hospitals and so had a strength of 2,576 ready for mobilization should the need arise. Standards and numbers were ensured; the staff of the new hospitals would be highly-trained professional women.

The busy and bustling Sir Alfred Keogh was quick to appreciate the BMA as an ally. Very soon after Mr Haldane took over his Department of State, the D.G. was addressing the British Medical Association — on the 20th January, 1906, in fact. His thesis was his concern for help from civilians and the relation of the medical profession to war. He was aware, he said, of the greater experience of civilians in surgery and medicine. He stressed however the importance of the Army Sanitary branch, saying how this was a specialty where the serving officer had more knowledge. He also noted the cooling of enthusiasm for civilian hospitals to go to another war as they had done in South Africa.

The speech came at the right time. Already letters were appearing from RAMC Volunteers advertising their military skills and boosting their units. In the background, too, was the new War Office scheme for a Medical Reserve, similar to the Army Emergency Reserve (AER) type of contract of later years, with a limit of 7 years of service, as well as pressure for an RAMC(Volunteers) as an entity which individuals were calling for. Lieutenant Colonel John J. de Zouche Marshall, commanding the East Surrey Volunteer Bearer Company went so far as to write a Medical Order of Battle (ORBAT) for such a Corps, to brigade level. There was no lack of interest in the medical profession at large.

On 5th May, 1906 the Scottish Volunteers Ambulance Trophy Competition was visited by General Keogh. At the dinner after, he spoke powerfully of the need for an entire reorganisation of the Volunteer Medical Service, throwing his weight behind the Territorials' demands.

In parallel, Haldane was making plans for mobilization of nurses, as just described. In his speech on the Army Estimates in 1906, he said that in war the preservation of the health of the army was one of the first considerations; he laid out the establishment for sanitary services and spoke of new methods of water filtration, as well as outlining his ideas for nurses and doctors.

It was at this time that the need for *local identity* of the Territorial Army was conceived. Perhaps General Evatt deserves some of the credit though he did not get it; his often outspoken criticism of the Regular Medical military establishment, usually justified, had not endeared him to military memory. He had suggested in 1903 that the new Volunteer Medicals should become "companies RAMC with a local prefix." He was very keen on volunteers having proper rank structure, something which also did not endear him to the Regular Army. He wrote that May: "There is no reason why county badges should not be worn on the collars of the coats or tunics of County Companies nor in the case of the Scottish Medical Volunteers of the dice caps worn by Scottish troops. We need local attachments with centralised direction to secure efficiency — we must never forget the county tie. I foresee that all these things will surely come true either in an evolutionary manner or in a rapid and hasty manner by the advent of a great war."

Events moved quickly. The support of the BMA for the proposals was immediate. In March 1907 they reported what they called "Mr Haldane's unfolding his great scheme for army reform: for the Field Force we want 331 MOs, 30 Q.M.s, and 4,400 men...a proposal to organize a large Territorial Army Medical Corps, analogous to the Regular RAMC. (It was interesting the BMA used the word 'Army' instead of the word 'Force'). The BMA is taking a great interest in it, and has suggested that we organize our Corps not merely as a local, but a great corps like the engineers and the artillery — one great corps organised under the D.G. of the A.M.S." The Journal reported the proposals fully. The National Forces were now to be in two lines — a Regular Army and a Territorial Army, the TA being second line. The Regular Army was to be fit to maintain itself for 6 months of war. The new Reserve was to take the place of the old Volunteers and Militia, and to be based on the County Associations.

There were to be 14 Divisions in this new Territorial Army, with supporting arms. It was hoped to have TA Brigades in due course. For an establishment of 250,000 rising to 300,000 after 6 months, the RAMC TA would have 1200 MOs, 70–80 Q.M.s, 12,000 NCOs and men. There was to be a post of Inspector of Hospitals and army sanitation — this was not new though described as such at the time — but what was new was that the officer appointed, Colonel W. Babtie, V.C., would be on the personal Staff of the Inspector- General of the Forces. (This too followed a suggestion by General Evatt). The support given by the BMA was so important that it should be recorded; its realisation that at long last the nation was going to have an adequate medical support in a future war was very obvious from the excitement of its reporting.

After the summer recess the momentum returned. Haldane's speech at North Berwick, where he was the Member of Parliament, on 10th October, 1907, made the point that he wished the new Force to bridge the previous social *and* geographical gaps between the Volunteers and Yeomanry. The medical element was to have *all the units presently in the Regular RAMC, and a full establishment of nursing sisters and nurses.* He hoped also, he said, to recruit a contingent of specialists, railway, engineer, but also medical, of in all 70–80,000. While all these would be reinforcements for the Regular Army, they would be available for home defence. It was unprecedented. It was revolutionary.[19]

Sir Alfred Keogh went to Scotland to inaugurate the new Medical Force. He held meetings in Edinburgh, Glasgow, but especially in Aberdeen, the home of McGrigor. On 16th October in Aberdeen he set out the sort of engagement which would suit civilians wishing to serve on a part-time basis. He saw in a way so many of his much more limited successors seemed totally unable to comprehend, that the part-time doctor needed to have a flexible contract and an attractive career.

Next he went to Leeds and Newcastle. At Newcastle, the very first TF Hospital was set up and remained among the best. He did not make the mistake of talking from London to the northern parts of the Kingdom and making them feel resentful. This time he showed by the use of diagrams his concept of the Order of Battle. Field hospitals must be maintained empty so that new wounded could get into them. He emphasised the crucial role of the School of Sanitation in Aldershot. And to end his speech, he criticised and dismissed the view that come a war, all would come flocking in. Such would be untrained. Keogh saw far into the 20th century.[20]

"Further", went on the Director General, "TA units will be allocated to their local brigades and divisions just as Regular ones are. There would be special sanitary staff. Regular adjutants would be appointed, but there was to be an administrative officer for each Reserve division — who later would become the Assistant Director of Medical Services (ADMS)." What the War Office must have thought of this decision to give a *reserve* officer such a high authority defies description. But Keogh saw that the civilians were men of ability and that they would have no difficulty in working successfully at such levels. Time fulfilled his trust.

With the reorganisation of both Regular and Reserve Medical elements came new titles — Director of Medical Services (DMS), Deputy Director of Medical Services (DDMS), Assistant and Deputy Assistant Directors — for the various levels of command. The old PMO title eventually disappeared.

Keogh had not forgotten his first experiences of the South African War when he was on the staff of general hospitals. He knew, as he kept saying, that the civilians had superior surgical and medical skills. So he created a large hospital establishment in his new Army Medical Corps of reservists. The 23 new hospitals were to be stationary and general, and to use local civilians, and include some on the new low commitment engagement so that their clinical skills and experience were not lost; had they been forced to fulfil the full requirement for training, they might well have resigned. Keogh also asked for the help of local experts in preventive medicine in the reserve hospitals. Although the new BGHs were to be raised in the locality of a TA division, they were to have no organic connection with them. A Lieutenant would be promoted Captain after 3 years, and a Captain promoted Major after 8 years. The senior clinicians were to rank higher than the officer commanding.

"The officer personnel", said the General, "both for hospitals and for sanitation, will, it is hoped, be sufficiently large — larger than the actual requirements — to enable the utmost elasticity as regards the assumption of duties in time of war." He made the same sort of arrangements for the recruitment of nurses, but theirs was related mainly to transition to war.

It was providential for the British Medical Services that Haldane and Keogh were in post together at the same time. Sometimes countries get the politicians and senior military they need, and these two men put together proposals far-seeing and, especially as far as the new Reserves were concerned, extremely shrewd. Sadly, their principles have been lost several times over the 20th century.

There was another major change made over these Keogh years. This was the replacement of the bearer company and field hospital by the field ambulance.

Experience in the late war had shown that separate BCs and FHs distributed work unequally and wastefully. Too often the BC was underemployed, the FH overwhelmed. Combining the two, as had been tried by the Volunteers, the Australians, and the Indian medical units, working alongside the RAMC, showed no such drawbacks. There was no duplication of control. Experience had also shown the need for divisibility of field units into functional sub-units with holding points — i.e. beds, and for a much larger proportion of stretchers and stretcher bearers.

And so the new unit was constituted. Its establishment was published in an Army Order of 1st March, 1905. It had a Bearer Division, a Tent Division, and a Transport Division. The commanding officer was a Lieutenant Colonel. The Bearer Division had 18 stretcher squads each of 6 men, compared to 8 squads of 4 men in the old BC. The tent Division had accommodation for 150 cases; interestingly, 3 of the officers could be civilian surgeons. The transport Division had 60 Army Service Corps men but no ASC officer.

The three sections of the field ambulance each had a bearer group and a tent section. It was a replica of the whole, permanently organised for instant detachment. 1 field ambulance was allotted to each brigade, and one to corps troops. There were 9 RAMC officers, 1 QM, 1 WO1(R.S.M.), 13 senior NCOs, 3 buglers, 9 corporals, 66 privates plus 90 special enlistments in event of war — a total of 192 RAMC. The 60 ASC included 3 sergeants and 57 privates and batmen: a grand total of 252. It was to become one of the most successful units over the century in the whole British Army.

The senior civilian surgeons had made many criticisms of the provision of forward hospital care, and this was another major part of the system needing modification. The first try was the clearing hospital, a unit to be established on outbreak of war. They were probably the concept of Colonel W.G. Macpherson. There had to be somewhere for the wounded to go after they left the new field ambulance on the way back to the major hospitals, and the role of the clearing hospital was regarded as highly important. They were, in fact, described in Field Service Regulations as "the pivot upon which the whole system of evacuating sick and wounded turns." To be located at an advanced base, they would "push up to within reach of the field ambulances to relieve them of their casualties and free them to follow their divisions" — if the army advanced, or if there was a retreat, to help the field ambulances in evacuating wounded before once again passing them back. They were also to serve as a relay for sick and wounded between active engagements.

But there were several question marks over this new unit. It had no transport of its own, but was supposed to obtain transport from the LofC; this, as medical officers commented, "was not ideal" — the clearing hospital was in front of the LofC at the advanced base and so outwith its command, said some accounts, but was within its command according to others! "But given a complete understanding between the C.O. of the clearing hospital and the Transport Authorities, the plan was workable."[21]

Although clearing hospitals were war establishment units only, and Regular units at that, criticisms soon appeared from TF medical officers about their proposed function and the rather nebulous remarks in the official regulations about where their transport would come from. They were not welcomed in the enthusiastic way that field ambulances were.[22] In spite of a few potential weaknesses like this, the Medical Services had undergone a transformation and that in a surprisingly short time. They had a College of repute, with visiting staff of distinction, passing some 70 officers through its classes every year. They had at last sanitary training and sanitary advice readily available, and the RAMC had the authority to see it was carried out. There were measures previously unknown to control infectious diseases. And there was a Reserve Medical Service as part of the Territorial Force which contained the nucleus (for the large TA hospitals had peace establishments of 3 officers and 42 men; those on "lower commitment" engagements being only included in event of mobilization) of skill, experience, and numbers to ensure that the embarrassment of 1899 would not be repeated. Had General Sir Alfred Keogh done nothing more than this, his reputation would have been assured. Were a major war to come, Great

Britain would have a better prepared Army Medical Service than at perhaps any time in her history.

Notes and references

CHAPTER 4

[1]Sir David Bruce was born in Melbourne in 1855 but returned with his parents to Scotland in 1860. He was an Edinburgh graduate of 1881. Commissioned into the AMS in 1883, he worked in Malta on Malta or Mediterranean Fever, and discovered the causative organism, *Brucella mellitensis*. For a time he was assistant Professor of Pathology at Netley. Later, in Uganda, he identified the cause of Sleeping Sickness as the Trypanosome named *T. brucei* after him. He became a Fellow of the Royal Society when aged 25. He served in the Boer War, having 7 clasps to his Queen's medal, and was in Ladysmith with his wife during the siege. In the 1914–18 War he worked on trench fever. He retired in 1919 as Major General. His scientific medals and awards are the greatest of any RAMC officer, and can be seen in the RAM College.

The first Advisory Board included, as well as himself, Major W.G. Macpherson, Surgeon General Hooper, representing the IMS, Colonel Dunne from the Quarter-Master-General's Department, representing the War Office, with the D.G. Sir William Taylor and General Keogh his deputy, *ex officio*. The civilian members were Sir Fredrick Treves, Mr A.D. Fripp, Dr C. Ball, Dr E.C. Perry, and Dr J. Galloway. The Matron-in Chief came to the Board when advice was needed or when nursing Service questions arose.

[2]Barnsley, R.E., Miss Nightingale and the College, J R Army Med Corps, 1965, Vol III, 66–73.

[3]Volume I of the Corps Journal began with a leader "L'ENVOI", by the editor Lieutenant Colonel R.H. Firth.

"This issue of this Journal is the realisation of a hope of many years. The necessity of such a periodical has long been recognised by the medical officers of the Army. It is not, as many suppose, a new idea. As long ago as 1864 a meeting was held at Netley to consider the question, and the establishment of a Journal was resolved upon, and its scope, character, and form were decided even to the most minute detail. The whole question was thought to have been settled and the greatest satisfaction was felt. But an old-world official opposition, together with "rules and Customs of the Service" effectively killed the proposal at its birth, and though many efforts have been made since to revive it they have all been without success."

The Journal's institution was yet another success for the new Committee. In addition to funds being made available for its publication and printing, the librarian for the project was to have £100 *per annum* in addition to his pay. The original advertisement for this post asked that applicants have special experience and know enough of a foreign language to translate from foreign material.

[4]Sir Ronald Ross (1857–1932) studied at St Bartholomew's Hospital and worked as a ship's surgeon before joining the IMS. In 1881 he became a Licentiate of the Society of Apothecaries. In 1884 Manson suggested to Ross, then his pupil, that malaria was probably transmitted to man by the mosquito. Ross returned to Secunderabad, and after long research, was able on 20th. August 1897 to demonstrate that a female anopheline mosquito had become infected from a patient with malaria. In 1898, in Calcutta, working with a species of bird malaria, he was able to show the complete cycle and to prove that bites of infected mosquitoes communicate the disease to man. He was elected F.R.S. in 1901 and awarded the Nobel Prize in 1902. He wrote articles in the RAMC Journal (Vol IV, 1905, 1, 450.) about his discoveries, though a former member of the IMS.

[5]*BMJ* 1903; **2** : 374. "We criticised Mr Brodrick's scheme for the reform of the Medical service of the Army, when it was first tentatively offered to the profession, with the frankness which is a duty as well as a privilege of true friendship…We were also the first to recognize that he had profited by the criticism…indeed, Mr Brodrick has shown a readiness almost unparralled in the history of the War Office, to leave the deep-rutted road of tradition, and to follow new paths of reform. The result is that the Medical Services of the army which, owing to the ineptitude of fossilised officials and the prejudices of a military caste had become a by-word and a reproach, has been rehabilitated." The leader also scorned Mr Burdett-Coutts, who had tried to claim credit.

[6]Sir Frederick Harris as D.G. gave an almost identical talk to the writer's National Service intake in November, 1952.

[7]Sir William Boog Leishman, of Scandinavian descent, (1865–1926) graduated from Glasgow University in 1886. He worked as an assistant to Professor Almroth Wright at Netley before succeeding him as Professor in 1902 at Millbank. He invented the Leishman stain for micro-organisms, and described the cause of Kala-Azar — the

Leishmania donovani. He also elucidated the life cycle of relapsing fever — the *Borellia duttoni.* He became an FRS in 1910 and was D.G. from 1923 till his death in 1926.

[8]The magnificent woodwork in the mess at Millbank came from the old House of Commons. The panelling in the Commandant's office is from the old Chapel of the hospital, closed on 1st March, 1977. The folding doors between the former senior officers' anteroom and the mess proper are said to be the tallest in London. I am grateful to Dr N.R.H. Burgess, the entomologist at the College, for this information. For his excellent short history of the Millbank site from mediaeval times to the date of closure of the hospital, see J R Army Med Corps, 1973, Vol 124, 96–104.

[9]Trombley, Stephen. "Sir Frederick Treves, the Extra-Ordinary Edwardian", Routledge, 1989, p149.

[10]The most able of these three, notwithstanding the fact that he was never in a post which gave Lieutenant General's rank, was General Galwey. A "tall soldier of arresting appearance and genial manner", as his contemporaries remembered him, was almost as famous for owning Hidden Mystery, the favourite for the 1900 Grand National. Sadly, it did not win. The best placed of his horses in the race was Leinster, placed 6th one year.

[11]*BMJ* 1904; **1** : 381. A letter was also sent to *The Times* on 17th February from Dr Andrew Clark, Chairman of Council of the B.M.A. An official reply cited the fact that there was no medical officer on the Admiralty Board. Dr Clark's further letter stated that his criticism was not *specifically* of the loss of the D.G., but of a person to represent preventative medicine in relation to war. It is not without interest that the R.N. Medical Services, who had failed to make any improvements, had at this time almost no candidates for commissions.

[12]*BMJ* 1903; **1** : 1051. "It is the old, old, story", said the British Medical Journal.

[13]ibid, 1905; **1** : 428–429.

[14]Leishman, W.B., et al, J R Army Med Corps, 1905, Vol V, 1.

[15]Leishman, W.B., ibid, 1907, Vol VIII, 32. See also Harrison, W.S., ibid, 472–491, and Luxmore, E.J.H., Report from Meerut, 492–503.

[16]Macpherson, Colonel W.G., The Geneva Convention, J R Army Med Corps, 1910, Vol XV, 607.

[17]"The Volunteer Service Gazette", 5th May, 1883.

[18]Prospective QAIMNS sisters for India were offered 175 Rupees/month (15Rs=£1), senior sisters 200Rs/month, and Superintendent sisters 300Rs/month. In addition to free quarters, fuel and light, they had free "punkah-pullers."

[19]See the *Aberdeen Free Press*, 16th October, 1907. The proposal was "to form an RAMC for the territorial force, which should be an exact counterpart of the regular RAMC, with corresponding ranks and appointments, and with medical units organized for war on similar scales to the war establishments of the medical services of the expeditionary force."

By 1908, as well as the Territorial Force RAMC as above, there were a Special Reserve of officers, a Special Reserve of other ranks, both for general service with the regular RAMC on the outbreak of war, and lastly a Home Hospital Reserve of St John's Ambulance Brigade in England and the St Andrews Ambulance Association in Scotland, for staffing the military hospitals in the UK upon the mobilization and withdrawal of the RAMC for duty in the field. See the Official History of the War, Medical Services General History, Vol I, pp 26,27.

[20]At a D.G.'s Exercise in the 1970's, the chairman said: "Yes, we are short of officers in the RAMC but we have enough soldiers. But if there is a war with the Russians, we will have no trouble — the doctors from outside will come flooding in."

[21]Russell, Lieutnant Colonel M.W., The Clearing Hospital, J R Army Med Corps, 1910, *XIV*, 603.

[22]See letters in vols *XV* and *XVI*, ibid, 1910. Many articles continued to appear in the Corps Journal up till 1914.

Chapter 5

The Great War of 1914–18. The contestants. Grand Strategy and attitudes. Medical mobilization. The early conflicts and the new RAMC

This was going to be a very different war. It was going to be fought on the continent of Europe, over well-known countryside. Doctors as well as others with a sense of history recorded passing by Malplaquet, a battle site two centuries in the past, or Harfleur and Boulogne, where Napoleon's Army had concentrated before its planned invasion of England a full century earlier. But while the terrain and weather had not changed, everything else had. The contestants had huge resources of men, and military material of a totally new dimension of killing power.[1]

A confident, newly united Germany had easily beaten the French in 1870; Napoleon III had surrendered at the head of his Army and walked out of history. In January 1871 the German Reich was proclaimed in the Palace of Versailles, from where France had once dominated the European scene. By the Treaty of Frankfurt that May France had ceded Alsace and Lorraine, with the ancient fortress of Metz, had to pay 5 milliard francs indemnity, and had to endure a German Army of occupation until payment was complete. It was a humiliation for France, and sowed the seeds of acrimony for the next 80 years.

Ever since this armistice, the Germans had made no secret of their determination to dominate. It was not just the steadily increasing size of their army and its obvious efficiency — it was clear that Germany had a technology large enough to launch and sustain a major war. Even their railway system was constructed as a strategic network, as the *Autobahnen* of their next attempt at military domination would also be. The railheads would in

August 1914 convey over 1 million men to launch the German offensive.

The concept of the whole nation at war — revived by Napoleon so successfully — had returned to Europe. With it went the concept that enemy civilians were legitimate targets for destruction if they proved awkward; the Germans would pursue a policy of what they called *Schrecklichkeit* (frightfulness) towards any such — the burning of villages, taking and execution of hostages. This would quickly produce the columns of frightened refugees which would block military vehicles going towards the front and ambulance vehicles coming from it, in this and succeeding wars.

Small armies of professional soldiers officered by gentlemen with a certain shared code of professional fairness — the eighteenth century pattern — were no longer enough. Increased size was mirrored in the much wider range of social classes now manning the European armies — even Russia, regarded in popular mythology as being officered by aristocrats alone — had very many peasant officers in her army. This implied, as far as all services including medical were concerned, that an even higher proportion of civilians without military tradition would be required if a large war broke out. Indeed, there was anxiety in the British General Staff that an army composed of workers and of young men whose only interest seemed to be watching Saturday afternoon football might have republican tendencies and be unwilling to fight for King and Country.[2] Happily, the clear-headedness of Lord Haldane and enough senior officers, including Generals Haig and Keogh, had provided the framework for an expandable reserve in the event of war; they knew what the expanded army would be for, even though it appeared many politicians did not.[3]

If the building of railway lines terminating at sidings on the frontiers of Belgium and Holland was something politicians in Britain might choose to ignore, the construction of a major fleet by the Reich was not. This, plus German moves to control finance and organize commercial espionage around the world, *did* alarm Great Britain and her Empire.[4] For centuries France had been the natural and bitter foe of Britain, but now all of a sudden the enemy was across the North Sea and not the English Channel.

The French reply to the major German military expansions of 1905, 1911, and 1912 was to increase the duration of their period of conscription from 2 years to 3. After his 3 years in the active army, every Frenchman fit for service had to spend 11 years in the Reserves. Like the German, the French Army was a national one. But this increase was not enough; by 1913 German forces were 4 million trained men in the Regular Army and as many more in the Reserves. France had half a million less; this nevertheless amounted to 5 Armies, 7 Divisions of Cavalry and a Cavalry Corps of 3 Divisions.

The British Army, by contrast, was tiny; 247,432 plus reserves including the new and untried element, the Territorial Force, of less than 270,000. It was about the size of the Belgian Army, which meant that, on mobilization, a country of 45 million population was only able to put into the field the same number of divisions as one of 7 _ million. The small size of the British Regular Army was the result of the principle of long service voluntary enlistment, described by Lord Roberts as "Conscription by Hunger" and by Lord Esher as "The Principle of Unequal Sacrifice."

It would be Germany which would determine the course of the War. The Grand Strategic Plan of Germany, the famous Schlieffen Plan, was to contain the expected French counter through Metz. The Germans would then, as the French pushed across their eastern frontier and northwards, march through Belgium, envelope the left wing of the French, and wheel onwards south and east, rolling the entire French Army against the Swiss border. It entailed fast-moving warfare; pre-war German manoeuvres had always included fast marching to the point of exhaustion by their infantry. The very impetus of the French counter-attack, and its direction, would allow the Germans to "slam the gate behind them." Then, having disposed of France, Germany would have its entire army available to attack Russia.[5]

The French General Staff had made no provision to meet a major attack through Belgium beyond plans to re-arrange their 4th and 5th Armies. They did not cover the gap between their 5th Army and the sea except by forts and local troops. The British Expeditionary Force (BEF) was if mobilized to take up position west of the French 5th Army, though what it was to do when it got there was not very certain.[6]

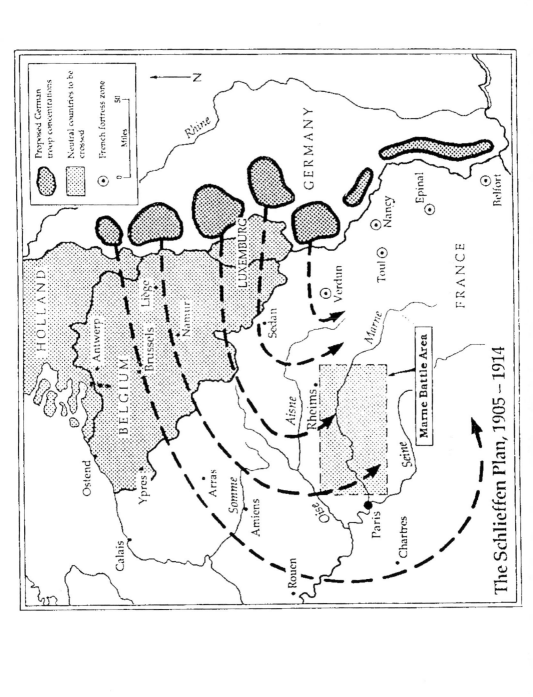

The Schlieffen Plan, 1905 – 1914

Proposed German troop concentrations

Neutral countries to be crossed

French fortress zone

0   Miles   50

N

Rhine

GERMANY

HOLLAND

Antwerp

BELGIUM

Brussels

Liège

Namur

LUXEMBURG

Ostend

Ypres

Calais

Arras

Somme

Amiens

Rouen

Oise

Chartres

Paris

Seine

Rheims

Aisne

Sedan

Verdun

Marne

Marne Battle Area

Toul

Nancy

Epinal

Belfort

FRANCE

French military thinking was imbued — obsessed is perhaps not too strong a word — with the notion of "attack." French Military Staff believed their defeat in 1870–1 was because of their departure from the Napoleonic principle of attack to throw the enemy off balance. The notion of the "attack at all costs", the "big push", and the inevitable call for more and more soldiers to maintain the offensive, was implicit in French theory, not least by Colonel Ferdinand Foch, when Chief instructor at the Ecole Superieure de Guerre from 1895–1900. Fortunately, General Joffre would be sensible enough, eventually, to put this doctrine aside in the first major battles of 1914. But it would re-appear very soon afterwards.

There is clear evidence that the major powers believed this European conflict would be short. General von Moltke, the Chief of the German Staff, considered that one great battle would settle the issue. Had he followed the original Schlieffen Plan to the letter, he could have been right. The French, equally, were so sure of a quick decision that they had made no arrangements for construction of new war material, but only for repair of what they already had. The British General Staff agreed. The later so often repeated jibe that "they all expected it to be over by Christmas" is, like most retrospective remarks made with similar insinuation, unfair. The strategists *did* have good grounds for believing it to be true.[7]

As far as expected casualties were concerned, the recent Russo-Japanese War had provided much evidence. To the credit of the Army Medical Directorate (AMD), they saw to it that up-to-date military surgical and medical innovations were available for study at the RAM College. This was in contrast to General Staff practice. It was known from Russian sources that shell and shrapnel wounds had increased in frequency and severity in that war from the much earlier 50:50 to the ratio, if trench mortar bombs and hand grenades were included, of 73 per cent shell to only 27 per cent bullet. It was also known that shell wounds were more likely to become septic. What was not yet known — and the Conferences at the Hague and elsewhere did not know either — was the effect of medium machine gun fire or of the very heavy artillery pieces recently developed especially by Germany and Austria. Ballistic work on the newest projectiles, while not neglected in Britain, had not produced more than predictable information. British experience in Southern Africa, while vital for fire and movement tactical training and for small arms efficiency, would not help the medical Services in such different conditions as North-Western Europe.

All these factors would be relevant to the task the new RAMC — the small Regular Force, its Special Reserve, but this time with a large and trained Territorial Force as part of its ORBAT — the numbers of men involved, the scale of the German offensive and the weapons it was to employ, the geography of the battlefield, the attitude of the military generals to warfare. The attitude of their government would appear in due course.

The events following the assassination of the Archduke Franz Ferdinand of Austria and his consort at Sarajevo on 28th June, 1914, led inexorably to war. Austria and Russia were fully mobilized by 31st July, France and Germany on August 1st. On August 2nd, Germany declared war on France. But the British Government refused to agree to its General Staff's request for full mobilization and the immediate sending of pre-arranged advance parties to the Continent. It also refused to cancel Territorial Force camps, saying that such cancellation would be construed as "menacing." When Great Britain did declare war on Germany at 11 p.m. on 4th August, it followed that her mobilization was later than that of France and would not be completed within the time scale the French had hoped for. Fortunately the strong resistance of the Belgians held up the initial German advance. Significantly, it was not till the biggest siege guns were used that the fortress of Liège fell — the gallant General Leman, its commander, was carried unconscious from its rubble. The power of artillery at Liège was a portent of things to come. Had Belgian resistance failed at this stage as it did seventeen years later, the outcome of the 1914–18 War might also have been different.

The initial British Force to be embarked was of four divisions with a fifth to follow, plus the Cavalry Division and supporting Arms. Two Indian Divisions were to be sent to Egypt but no farther. British troops (in fact Indian) were to come from South Africa. The total war establishment of a division was now 18,000 all ranks, 12,000 infantry with 24 machine guns and 4000 artillery with 76 guns of various calibres. The Cavalry Division had 9,000 men and 10,000 horses. It was said of the Regular British Army:

"In every respect the Expeditionary Force of 1914 was incomparably the best trained, best organised, and best equipped British Army that ever went forth to war."[8]

The Medicals mobilize.
The medical plan had been carefully worked out and was quickly set in motion. Each British division was to be covered initially by 2 BGHs and 2 SHs. There were to be clearing hospitals (CHs) of Regular RAMC, No 1 at St Omer, No 2 at Bailleul, No 3 at Armentières, No 4 at Poperinghe, and so on. Because the Indian divisions appeared so quickly, the Lahore CH was set up at Ballieul and the Meerut CH at Bethune. (By November, No 2 Canadian SH was working at Le Touquet).

In the LofC, at Rouen, there were 6 BGHs and 3 SHs, at Le Havre there were 6 BGHs, and at Etretat, 1 BGH The Surgeon General in France, General T.P. Woodhouse, actually wrote to the new D.G. Sir Arthur Sloggett in August to say there were too many General Hospitals and that they might have to send 3 general and 4 stationary back to England. Another reason he gave the D.G. was that there was no accommodation for the nursing sisters.[9]

In the U.K., there was a very large system of support, Regular but mainly TF.[10]

Evacuation was to be by empty stores waggons returning from the front, by field ambulance waggons, to hospital trains to the base ports and thence over the Channel. The new Clearing Hospitals were to act as both holding and evacuation elements. The other new evacuation element was the Motor Ambulance Companies (MACs), of whom much would be heard from the time of their first use, at the Battle of the Aisne in September. All divisions were to have 2 or more MACs — No 1 had 40 ambulance cars and was working from quite soon after the start of hostilities. Nos 2, 3, 4, and 5 did not arrive until October and early November. Their own workshops accompanied them. Ambulance trains were also not organised until 11th October; these late arrivals had some repercussions shortly to be described. Nevertheless, the medical Order of Battle was impressive in scale and quality.

RAMC medical orderlies wore warm service dress with flat topped peaked hats, black boots and puttees, a red cross in a circle sewn on the right arm, a large red cross armband on the left, and, slung over the left shoulder, a water bottle and a large flat satchel to hold sterile first field dressings, unsterilised bandages of various sizes, sticking plaster, and so on.

The basic MO's drug box in 1914 included phenacitin for headaches, "adrenaline in injectable form, 0.0003gm, one dose to be used as a stimulant… the adrenal glands are just above the kidneys", Dover's powders for colds, Bismuth salicylate for the stomach, cough medicine, a light aperient calomel, and a strong one, unspecified; quinine sulphate, 2gr. (60mg) as a tonic, lead and opium tablets to be made into a lotion as an application for sprains or as an anti-diarrhoeal and, for the doctor to hold safely, morphine sulphate gr1/4 or gr1/2 (15 or 30mg). Morphine was to be given "under the tongue or by injection." There were also methylated spirits, iodine, boric lotion and carbolic acid 1 part in 60 as antiseptics for wounds. Lastly there was sal volatile, to be given for "fainting, a few drops in water."

It is of interest that these apparently "simple" remedies were provided at the very outset. Seventy-five years later, medical officers in the Middle East would complain about being supplied with surgical equipment of complexity, but finding themselves short of remedies for the minor ailments, the first to appear at the start of any campaign, as they always do.

New for hospitals was the universal provision of X-ray apparatus with even a few trained specialists to work it. But the most important novelty was the number of picked bacteriologists plus their laboratories, who were already in post waiting to evaluate the septic and other infections the European Theatre would bring. They were also primed to evaluate anti-typhoid inoculation, still declared voluntary by the desk officers of the War Office in 1912 but in practice almost universally accepted by the Army at large, and anti-tetanus serum prepared in what was fervently hoped would be adequate amount.[11]

As far as mobilization was concerned, the RMOs had few problems. Hugh Shields was one of them. He had been born in Calcutta in 1887. In 1910 he graduated with honours at Cambridge, where he was a rowing blue. At the Middlesex Hospital in 1913 he was a prizeman. He was a committed Christian. He joined the Regular RAMC, had been posted to

Poona, but now found himself posted to the Irish Guards. Because of the war, he had postponed his wedding.

The Irish Guards marched out of Wellington Barracks on August 12th. Shields was with them. They were themselves a "new" regiment. Southampton to Le Havre was the next leg; they marched into France "at 1300 hrs on the hottest day I have ever felt", said their RMO. Many guardsmen fell out; their RMO took a hard line with any he thought were not genuine. On 17th August he inoculated 750 of the battalion against typhoid. On the 23rd they passed the site of the Battle of Malplaquet.

Also in the Guards Brigade was Lieutenant James Laidlaw Huggan, an Edinburgh graduate of 1911, RMO to 3rd Bn Coldstreams. A very fit man — he had been a Scottish rugby international — he, too, marched with his regiment, and he, too, inoculated everyone on the way to war.

William Pennefather Croker was RMO to the 1st Bn Royal West Kent Regiment. He was a graduate of Trinity College Dublin where he had an honours certificate in surgery. He had previously been a cavalry RMO, but had had to take a course of instruction in riding first. He was a little disappointed at being with infantry.

These men had their own number of regimental medical orderlies, whom they had trained themselves to good standards. They had given the standard instruction in all aspects of hygiene as it affected the infantry soldier and officer. They were "attached" to their regiment, but felt themselves part of it and shared its pride.

The teeth arms marched north. Because nearly 50 per cent of the troops were reservists, (a fact very often not realised by commentators) and so out of training, and with new boots, many fell out. The pavé roads took their toll. Older men who could not stand the pace had to be left behind. The field ambulances following picked up stragglers. Horses cast shoes, waggons and harnesses needed repair. The medicals were short of farriers, wheelwrights, and saddlers, so they had to beg help from their colleagues in the Advanced Surgical Centre (ASC).

Cavalry Fd Ambs were the first to see action — perhaps on Sunday August 23rd when a Scots Greys officer was wounded in the thigh and was passed by his RMO to 2 Cavalry Field Ambulance. But he was not the very first British casualty; these were 2 Royal Flying Corps (RFC) officers whose plane crashed on August 18th. The field ambulances, like the regimental medical officers, were very early on the scene; now comes the story of some of them as they mobilized.

Captain John Patrick Lynch had joined the Regular RAMC as Lieutenant on probation in 1904. He had graduated with Honours from Queen's University, Cork, the year before, after winning undergraduate prizes. Cork was one of the new medical schools the British government had set up in Ireland. Lynch was yet another of the new, bright clever doctors the RAMC was attracting.

But on 30th July, 1914, he was living at Eastbourne on half pay. That day the order came through by telegraph ordering him to re-join at Canterbury for full duty. Most reservists did not get their telegram to "mobilize" till about 5th August. Inside were their mob orders, "SECRET" in red letters on the envelope. "Report at... join...." So he set off in his motor cycle and side-car, taking his wife Rosie and their small daughter with him. They all had a pleasant journey in sunshine *en route*, with no mechanical breakdowns.

Captain Lynch had been at Canterbury before, as a cavalry RMO. He was delighted to be back, because he wanted a posting again to a cavalry regiment — the one he fancied was the Carabiniers. He thought his chances quite good because he knew Colonel Hunter, their C.O. When he arrived, he talked excitedly to old friends at the small military hospital about the war they all agreed was now inevitable.

On August 3rd, after hostilities began and the Germans invaded Belgium, he was detailed to carry out medical examinations on the troops of the garrison "for fitness for field service." He completed the medical check of the Carabiniers in 70 minutes! "The air in the barracks was full of electricity", he wrote in his diary. "But next day, after the order to mobilise came through in the afternoon, the atmosphere changed: ...during the tea party we did not say very much but thought a great deal." John Lynch was *not* to be with cavalry, but was posted to one of the new field ambulances, No 4. It was a disappointment. He was to be transport officer, because of his previous experience of horses!

On August 5th he packed, said good-bye to his wife and daughter, and got the train to Cannon Street with a change at

Faversham. The train was late. He missed his connection. With time to spare, he went to buy a new waterproof at Cording's shop and a packet of instruments at the Junior Army and Navy stores. He was overcharged for these, being told "there was a war on!"

On arriving at Aldershot station, he walked up Gun Hill to the McGrigor Mess as so many of us have done: "The old mess was strangely familiar, and on getting there I asked about No 4 Fd Amb. There were only two subalterns of the ambulance present, Hattersley and Brown, so I found myself the senior officer present, and as such I had a lot of papers, pamphlets, and books of instruction, thrust upon me by Major Fell, DADMS Aldershot Command...my next step after sorting out the papers was to hunt for the Depot Sergeant Major. He found Sgt. Mackay for me — who called out the recruits from the depot to help in collecting rations, groundsheets, pitching tents...later got a letter from Major Collingwood who is to be O.C. Fd Amb asking me to take command of C section...various civil surgeon subalterns arrived[12]...I met a good many old friends in the old mess in McGrigor Barracks...had a long talk with a Captain Egan, who comes from Duncarvan..." and they had a game of billiards on the very same billiard table some of us have played on. Captain Egan was to join No 6 Fd Amb attached to 2 Division. They would work with No 4 at Mons and during the retreat.

The rest of Captain Lynch's story must strike a chord in the memory of those who have also mobilized for war, and for those, especially in the Territorial Army, who have repeatedly practised mobilization as part of their peace-time training. As Transport officer he had to collect, not vehicles, but horses — 13 light draught ones the day after he arrived at Aldershot, 39 heavy ones the next morning. Mobilization stores came next, but the harness and saddlery were all in a jumbled mess in the waggons and took ages to sort out. They could not get the horses tethered properly at their site on Redan Hill and he went to bed certain they would all stampede in the night.

Soldiers arrived in batches, including some infantry reservists who had transferred to RAMC. His section Sgt Todd had been a permanent staff instructor (PSI) with Aberdeen University's OTC. Medical Unit. His batman was "an old Dublin Fusilier... O'Conner — has been through the South African War and knows what's what." (Perhaps O'Conner had used a touch of the blarney on his new officer).

The unit began to find its identity. Drizzling rain depressed them all as they put together the personnel for the various departments of the field ambulance, revised their drills and procedures and taught them to new arrivals with no RAMC knowledge. They got to know one another. On the 15th of August they left "from the Government siding, still in the rain", watched by his wife and daughter, *en route* for Southampton.

The scene there too was familiar to those who have gone through the process: "Arrived at a large shed, already three-quarters full of cavalry — 19th Lancers and 18th Hussars…rained all day… had nothing to do; a weary day…heard my friend Dunn is RMO to the Carabiniers…poor food arrangements… officers went out in town for dinner, where we were charged 100 per cent more than the usual price…about 9pm began to embark on *SS Armenian*."

No 4 Fd Amb marched into action at once. On the way to the front were usual events and difficulties: a horse kicked Lynch on the thigh through the canvas of his bivvy tent. Feet were sore. Soldiers gave their cap badges to French girls. Everyone got used to sleeping out. Their food was bully beef and biscuits; the officers, having the luxury of a horse, could put these in a saddle-bag. They had a serious argument with some Guards they found in possession of their billets, and had to obtain help from Major F.S. Irvine, the DADMS, and Staff Captain Soames, to get them out. They liaised with their ASC compatriots about evacuation of casualties. Lynch was given a telling off from the ADMS for not being prepared for reception of sick — "so up to this I thought the war is exactly like manoeuvres", he reflected sadly. They wired to medical stores for re-supply. They had small all ranks parties in their lines.

As ever, they were proud of their Corps. They were a Medical Unit, not RMOs. Marching by now within their brigade, their section was placed at the rear of the Coldstream Guards: "The bde marched with an easy swing under their heavy packs", remembered John Lynch, "and though I say it myself, my little lot trekked as well as the best of them." As he marched, he had gruesome thoughts about the ambulance waggons and their contents to come.

On Sunday 23rd August "it was rumoured there would be some fighting around Mons today" and they saw their first shell bursts in the distance. That evening they came on their No 3 section open and receiving. He made his will and sent it off urgently to his wife. So far all their patients had been sick, but now the war would start for No 4 Field Ambulance when at 5am the ADMS came to tell them " a retirement had been ordered." John Lynch would not see the retreat through; he was captured with his field ambulance section and its wounded.

This BEF of 7 divisions i.e. two army corps — plus one cavalry division of 5 brigades, was what the new field ambulance units were supporting. The cavalry, with 1,2,3, and 5 Infantry Divisions were to take part in the fighting at Mons. 4 Div left the U.K. later and did not arrive at the front till a day after the Mons battle began, and 6 Div did not arrive until the retreat from Mons was over.

At this opening stage in the Great War, there were 3 field ambulances per division, 4 with the cavalry division, and in the next point in the chain of medical evacuation, 1 clearing hospital for each division i.e. 6 in all; farther back, it is worth recalling, 12 SHs, 6 ambulance trains; farther back again there were the 12 base hospitals already referred to. There was an Advanced Medical Equipment Depot (AMED), and there were specialist sanitary units.

The TF was involved: of the new cavalry Fd Ambs, the 6th, 7th, and 8th, which went out in August, were formed of volunteers from various Territorial units. The 8th was the 1/1 Yorks Mounted Brigade Field Ambulance of the Territorial Force. The 7th, 8th, 27th, and 29th Divisions, formed from Regular battalions withdrawn from British Garrisons overseas and India, were provided entirely with their field units from existing T.F. field ambulances, with the exception of the 21st, 22nd, and 23 Fd Ambs of 7 Div — these were mobilized at Southampton from Regular RAMC who had also returned from overseas Garrisons.

Troop movement across the English Channel was wonderfully smooth. The summer weather meant the water was smooth too, and this was providential. In the first 5 days of greatest activity, 1800 special trains ran in Great Britain and Ireland. An average of 13 ships crossed over. "Thanks to the courageous initiative by the First Sea Lord, Prince Louis of Battenberg, supported by

Churchill as First Lord, the Royal Navy was at its war stations by 1 August, three days before war was declared. It was the Royal Navy which would make all this mobilization possible, so that by 1918 5 million men would be transferred across, closely adjacent to the German Navy, without ever losing a man, horse or gun while at sea".[13] While there is evidence that the Germans made no attempt to stop the original BEF crossing the Channel, because they believed the British would thereby be beaten in battle with the French, this did not pertain after, when the Germans began to realise who their main enemy were. Hospital ships were less fortunate; 6 were mined and 8 torpedoed. Thereafter they were darkened and camouflaged.

But as well as fit men crossing to war, there were the casualties coming back. S.G. William Donovan was appointed "DMS Embarkation, Southampton Docks" on August 24th 1914, and his contribution was one of the most important any Corps member made throughout the whole War. His task was "to supervise arrangements for reception and distribution of patients", and he began with a tiny staff. The first real flood of wounded arrived on September 8th, direct from the field, and did not cease for 4 years. The ambulance trains which took them onwards were also under his direction, and his co-operation with the railway staff was excellent from the first. He had IMS officers on his staff to supervise the Indian hospital ships carrying Indian casualties. Recalled from retirement for the job in 1914, he was "relegated to the retired list as from 15/7/1919" — his record of service stated!

General Sir William Donovan, as he became, did a huge job with great success. By 1916, over 600,000 patients had passed through Southampton. The records his staff kept were also clearly first-class, as accounts of complaints by individuals being successfully answered showed.[14] His success was commemorated perhaps more by the Americans than by his own people, as he had to work with their casualties also. He must not be forgotten.

Clearing Hospitals were the next in the chain of evacuation. No 6 was mobilized at the Carlton Hotel, Southsea on August 6th. They were at Rouen by the 17th and went straight into action.

No 6 Clearing hospital personnel *marched* from their disembarkation. "As we marched along the cobbled roads, singing It's a long way to Tipperary", said one MO, "I thought the spirit of soldiering is to forget tragedy in the acceptance of the joys of the moment." They found themselves in a slower stream of traffic. They gazed at the French officers in their gaily-coloured uniform — much brighter than the "sadder khaki", recalled another doctor. This was before they had seen action — the value of the sadder khaki became apparent at once. Two other hazards of mobilization were recorded in the diary: "Our heavy stuff was left on the quay. Our stores consisted of every detail from a marquee to a lemon squeezer", and "We had no transport." Soon they boarded a troop train, and wondered even more if they would ever see their equipment again.

But in spite of the shortage of equipment, their C.O., Lieutenant Colonel Bernard Forde, a graduate of 1886 from the Catholic University of Dublin, was able to open at St Quentin. No 6 were withdrawn to Versailles, put in place for the approaching Battle of the Aisne, and will be heard from again.

No 1 CH, under command of Major Symonds and his 2 i/c Major Storrs, had a different story. They camped overnight at Harfleur and moved without mishap to Merville, where they set up in a large convent, "Collège St Joseph." Sir Anthony Bowlby, the TF officer who was Consulting Surgeon to the BEF, visited them there on the 14th of October and found their patients "in good long wards and all dressed." He operated the next day, amputating patients with gangrene of legs and hand. This was the new surgical complication; Bowlby took bacterial swabs, which Captain Rowlands, the bacteriologist of No 1, cultured in the mobile laboratory he had brought out with him from England.

Colonel Leishman was with Sir Anthony Bowlby, and together they visited No 5 CH at Hazebrouck (under command of Lieutenant Colonel Bewley) and No 6 who were by now at Béthune and back in action. Their surgeon was Captain Wilson.

The last line in the chain of evacuation was the General Hospital. And now the TF Hospitals which General Keogh had planned so carefully came into the system. At this early stage, the TF personnel were supposed to be for home service only. But in the medical master plan, the home-based hospitals were to be the ones with the highest clinical level of skill and competence. As the example, 3rd London GH TF containing staff from the Middlesex, St Mary's and Charing Cross Hospitals, can have its mobilization story told. The large series of others, countrywide, had very similar experiences.[15]

No 3 London was mobilized during its annual camp. But it had never practised mobilization as a training exercise, and this became very obvious as the days passed. They had no shortage of staff — 42 officers, 204 NCOs and men, 114 TF sisters and 134 Voluntary Aid Detachment (VAD) probationer nurses. Their own surgeons ("who included Sir Alfred Pearce Gould and Sir Victor Horsley" said one of their doctors casually) had procured all surgical kit necessary. But their Service kit was for a Field Hospital, not a General one; the equipment scale was quite unsuitable. Next, the firms who had assured them they would supply beds on the 4th of August said some days later they could not. 150 beds were promised, but when they arrived they were found to be bunks. Eventually the hospital, in its war location in the Royal Victoria Patriotic School in Wandsworth, managed to set up its requirement of 500 beds. Casualties from the opening battles of the conflict arrived within no time, the first at Southampton on 31st August — 3 officers and 121 soldiers. All casualties arriving in the U.K. base later had their primary care on the continent, but these first included some who still had on their first field dressings. They were treated to their conclusion by the teaching hospital medical and especially nursing staff. The TF staff also had the great advantage over Regular colleagues of knowing one another and having trained together — even if not at mobilization.

All the usual summer sports events of the RAMC had time to happen that summer of 1914. There was only one exception — the Army Golf Meeting was arranged for October, and had to be cancelled. So the army teams missed the chance of playing over the Links of St Andrews, and the members lost the opportunity of temporary membership, for the duration of the tournament, at the Golf Holy of Holies, the Royal and Ancient Golf Club.

In the large historical sweep of the 20th century, the first battles of 1914 would have, as far as the RAMC was concerned, their most significant features in the development of the field ambulance, which could not have had a worse baptism than the retreat from Mons now to unfold, and in the development of the CCS from the Clearing Hospital. On the clinical side, the first large casualties produced sepsis of a type and ferocity at which the medical officers, including General Keogh, were appalled. Other clinical problems, though appearing very quickly over the late autumn and winter, would not at this date loom so large as that of gas gangrene. The appearance of this kind of sepsis would have political repercussions as well as surgical, which, allied to an apparent failure in the evacuation system, would lead to doubts about the efficiency of the RAMC at the highest military level.

On August 14th the BEF moved to concentration areas between Maubeuge and Le Cateau(map of early BEF). Their first contact with the enemy was at dawn on the 22nd, when C Sqn of 4 Royal Dragoon Guards sent out two patrols from the town of Oburg on the Condé Canal north towards Soignies. One of these met a German picquet, fired on it, and withdrew. Quite soon afterwards, a local attack brought in some German prisoners; the Dragoon Guards discovered the enemy were fallible after all.

But that very day major French attacks had been unsuccessful; their attacks the two preceding days had also failed. The French first objective, to "attack with all forces united and wrest the initiative from the enemy and to break the German centre" had failed with them.

There was confusion. The French 3rd and 4th Armies began to move into the Ardennes. Their 5th Army, under General Lanrezac, and beside the BEF, was heavily engaged.

The BEF had marched to Mons, passing the coal dumps and ugly coal tips of the region, and on August 23rd the Mons-Condé Canal was their front line. The Canal was held by General Smith-Dorrien's II Corps, 5 Div holding the main canal line, 3 Div the right of the line including the town of Mons. I Corps was to the east; it included the Guards Brigade. Already the noise and destructive power of the new big artillery was evident. As a British officer quoted by Sir Edward Spiers wrote, as he watched the flames to the north: "A chill of horror came over us. War seemed suddenly to have assumed a merciless, ruthless aspect that we had not realised till then."[16]

As soon as it was realised by General Joffre, the French Commander-in-Chief, that the German aim was to turn the left flank of the Allied Armies, the BEF began to fall back on Maubeuge and Valenciennes. Now rapid rifle fire, and tactical tricks learned from the Boers, helped II Corps to defend effectively and disengage rapidly. From 24th August I Corps was fully

HOLLAND

Rhine

BELGIANS

1

Brussels

Maastricht

Lille

Tournai

Aachen

Cologne

Scheldt

Maas

Mons

Meuse

Liége

2

Charleroi

Namur

Sambre

Le Cateau

B.E.F.

Dinant

3

Amiens

Guise

LUXEMBOURG

La Fère

4

Moselle

Oise

Soissons

5

Meuse

Rethel

Reims

Verdun

Thionville

Marne

4

Metz

5

Morhange

3

Paris

Nancy

GERMAN OFFENSIVE

Toul

2

6

1914

Meurthe

1

Épinal

Scale of Miles

0   10   20   30   40   50

7

Langres

Saône

Allies

Dijon

Germans

Besançon

Fortresses

SWITZERLAND

involved. Sir John French, the British C-in-C, showed good tactical sense in deciding the BEF's line of retreat. It and the French 5th Army fell back for two weeks on end to aid Joffre's re-grouping; the Battle at Le Cateau held up the German advance momentarily. By September 4th the Retreat from Mons was over. The following Battles of the Aisne, the Marne, and finally the First Battle of Ypres, meant that the Schlieffen plan had finally failed. Now the mighty armies would face each other across fixed fronts for three years, until once again a battle of movement was fought.

For 1st Irish Guards and their RMO the retreat began on the night of August 24th. Hugh Shields had seen and heard his first shrapnel, and ducked to escape his first machine gun bullets, only the previous day. (This was the day, the 23rd, which The *Official History* of the Medical Services said was the date the war began for the AMD.) He helped to carry stretchers, did casualty sweeps with his SBs, dressed wounds. On the 25th the field ambulance was open. Returning from putting wounded into a Belgian Red Cross Hospital, he found he had lost his horse and all his kit. Days later on the way back he saw guardsmen of the Coldstream battalion so tired they were given bread and automatically put it into their rifle magazines.

He was briefly captured by the Germans, marched with a bayonet at his back, and had to give chloroform for the German MOs. He remembered the stink of suppurating wounds. He worked with three other British RAMC officers, also prisoners, Captain Sinclair, Captain Wetherall and Lieutenant Rankin. The Germans, who had once appalled him by driving Belgian village women in front of them as they advanced, allowed the four doctors a mess of their own and provided a cook.

Re-joining his unit when the Germans retreated, on a quiet day he had time for a chat with Lieutenant Huggan of the Coldstreams. "The guardsmen brought us a magnificent lunch." They sat and smoked, and talked of what they would do after the war. Huggan was killed a few hours after.

Hugh Shields can speak for all the Regimental Medical Officers.

"I make a point of entirely disregarding fire when it comes to the point of seeing a wounded man and paying no attention. I don't believe in precautions beyond the ordinary ones of not exposing oneself more than one can help does any good. After all I always think if one is killed doing one's duty, one can't help it and it is the best way of coming to an end, and I mentally repeat that to myself when I am getting plugged at. Somehow I don't feel that God means me to get killed yet, though before I came out, I had a conviction that I shouldn't come back alive."

"Almost everything I now possess belonged to officers now dead, but I had nothing after the Germans took everything..."

"of the original 28 officers in the bn now only 12 are left...we have plenty of tobacco and chocolate...we take it off all officers who have been killed...."

And after the Battle of Ypres was over, on October 23rd, he wrote: "The battle is now over and I am sitting with a wounded officer waiting for the ambulance waggons to come up. I had an exciting afternoon running down the line behind the trenches to see wounded men. The men appreciated it very much, but on the whole I doubt if it is good enough and whether the benefit derived is proportionate to the risk run...." Hugh Shields was killed three days later.

A friend, Lieutenant (later Captain) the Hon Harold Alexander, Irish Guards, wrote to his parents: "You know Hugh was a great friend of mine, and a pluckier fellow never lived. I think the nicest thing I ever heard was said by one of our men, who said 'Mr Shields is the bravest man I ever saw'. The officers said he was too brave and told him, but he always said it was his duty to help wounded men whenever he could. If anyone has done his duty and a great deal more, he has."

Lieutenant W.P. Croker wrote of the clinical cases he saw. As early as October 28th, he described a case of something he thought unusual. Captain Tulloch, a company 2 i/c in the Royal West Kents, became hysterical and burst into tears after a shell burst near him. Croker gave him "1/4 gr of morphia (15mg) + tea boiled eggs and bread...told him to go back to 2nd line transport, live out in the open, and in 10 days he would be himself again." He was "a case of spinal concussion from a shell bursting close to him."

He also recorded in his diary another case, of Lieutenant Newton, the Transport Officer, who came up to the front to deputise for the adjutant and who went at once to Croker to say he had "nervous exhaustion from the extra work being thrown upon him and also not being accustomed to living in dugouts and under heavy shell fire. I had to send him back also."

Croker, however, had a very different attitude to casualty collection from Hugh Shields. From his own account, he stayed in his RAP and had others do the collecting. He spoke of "giving a SB 1/4gr Morphia to take out and give to a wounded officer!"

He was captured after his RAP was overrun by the enemy and spent time in a POW camp at Krefeld. Later exchanged, he served in the U.K. and became a Regular RAMC officer. A good hockey and cricket player, he soldiered in Peshawar and Malta. He was DDMS of X Corps in 1943, and his last posting was as C.O. of Netley.

Owen Spencer Watkins was a padre with 14 Fd Amb, which was in support of the 1st Royal West Kents. He spoke of the terror-stricken refugees; "some of the outrages made the blood run cold and caused men to set their lips tight." He spoke too of "the spies and of villagers signalling to the enemy", of his first experience of digging in as the ADS was being set up, of General Smith Dorrien cheerfully waving to the troops. They found themselves also in the rearguard and had to leave MOs behind with wounded. Finally they disengaged: "We slept as only men who during 3 hard days have had only 6 hours' sleep and 2 square meals can sleep."

An RMO who was with 1st Bn Royal Fusiliers in 17 Infantry Bde of 6 Div. and who therefore came along a little later that summer, was Captain John Hare from Belfast. When his unit landed in France he saw groups of German officer and soldier POW being taken to internment. He thought they looked fine men, and was surprised to see how they had to be guarded from Frenchwomen until he learnt that French women had been recently mutilated by German soldiers.

On the way to the Marne, sometimes marching and sometimes riding, he watched the German planes which were carrying out aerial spotting for their gunners, and a German observation balloon. This was the shape of warfare to come. As his battalion marched in the tedious rain, he saw the "men returning dead beat — officers unshaven and haggard." (Many medical accounts spoke of the depression and exhaustion of the casualties from Mons and contrasted them with the much more cheerful men wounded at the Marne and Aisne). John Hare envied a friend called Poole who was in the LofC — " a lucky dog", he called him.

Arriving at the front line he found his "home a small cave and the bn HQ 2 feet high (60 cms) and littered with straw. The trenches were only 1000 yds apart (900 m) and 'marked with crosses'. The first night in the line was marked by 'trench panic', but from the second night they were all right."

He saw their Brigadier and Brigade Major visit the Battalion: "the fools kept on staff caps and warned snipers." He and his infantry friends applauded the bravery and skill of Gunner officers in support, as predecesors had done in South Africa.

"There was a bad smell in front of us" — the C.O. blamed it on a dead cow, but when Captain Hare investigated, he found a graveyard. "Never properly buried", he told his commander. Aware of the health risk, as RMO he insisted on proper burial, and with the help of his own and neighbouring King's Own Scottish Border men "and self dug up dead horses Germans and guardsmen. All black and maggoty. Some men vomited. We buried them in a large pit." The burial of the dead was a job the RMOs were often involved with, as well as the padres, and it was an exhausting and highly unpleasant task. Captain John Hare will be met with again in Gallipoli; he was posted away from Flanders in December 1914.

The field ambulances were the first RAMC units behind the front. Their role was to collect, hold and treat where necessary, and pass back, the casualties their waggons had brought from the fighting units. At the start of the War, they were set up behind their division, being divisional troops. But the speed of retreat and their initial lack of transport and hence of mobility tested them and their officers sorely. Behind them were the Clearing Hospitals, styled before the outbreak of war as the key medical units in the chain of evacuation from the field.

The Fd Amb of 6 Div was No 17, commanded by Major J.P Silver, MD, RAMC When he arrived at the front, like Captain Hare, he looked at "A.G. (b) 28 dated 23/8/14", signed by Major General C.F.N. Macready. It told him what to do with his casualties — what is called in military (and indeed civilian) terms "their disposal."

"DMS on receipt of instructions...the battlefield CHs sufficient to cope with the numbers estimated wounded (own, allies, en (enemy)) will in the first instance, be collected at easily distinguishable points, such as outskirts of villages, farms, or small woods…these localities to be, if possible, on roads or railways…removal from CHs to be arranged by DMS direct with QMG's branch. Cases which can in the opinion of the MO be removed, without detriment, in waggons or supply columns, will be collected at spots on the routes traversed by the supply columns, and be taken by them to refilling or other convenient places on their route. Every care will be taken that supply columns are delayed as short a time as possible, and on no account will they deviate from their route…amn (ammunition) park lorries, if possible, will be used in the same manner."

"ALL OFFICERS TO SEE AND INITIAL."….[17]

These orders did not take account of the shortage of transport which the AMD, and the TF doctors, had warned about. They also did not take into account the fact that the railways system was French controlled. And the General Staff planners did not seem to have anticipated that the first phase of this Great War was to be a hurried and frightening reverse.

The speed of the reverse took everyone by surprise. "Withdrawals" had never been practised by field medical units, only "setting up" and movement in a somewhat leisurely fashion. There is perhaps a lesson from history for even the present here: all major wars where Britain was involved in the 20th century began with withdrawals, and usually hurried ones at that.

Major Thurston, for example, was C.O. of 13 Fd Amb. He expected his neighbours of 14 and 15 to be there when he arrived at his ordered destination of the town of Dour — they and all their equipment were still on the train to Valenciennes. So he had to split his No 13, to support 13 and 14 Bdes, keeping his HQ at Dour in a girls' school. In 3 Div, Lieutenant Colonel A. Kennedy had to split his 7 Fd Amb into 3 because 8 and 9 Fd Ambs were also still held up in a French train *en route* to Valenciennes and 5 miles (8Km) away. Medical Officers watched while waiting for casualties the French cavalrymen passing, leading horses "whose ulcerated backs and limping bore witness… the French station master, listening to the telegraph, fled…." One doctor in a Clearing Hospital actually wrote in his diary "we had not been trained for a retreat, only for an advance."

Normally, one thinks of falling *back* along the LofC, but from Mons it was actually carried out *at right angles* to this line. So field ambulances were not falling back towards the medical units of the LofC, but were actually marching away from them. Railheads were constantly changing, there were no CHs at the sort of positions described in A.G. (b) dated 23/8/14, ambulance trains were just beginning to run, and there was no Motor Ambulance Company (MAC) at all with this division. This last unit did not appear until the Battle of the Aisne began.

It was however doubtful if an MAC would have helped in the retreat from Mons. It would have had to cross and re-cross the line of retreat. There was severe congestion on the roads, and it would have had great difficulty in finding the rear medical units. Thus the field ambulance C.O.s had to utilize every form of transport they could find. Their experience in their first battle taught them a lesson which was never forgotten, and went into the instinctive lore of those officers from then onwards.

For in spite of all the difficulties, casualties came back. A clearing hospital officer "watched a Fd Amb, officers and men, and horses, march back in perfect column of route — no disorder, their waggons full of wounded men they took them to the train themselves. They were weary, but in good order. One told me a staff officer told the doctors 'this is a strategic retreat'!" The medical officers had not lost their doctors' sense of humour!

But they saw other things which were less happy. Major Florrs, No 1 CH 2 i/c, saw " a dirty young MO — his regiment all killed, he said. It was the way he was shaking...an English private, whom they asked for news, but he stared vacantly to his front and then began to cry."

No 6 Fd Amb was with 2 Div at Mons from the start. Major T.J. Potter was C.O., and Captain W. Egan who had chatted with Captain Lynch in the McGrigor mess at Aldershot was one of the nine RAMC officers. They had had time to set up; they worked with No 4 from August 18th. The first casualties went back to Givry where the Advanced Dressing Station (ADS) was "as described in the Corps Journal", as Captain Priestly put it.

Then the fog of war descended. Messages to the ADMS did not reach him. The rains came and the usual results followed. A section was sent with its ambulance waggons and a forage cart with Captains Priestly and Egan and twelve soldiers to collect casualties at Maroilles. All were captured, as were the ADMS Colonel H.Thompson and the DADMS Major F.S. Irvine. This last officer was later liberated from the enemy.

There were no orders, so the C.O. decided to follow a battery of artillery in retreat. The exhaustion of marching, setting up, closing down, setting up, and for 8 days on end, was vividly told in the unit's diary. It contained a minimum of military detail: "We crossed the Marne on 2nd (September). Sept 4th was the last day of the retreat. In 12 days the Army had covered 140 miles (200 Km) as the crow flies. Battle of the Marne (Sept 5–14) followed. Battle of the Aisne began 12/9. Torrential rain."

There was undoubtedly some disquiet. "When the Army doesn't know what it wants", wrote one MO, "what can a wretched (medical) C.O., whose duty is to follow, decide upon his movements?...some of us who had been in S.A., compared our position with that following Colenso...a repulse is an excellent stimulus."

The medicals watched the other units retreating. They had little or no information. At this early stage in the war they were not as "netted in" — to use a signaller's term — as they became later. They were aware that field ambulances holding wounded would be captured — like Captain Lynch and his fellows. The clearing hospitals were in exactly the same position — in fact, not having the contact the field ambulances officers had with the RMOs they were less well off for news. Some of them put out what were in effect sections of field ambulance pattern, with an MO and RAMC soldiers to clear areas. "Our tentacles were to clear" (sic). They had the railways as their best hope; "the C.O. had to spend most of his time negotiating with French rly staff — including drivers...one train took them to the wrong place!"

The CHs had in theory 3 main functions: 1) to treat till fit for evacuation sick and wounded, 2) to expedite immediate removal to base, 3) to retain till fit to return to unit. To some extent these overlapped at this stage of fighting; field ambulances, having more transport, could cope much better with evacuation. The CHs were supposed to be mobile, but they were not.

A further difficulty for the CHs — which was no fault of theirs — was that their stretchers were impounded for use on ambulance trains. On the outbreak of war the ambulance trains were seriously deficient in stretchers and other stores. Urgent letters passed from General Woodhouse to the D.G. including one saying: "I shall have to rob clearing hospitals." The CHs were given cots instead of stretchers. The deficiency in ambulance trains was called "the one blot on the mobilization of the medical units" by the official historian, General Macpherson.[18]

Because they had to move in the retreat, they could not carry out their treatment and holding functions. Major Florrs summed it up well: "A CH is the field hospital nearest the fighting line. It must follow within a few miles of the Fd Ambs of the div and receive all pts evac nightly by the latter units. When the distance between the 2 becomes inconveniently great, the CH must pack up, follow on, and reopen. The tide of war decides the number of moves."

Empty supply lorries were the sole means of transport. (The *fourgons* (cattle trucks) of the French were very quickly discarded). But from the start of the Aisne battle, the MACs they had previously asked for but were denied, appeared.[19] One section had 20 cars, the other in the company had 15 each. Special road circuits appeared at this time — the beginning of what became the routine. So the medical and transport authorities learned together from the Mons defeat, and it was to their credit that they learned quickly.

After the haste and disorganisation of the retreat, the Medical Services re-grouped and stood ready for the next German attack. Sir Anthony Bowlby, who had gone to France on September 23rd, recalled the anxiety of GHQ BEF as news came in of the arrival of yet more German reinforcements. It is very significant that it was he, and not the DMS, who ordered that some surgery be done at field ambulance level as soon as he realised that the clearing hospitals could not cope and that the speed of the retreat made casualty evacuation to the base difficult. Some of the German reinforcements constituted the German 4th Army, made up of very young men and older, and they would be slaughtered at Ypres; after one day of heavy German attacks a platoon of Gordon Highlanders counted 240 dead on its platoon front. One of the survivors was a young man called Adolf Hitler. Nevertheless Messines fell, the hospital at Ypres had to close and retire, and medicals as well as Generals knew how serious things were. "Evident that this fight is very critical", wrote Sir Anthony. "1st November the critical day. The German Emperor has arrived and personally ordered the attack! By November 4th we heard the great attack of last week has failed."

The DMS on this front was S.G. T.J. O'Donnell, DSO, a Deputy D.G. in France. Always called by his contemporaries cheery and helpful, he had sole responsibility for the medical cover for the First Battle of Ypres. Because of his honesty and complete lack of self-interest he was respected and popular; his contribution, his energy and his clearness of what was required, was just what was needed. In particular, he organised the MACs for the first time, and the hospital trains. He was ably supported by Major P.Evans, RAMC. The short breathing space before the battle was well used by General O'Donnell to place his units in conjunction with the General Staff, to hurry forward MACs, and to make firm the whole system of medical organisation. If "First Ypres" was a turning point for the BEF, it was no less a turning point for the RAMC in France also.[20]

Early problems for the AMD were not confined to the land of France. Many occurred at home, and the first of these was that the numbers of men being processed for the Army were enormous. One of the biggest problems was that of recruit medical examinations, and it took a little time to solve it. The normal number of recruits drafted into the Regular Army in time of peace was about 35,000 annually. But by a month into hostilities, the Prime Minister Mr Asquith announced in a speech at the Guildhall that between 250,000 and 300,000 men had been accepted for military service. These were not Territorial Force, but part of the "New Army" called for by Lord Kitchener. Kitchener, unlike many senior officers, realised very early that this would be a long war and that the whole population would have to be mobilized. The press had quickly alleged that the recruiting offices were unable to deal with the numbers, and medical examinations were inadequate. Because the AMD insisted that entrance medical examinations had to be carried out by Regular officers, there was some delay, but it was soon overcome as civilian practitioners became enlisted to help after learning the requirements necessary. It is interesting that "The Territorial Force was considered to be on a different footing, and the medical tests and standards are far less stringent."[21]

The difficulties which had arisen with the lack of transport for the evacuation of wounded, and which had affected both field ambulances and CHs, had led to delays in surgical treatment. There had also been delay in the actual collection of wounded at the front line because of the impossibility of moving during daylight, but this was not at first appreciated at home. What intensified the media complaints was the appearance of seriously infected wounds, wounds infected with what appeared to the lay mind as the infections of neglect. These infections were naturally made much worse by the time between wounding and the soldier's coming to the operating theatre. Because the infection was from bacteria which existed in large numbers in the tilled soil of Flanders, called anaerobes, and because the gas gangrene resulting was so horrible, it was not surprising that alarm arose. Lords Esher and Barron, who visited in the third week of September, were very critical, attributing the appearance of gangrene and tetanus to neglect.

Lieutenant General Sir Arthur Sloggett had only been D.G. at the War Office since 1st June 1914. His deputy was S.G. W.G. Macpherson, who himself had only been in post since March. Macpherson had succeeded S.G. W. Babtie, V.C., who had gone to India as DMS in succession to General Sloggett.

There were five branches in the AMD, one dealing with personnel and training, one with sanitation, hospital accommodation, recruiting, and statistics (a very odd collection), one with hospital equipment, surgical and medical supplies, medical boards, professional matters, and voluntary aid, one with organisation, mobilization, and preparations for war, and one for Nursing Services.

Sloggett was sent to France on October 28th by Field-Marshal Kitchener, the Secretary of State, ostensibly to sort out problems with the British Red Cross Society and the Order of St John. These voluntary bodies had very rapidly built a series of active agencies, all determined to provide help, and to play a prominent part, in caring for the Army sick and wounded in France. They were producing friction with the Army Medical Services, and they had the strong support of influential sections of the press.[22] At the same time, Sir Arthur Keogh, who was already in France as Chief Commissioner of the BRCS overseas (then as now retired Directors General moved into such posts on leaving the army), was returned to London to take Sloggett's place as D.G. at the War Office. He took up his second tour on October 8th.

With Sir David Bruce at the RAM College as Commandant and superintending the background research and development, there was now a powerful team in place.

There can be little doubt, especially having regard to the fact that Kitchener sent out at the same time a confidential envoy, Colonel Arthur Lee, M.P., to investigate how the medical services were functioning and report back to him, that the posting of General Sloggett to France was a demotion. Had he had to do no more than settle difficulties with gentlemen and ladies of the Red Cross and St John, he could easily have come back to his Director's post. He appears as an almost shadowy figure in the rest of the War, and is mentioned only twice by Haig in his personal diaries, the first in April 1915, when he wrote "S.G. Sloggett, who has recently taken over duties of DGMS, came to see me, very pleased with all the medical arrangements. Says he is much troubled by Lord K. listening to wishes of certain titled ladies and sending out ambulance cookers and other appliances, which are encumbrances", and the other on the occasion when he congratulated General Haig on the birth of his daughter. Sir Anthony Bowlby also mentions him rarely, and then usually in a critical way, speaking of his failure to understand surgical problems.[23]

The other reason for Colonel Lee's visit was perhaps that complaints about the RAMC had been appearing in the press. There were undue delays, it was said, in passing wounded back to base hospitals at the coast. Motor ambulances were required — it was all too obvious, from no more than a glance at the map, that the journey of some 50 miles(80Km) from the Aisne to the Channel Port of Boulogne could be done in a modern vehicle in 2–3 hours. And why were the hospital trains so slow? Men lay for 12 hours on the train journey. The diseases of tetanus and gangrene were rife. The Army Medical Services were failing in their duty. Mr Douglas Hall, M.P., in the House on Wednesday November 25th, criticised the use of horse-drawn ambulances. He suggested that barges be used, to float the wounded back to hospital. The fact that this bad medical news was being reported in parallel with the bad news of retreat and disorder made things worse. And the Senior General Staff were privately expressing anxieties. It was all good headline material, especially for the tabloids of the day. The demarcation disputes between the voluntary organisations and the AMD was naturally a smaller issue.

The confidential letters of Lee are of the greatest interest. They cover the major age-old problems of medical care in war applied to the current conflict.

Colonel Lee at once stated that there was "no foundation for the condemnation which has been visited on (the AMS) in certain quarters."[24] There had been initial friction between the RAMC and the BRCS because, in his opinion, both "were suffering from a surfeit of well-meaning but conflicting advice — neither knows how much is officially inspired or how much is totally unauthorised." But as the BRCS was coming to realise where its spheres of activity were, and as sharing of responsibilities was being agreed, this was disappearing. The two sides should be left to sort themselves out,, he said very sensibly. "The War Office should publicly recognize the help being given by the Red Cross, as it is an organisation wholly dependent for its existence on public esteem and private financial support." Also, he warned, perhaps recalling problems caused by the number of well-meaning individuals who had appeared in South Africa, "No *voluntary* organisation, however influential, should be officially recognised except through the British Red Cross."

Next he demolished the ignorant utterances of the press. "How easy it is to look from London, or after scanning a map, to criticise", he said. "The transport problem might appear simple to reporters, but the facts were that the BEF formed less than one-tenth of the Allied Armies, and the French organisation overwhelmed the system. The railways were under exclusive French control, the bridges, signalling, and telegraphic systems (and many roads) had been destroyed by shelling, most of the French employees had deserted as soon as the Germans approached, so there was no-one to man the system, and all these occurred when there had been the heaviest fighting and greatest influx of wounded. The railway system belonged to the French; and their exodus of government and civilians from Paris was absorbing over 100 trains daily."

Roads — in France but more so in Belgium — were of the highly convex, pavé variety, on whose cobbled surface ambulance cars were so shaken that casualties dreaded being transported by them. The roads were filled with columns of marching troops, military supplies needed priority, and ambulance cars as often as not found themselves in the depths of the road-side depressions. "Considering the difficulties and abnormal circumstances of the opening stages of the campaign", was his conclusion to Lord Kitchener, "the Army Medical Services are on the whole deserving of credit rather than condemnation."

As the weeks passed, the pattern of necessity became clear. By the end of October it was evident that motor ambulance cars were best for that short carry between dressing stations at Fd Amb level and CHs or trains. Military traffic of higher priority always had to be given precedence. This age-old rule of war was re-stated for the benefit of the press. The French "Commission Regulatrica" was pressed to provide more trains for the BEF and to allot the British more suitable buildings for hospitals — something they had not been doing — especially since winter was fast approaching.

As far as infections were concerned, there was no justification for the press charge that tetanus was rife. On October 31st, the Army Sanitary Committee[25] reported "the absence of typhoid fever is most gratifying, and that only a dozen cases of tetanus out of 1000 casualties had occurred." The symptoms had appeared in the third week after injury. They were in men with extensive lacerated wounds contaminated with soil and clothing. Though given repeated doses of anti-tetanic serum (A.T.S.), all had died in 3–10 days.

But as far as "gangrene" was concerned, things were very different. It had been noted, especially by French surgical reports, that men wounded in what were called "entrenchments" had injuries of the backs of the hands and forearms because they were holding their knapsacks over their heads to protect themselves from the shell debris which was a major horror for them. Those lying prone outside cover had suffered severe injuries to their buttocks and backs of thighs, and some had their buttocks almost blown away, with their genitals. Pelvic injuries were common. There was also "Concussion from being blown up, with loss of consciousness, later loss of words" — more examples of what Croker had written about in his notebook.

"Emphysematous gangrene" called for operation. "Although the adipose tissue in the (skin) flaps was yellow, offensive, and gelatinous, these casualties did well with some sloughing. There have been many cases with blue or bluish-green pus. They were characterised by profuse suppuration and a horribly offensive odour. Iodoform was useful."

This description detailed the local changes of gas gangrene, caused by Clostridium welchii, but it did not include the toxic changes which could bring death in a few hours. The surgeons, more especially those who had experience of South Africa, were horrified. They had believed they knew how to treat wounds by the antiseptic method. "But now", said the Director General Sir Alfred Keogh himself, "we seem to have gone back to the infections of the Middle Ages."

This dramatic incidence of infection was the greatest worry by far — the alleged shortage of chloroform, magnified by the press (and there was indeed a shortage, for a short while in early November) — was insignificant in comparison. It would tax the surgeons, soon to be almost entirely Territorials and civilian consultants, to the uttermost. The Germans had the same problem: they called it "gas-phlegm", and Müller of Rostock suggested giving subcutaneous injections of oxygen gas. Hydrogen Peroxide, especially in solid form, was widely recommended.[26] Its management, which led to the evolution of a surgical treatment of war wounds, will be described in the next chapter, along with a survey of the development of the RAMC's surgery of the War.

The RMO would have to be the bravest of the brave in this Great War. Hugh Shields said of his friend Huggan's being recommended for the V.C. for pulling wounded Germans out of a barn where they were housed and which had gone on fire: "I doubt if he was recommended really, as people told me I had been and nobody in their senses would consider it worth a V.C., as if they got V.C.s for so little they would be as cheap as dirt."

Lieutenant Arthur Martin-Leake, re-joined in 1914, was awarded "a clasp to the V.C. for most conspicuous bravery and devotion to duty throughout the campaign, especially during the period October 29th to November 8th, 1914, near Zonnebecke, in rescuing whilst exposed to constant fire a large number of the wounded who were lying close to the enemy's trenches." Our Corps had been awarded the first double V.C. in the country's history.

Notes and references

CHAPTER 5

[1]For an easily-read assessment of the military power available, see "White Heat — the New Warfare 1914–18" John Terraine, 1982, Sidgwick and Jackson, London, chapters 1 & 2.

[2]"The Killing Grounds — the British Army, on Western Front and the Emergence of Modern Warfare, 1910–1918." Tim Travers, 1987, Unwin Hyman, London, p 42ff.

[3]Colonel Repington, *The Times* correspondent, wrote in 1919 that the apparent failure of many in the Liberal Party (with its strong anti-militarist tradition) was due to "the complete disbelief of both great political parties that such (European) war would ever come, and their determination that we should never take serious part in it...if it came, the chance that such a war might be forced on us by the aggression of a foreign power was too inconvenient to be considered." Vestigia, 1919, Constable, London, p 256.

[4]Admiral von Tirpitz believed the power of the British Fleet was the factor which had to be overcome if Germany was to be a world power. His Navy Law of 1898 initiated the building of a battle fleet, for reasons not dissimilar to the building of the Soviet fleet 60 years later.

[5]General Count von Schlieffen was Chief of the German Staff in 1891. His plan looked towards a decisive victory for Germany, as decisive as Sedan in 1871. But when put into effect by his successor, von Moltke, the original plan had been considerably whittled away. See also Sir Basil Liddle Hart, "History of the First World War", 1970, Cassel and Co Ltd., London, Chapter 3.

[6]Official History of the Great War, Military Operations Vol I, France and Belgium 1914, Brigadier General J.E. Edmonds, 1925, Macmillan, London, p 14. "From 1911 onwards the French and British Staffs had worked out in detail a scheme for the landing of the Expeditionary Force in France, and for its concentration in the area Maubeuge — Le Cateau -Hirson, but, though there was 'an obligation

of honour', there was no definite undertaking to send the whole or part of this force to any particular part, or, in fact, anywhere at all."

[7]ibid, p 11. "No steps had been taken to instruct the army in a knowledge of the probable theatre of war or of the German army, except in the publication of a handbook of the army and of annual reports on manoeuvres and military changes. Exactly the same, however, was done in the case of the armies of all foreign states. The study of German military organization and methods was specifically forbidden at war games, staff tours, and intelligence classes, which would have provided the best opportunities for such instruction."

[8]ibid, p 10–11.

[9]Tom Percy Woodhouse enlisted as a surgeon in the AMD in 1881. His postings alternated between the U.K. and India until the Boer War, and apart from a special mention in connection with his promotion examination, a good confidential report in 1891, and a mention in despatches in Natal, he had nothing whatever that was outstanding in his record of service. He was put on half-pay as a Colonel in November 1913. He was recalled in July 1914 as Surgeon General. It is hard to see why he was promoted into this command of the highest importance. He was made CB in 1915, and KCMG in 1917 when he retired.

[10]These were based on Teaching Hospitals. In London No 1 was staffed by St Bartholomew's Hospital physicians and surgeons, No 2 by St Thomas', No 3 by University College and Middlesex, and No 4 by Guy's men. Birmingham staffed No 1 Southern General Hospital of the Territorial Force, and others were set up near the south coast.

In the north, 1st Northern General can serve as the example, as it was the prototype. It mobilized at Armstrong College, Newcastle, on August 5th and by September 1st had admitted 546 sick. Major T. Gowans was C.O., the consultant staff were Lieutnant Colonels A.M. Martin, H.B. Angus, T. Beattie, and W.E. Hume. Among the assistants was Major C.G. Turner, later the great Professor Grey Turner. By Keogh's establishment, rank was given to staff depending upon their clinical seniority, and the senior clinicians ranked higher or as high as the Commanding Officer.

In Scotland there were four BGHs, TF (British General Hospitals) No 1, fittingly, was at Aberdeen, 2 in Edinburgh, and 3 and 4 in Glasgow. The Glasgow Hospitals were at Yorkhill Parade, still a TA centre. The names of the senior medical staff included many famous names, especially in Edinburgh.

In Wales a hospital was set up under command of Lieutnant Colonel W. Sheen, who had worked with the Welsh Hospital in South Africa, but was now a Territorial officer. Now MD, MS, FRCS, and a senior surgeon, he, along with Colonel David Hepburn, C.O. of the larger Cardiff Hospital and Professor of Anatomy at Cardiff with a gold medal MD from Edinburgh, was the prototype of the very typical TF officer of the time.

[11]Outstanding research was done by the TF bacteriologists enlisted under Keogh's "new deal." Typing of tetanus was the work of Captain W.J. Tulloch, later Professor of Bacteriology at St Andrews University. See "On the Bacteriology of Wound Infections in cases of Tetanus and the identification of *Bacillus Tetani* by Serological Reactions", Captain W.J. Tulloch, RAMC, (later Captain Tulloch was awarded the OBE) from the laboratories of the RAMC College and the Lister Institute of Preventive Medicine, J R Army Med Corps, 1917; *XXIX*; 631–661.

[12]Before the TF was formed, a succession of Reserves for the RAMC was created and then modified between 1904 and 1909. They were given peace time commissions, a minimum of annual training, and were liable for service in time of war. Because of their poor career prospects and unsatisfactory training, they were not recruited with the same enthusiasm as the Territorial Force. They continue as the Army Emergency Reserve "Specialist Units." (In 1914 there was still an establishment for "civil surgeons" to join the Regular medical units on mobilization, to a total of 381 for the whole BEF. But those who created this establishment had apparently little knowledge of the TF and how it would function).

[13]John Terraine, *op cit*, p 76.

[14]The excellence of the records can be confirmed by two random examples: Two Austrian POW later claimed that combatant troops had been carried with them — the charge could be answered by reference to records. A Kensington vicar wrote to the War office claiming a man had died as a result of his treatment on disembarkation — this too was dismissed by reference to the records.

[15]But many TF medical units were not mobilized until much later. See below, p 98.

[16]Major General Sir Edward Spiers, *Liaison 1914*, Eyre and Spottiswoode, 1930, p 106.

[17]Another Order concerned burial of the dead. This was "Procedure for Clearing a Battlefield, AG (6) 28 dated 23/8/14", signed by Colonel A. Cavendish, for the Adjutant General, BEF.

[18]Major General W.G. Macpherson, op cit, p 46.

[19]Colonel Holt, ADMS of 2 Div, wrote excitedly in his diary on 23rd October: "DDMS 1st Army informs me that 5 motor ambulances are parked at my disposal in Market Square." Till then, he had always spoken of ambulance waggons. His diary went on: "3.0 p.m. 3 Bearer Subdiv of 5 F.A. sent with Captain Holland and Captain Martin-Leake

to point where lane leaves WIELTJES — PASSCHENDALE Road — in NW direction just E of stream HANNEBECK & W of point 37 to report to O.C. 4 Gds Bde."

[20]See "Medical Narrative of the Arrangements of the 1st Division at the Battle of the Aisne", by Colonel G. Cree, CMG, which brings out many other difficulties apart from medical ones, handled largely by RAMC soldiers — problems of feeding the wounded away from their units, disposal of arms and ammunition (which the NCOs kept at dressing stations, so that they could be used to make up shortages by the teeth arms), and so on. Two of Colonel Cree's comments are significant: "The C.O. of fd amb selected the sites for dressing stations, **not** the ADMS," and "The replenishment of medical and surgical material is now much simplified by the same MA (motor ambulance) convoys, as they are able to bring up as much as required and wherever wanted." J R Army Med Corps, *XXIV*, 201–220.

[21]*Lancet* 1914; **2**: 720. It was known that Kitchener was doubtful of the usefulness of the TF. This was partly because of their initial contract being of service within the UK base, which made them appear fit for home service only, but also because his ideas had been fixed some years before the concept of this new force came along. Another possible cause was that very early in the War annoyances arose which would be repeated for the rest of the 20th Century; the Territorials were jealous of their status and resented apparent or real snubs. For example, Mr Sanders M.P. asked the Under Secretary of State for War why TA officers were paid 15/6 (80p) per day but civilian practitioners newly joined for war were paid 24/- (£1.20p) a day during the war and assured of a bounty of £60 at the end of it.

Mr Baker, the Under Secretary for War, made a reply which is a classic and would be repeated again later in the century:

"All such officers commissioned in peace draw under the terms of their contract the pay and allowances of the Regular Army, varying according to the ranks which they hold. The rate quoted, 15/6 a day, is that of a Captain of the Royal Army Medical Corps, but field allowance of 3/6 (17p) is also allowable, so that the total drawn is 19/ (95p) and **not** 15/6. It is necessary to give higher rates to those commissioned on emergency, but there is no intention of making this universal." The failure to answer the question was probably inevitable !

Mr Bridgeman: "Is it not the case that the former class are getting less than the civilian practitioners newly joined?"

Mr Baker: "They are serving under a running contract under which they have engaged. It is always necessary when you take on specialists to deal with them on special terms in times of war." (House of Commons, Wednesday, 26th August, 1914).

[22]Although voluntary aid organizations were far from being in a better position to deal with the situation than the Regular Army medical service and the responsible military authorities, there was a tendency to create a different impression in the public mind, and an appeal in *The Times* of the 29th August, 1914, was to the effect that 'The British Red Cross Society is in urgent need of more funds *if effective and immediate aid is to be given to the sick and wounded at the front* ' (author's italics). See Macpherson, *op cit,* Vol I, p 60.

[23]Sir Arthur Sloggett, who graduated LRCP Edinburgh and MRCS London in 1880, had not had anything exceptional in his career. Letters and papers of the senior consultants in France — holding temporary Major General's rank — do not show him as in any way an innovator or an outstanding mind. Sir John Rose Bradford, consulting physician, wrote to Major General Sir Anthony Bowlby in early 1918 asking that General Sloggett be allowed to carry on and not be replaced, saying "Sloggett was always most sympathetic to the suggestions made by physicians and surgeons, drew no distinction between civilian consultants or Territorial officers and those of the Regular service, and has always placed the welfare of the soldier first." But the War Office said that they would not make an exception, especially in view of the long strain on the General over three and a half years, and he "had to go." And when his successor Major General C.H. Burtchaell was appointed, he was given the temporary rank of Lieutnant General while holding the appointment of DGMS France. The *real* D.G. remained General Keogh.

Obituries of "Old Sloggo", as he was affectionately called were somewhat guarded; Sir George Makins' account of the circumstances of his appointment to France is incorrect(*BMJ* of December 9th 1929).

[24]For Colonel Lees' confidential letters, see Wellcome RAMC archives, No 446, Lieutenant General Sir Charles Burtchaell's (DGAMS France 1918) reports.

[25]The Army Sanitary Committee in October 1914 consisted of: Brigadier General F.J. Anderson, RE., Chairman, Arthur Newsome MD, Government medical officer, Colonel W.H. Horrocks, Sir Fredrick Treves, Major C.E.P. Fowler, RAMC, who had just finished as Officer Commanding the School of Sanitation in Aldershot, and 2 civilian experts, Henry R. Kenwood and Dr John Robertson MD, MOH Birmingham.

[26]German records, reported in the Lancet and the BMJ, both at the time and after the War, are of the greatest interest. (See e.g. *BMJ* 1914; **2**: 1080–82.) Two months after the beginning of the War, the Medical Chief of the German Army, Dr Otto von Schjerning, issued as official report on the western battles. In one week 40–50,000 minor wounded

were sent home, largely by train. The Germans had expected a quick victory, and had made limited evacuation plans accordingly. Severely wounded were treated in field ambulances (which were thus different from the British version) and war hospitals. But the same month, in October, Professor Czerny in the *Munchener Medizinske Wochenskrift* made what he called "friendly criticisms" almost identical to those Colonel Lee replied to — slow evacuation, serious sepsis. See *Lancet* 1914; **2** : 1023–1024, 1123–1124, and later. For a résumé of the German Official Medical History of the Great War, completed in 1920 under the editorship of Lieutenant General von Schjerning, see J R Army Med Corps, Vol XXXIV, 554ff.

Chapter 6

The Major War Theatres. Casualty collection and management. Delayed Primary Suture.

PERSPECTIVE

Verdun was to become an anvil upon which French military manhood was to be hammered to death by the Germans.... By the end of April 1916, nearly a quarter of a million French and Germans had been killed or wounded in the total area, though influencing in no decisive way the balance of the World War.

Winston Churchill, The World Crisis, p 993.

The Somme

In *personnel* the results of the operation have been disastrous; in *terrain* they have been absolutely barren... from every point of view, the British offensive *per se* has been a great failure.

Winston Churchill, The World Crisis, p 1088.

The Dardanelles

We spent 5 months on SUVLA BAY which was hell on earth, because it did not matter which place we went, we were always under shell fire.

Clarence Whittaker, Private RAMC

Very soon after the German onslaught had been halted, events happened quickly behind the new British front line. King George V visited from November 4th — no time at all, it seemed, since the Battle of Ypres was over. He stayed a whole week, went to the line, and visited many medical units. Subsequent visits by the King were a great contribution — his genuine affection and concern were at once evident to everyone. Comments during his visits throughout the War, recorded by many including medical officers, and recorded by Field Marshal Haig in his personal diary published much later, confirmed that the King's advice was sound, always constitutionally correct, and regularly extremely helpful. Diaries from especially Territorial hospitals in the U.K. base told the same story; staff and patients were impressed by his — and Queen Mary's — interest and care. Nor was their interest only morale-building; they personally donated several ambulances to the Medical Services. It is obvious from the records that he provided a unifying influence of the best kind.

One of the people King George met and talked to the day after he arrived in France was Sir Anthony Bowlby, newly promoted Lieutenant Colonel, and Consulting Surgeon to the 1st Army. They discussed septic wounds, hospitals, stores, and the frost-bite which was now appearing. The RAMC was filling fast with Territorial and wartime doctors and surgeons — the astonishing transformation is told in the detailed, neatly-written diary of Maurice Holt, promoted Colonel since his Boer War days and now ADMS of 2 Div. At the beginning of 1915 his divisional MOs were all Territorial or War-time officers except for two Regular and two S.R. Of his field ambulances, Nos 4 and 5 were now commanded by TF Captains and No 6 by a Regular Major, with only one SR (Special Reserve) officer in each. This was the "New RAMC", which had moved from reserve to front line. All of them were fearful about the management of wounds, which at this stage seemed to be going so badly wrong. While the *British Official Medical History of the War*, written under the editorship of Surgeon General Sir W.G. Macpherson, tells of what happened when and where very much from the point of view of the administrative officer, the history of the clinical advances was told by Colonel Bowlby and his colleagues of the "New RAMC" in a large number of very personal accounts. What those clinical problems would be would depend, as always, on the battlefields where they arose.

After the First Battle of Ypres the front lines became fixed for four years. Both sides would make a series of attempts to penetrate the enemy defences and destroy his manpower. But Churchill was wrong; the Germans did not achieve their aim at Verdun and the British destroyed enough German soldiers to matter during the Somme Battles.[1] The balance *was* tipped in the

Allies' favour as a result. The reason there was so little ground advantage was because neither side had the means of achieving a decisive victory.

Artillery bombardments did not wipe out the opposition; the defenders came out of their underground shelters or advanced from their reserve trenches; their machine guns mowed down the attackers. The tank was not yet an armoured vehicle capable of exploiting a battlefield attack by rapid movement and fire power. Nor was the new and fearful poison gas, launched from 1915 onwards, able to break the deadlock either.

On the Western Front, which remained the most important theatre of war, the commanding generals were attacked by a long succession of writers for their continued insistence on mounting major offensives with great loss of life. Like the majority of critics, they did not have any better ideas.

In 1915 there was an attempt to shift the centre of gravity away from the European stalemate to Asia Minor and achieve a strategic victory. After its failure, which taught naval as well as military lessons for Britain, the centre returned to the west. General Douglas Haig, who replaced Sir John French as British CinC, had his detractors, but although he "is sometimes portrayed as the embodiment of military stupidity, this was not the view of those who had most reason to know."[2]

Lastly, there was an important and much more mobile campaign against the Turks in Mesopotamia, which produced its own set of medical as well as military problems. It resulted in victory, as did the campaign in the west. Some medical difficulties overall were the fault of the generals who commanded generally, but in Mesopotamia the medicals themselves made culpable errors.

From January 1915 onwards the TF RAMC mobilized steadily and units went to all theatres of war. Because of Kitchener's ignorance and contempt of the Territorials, his "New" or "Kitchener" Armies trained in parallel with the teeth arms of the TF, but the medical plan Keogh had set up was sufficiently well-established to be unaffected. Kitchener did not need a "New" medical service; there was one in training already.

There was no shortage of medical units to follow the British Forces not only to France, the Dardanelles, Egypt and Palestine, but also to the Mediterranean Garrisons, Hong Kong, the Straits

Settlements, Ceylon, Tsingtau in the North China Command, Africa — Togoland, the Cameroons, South Africa, Salonika, and even Russia.

Some TF field ambulances were retained in the U.K. base, however, until their Territorial Division had been trained and moved to its overseas posting. Thus 2/3 Home Counties Field Ambulance of 67 Home Counties Division, for example, trained at Sevenoaks throughout 1915–16, and did not arrive at Le Havre till January 1917. They are noteworthy as they took with them two United States medical officers, Captain J.F. Doolong from Long Island, and Captain J.R. Travis from New London, Virginia. Both were awarded the M.C. for bravery in action with 175 Bde.

As in the South African War, the major medical units to be set up behind the battlefield were the British General Hospitals. No 26 BGH may serve as the example of them.

26 mobilized on June 18th, 1915, at Aldershot. Colonel H.E. Cree was their Regular Commanding officer. By June 26th they were at their war location near Etaples, with its memory of being one of Napoleon's concentration areas; their 150 tons(153 tonnes) of equipment de-trained with them. Mobilization was by now a well-practised process.

Soldiers, doctors, and nursing sisters were in Aylwin huts — the biggest for the sisters — No 26 was the third of a series of big BGHs to take 1040 patients. Nearby were 23 BGH, No 1 Canadian, and beyond them a St John Ambulance Hospital. There was also a Liverpool Merchants' Hospital building in course of completion.

26 BGH had 35 wards plus a hut for 12 psychiatric patients. The surgical division had wards A,B,C,D in huts 1–13, the medical division huts 16–22, skin patients huts 22–30, including special scabies huts. Reception was in huts 14–15. Only the surgical side was in "wards"; the rest were in "huts." There were 27 patients to a hut and 23 to a ward. Wards ran east-west, with the two theatres and the X-ray department centrally. Ward buildings were constructed of galvanised iron with inner walls and roofs of malite slabs. Lighting was by hopper windows, heating by two stoves per ward or hut. Huts had tanned canvas roofs and wooden boarded outer walls lined inside with malite, 15 feet by 120 feet(450 by 3600cm).

Beds were arranged in a single row, with extra beds placed lengthwise on the opposite wall. Up to 40 patients could be accommodated, the additional on trestles. Non-smokers were a tiny minority in those days — they had a small day space set aside for them as a special favour.

All hygiene and washing facilities were in place, waste disposal, sullage pits, and so on; the water supply and electricity came from French sources. Food and special diets, including "no diet"[3], were purchased locally "with various economies in purchase and choice."

Sisters and nurses had not mobilized with the men. The first arrived on July 13th with Miss Allen in charge. Later Miss Stewart, a pretty lady, arrived as Matron on the 22nd. She had with her 26 sisters and 46 staff nurses QAIMNS in total. On 28/7/15 No 26 could report "ready to receive."[4]

Apart from the C.O., 2 i/c, administrative registrar, and one quartermaster, all medical officers were Territorials — 2 Lieutenant Colonels' appointments — held by Captains, in spite of their major clinical responsibility, 4 Majors General Duty (GD), 24 Captains, 2–3 chaplains, 2 Quartermasters, 2 Warrant Officers, 21 S/Sgts and Sgts, 181 soldiers including carpenters, X-ray and operating department assistants, laboratory technicians, cooks with special certificates in dietary cooking, and 2 buglers. Apart from the GD officers several of the others though of junior rank were of senior clinical status; Captain F.L.A. Greaves, a St Thomas' graduate of 1897, FRCS England of 1902, and General and E.N.T. Surgeon from Derbyshire Royal Infirmary, was O.C. Surgical Division. He had been Lieutenant RAMC (TF) attached to 4th N. Midlands Bde. and honorary secretary of the Midlands Division BMA before leaving England. Captain Maynard Horne, anaesthetist to the Hospital for Women, Soho Square, and to St George's, a Cambridge graduate of 1901, was Senior Anaesthetist, Captain S.F. Macdonald was Radiographer, and Captain H. MacCormac of 15 Harley Street, Assistant Physician and Assistant at the cancer laboratory in the Middlesex Hospital, was Consultant Physician and O.C. Medical Division. The Psychiatrist was one who would become most famous of all — Lieutenant Henry Yellowlees, Assistant Physician, Royal Edinburgh Asylum, a Glasgow graduate of 1910. They were together the typical Territorial medicals who were now in clinical charge — some had left their original post in a U.K. TF General Hospital and volunteered for France or been specially posted because of their experience and skill.

The first and most pressing aim was to solve the problem of gas gangrene. As early as December 7th, 1914, it was decided to begin a clinical trial comparing pure carbolic and tincture of iodine for wounds, in addition to the incision and drainage which was current practice. (The frostbite which Lieutenant Colonel Bowlby and the King had discussed was more easily managed — Bowlby wrote to General Keogh in November asking for Canadian high boots, but none arrived till the General Staff became really alarmed in January).[5]

Over 1915, various antiseptic substances were used for infusion into wounds to try to cure the infection. Active bacteriological and pathological investigation proceeded, in parallel with clinical studies.

The second aim was to bring the surgeon nearer to the front. As early as mid-December, Colonel Bowlby, as he now was, was writing in the *BMJ* that the clearing hospital is "in future to be called a casualty clearing station." ...because..."a CH is not a hospital...has no tents or huts...no such luxuries as X-rays and a pathological outfit." This was to be changed. (Sir Anthony Bowlby's hand was strengthened by Colonel Lee, who had also, in his confidential report to Lord Kitchener, advised that "CH become CCS").

What the surgeons envisaged was a forward surgical centre, with a larger staff, more investigatory equipment, and best of all, nursing sisters. Bowlby's South African experience had taught him their immeasurable worth. Moreover, the forward positioning of the CCS had become a matter of some urgency, to reduce the time between wounding and surgical intervention. Delays incurred by awaiting darkness before recovering casualties from the field, and by long journeys to hospital afterwards, permitted rapid proliferation of anaerobic and other organisms in wounds with devastating effects which were all too often lethal. Clinical arguments were powerful: "wounded left lying in wet mud of manured fields — wounds soaked and impossible to get them even mechanically clean — new-pointed bullets different from the old blunt Mauser — do not make the very small punctures of the Boer War — very short ranges, 100–200 yards(110–180m), so *apparent* explosive power of rifle bullets." The notion of the "explosive bullet", especially by the populist press, had as usual made its re-appearance.

Shell wounds were "of two kinds, shrapnel, with fragments driven into men with great velocity — limbs shattered, such carry gravel, soil, much more than rifle bullets…howitzer shell contains no bullets, but only a bursting charge, and this is made to detonate when the shell strikes the ground. These the most severe of all — gross tissue destruction. Far beyond the actual wound the tissues are so injured that they slough in large masses."[6]

The other arm of research was bacteriological. Lieutenant S. Rowland as early as November 1914 was able to grow from an infected wound "a bacillus which when inoculated into a guinea pig produced fatal gangrenous cellulitis. A second guinea pig sent to the Lister Institute…earth from trench cultured grew an anaerobic spore bearing organism."[7]

Through the next year the management of wounds was subjected to constant clinical research and development. From November 1914, after the King's visit, the best surgeons of the New RAMC were systematically posted from the U.K. Territorial hospitals to the CCSs being set up; by the end of the year, the consulting surgeons could report that good work was being done in 8 of these units. Antiseptic infusions were found not to be the answer to the problem, neither hydrogen peroxide, the first tried, nor Eusol (Edinburgh University solution of lime) or Carrel-Dakin, both basically hypochlorous acid derivatives, tried later. These solutions released oxygen into the tissues, which killed the organisms which could not grow if oxygen was present. Wounds were "enlarged" rather than drained. And then by 1916 the technique which remains the only safe and satisfactory one was evolved: the excision of all dead and devitalised tissue from a wound, together with all foreign matter. The wound is not closed, but the skin is approximated by loose stitches over a dressing. Four or so days later, when all tissues look safely clean, the skin is stitched and closed. The method is called Delayed Primary Suture. Its importance demands it have capital letters; it is still ignored by surgeons who should know better. The most powerful antibiotics are no substitute. Nothing else is. It was a discovery of the surgeons of the 1914–18 War.[8]

Where all this wound excision, as the first stage in delayed primary suture is called, took place, was in the CCS. But not at once — during 1915 the RAMC surgeons had to fight hard to get their way. War Office policy held them up for a time. Delay was still producing infection too advanced to be treated satisfactorily because the first excision opportunity was too distant in time from the front line. In June 1915 the CCS for the 1st Army was thought to be too far back, Colonel Bowlby insisted. Cuthbert Wallace, another war-time consultant surgeon now an RAMC officer in France, agreed with him. They had the agreement of Surgeon General O'Donnell, "but he saw Macpherson, (now DMS First Army) but the latter never stirred in the matter until he, at the last moment, enlarged a Fd Ambs", Bowlby wrote in his diary. Macpherson was also criticised for failing to bring forward medical reinforcements at the Battle of Loos in late September, and General Sloggett was criticised by the surgeons the next spring for not seeming to understand the surgical position. That year — 1916 — had brought out a number of attacks on the RAMC in Parliament and press, and the consultants had to spend their valuable time taking visitors around to explain what was actually happening.[9]

By the early summer of 1916 there were CCSs along the entire front. They were placed at or near railway sidings for evacuation, where good roads could connect them with the front, and where they had a good water supply. These were the three essential conditions for their proper working.

They were arranged, for practical reasons, in two series: the first from 6 to 9 miles(8.5 to 10.5km) from the front trenches, the second from 3 to 6 miles farther back, to act as a reserve during active operations, or as units for special cases during quieter times. The staff increased steadily; in 1914 there were never more than 6 MOs in a CCS, by 1917, 24 or more.

The weight of operating increased steadily as well. In 1914, less than 1 per cent of casualties were operated on in CHs, (more were in fact operated on at Fd Amb level); in 1915 work increased throughout the year, with 15 per cent in so-called "quiet times" and 5 per cent of casualties if fighting was heavy. In 1916, the number went up to 25 per cent in quiet times. During the Somme Battle, 30,000 operations were carried out in about 300,000 cases, i.e. 10 per cent. By 1917, 80 per cent of wounded were operated on in quiet times, with 24 per cent rising to 30.6 per cent in the third Battle of Ypres. This was the highest attained in any major battle. The CCS, the product of the new RAMC, was the operating power-house of the Medical Service. Staff of the BGHs, farther back, commented on the increasingly good results.

Casualty numbers were the other overwhelming fact for the Medical Services. Medical officers' accounts paint a vivid picture:

"Picture a large space surrounded by buildings…a motor ambulance drives up, 4 stretcher cases slid out and carried to a large receiving room, 30 or 40 feet long(9–12m)…as many as 500 to 1000 wounded may come in during a 24 hour period…all clothes thick with mud.

"And now look inside the receiving room. Here are half-a-dozen or more surgeons, often with dressers some of whom have been medical students, and a score or so of well-trained, efficient orderlies…dressing…all degrees of wounding…. In addition you will see that one surgeon is detailed to inject every man with anti-tetanic serum, and you will notice that all men are given hot soup or milk, or perhaps stimulants, while they wait their turn to see the surgeon.

"And so on for some days hour after hour, and for most of both day and night…but consider what forethought has been necessary for such a condition to be successfully dealt with…what stores of dressings and bandages… and drugs.

"When I think that in a London Hospital with ample space and permanent equipment the resident staff are really very busy if they have 20 broken legs to treat in a day, and that if an operating surgeon who gets through 6 or 8 operations in an afternoon, with plenty of assistants, has done a hard day's work, it is possible to get a faint idea of what it is like to treat 100 or more compound fractures besides caring for 5 or 600 other men shot through the chest, the abdomen, the head, etc, many of them requiring immediate attention."

This was the CCS in full swing, as the officers of No 6, who had started early in the war as No 6 CH, described it. And one of their war diary notes of April 1915 is of the greatest significance: "The CCS became the initial and most important link in the surgical treat. of the wounded. CCS policy, devised on the spot, called for *in effect a triage of casualties.*" The word "triage"(the clinical division into three categories of priority for treatment) may have been used elsewhere or earlier, but its appearance on this date shows that the medical officers were thinking in terms of a procedure which would pass into the standing operating procedures of war surgery. They even anticipated the "fourth category" of the nuclear casualty era.[10]

Farther back, at the BGHs, it was the same story of massive effort, though many of their patients had already been through a CCS and were less acutely ill. Captain Greaves of 26 recalled: "Patients admission — convoys arrive almost invariably at night. Large reception tent. C.O, and registrar always present. (So were Matron and the padres). pts take a bath on admission if able. V.D. pts if any are held overnight before transfer to HAVRE. (A special venereal diseases hospital). Supper served if any delay. Av convoy 115."

"Standard procedure. Facsimile of A and D book (Admission and discharge book) and diet sheet used on admission. 2 clerks to each table. 1 pharmacist at another table, plus the night clerk — 4 tables in all, 6 clerks. plan of wards used — vacant beds on the plan. Inventory of kit, etc.

Each vacant bed has a complete hospital kit beside it; sisters handle this. All cast clothing from reception & bath hut removed for disinfection the same night. Boots, caps, personal items retained. OMO (Orderly Medical Officer) sees any local cases."

By this stage on "the way back" the evacuation was often to the U.K. base: "Evac — 2 labels attached. A.F. (Army Form) 3083 with name, regiment, classification, and diagnosis. All cases of importance to be given a transfer certificate A.B. 172 to give to the MO in England. All infectious pts to be NOTIFIED on A.F. 3310 in usual way. Trench Foot to be notified before discharge on special form. A.F. B117 accident report if reqd." The keeping of careful records was the responsibility of the AMS, medical and nursing, and was, as ever a vital one.

The work of the RAMC nursing orderlies was hard. Captains Greaves and MacCormac made the point that as the bulk of their patients were evacuated as soon as possible; those remaining were the helpless ill ones or the serious new admissions. There were no convalescents. The postal and clerical staff were always harassed — the numbers of answers to queries, the sheer volume of letters and personal items to be taken care of, gave them no respite. And this was in addition to the 60 daily returns a BGH had to make.

The supply and quartermaster departments had to produce the necessary and vital things of every kind a large hospital needed, and those things the other units they had responsibility for supplying had to have as well. Their task was endless.

As the Great War progressed, there were further improvements. More nursing sisters worked farther forwards. At CCS level their numbers increased from 5 to 25. Many of them worked as anaesthetists — a fact little-known. By 1917 there were 200 female anaesthetists. It was not until 1917 that the Consultant surgeons managed to have specialist male anaesthetists appointed in adequate numbers, and even then, ladies were still needed.[11] Field Surgical Teams, of consultant surgeon, theatre sister, assistant MO and one or two theatre orderlies were invented in 1916–17 to be attached to CCSs as reinforcement or to provide specialist expertise. They are still a vital component of the AMS surgical ORBAT.

It was the Somme Battle at which the new surgical unit was first tested seriously. The most comprehensive medical account is in the *Official Medical History* of the War, and tells of the temporary failure of the system because of the unexpectedly large numbers evacuated in the first hours of the first attack — the field ambulances functioned almost too well. Also, for tactical reasons the General Staff had forbidden a CCS group to be placed beside a railhead.[12] In the 4th Army alone, out of the total of 29,993 wounded who had been collected by the field ambulances during the first 24 hours, 14,416 had been brought to the CCSs, "a number greatly in excess of the accommodation available in the latter", as General Macpherson's History flatly tells. The individual recollections are more expressive and memorable.

Major Neil Cantlie, who was to become D.G. one day, was one of the D.A.Ds.M.S. during the Somme Battle. His account is as the staff officer saw it, beginning with a "rough draft" a full eight pages long, naming the various units and their disposal — a corps ADS, a corps walking wounded CP (Collecting Point), a corps rest station, and the single line of evacuation for the divisional front. At this time Major Cantlie had not got used to the concept of the new field ambulances; he clearly thought in terms of the "Tent Divisions" of the pre-war Colonel Macpherson era, and talked of "Bearer personnel" as if they were a separate unit like a Bearer Company. It is curious how matter-of-fact, almost distant, his war diary reads, and it is rather humourless. He seemed to have always accompanied his ADMS, rather than to have gone on his own. Yet it is always very cool, the essence of the good staff officer.

Major Cantlie regularly spoke of the most important men in the whole Medical Services in this Great War — the stretcher bearers. He described their work from the staff officers' point of view. "In active operations, the large no. of cas meant that extra SBs from bns had to be employed...4 SBs if fine weather, 6 if wet. Carry — relays every 1000 yards(900m). (But in practice bearers so tired that they had to be relieved)."

The stretcher bearer was the most important man in the medical ORBAT; the greatest medical hero of the World War of 1914–1918. While individual RMOs rescued wounded with great bravery (and Captain Noel Chavasse became the second man to be awarded a bar to the V.C.)[13], they did not have the sustained physical strain and emotional stress of the parties of SBs who spent their every day carrying, over and over again. The MOs, at whatever level they worked and whatever their skill, could do nothing until the casualties were brought to them. As far as the casualties were concerned, the RAMC soldiers were, as in South Africa, the nurses of the front line. Their many decorations testify to their bravery.

A multitude of men told of what they owed to these first members of the Medical Corps they met. Frank Fox, an Artillery officer, was on Forward Observation Post duty and was badly wounded in the arm by a sniper's bullet. "That was the moment I blessed the RAMC and the knowledge that I, and the rest of the British Army, had of its works", he wrote after the War. He spoke of the bravery of the SBs taking him "over the top" to save time; of being at the RAP in 20 minutes: "a little anxiety might have made all the difference to me" ... his morphine, china tea, and then the carry by MAC to the ADS and 'marked for Blighty'." The medicals were equally sustained by the behaviour of the wounded. Lieutenant Colonel James Young, C.O. of a Fd Amb with 52(L) Division at Gallipoli, spoke of "the courage of the wounded — men, and officers — more concerned for their men...the doctor's smile and word of cheer and encouragement seem puny and irrelevant beside such a thing as this."

As in all British wars, the chaplains were colleagues of the doctors. Many clergy and Divinity students joined the Medical Services and served as RAMC orderlies in this war. In the hospitals and CCSs, they too were on duty as the convoys came in, and at RAP level they worked with the RMO, sharing his dangers and dressing wounds. A CCS doctor wrote a typical comment: "A zealous and manly padre can do much. Morale in trenches is no more a negligible quantity than ammunition. A chaplain of the right sort on the eve of battle is worth his weight in gold. He must, however, be a man as well as a priest."

GALLIPOLI

The Dardanelles campaign, like all other First War battles, has been written about so much that it requires no description here. Though a failure, it might have been a success — the superlative bravery of all the troops taking part, the advance in spite of all odds; the ANZAC reached the top of Sari Bair ridge and the peak of Chunuk Bair. Victory seemed in sight. And then the Turks, usually a brave and chivalrous enemy, counter-attacked and drove them back.

Private Whittaker gives us this part of the RAMC's history. Although only a SB attached to 11 Division, his diary tells the story of the Gallipoli Campaign in miniature.

Whittaker was not enamoured at his first sight of the Dardanelles on the 28th of July, 1915. He had been "fed up" at the base at Lemnos, and found the transport SS *Lake Michigan* full of "cattle and vermin." He heard the guns firing. Their camp was "a ploughed field infested with locusts, very hot, no cover, no bread, little water, nothing but bully beef and biscuits." There were "thousands of men — Gurkhas, Sikhs, NZ, Australian, Egyptian, Greeks." He bought grapes at a Greek shop and got such bad diarrhoea he had to be admitted to hospital.

On the lighter going ashore, he had his helmet knocked off into the sea. They found their field ambulance was landed in the wrong position, and had to get back into the lighter. He managed to find time to write:

"6/8/15 troops had to swim ashore. many were drowned. that night we were bombed. 10 Div landed by us, at 0730. Many wounded the moment they landed.

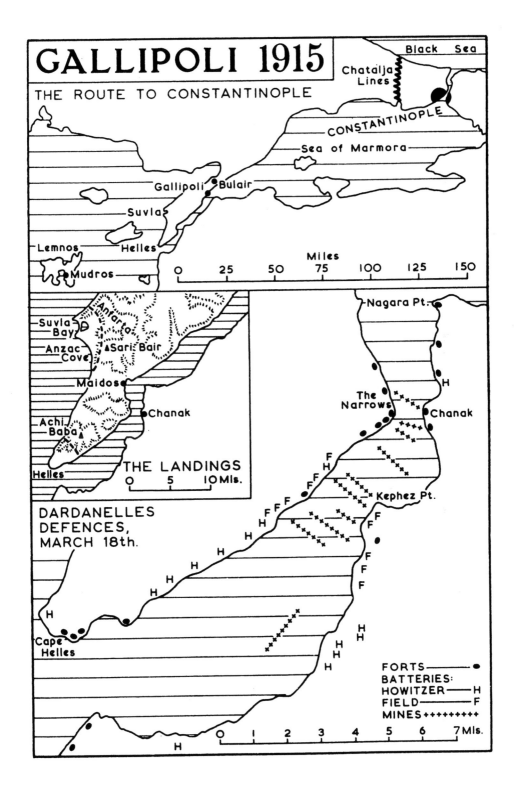

GALLIPOLI 1915

THE ROUTE TO CONSTANTINOPLE

Black Sea

Chatalja Lines

CONSTANTINOPLE

Sea of Marmora

Gallipoli • Bulair

Suvla

Lemnos • Helles

Mudros

Miles

0   25   50   75   100   125   150

Anafarta

Nagara Pt.

Suvla Bay

Anzac Cove ▲Sari Bair

Maidos

The Narrows

Chanak

Achi Baba▲

Helles

Chanak

Kephez Pt.

THE LANDINGS

0   5   10 Mls.

DARDANELLES DEFENCES, MARCH 18th.

Cape Helles

FORTS————•
BATTERIES:
HOWITZER——H
FIELD——F
MINES+++++++++

0   1   2   3   4   5   6   7 Mls.

"I shall never forget this sight. Hundreds of wounded lying round bleeding to death for want of being attended too. Some with there (sic) eyes shot out, others with their intestines protruding some with legs shot off and many other awful sights. The heat was terrible and the flies made things worse. While we were dressing them the Turks were shelling all round us...

"We could not get the wounded away to the hospital ships very quick as there was only rowing boats that could get near enough to get them we had to carry them on stretchers and on our backs out to (the boats) up to the waist in water. had a wounded Turk brought in to our DS.

"7/8, 8/8 Packed with wounded. hundreds lying around both dead and wounded. Buried those who died thro the night at the back of the DS Under constant shellfire — then stopped — we hoped our guns had silenced theirs — then they started again.

"10/8 Had a night's sleep, the first for 4 days. When I woke up I found I had been lying aside of 2 dead men and then I wondered how long it would be before I was like that.

"August 17 last night a huge battle. The ADS on OPEN GROUND — marked with flags. (Colonel Young, with his Fd Amb of 52 Div, was luckier — landing with the first party on July 3rd on Lancashire Beach, where the Lancs Bn of 29 Div gained eternal fame, managed to dig in 1 Km from the shore. They finally had a below-ground hospital. They put up a Red Cross, which the Turks respected; he could see, across the battlefield, the sun shining on the Red Crescent of the enemy medical unit). A grand night — the flashes from our guns...

"Now the 11th day since we landed. No bread only iron rations."

He described the intense British shelling of the Turkish trenches: "they must all be dead — shelling stopped — our troops advanced — Turks got up and mowed them all down.

"Turks set fire to bushes near where Br wounded were sheltered — Hundreds were burnt alive. The F.A. (Fd Amb) brought as many as they could...I don't know which to dress first. I am covered with blood."

In late August he moved to Lala Baba, where they opened a "sick hospital." "now sickness, dysentery, jaundice, heat exhaustion."

On the 6th September, their landing stage was blown up.

By December there was frostbite by night. "It is terrible to see such big strong men crying like children with frostbite and scores have been found frozen to death."

"6/12 published today in Corps Orders. The weather during the last week was probably worse than any our tps experienced during the whole of last winter in France and Flanders."

"15/12 The whole army ready to evacuate. Some men began to report sick lest they be made prisoners. I intend to stick it."

"20/12 We left Suvla Bay and very pleased we were. had been there 4 months & 14 days."

"The landings and the evacuation of Suvla must be two of the finest things in British history. I am pleased to say I was among the first to land and amongst the last to leave."

Whittaker also wrote of how he saw his own grave dug — as an RMO in 1945 in Formosa would also see — since the troops expected to be killed if they did not get away — as 11 Division prepared to evacuate.

After a 6 month spell in the desert in their ADS, he sailed back to Marseilles by July 2nd 1916. He then went to Amiens, where he resumed stretcher bearing. Only now he carried a respirator and tear goggles.[14] His job was to carry wounded on a stretcher and this is what he did.

Arthur Morgan, of the Munster Fusiliers, was a patient. He was early into Suvla Bay and his unit had some success at first. But "we held on till evening, hoping for reinforcements. This was the blunder of the general who was recalled. If we had had reinforcements then, we would have had Achi Baba in our grip."

Wounded in the shoulder, he lay among "trenches choked with wounded...dying asking for water." He was evacuated to the CCS at Imbros, where he lay for 3 days as he was so weak from loss of blood. He then went to No 3 Australian GH at Lemnos, where the bullet was removed: "a model hospital and the Australians should be very proud of it." He was then taken straight back to England: "36 dysentery cases died on the way...eating fruit their friends got from the canteen...was 4 days at East Leeds Hospital...saw the King there...then convalesced."

Pte Cockfield, an Australian soldier, told of his affection for the "Tommies", the rum issued before he and his mates had "to do a burial", and of the sanitary staff being unable to work because they all had dysentery.

These accounts include all the items of the Dardanelles campaign which writers have filled books discussing — the naval bombardment, which did not eliminate the well-prepared enemy defences, the bravery of the soldiers, the quiet, cheerful, likeable New Zealanders, the flamboyant but touchy Australians, the majority British, and the wonderful Gurkhas and Indian troops. There were French too. The diaries highlight the terror of the landing sites, the constant shelling from the Turkish batteries whose range cards they had had so much time to prepare as the politicians delayed, the inadequacy of the evacuation system, the total lack of cover and of sanitation on the beaches, the heat, the dysentery, and finally the intense cold. The final mood of Whittaker's unit was however one of pride and defiance.

Other RAMC persons saw the campaign from their own point of view. Captain John Hare, whom we recall starting the War as RMO to the 1st Bn Royal Fusiliers, found himself General Sir Ian Hamilton's MO. He mobilized on 17th March at the Tower of London, reporting to Major Cole, RA, attached to HQ 2nd echelon. His voyage was somewhat different from Pte Whittaker's. He enjoyed the "glorious harbour" of Malta, in spite of the heat and the horses dying *en route*. He was critical of the French, especially their navy, but played bridge with them happily. He liked and respected the Australian medical officers he met. He, too, had an attack of dysentery on the way.

His account complements Pte Whittaker's, from the medical point of view. Arriving on April 25th at the mouth of the Dardanelles, he watched the landings and looked up at the German aircraft overhead. He described the medium machine guns which held the troops up, the mines in the sea channel, and the wire defences made by the Turks.

As acting DADMS, he advised the Surgeon General, W.G. Birrell, about the placing of a hospital and a convalescent depot, and the DMS agreed.[15] He went round the beaches, and was quickly aware of the failure of the attack: "We have not sufficient howitzers or big field guns…their lack…means an unnecessary wastage of the best lives…our troops' position precarious."

But among all the anxiety, some of his comments make amusing reading. A Durham graduate, he praised the English above the Scots and Irish — "they (the English) never murmured." The RAMC were looking after sailors — "I was annoyed at a

Naval MO. They really believe the Navy is better and a more proficient Service. It is still unfortunately called the Senior Service. Rot!!! All braggards…"

By May, Captain Hare was writing: "My humble opinion is that we should never have landed here…an Australian bn almost wiped out. The French retreated." And on the 8th of September, before he became ill with Typhoid Fever, he wrote: "landing at Suvla Bay an abject failure." His illness was so severe he had to be evacuated to Egypt.[16]

The catalogue of errors in the medical plans for the Gallipoli Campaign makes sorry reading. The War Council sanctioned the naval attack on the Dardanelles on 28th January, 1915; Colonel J. Maher, the nominated DMS, arrived in Malta with his deputies including Lieutenant Colonel Dorgan, a hygiene specialist, six weeks later, none of them knowing what their task was to be. Colonel Maher persuaded the G.O.C., General Sir Ian Hamilton, that the proposed base at Lemnos had insufficient water, and it was moved back to Alexandria.

Next another DMS, Surgeon General Birrell, arrived in Alexandria on April 1st, with his staff but no hygiene specialist. When he arrived at Mudros 2 weeks later, he learned *for the first time* what the plans for the attack were. He was told 1,000 casualties would be expected, but at once insisted that 10,000 was a more realistic figure. Urgent messages passed to London asking for more medical manpower, more launches and more hospital ships. The General Staff decreed that wounded must be treated on the shore, because they could not be evacuated while fighting was in progress. It was doubtful, they said, whether any could be evacuated for 3 days. So the medicals decided that they must allot only part of a Fd Amb to each landing force, one CCS for 29 Div and one for the ANZAC Corps. They would manhandle as much medical equipment as they could on the landing beach areas.

The map shows the areas of operations. From the attackers' point of view, and from a casualty evacuation point of view, the critical features were the narrowness of the beaches, especially where the ANZAC Corps was to land, the cliffs overhanging them, the gullies, ridges, and fierce scrub. Beyond was a range of hills.

Nowhere was there any water supply apart from shallow wells and springs, so tanks had to be placed on shore and refuelled from lighters. The only means of evacuation was by boats and small craft, and, as it would soon turn out, directly by hospital ships and troop transports improvised as carriers. This meant that these last were not available to carry out their proper function. And since the arrangements for the actual deployment of this array of mixed craft were poorly organised, it was not surprising that inevitable breakdown occurred.

Yet, after 48–72 hours the Army Medical Services were beginning to cope with the problems. Their tenacity in carrying out the task given them by the commanders deserves more praise than has been perhaps given in the past. The plain fact was that no provision had been made for the possibility of the landings being held up and casualties having to lie on the beaches as a result. What the DMS and his staff could have done better was to demand at the planning stage that hospitals be set up at Lemnos before the landings began. It would then have then been much easier for wounded and sick to be evacuated there, and held in quieter surroundings, following tried and tested medical evacuation principles, until proper arrangements were made for their disposal.

Complaints soon came back to the front from the Medical Headquarters in Egypt, and onwards from Egypt to Kitchener. As always happens in such circumstances, more senior AMS officers were called from Egypt to Gallipoli to try to strengthen medical control.

Hospitals in Egypt and Malta became filled to overflowing over the summer as things got worse. Hospital ships sailed directly back to U.K., without adequate provision for a voyage of that length. The D.G. then ordered General Babtie from India to act as Principal DMS in the Mediterranean. Babtie altered the arrangements which were now beginning to work, and his intervention only made things worse.

For a short spell Sir James Porter, former S.G. of the Medical Services, RN, was appointed "Hospital Transport Officer in the Mediterranean", with the agreement of the DGAMS and in spite of protests from Babtie and General Hamilton. His intervention added further to the troubles and fortunately he soon left, after General Keogh wrote to S.G. Babtie on 1st October: "The dissatisfaction which has all along existed with the arrangements for the care and comfort of the sick and wounded has never abated and has grown in intensity."

The last word can be given to the *Official History*: "For the state of affairs and the confusion that occurred in the distribution of casualties to hospital ships and transports it would scarcely be fair to blame the medical services of the Expeditionary Force. It arose from a variety of causes over which they had little or no control…".[17]

THE MESOPOTAMIA CAMPAIGN

While the errors over casualty evacuation at Gallipoli were grievous enough, they were largely the result of the military decisions and the terrain involved. The same cannot be said of the errors of the early part of the Campaign in Mesopotamia. Here there were cruel deficiencies in the medical chain of evacuation which were the result of grave errors on the part of the Army Medical Services.

The background to the medical failures was the constantly-recurring theme of reductions in the strength of the British Army which went below a safe level and which were exposed when as always hostilities began in an unexpected part of the world. The Army of India had been told, prior to 1914, that because there was no longer a perceived threat from Russia, it was to reduce its manpower and weaponry and leave only adequate forces to deal with terrorist attacks in the North-West Frontier Province. When war broke out in 1914, the Indian authorities found the enemy they had to deal with was Turkey, in the Middle East. Although no active operations were called for in Mesopotamia for a further year, the deficiencies were not made good. And the branch of the Indian Army reduced as savagely as any was its Medical Services.[18]

The first British aim was to occupy Abadan, to protect the oil refineries there. When the Turks concentrated troops to attack Basra in early 1915, threatening the oil pipe, a force of divisional strength (initially the 12th Division) was sent by the Indian Government. More troops followed. Basra was taken, and on September 29th, the 6th Indian Division took Kut-el-Mara. The terrain was hot desert, and the Tigris River a shallow-draft channel. It was planned to advance to Baghdad, but the British were repulsed at Ctesiphon. As the army advanced, its LofC became increasingly difficult to maintain. At Ctesiphon they lost 700 killed and 3,800 wounded; General Townshend's Force was surrounded at Kut and attempts to relieve it failed.

It was after the defeat at Ctesiphon that the medical arrangements broke down. The failures were so gross that a commission was later set up — the Vincent-Bingley Commission[19] — to examine in detail what went wrong. Its findings were that S.G. Baptie was seriously to blame for lack of foresight, and that S.G. Hathaway "showed himself unfit for the high administrative office which he held"(Hathaway was DMS Mesopotamia but in Indian Army terms was still given the obsolete title 'PMO'). But both had tried to maintain that all was well when it was not. S.G. Macneece, who succeeded Hathaway, was also criticised, although it was agreed that he had made efforts to improve the system. The G.O.C. India, Sir Beauchamp Duff, and the Viceroy himself, Lord Hardinge, were also censured by the Royal Commission.[20] It is of interest that when S.G. MacNeece left, he was succeeded, but only for a short time, by S.G. Sir Pardey Lukis of the IMS. He worked with great energy to make good the many deficiencies until he had to make way for S.G. O'Donnell (whom Bowlby missed so much, and so regretted his replacement by Macpherson), "in accordance with the unwritten law that forbids a Surgeon General of the IMS to serve as DMS India." It was incredible that this insulting practice was allowed to continue, but it has to be remembered that even an officer of the calibre of Field Marshal Slim was felt by some to be unsuitable for the post of CIGS because he was an Indian Army officer, very many years later.

Worst of all, and reflecting no credit on the senior AMS officers, was that Lieutenant Colonel R.M. Carter, IMS, "the first man to report truthfully to his superiors what was really happening, was snubbed and even threatened."[21] Colonel Carter was not the first, and certainly not the last RAMC officer, to be treated in this way by malicious superiors.

The new régime of Commanders and Medical leaders saw the Mesopotamian Campaign to its successful conclusion. S.G. Treherne arrived in 1916 and with him as his DDMS LofC, Colonel Matthew Fell. Another officer who deserves recognition was Lieutenant Colonel Graham, IMS, C.O. of the Sanitary Department of the Medical Service in Mesopotamia; he worked steadfastly throughout the campaign, but got no recognition or reward for his labours.

The two new Medical commanders faced a daunting task. Both at the front, where sickness was as much a daily hazard as injury, and on the LofC, which stretched to 500 miles(750km), the collection of casualties and, perhaps even more difficult, their transport on the newly acquired boats and carts with springs (the earlier régime had actually made men travel on unsprung carts over the desert surface), was a constant anxiety. The problems were very different from those of Western Europe, but just as great.

Letters between the two medical officers give a fascinating insight into the difficulties at command level. While unit C.O.s were concerned with local difficulties and the actual things requiring to be done for their staff and their patients, the Medical Commanders were concerned with planning, and especially with personalities.

General Treherne wrote of his planning of moves of his Fd Ambs and CCSs. He was often in conflict with the General Staff: "Sloan has not been playing the game and I hope will get scrubbed. He has a down on Wimberley (a medical C.O.), who has done well...evac of cas at a (river) crossing was delayed, and he was responsible (Sloan), but W. was given the blame, and a report sent in spite of pleas by Sir A. Lawley not to..."

"Wale had turned out a rotter as ADMS cavalry...Beit O/C 131 Cavalry Fd Ambs I have removed for being inefficient and too slow...the new org of F.A. is not quite my idea — the D.G. has put his finger in and upset all my ideas — but I am sick of it and so will have to let it go."

"as usual, I do not see eye to eye with the Army Commander. Being a guardsman, I suppose he regards me still as a Regimental Medical Officer and all initiative is taken out of my hands. If he had been in command when we first arrived in this country I wonder how the medical arrangements would have fared. It makes very little difference now. He says to (his Staff officers) 'how are your clearing stations? where are you putting them now? what arrangements are you making for the evac of Keary's Column'? etc. while I am referred to on matters of sanitation or the nature of sickness. But I do not care — I have now drawn up what *I* require and how I propose dealing with the systems of evac. He can agree or not as he likes — if he does not I use my second string..."

General Treherne spoke of the G.O.C. refusing to let a CCS take *sick* in a quiet period: "If he insists, of course, I shall have a large body of medical officers and personnel available for duty elsewhere…but of course he cannot insist, so I go my own way."

These very frank letters between the DMS and his Deputy are indeed fascinating to read, and most revealing of the personal relations between senior staff. They do not show any rancour or malice, and are for that reason the more valuable. The working notes are also of great interest. Discussing the limitations of the transport steamers and barges from the Tigris front to Aman and Basra, the doctors covered all the sorts of things one would expect — use of CCS personnel to man the barges, shortage of water and latrine accommodation, distances and timings, the later use of permanent personnel for the river convoys of sick. The notes tell of the dejection of the troops after the fall of Kut, the poor rations (inadequate and unsatisfactory food was one of the complaints against the earlier Medical Commanders), poor cover from the sun, the rush of sick as the weather became hotter, and so on.

The notes also tell of success — writing from Baghdad to Fell on 23rd March, 1917, General Treherne could say: "the rapidity of our advance had often made evac difficult but everything went off without a hitch.…Even General Cowley had nothing to find fault with!"

Treherne was knighted before he left; he thoroughly deserved his honour. He and Fell got on well together. Before he left, he wrote to Matthew Fell that he doubted if his successor would get on so well with him, as "you are so honest and direct."

By contrast, the Syrian/ Palestinian Campaign was rapid and straightforward. The diary of Pte Charles Cyril Ammons, a young intellectual who admired Mr George Bernard Shaw and had grave doubts about whether he would ever have served unless conscripted, written from October 1917 till May 1918, makes the advance to Jerusalem with the London Mounted Brigade Fd Amb sound almost like a holiday!

Pte Ammons was probably right in some of his descriptions. With the arrival of General Sir Edmund Allenby in July, 1917 — an officer of true greatness, the war moved steadily forwards. A motor ambulance convoy arrived in time for the operations in Gaza, and from then until the campaign ended they gave excellent service. The expansion of Allenby's Force required five new CCSs and one Indian Hospital; before there had been only two in total. 5 new Stationary hospitals were provided, making 8 in all, and 4 new 1040 bed BGHs, in addition to the 7 already in place and working.[22] It was a remarkable transformation, and gave the British a major superiority in manpower.

Private Ammons' diary does not tell, however, of the Megiddo Battle which began on September 19th, 1918, and ended with the annihilation of the Turkish armies within a few days. As well as Jerusalem, Damascus fell; the success of the Royal Flying Corps in the action, which included the dropping of propaganda leaflets as well as bombs, was a hint of how this new arm of warfare would dominate in the future.

One war-time officer who served in Mesopotamia and later reached the top of the profession was Major G. Grey Turner. His medical and surgical notes make interesting reading, and he found time to send articles to the Medical Journals at home. Colonel W.H. Willcox, a St Mary's Hospital physician, was Consulting Physician, and his account is also of the greatest interest. He, however, had a different opinion of Sir Percy Lake, the Army Commander of 1916: "He took the greatest interest in the medical arrangements, and did everything in his power to ensure the supply of everything in the way of hospital units, personnel and equipment that was required. This work of organisation laid the foundations of the future success of the Medical Service in Mesopotamia, for in a few months the medical arrangements throughout the Force were such that they would compare favourably with those in any other theatre of war." Perhaps both he and his Medical General were right.

While the actual amount of surgical work in Mesopotamia was small compared to that in France, warfare was mobile, there was one prolonged siege, and the first Battle of Gaza ("the nearest thing to Cape Helles for anxiety", said one Medical Commanding Officer) required special surgical help. The great Sir Victor Horsley died of heat stroke, and was succeeded by Colonel Wade of the Scottish Horse Mounted Fd Amb, later Sir Henry Wade of Edinburgh, as Consultant Surgeon. He set up mobile surgical units, then an innovation, using fellow territorials from 53 and 54 CCSs and other surgical and anaesthetic specialists from 52 Div Fd Amb.. To deal with the long carry for casualties, he formed an Australian mobile advanced operating unit under

Colonel Story. To it was attached a surgical operating car which he designed himself.

LATER PHASES OF THE WAR. MOVEMENT RETURNS

In 1917, the Western front continued its set pattern. Because of the need for protection from artillery fire and from gas, medicals — and indeed all — lived underground when within the divisional area front line. Captain Andrew Macphail of the RCAMC, war-time Fd Amb medical officer but peace-time Professor of Medical History at McGill University, described the earthworks at Vimy, and the preparations for the 1917 attack.

"The medicals spent 2 months excavating 10 dugouts, 20 feet (7m) below the surface, roofs and walls and shored,(up) fitted with racks for stretchers. Large blankets at the entrances were a protection against gas.... Rehearsal of the attack on ground similar to that of the actual battle. Timings especially important. Evac from the front was so perfect and rapid that cas began to accumulate at the A.DS — but all were treated and sedated." He spoke of "the long years the RAMC had worked on the plan — we Canadians knew of it and worked together with no problems".[23]

In the 1914–18 War the Canadians were a truly wonderful part of the British family. "The Canadians were always welcome." Not only did they hold their position when the first poison gas was released in 1915, but the charge of the Canadian Cavalry Brigade at Moreuil Wood in March 1918, under Major General Jack Seely, halted the German advance at the time and place where it might have been decisive. It was the last mounted cavalry charge of high significance in history. Quiet and unassuming, the Canadians were — and still are — greatly respected by their British colleagues and relatives.[23]

Things changed when the 1918 German offensive almost succeeded. After years of fixed trench lines, movement returned to warfare again. Five British Divisions operating with the French were driven out of their positions; casualties were scattered as far away as Biarritz, and 20,000 beds at Etaples were put out of service because of German air attacks which destroyed the railway leading there. The Germans also bombed the major hospital complex. It was the nearest the AMS came to being overwhelmed during the whole War. They had to evacuate faster and farther. If at the time of the Calais Conference in 1917 it is true that Lloyd George held back reinforcements from the British generals and Haig their C.in C. to prevent their making another attack which would be costly in lives, and that he tried to put Haig in a subordinate position to Nivelle, the headline French General of 1917, it reflects no credit on the Prime Minister. But the failure of Nivelle's offensive of 16th April, 1917, and the ugly French mutinies which followed, forced him to drop his scheme. In the end, it was the British Army which carried the brunt of the later part of the war — notwithstanding the appearance of U.S. troops — the only time in her history when Great Britain's Army was the senior partner in a major European War. In all others, Britain has been the junior in terms of numbers and command.[24]

Notwithstanding the change in tempo of fighting, casualty evacuation continued to follow a standard and well-practised pattern. The MAC had revolutionised evacuation; the Fd Ambs procedures were developed into the flexible form they have retained since — the ADS/MDS set up, the sections out, liaison with the units of the Brigade, the resupply of the RMOs. Lieutenant Colonel Young, whose 52(L) Div Fd Amb was in France after their baptism in Gallipoli, set out the principles of field ambulance procedure in the advance which are hard to better:

"During a battle the intense activity for us usually comes with the night for it is late before the wounded collected from the field reach the stations."

"You must have stores of blankets, but you must have stores of food also."

"As the base recedes farther and farther back as the army advances, the problem of getting the wounded and sick back is greater and greater. You must have ample transport, therefore."

"An axiom, which you break at your peril, is to keep the forward section empty at all times of the night or day, so that at a moment's notice, it can set off in the wake of the moving troops. Where, as must always recur on occasions during heavy fighting, you have to compromise between mobility and immobility, this compromise must never touch the mobile section."

"Communications: you have to know your job but also every other man's job. For during the stress of the fight you are apt to be forgotten unless you obtrude your presence to the risk of annoyance. In an ambulance, you have to keep in constant touch with what is going on in front, and you have to know what is taking place behind. You must be *au fait* with the movements of the bde and the changing dispositions of the bns of that bde."

"You must also keep in touch with HQ of Division. The ADMS must know where you are…and you must know where the ADMS is, for he can help you out of difficulty when no-one else can."

Although the waggoners were replaced by motor cars, the ASC remained strong opposite numbers of the RAMC. "All the troopers swore hard", said Colonel Brebner, "but they were good fellows." Recruited originally into the RAMC, the troopers who understood horses were later transferred *en bloc* into ASC. But they remained part of the unit, as the RCT did later. They were the carriers of the wounded, and were respected and admired for their professionalism. "During stunts they had many casualties." By the later war years, they were the drivers and maintainers of the lorries, with their workshop mechanics, the forerunners of today's REME.

In their times of rest and respite, away from the line, the medical field units enjoyed themselves. In the last year of the War, the tensions of the diary writers seemed to lift. Concert parties were popular — 2/3 Home Counties Fd Amb had a particularly good one called "The Merrie Needles." They joked, Old Bill like, about everything, especially the length of the War.[25] "Pantomime in France", put on by 17 Fd Amb, announced:

> Babes in the W (censored).
> Production by Divisional Pierrot Troop.
> Doors open 5.30. Commence 6 p.m.
> Admission: offrs 5d (2p), NCOs and men 1d.
> Stretcher Bearers at 8 p.m.

"Try our Xmas crackers — Loos specials, A 1 Hohenzollerns, Super Sommes.

Are you troubled by gas? A few whiffs of our extra special inhalation gives INSTANT RELIEF. Is your breathing distressed? Use our latest pattern fox respirator. All victims of neurasthenia should try our MANIN REST CURE. When in delicate health consult Monsieur Balfour. Mlle JOLIE de la VIE writes: Six months ago, I consulted M. Balfour. Since then, my appetite has improved, my figure has become noticeably rounder, and my weight had considerably increased. I attribute these happy results to the efforts of Monsieur Balfour only."

Christmas parties in all theatres became elegant. In Macedonia, called by those in it "the forgotten front", T/QMS Frank Wheatly, DCM, (Distinguished Conduct medal) enthused over the Sergeants' Mess of 80 Fd Amb of 26 Div Christmas Dinner in 1917. "Roast goose, Xmas pudding, etc — dessert, fruit, cigars. Caterers — own unit."

The advice given above about action in the advance became real again in the last months of the War, when movement returned to the battlefield. One major disease to appear was influenza. But otherwise the surgical side of things continued to develop in the last year of war. There was the beginning of resuscitation wards, called the "Réchauffment" ward, and run by nursing sisters. Documentation improved — the "medical label" was put on at the ADS within the Field Medical Card. But a post card was also included, so that a report could be returned to France from the disposal hospital in U.K., and the first man seeing the case would know the outcome. At the start of the War, because little was done in the CHs, little documentation was done there; by the end, the forward units, Fd Ambs and CCSs, made full notes. More specialist dental surgeons were recruited, and their work increasingly praised. They shared the first beginnings of what would become a major specialty in the next war, plastic surgery.

At the very end of the Great War, all were amazed at the increasing speed of the advance. The diary of 6 Fd Amb recalled: "In all, 600 officers and soldiers served in the Fd Ambs between 1914 and 1919. 24 were killed — 3 the day before the Armistice."

Many moving accounts of the minute of 11 o'clock on November 11th are found. Two will serve. Captain H.L. Chase, RAMC: "We noticed how the guns kept firing till 11.0, *then suddenly silence*. A wild impossible dream had come at last. *Not* excitement, but a strangely mixed feeling of indescribable relief combined with a sudden realisation of an intense and almost overpowering weariness…"

And Captain E.P. Dickie, MC, KOSB, (King's Own Scottish

Borderers)later Professor of Divinity at St Mary's College, St Andrews University, whose Armistice sermons have been described as the finest ever written: "I had actually fallen asleep beside a pile of shells. *I heard the guns stop.*"

Major G.A. Kempthorne, DSO, a field ambulance officer and a Regular, wrote what he called "a review" on 4th August, 1918, the fourth anniversary of the outbreak of the War: "The past year has seen a good many changes in the RAMC, perhaps more marked in the world of spirit than of matter, and typified by the selection of the present Surgeon General (Goodwin). It points to what might be called the waning of the 'PMO spirit!'"[26]

"What is being looked for is men of a more constructive spirit. Efficiency and 'staffing' are no longer regarded as complementary terms. Young men are being appointed as ADMS; a certain amount of unconventionality is to be found in F.A.s with no loss of efficiency."

"It should be noted that the whole of the forward work — of RMOs and Bearer officers clearing the line, and the MOs in the field ambulances, is in the hands of Temporary Commissioned officers. They have standardised the collection of the wounded, have undertaken the training of new men, and of the American MOs, and have brought to their work an independence of thought and action; and exercise of common sense not always to be found in the Regular officer, while matching him in courage and sporting spirit. Promotion of the TF officer is often tardy — to more responsible positions."

"The role of the Regular officer is that of the necessary machinery co-ordinating on the one hand the brains and initiatives of consultants and civil surgeons at the bases and LofC and on the others the bravery and resource of the RMOs and Bearer officers in the field. Necessary but not heroic."

The story is told of a DDMS of the old type (he was referring to General Skinner) at a conference with the MOs of the 51[st](Highland) Division. "They were holding the line in the Miraumont sector, parts of which were quite waterlogged, and very little movement possible in isolated posts in the front line. The General had been dilating on the disposal of sewage in the front line — digging pits behind the trenches etc and other matters quite impractical in the sector, and then asked for comment. The MOs of the Division, mostly hard-bitten country practitioners from the north of Scotland to whom military rank meant nothing, then fell upon him, and the General emerged with this remark to his credit —'gentlemen, this is one of the few conferences from which I have learned anything'."

There was no need this time for any Royal Commission as after the South African War. On the battlefield the Royal Army Medical Corps had no detractors in 1918. There were official tributes from Commanders in Chief, but one from an intermediate rank officer who was carried to safety by the Medical Corps summed up the significant change which had come about since 1902. Frank Fox wrote in 1919: "In this War the Medical Service has had unstinted power within its own sphere, and after some slight inevitable friction at first, has settled down to a comradely partnership with the fighting command. The ADMS in planning, has a voice in movements…he studies the maps with as much care as artillery or engineer commanders — especially for roads. He claims, and gets, his share of the roads available."[27]

Notes and references

CHAPTER 6

[1]Official final casualties for the entire Somme Battle (killed and wounded): Commonwealth — 418,654, French — 194,451, German — 650,000. "The Fallen", John Garfield, Lee Cooper, London, 1990, 111.

[2]The Private papers of Douglas Haig 1914–19, edited by Robert Blake, Eyre and Spottiswoode, London, 1952; Introduction, p 27–28. See also John Terraine's assessment, in "The Western Front." By contrast, the War as seen by poets is well summarised in: The War Poets. "My subject is War and the Pity of War, The lives and writing of the 1914–18 War poets", ed. Robert Gidding, Great Britain 1988, Bloomsbury Publishing Ltd.

[3]The term "No Diet" referred to a system in the AMS hospitals where a patient, if specially authorised by the medical officer, could order any food he wanted. The authorities would go to great lengths to obtain such. The diet was used for patients with mortal disease. It is no longer available.

[4]The original TF hospitals had their nursing and medical staff in post from the first day, following Keogh's plan, and had worked together in their home location. They were described as "à la suite", a mysterious term, which meant that they were available for mobilization as soon as required. The reinforcement problem was such, however, that these hospitals did not move abroad as entities. In 1939, the nursing staff did not train with the male medical staff prior to the start of hostilities — a less satisfactory situation than existed in 1914. General Keogh had thought things out better!

The appearance of nursing Sisters was welcome in the CCSs perhaps even more than in the general hospitals, because no field unit had had an establishment for them. Pte Campion, in No 1 CCS, wrote "How happy we all were when we learned the Gallant Band of Hospital Sisters had arrived from Great Britain."

[5]Frostbite was clearly a huge problem in November 1914 and over that winter. Colonel Lee mentioned it in his report to Lord Kitchener. Most of the measures were military as much as medical — General Munro of 1 Div told Colonel Bowlby that as soon as men were only allowed in water for 8 hours and not longer, their feet improved. Soldiers' diaries told of regular protection by rubbing with whale oil supervised by their NCOs and officers. The disease of "trench foot" appeared later in the War, and was due to immersion, not necessarily cold.

Frostbite was the subject discussed at the inaugural meeting of the "Rouen Medical Society" on January 16, 1915, at No 11 Stationary Hospital. Colonel Skinner, one of the ADsMS was in the chair. Lieutenant Beckwith Whitehouse was elected secretary. The newly formed Society was to hear "papers and matters of medical and surgical interest", and there was a large attendance, including MOs from all the nearby hospitals and other medical units. The first paper was by brevet Colonel C.B. Lawson, on his experience of frostbite cases in No 8 BGH. He was followed by Mr J. Skeffington, Senior Surgeon at the nearby No 2 BRCS(British Red Cross Society) Hospital. This Society catered for post-graduate training and what was known in the late 20th Century as "in-post" instruction.

[6]The surgeons understood very soon how different the wounds were; Bowlby wrote in his diary in November 1914 "Almost all the experiences of bullet wounds in the Boer War have been set at naught." With experience they came to understand that the injuries to tissue extended far into limbs or trunk — beyond the obvious naked-eye damage. This realisation led to the concept of "full excision" and not just "enlarging" of wounds. It is of interest that the same fact, of damage far beyond the apparently obvious, was rediscovered in the 1960s when Major General John Matheson told with pride of the "brilliant work" of Lieutnant Colonel Owen-Smith in describing the effects of the high velocity small arms projectiles of that time. It had all been described before.

[7]For a comprehensive account of gas gangrene and other clostridial infections, see Topley and Wilson, Principles of Bacteriology, Virology and Immunity, Seventh Edition, 1983/84, Vol 3, chapter 63 (J.W.G. Smith and Geoffrey Smith). The chapter references include papers from both First and Second Wars.

[8]The increase in early operating, the surgeons of CCSs reported in 1917, "is based on the knowledge acquired by experience that by far the most important treatment is the early mechanical cleansing of the wound and the excision of all badly torn tissues under an anaesthetic. Nothing that can subsequently be done can compensate for the want

of this, and if the treatment is thoroughly carried out any subsequent line of treatment is simplified, for early excision and cleansing is the necessary basis for all methods yet devised to obviate sepsis…it is also absolutely essential for success that this excision should be done as soon as possible after the infliction of an extensive wound because in such cases gas-gangrene may become widely spread within 24 hours."

"This method of treatment has entirely superseded the application of strong antiseptics to a recent wound, or the use of continual saline infusions…it is agreed by all Allied surgeons." (See also Bowlby and Wallace, Development of British Surgery at the Front. *BMJ* 1917; **2**: 725–726). The irrigation system propounded by Almroth Wright, (*Proc R Soc Med* **9**, 1915–16, 1–16, 60–72), showed an amazing ignorance of surgery, and can be dismissed as irrelevant.

Dr D.P. Penhallow, Chief Surgeon to the American Womens' War Hospital in 1916, advocated, on his arrival in France, *primary suture* of war wounds. He made no mention of prophylactic ATS (anti-tetanic serum). Even more foolishly, he wrote a book trying to embrace the whole field of military surgery in which he continued to advocate primary suture, showing the ignorance of the civil surgeon which still manifests itself at the time of natural disasters where military surgical principles are needed for the correct management of devitalised or hours-old injuries. Major General J.P. Coull, the Director of Army Surgery at the time of the 1990 Gulf War, told the writer of his horror when two men were evacuated to UK with their wounds closed by primary suture by Regular RAMC who should have known better.

⁹The British Press, although not exhibiting the vicious writings of the so-called tabloids of the late 20th Century, was run by dictators who considered themselves able and willing to destroy individuals and bring down governments. The behaviour of Lord Northcliffe and his changes of side are a study of selfishness in themselves, and the *Morning Post*, to which Colonel Repington, the military correspondent of *The Times*, was driven by Northcliffe, took the side of the General Staff against him and indeed against the perfidious Lloyd George. (See Private Papers of Sir Douglas Haig, *op cit* , p 155). Sir Max Aitken, owner of the *Daily Express*, was pacified in 1917 by the title of Lord Beaverbrook from Mr Lloyd George.

Early in the War Colonel Lee was prepared to take the barons on — he used the word "lies" to refute claims that soldiers were being operated on without chloroform, because the RAMC had failed to provide it, and about the numbers of cases of tetanus, in his despatches to Kitchener. "Figures", he said, "should be published to surprise the critics and to reassure the public mind which has been naturally disturbed by the cruel exaggerations which have been indulged in so freely at home." The Order of St John he also castigated for spreading the story about lack of chloroform, on the word of the press. The BMA made its own enquiries, and found it possible that a few private hospitals, working under the aegis of the French Red Cross, might have run short. See *BMJ* 1914; **2**: 1079.

The press were distrusted and disliked by the RAMC soldiers, as they had been in the South African War. "The war correspondent", wrote Lieutnant Colonel Bruce Porter, commanding 3rd London GH, "is commonly esteemed a very great personage by the civilian population at Home, but by the Fighting Men in the line he is an object of some scorn and amusement."

In 1916 there were attacks on the AMS and in April of that year, Mr R. McNeill M.P. proposed a Commission of enquiry into the RAMC consisting of Lord Milner, Mr Dent who was a railway manager, and Dr Cooper of Guy's Hospital who had been previously dismissed from the Army Board. Mr Asquith and the D.G. refused it, and the Under-Secretary of State, Mr Tennant turned it down in the House of Commons. The senior Consultants in France were furious. Sir Anthony Bowlby wrote angrily in his diary against Keogh, saying he would have granted the request when it first appeared, "like the weak little creature he is !"

Attacks also came from medical men. The most persistent for a period was Sir Alfred Fripp of Guy's Hospital, and were against the D.G. "Many people are grumbling… it is useless to shut our eyes to the fact that there are substantial complaints, and that there is room for improvement. Complaints hidden from senior members of the Corps…problems too big for one man to carry — there must be many things beyond the cognisance of the Director General, on which a committee could shed light." His list of complaints, backed by Sir Cooper Perry, Guy's, Dr T.J. Horder, Bart's ('just returned from France') and Sir Alexander Ogston, was petty in the extreme.

It seems to have fallen to the lot of the war-time senior medical officers to take round difficult visitors. In June 1915, Mr Ben Tillet, a leader of dockers and strikers, was converted to "the British officer" after his public relations tour; before, he had "been full of press reports." On June 25th, 1916 Major General Bowlby wrote in his diary: "Met Lord Charnwood, who came out to see how the RAMC work is done, and of course he had been filled with lies by Fripp and Hector(Munroe) who is a scoundrel. Lord C now disgusted at the lies told him." (Bowlby was most entertained by the fact that his elevation to General's rank at once made his opinion much more worthy in the eyes of the Generals of the "Big Army !" He would surely have been equally amused by the letter, written in May, 1966 in reply to a request for information about him and Sir Cuthbert Wallace, and sent to the War Office. It read: "Neither officer had a regular or permanent commission and no record is available here or presumeably in AMD2"). Major Generals Sir Rose Bradford and Sir Wilmot Herringham, Consulting Physicians, had the same experiences, as far as non-medical Generals were concerned.

[10]Captain Francis Greaves, O.C. Surgical Division of 26 BGH, categorised the casualties as: a) lightly wounded — likely to be fit for convalescence in 3 weeks or less; b) severely wounded — to be retained for operation; c) an adequately treated lesion but no chance of return to his unit — to be discharged to U.K., and 4) "if obviously incurable." An earlier division was into "lightly wounded, seriously wounded, and very seriously wounded."

[11]As well as nurses carrying out doctors' work as anaesthetists, women were employed in TF BGHs as orderlies from 1915.

No 3 BGH said it was a "novel scheme" and called its women "orderlettes !"

There were a number of Women's hospitals abroad — the best known being run by Dr Elsie Inglis in Salonika, but Sir John French's sister, Mrs Harley, ran an all-women's hospital at Royamount, in a converted abbey. The operating here was all done by lady surgeons. In London the Endell Street Military Hospital was staffed almost entirely by women and commanded by Dr Flora Murray. The work of the volunteer ladies who went to France to nurse is told in "The Roses of No Man's Land", by Lyn Macdonald, 1980, Michael Joseph: 1993, Penguin. ISBN 0–14–017866–X.

[12]2/1st London Fd Amb was the successor to 1st London (in fact the 1/1st), one of the first TF units to go abroad. Their description of the battle of the Somme, from a fd amb's point of view, is one of the most compelling accounts. Their narrative tells of their familiarisation with 14 Div before going to their location, the streams of walking wounded from Gommecourt and Heboterne to the ADS. The MDS was at Couin with the MAC waiting beside it. In 24 hours they had evacuated 2,000 casualties to the CCS.

On the first afternoon, the Germans asked for an armistice of one hour for each side to collect. They agreed, but "Div HQ refused and the guns kept firing..so the Germans countermanded their offer, and our SBs had to run back."

"The most exhausting period in the unit's history" ended in early September, when they were allowed to set up a Divisional Rest Station. They saw the King pass by in his car on his return from the front. But they had no real rest; "squads of 8 RAMC were sent to each of the 4 bns of their bde and remained in continuous action for 6 weeks. The remainder then pooled under command of one of the fd ambs for the duration of the stunt" ('stunt ' was the term they had begun to use for an attack). The war diary went on: "Because of no roads, SBs had long carries, so relays of bearers till the horse ambulance was reached. Then by horse amb to the MDS, and next to the CCS Squads were switched from front to rear. From Sept 9 rain fell and the ground became indescribably bad. Nearer the line we called 'The valley of Death'. I overheard infantry soldiers (loaded) saying they wouldn't exchange with a stretcher bearer !"

[13]Captain Noel Chavasse was a son of the Bishop of Liverpool and a graduate of Liverpool and Oxford where he gained a double blue. Commissioned into the 10th (Scottish) Territorial Battalion of the King's Liverpool Regiment, he went to France with them on the outbreak of war. In 1916 he was awarded the Military Cross and the V.C. later that year for gallantry at Guillemont.

"For most conspicuous bravery and devotion to duty. During an attack he tended the wounded in the open all day under heavy fire, frequently in view of the enemy. During the ensuing night he searched for wounded on the ground in front of the enemy's lines for four hours. Next day he took one stretcher bearer to the advanced trenches, and under heavy shell fire carried an urgent case for 500 yards into safety, being wounded in the side by a shell splinter during the return journey. The same night he took a party of twenty volunteers, rescued three wounded men from a shell hole 36 yards from the enemy's trenches, buried the bodies of two officers, and collected many identity discs, although fired on by bombs and machine guns.

Altogether he saved the lives of some twenty wounded men, besides the ordinary cases which passed through his hands; his courage and self-sacrifice were beyond praise."

After serving another year at the front with the Liverpool Scottish, he was awarded a bar to the V.C. for outstanding service in the action at Wieltje in Belgium:

"His Majesty the King has been graciously pleased to approve of the award of a Bar to the Victoria Cross to Captain Noel Godfrey Chavasse, V.C., MC, late RAMC, attached Liverpool Regt. Though severely wounded early in the action whilst carrying a wounded soldier to the dressing station he refused to leave his post, and for two days not only continued to perform his duties but in addition went out repeatedly under heavy fire to search for and attend the wounded who were lying out. During these searches, although practically without food during this period, worn with fatigue and faint with his wound, he assisted to carry in a number of badly wounded men over heavy and difficult ground. By his extraordinary energy and inspiring example he was instrumental in rescuing many wounded who would have otherwise succumbed under the bad weather conditions. This devoted and gallant officer subsequently died of his wounds."

He died near Ypres on 4th August, 1917. At the memorial service in Birmingham it was said in the address that "it was no wonder the King felt that the whole Army would mourn the death of so brave and distinguished a man."

[14]Anti-gas goggles and hoods (the name for the respirator then in use) were available in the Dardannelles Campaign, but were never required.

[15]The choice of William George Birrell as DMS was a reflection of the paucity of Regular AMS officers of distinction. He had joined the Army Medical Department in 1881, and had had what could only be called an undistinguished career. Indeed, he was "censured for rejecting militia recruits on unsatisfactory grounds" in his earlier days, though mentioned in despatches for work in Upper Burma in 1887. He does not appear to have undertaken any postgraduate training. As a Colonel he had been employed "on the home establishment" from 1910 till his appointment in 1915. He died in 1918.

[16]Perhaps the best account of an RAMC unit in the Dardanelles campaign is that of 87 Field Ambulance of 29 Div. It is both exciting and sensibly critical: "We had leapt from a common and very ordinary unit of the Territorial Army (weekend soldiers we had been called!)...we were now Regular soldiers and an important adjunct to a Regular Army Division...that was to send its name echoing and re-echoing throughout the Empire.... On Sunday, 25th April 1915, the dawn broke fine and clear at 5.0 a.m. upon a perfect Aegean spring day.... B section of the fd amb went with the KOSBs and SWBs(South Wales Borderers) on 'Y' beach at Cape Helles...at Gallipoli, theory had to give way to ingenious improvisations in the early operation of landing. The cas were so enormous that there was a serious deadlock at the various DSs on the beaches. Here it may be said at the outset there were no CCSs or base hospitals at Cape Helles, and only 2 hospital ships at anchor off the coast...a breakdown of all medical arrangements on the lines of communication, a description which was just as apt to all beaches." See RAMC archives in Wellcome, No 493.

[17]Official History, *op cit*, Vol 3, p 31.

[18]Mesopotamia Commission. Report of the Commission Appointed by Act of Parliament to Enquire into the Operations of War in MESOPOTAMIA. London, HMSO., 1917, Part 1, p 10ff. Because of the perceived absence of a threat from Russia, the Indian Army was reduced to a size and scale of equipment to take account of the needs of "frontier warfare alone", and no more.

[19]The Vincent- Bingley Commission was set up in March 1916 by the Indian Government to enquire and report "upon the arrangements for dealing with the wounded and sick in Mesopotamia." Its critical findings were not immediately published.

[20]Mesopotamia Commission, *op cit*, p 79ff. Harold George Hathaway joined the AMS in 1885, did moderately well in his early career, and had been specially promoted to Lieutnant Colonel for service in South Africa. But after being on half pay he was sent to India in 1912, where he became a CB in 1914. In spite of being censured for his failures in Mesopotamia, his name was "brought to the notice of the Secretary of State for War for valuable services rendered in connection with the War" in 1917. James Macneece had a better record than Hathaway. A much older man — he joined the AMS in 1878 — he was however at the very end of his career in 1916 and died in 1919. Sir Francis Treherne, FRCS, DPH, was outstanding in every way and it was perhaps only his age which prevented his being D.G. after Keogh.

[21]Major Carter IMS was in the hospital ship *Varela* at Basra, waiting for the wounded from Ctesiphon. His description of what he saw, made to the Commission, made appalling hearing:

"I was standing on the bridge in the evening when the *Medjidieh* arrived. She had two steel barges without any protection against the rain, as far as I remember. As this ship, with two barges, came up to us, I saw that she was absolutely packed, and the barges too, with men. The *Medjidieh* was brought alongside the *Varela*. When she was about 300 or 400 yards off it looked as if she was festooned with ropes. The stench when she was close was quite definite, and I found that what I mistook for ropes were dried stalactites of human faeces. The patients were so huddled — and crowded together on the ship that they could not perform the offices of Nature clear of the edge of the ship, and the whole of the ship's side was covered with stalactites of human faeces.... Then we found a mass of men huddled up anyhow — some with blankets and some without. The were lying in a pool of dysentery about 30 feet(10m) square. They were covered with dysentery and dejecta generally from head to foot. With regard to this first man I examined, I put my hand into his trousers, and I thought he had a haemorrhage. His trousers were full up to the waist with something warm and slimy. I took my hand out, and thought it was blood clot. It was dysentery. The man had a fractured thigh, and his thigh was perforated in five or six places. He had apparently been writhing about the deck of the ship. Many cases were almost as bad." He went on : "In my report I describe mercilessly to the Government of India how I found Men with their limbs splinted with wood strips from 'Johnny

Walker' whisky boxes, 'Bhoosa' wire, and that sort of thing."
Mesopotamia Report, *op cit* part 10, p 76–77.

Yet General Sir John Nixon, the Army Commander during the
Battle for Ctesiphon, sent a report to India afterwards to say: "General
condition of wounded satisfactory. Medical arrangments under
conditions of considerable difficulty worked splendidly" (quoted in
"The Campaign in Mesopotomia Vol 2, HMSO chapter vii. and also
in "Kut — the Death of an Army", Ronald Millar, London, Secker and
Warburg, 1969, chapter ii, p44. "Edwin Chandler, an official eye-
witness, visited the scene of the Battle for Hanna afterwards and
described the litter of broken wheels and débris of war as a twentieth-
cnetury battle with eighteenth-century arrangements. He was so
appalled that he cabled home for medical supplies. Knowing the
stringent censorship he referred to the shortage of 'medical comforts.'
He later found that even this had been suppressed." (ibid, chapter viii,
p 162)).

[22]See "The Advance of the Egyptian Expeditionary Force, July 1917
to October 1918", Cairo, Government Press and Survey of Egypt, 1919,
pp 79–81, 104–105, for details of the part of the campaign under
command of General Allenby.

[23]Captain MacPhail wrote philosophically of his life as a medical
officer. "To each man it appears as if he alone is carrying on the war,
and in a sense he is. If he fails, something else goes wrong until all may
be in jeopardy", he wrote. And of the conditions in France: "On earth
one can walk; through water one can swim; but progress can only be
made inch by inch when earth and water are mixed in due
proportion…." The New Zealand men, as well as the Canadians, were
equally well regarded, but many instances of desertion and unhelpful
behaviour — as for example when gangs of deserters held up civilians
and other soldiers at gun point — marred the reputation of Australians
in France. Further, many of them were so revolutionary that they were
put in hospital accommodation apart from other troops. This was in
contradistinction to their universally admired bravery at Gallipoli. For
an interesting assessment of behaviour under stress amongst various
groups, see "The Thin Yellow Line", William Moore, 1974, Lee
Cooper Ltd, London.

[24]See Robert Blake's Introduction to "The Private papers of Douglas
Haig", *op cit*, p 43ff. Other senior officers apart from Haig were
amazed and contemptuous at the deviousness and malice of the
politicians they encountered.

[25]The most famous soldier character of the First World War was
"Old Bill", created by the cartoonist Bruce Bairnsfather. His cartoons
"If yers knows of a better 'ole, go to it", "Who made that hole ?" —

"Mice", "According to this 'ere almanack, the seventh year is to be the worst, and after that every fourteenth", are timeless.

[26]Photographs of General Keogh, taken between 1915 and 1917, show him looking old and tired. The same applied to General Sloggett. S.G. Woodhouse, with his very Prussian moustache, however, looked much younger by contrast. Goodwin, though described as a "dark horse" when he was appointed D.G., had an unassailable record. Born in Ceylon in 1871, his father was Surgeon Major John Goodwin. He commanded No 4 Fd Amb during the Retreat from Mons, then as ADMS 2 Cavalry Div went through Marne, Ypres and the Somme; was C.O. 14 BGH at Wimereux, and awarded the CMG in 1917. That year he was recommended by no less a person than Major General O'Donnell to go with Mr Balfour's mission to Washington as the representative of the AMS, where he made his name as an outstanding diplomat. His DSO was gained as a junior officer in Egypt. He was first Colonel Commandant of the RADC.

Gerard Ainslie Kempthorne joined the Corps in 1903. Because of his qualifications, he was recommended for accelerated promotion. He specialised in hygiene, taking the DPH in Dublin in 1913. Mentioned in despatches in October 1914 and awarded the DSO in 1918, he had a distinguished Regular career. He retired as a Lieutenant Colonel in 1931.

[27]The RAMC on the Battlefield. Frank Fox, Cornhill Magazine, Jan-June 1919, p 265. At the beginning of the War in 1914, the ADMS was not even listed in the divisional ORBAT. Medical units were merely referred to as "(x)Fd Amb."

Chapter 7

Diseases of the First World War. Army Health and Hygiene.

Since the days of Sennachrib military historians have time and time again reminded their readers that morbidity and deaths from disease far outnumbered those from the wounds of battle. An exception was in Classical Greek times when disease on campaign was rarely mentioned. It is often supposed that this was not so in the 1914–18 War because of the severity of battlefield losses, and it is certainly true that on the fronts of France, Egypt and Palestine, and in Mesopotamia, more were killed and died of wounds than died from disease. But in the smaller front of Macedonia, and Italy, more died from sickness. And if *total* admissions from sickness are counted, these were over fourteen times as great as those from battle injuries in theatres other than France. Even on the Western Front, medical *admissions* outnumbered surgical.[1]

The medical and surgical diseases of the Boer War have been recorded in detail. They reappeared in 1914 as they will continue to do in all future wars, and do not need to be mentioned further. A few, such as Desert Sore, had their cause discovered and were eliminated by specific treatment — in this instance, by anti-diphtheritic serum.

The World War saw the first control of a number of major diseases of warfare when a specific preventive measure was used. The hectic research into inoculation against enteric fever, which so dominated the AMS in the first decade of the new century, bore fruit. As the direct result of inoculation now being standard and compulsory (there was an anti-typhoid inoculation movement by cranks in Britain in 1915 which was fortunately suppressed), the rate of admission for typhoid and what could now be recognized as paratyphoid was nowhere over 10 per 1,000 except in Egypt for a time in 1916 and in Mesopotamia in 1916 and 1917. On the Western Front, it fell from 3.1 in 1915 to 0.7 per 1,000 in 1917 and 0.2 in 1918.[2]

The control of tetanus was another success. Again, new knowledge about protective antiserum could be applied for the first time. But the early weeks showed that control was not going to be quite so easy as some had supposed, owing to the *range* of types of tetanus bacillus not yet being known, and it was not till 1916 that Sir David Bruce's staff managed to produce a really satisfactory anti-serum.

Early cases occurring during the Retreat from Mons, as already seen, resulted in media comment and criticism. But the final figures speak for themselves; of a total wounded of 1,710,369 on the Western Front there were only 2,529 cases — an incidence of 1.47 per 1,000 wounded. And in all other theatres of war, there were only 20 cases out of 286,830 wounded. "A.T.S." had proved its worth; its continuing ability to produce sensitivity reactions was its only drawback. That would be solved in the future when "Tetanus Toxoid" appeared as the inoculating agent.

Bacillary Dysentery, too, had its incidence reduced on the Western Front from 4 per 1,000 in 1916 to 0.79 in 1918. This was not due to any form of inoculation, but to effective sanitation control. The first outbreak on a large scale occurred during the first Battle of the Somme when German lines were occupied, and again in 1918 when the army overran German positions. On the other hand, bacillary dysentry remained a prevalent and very serious disease in the Middle East and in East Africa. New Zealand and Australian troops imported amoebic dysentery to France, as well as Relapsing Fever, when they returned there from Egypt; Captain MacCormac of 26 BGH had to deal with these, as well as Malaria and some of the Captain of the Men of Death — Pulmonary Tuberculosis. The greatest disease in the world — Malaria — remained a constant danger in Mesopotamia and even more so in Macedonia.

Cholera occurred in Mesopotamia and Sinai, especially during the attack to relieve Kut in 1916. It affected mainly the Indian Divisions, and was treated by the novel method of intravenous saline given by transfusion. Vaccines were tried from 1916 onwards.

Typhus, "the results of which are written in the darkest pages of human history", persisted in the Eastern Front areas. On the Russian Front there were thought to have been 10 million cases, with 2 million deaths. But although an endemic disease in Turkey, there were no cases among the Commonwealth troops in the Gallipoli Campaign. In France only 5 cases occurred. RAMC hygiene methods were quickly introduced by the British Mission to Serbia when the 1915 epidemic there broke out; this was a striking example of the application of modern scientific methods to the aid of those who lacked them. Colonels Hunter and Stammers supervised delousing and made available to the civil population their own design of disinfector, and the epidemic was controlled. Till then the time-honoured procedure in Serbia had been to disperse the inhabitants of the place where the epidemic had appeared. These officers stood that on its head by preventing the population from dispersing, and disinfecting them where they stood. It is of interest that Typhus broke out once more at a later date when the locals ignored these measures the RAMC doctors had applied with such success.

Venereal Diseases were unlike most others as prevalent in the U.K. as overseas. This was because most military were stationed and trained near large centres of population. In France, the conditions of life in the trenches made it not at all surprising that so many soldiers on leave sought solace in brothels. Many men were infected when on leave in Britain also, and returned to France with Syphilis or Gonorrhoea.

Attempts at prevention were by "exhortation, lectures and posters", and by closing of brothels in Middle East Countries. There were various penalties for officers and soldiers. Similar measures were applied by the Medical Services of the Commonwealth. From 1916 onwards treatment was by personal disinfection, when Potassium Permanganate and Calomel cream were used. Australian troops, whose higher rate of infection from professional prostitutes was supposed to be related to their higher rates of pay than British soldiers', had their treatment — urethral irrigation — given by trained Medical Corps soldiers. This initiative was copied by the RAMC.

As the War went on, special hospitals for V.D. were set up — in France at Le Havre, Calais, Etaples and Rouen — a total of 9000 beds being made available. There was a hospital of 1000 beds in Egypt. Salvarsan, a new anti-syphilitic drug, became a standard treatment.

Meningococcal meningitis had been described in military garrisons during the 19th century, but became very prevalent from the start of the 1914–18 War, both among the military and civil populations in Britain. The epidemic was the most severe yet seen.

Meningitis was at this time called cerebro-spinal fever — as with a number of diseases, this was a better description than the later 20th century one. The interest in the British military epidemic lay in the preventive measures adopted. The causative organism, the meningococcus, was already known to the bacteriologist, but not its mode of spread. It was discovered that whenever soldiers were placed close together, numbers of carriers (persons having the germ in their noses but not being ill with the disease), rose sharply. Captain Glover noted its association with overcrowding in recruits' billets; Captain W. J. Tulloch, who worked on the disease and published a key monograph in the Corps Journal,[3] put it in homely terms. "The meningococcus could 'jump' 18 inches(0.5m) and infect the next soldier. It could not jump 3 feet(1m). So if soldiers' bunks were placed more than 3' apart, the disease did not spread. If soldiers had to have their bunks closer, you made them sleep head to foot." As clinical treatment was only symptomatic, and anti-serum unhelpful, prevention was imperative. But when it was eventually discovered that the serum had to correspond to the infecting organism and be standardised (the M.R.C. serum), results became better.

Infective jaundice had more than one cause. Jaundice is not a disease in itself, but a symptom of some disease which interferes with that part of liver function concerned with excretion of bile. A few munition workers became jaundiced from poisoning by the explosive tri-nitro-toluene, (T.N.T.). When the cause was known and precautions taken, this kind of jaundice disappeared. A second type was Spirochaetal jaundice, or Weil's disease, caused by a micro-organism discovered in 1914 by Japanese workers. The organism was carried in rats, and soldiers were infected by way of rats' urine. Rats being plentiful in trench warfare, the potential danger was obvious.

But it was "epidemic" jaundice, also called "campaign jaundice", which became an important disease in the Middle East and especially in Gallipoli. There was a co-relation with diarrhoea, but the causative virus would not be discovered till later. The 1915–17 outbreaks foreshadowed the major ones of 30 years later in the same war theatre.

Skin disease is often relegated to a lesser place in descriptions of campaigns, perhaps because it is so seldom life-threatening, but it deserves a place high in the list as far as the Great War is concerned. In 1914–18 skin diseases were a major source of disability, and some of the best brains in the AMS worked hard to control and eradicate them. As well as scabies, septic infections of the skin were a serious cause of admission to hospital — impetigo, boils, infected eczema. All these, plus psoriasis and ringworm, gave rise to nearly 2000 admissions a month in grand total.

Skin disease was related to the apparently new military disease of trench fever. Described as "an infectious disease characterised by febrile periods which tend to recur at regular intervals, by local pains, by an erythematous rash, and by enlargement of the spleen", it differed from any disease known to medicine before the War. Also called shin fever, trench shin, and gaiter-pain fever, because of the pain in the legs and ankle regions, this febrile illness originated in the front areas and for a long time was hardly seen at the base. It appeared from 1915 onwards, was worst in 1917, and probably produced 15–20,000 cases. Because of the prolonged low-grade fever and vague symptoms, it was at first thought to belong to the enteric group, being a type of enteric fever modified by preventive inoculation. Dr Jex Blake was a woman doctor, one of the base MOs, who studied it at Boulogne. The definitive paper was published in the Corps Journal in 1916 by J.W. McNee (later Professor McNee of Glasgow — one of the long list of war-time RAMC doctors who later became famous in civilian life), Renshaw and Blunt.[4]

The disease was caused by a louse-borne Rickettsia, smaller even than a germ, but now demonstrable by the bacteriologist. (The Rickettsia were formerly regarded as large viruses but are now classified with the true bacteria since they contain the murein and diaminopimelic residues that characterise the Gram-negative bacterial cell wall). No fatal case was recorded, but the care of the skin was a vital part of prevention. Sufferers were kept in bed for 21 days. No drug then available was curative — quinine, arsenic, salvarsan, antimony, colloidal silver, and mercury perchloride were all tried. The often severe leg pain responded to Dover's powder.

Trench foot appeared in 1915 as the inevitable consequence of soaking for long periods in trenches. It overlapped with frost-bite, which arose when the temperature fell to freezing. Regimental procedures did not always prevent trench foot.

There were four classes of the condition — patients with recovery from cold but with residual tenderness and stinging, patients with initial swelling of the legs following immersion, but with residual pain and difficulty in walking in spite of disappearance of swelling, and most severe, local gangrene of toes or foot. The worst of these made up the fourth category; they had sepsis added to vascular changes, producing spreading gangrenous cellulitis.

Measures ranged from dressings and nursing care to free incision or amputation. A.T.S. was given routinely. Because the nerves in the limbs were damaged as well as the blood vessels, pain took months to disappear. Intravenous antiseptics — 10 ml of 1:1000 mercury perchloride or 100 ml of eusol, were given: to late 20th century ears these sound highly dangerous.

As bacteriological culture was now routine, the infecting organism could be determined. For streptococcal infection, polyvalent anti-streptococcal serum was given, 30 ml, followed by 20 or 10 ml. It was able to produce marked improvement in some soldiers.

McNee's monograph on trench fever is very worth mentioning in our account, because it is one of the best examples of a short description of a disease and its management which was forgotten when the next war came along. Had MOs of 30 years later gone back to the records of the 1914–18 War, they could have saved themselves time and anxiety.

Another of the great diseases of mankind, influenza, affected the troops from 1916. During that year there were 36,072 admissions and in 1917, 28,980. Numbers increased in winter. In 1918 what was subsequently realised to be the first wave of the pandemic, appeared in June. There were 4,737 cases in May,

31,138 in June and 25,480 in July. After a fall, the epidemic proper began in the First and Second armies, with 25–30,000 cases each month. Of 112,274 cases in 1918, there were 5,483 deaths. The pandemic began from autumn 1918 (it had begun in fact in 1917 in the USA and came to Europe *via* Spain in early 1918) and continued over the winter, moving from west to east, weakening the national populations of both sides, with millions of deaths, from "the purulent bronchitis and heliotropic cyanosis (the blue colouration of the face which meant a fatal ending)…even the mildest case had to be regarded as potentially grave." The strain on the medical divisions of the BGHs, already exhausted by years of work, was enormous.

ADVANCES IN CLINICAL SURGERY

Delayed Primary Suture was the major surgical advance of the Great War. There need be no apology for repeating the fact. Interestingly enough, it was the very fact that *muscle* was realised to be the critical tissue involved in gas gangrene which led to the surgeons in 1915 beginning to excise muscle "systematically", as the *Official History* put it. "It was within the next year that the excision of any and all devitalised tissue, at the earliest possible time, was found by the surgeons to be the key to success. Soon they learned to leave the skin flaps open, to be closed some time later. Later another basic concept was enunciated: *The chief lesson learned by the experience of war was that the training of the military surgeon must be undertaken in peace.*"(C.J. Bond, CMG, FRCS England, Hon Colonel(T).[5]

Other standard surgical military problems were taken farther in 1914–18. Colonel Sir Cuthbert Wallace, reporting his experiences in the *Official History*, summarises the views on one of the areas where anxiety will always remain:

"Abdominal surgery. There is no doubt that laparotomy and repair of whatever damage had occurred became a common procedure as the War went on. Older views, such as the belief by Makins that a projectile could traverse the peritoneal cavity without damaging hollow viscera, was from his experience in South Africa. It was also because surgeons at that time had been extremely hesitant about opening the abdomen. All the records of their case reports make us conclude that it was the fear of operating which led surgeons to conjecture about spontaneous healing of bowel or traumatic entero-enterostomies, where two adjacent loops of bowel were transversed by a fragment and a hole between them formed spontaneously; as the fear of laparotomy lessened, surgeons explored and repaired what they found damaged. In time laparotomy became less dangerous than expectant treatment. Haemorrhage, of course, remained the lethal enemy of the abdominal surgeon…. The physical signs — of tenderness, guarding and rigidity of the abdominal wall, were still there for the surgeon to elicit. His decision to operate remained, as in South Africa, his alone. But now laparotomy (and anaesthesia) was much safer." He included a piece of clinical knowledge which does not change: "The point of maximum tenderness may coincide with the position of the gut lesion."[6]

This conclusion can be compared with the views in Chapter 3, pp 73ff. They can be compared with the view later in this century when blood transfusion had made haemorrhage less of a hazard. (p291, 341)

It is also of interest that in the earlier stages of the campaign in Palestine, when the majority of wounds were bullet and the climate dry, that GSW wounds did as well as in South Africa and healed readily.

Other surgical specialties developed, some more than others. There was no improvement in neurosurgery until specialist neurosurgeons began to attract referrals, and even then the results were similar to those in the South African War. Steel helmets were issued from 1916, and they improved the outlook perhaps more than the doctors did. In orthopaedic surgery, the value of early splinting was recognised very soon. The Thomas Splint showed its worth, and became the standard appliance for femoral shaft fractures and major thigh wounds. "Its use prevented shock and reduced sepsis." This remark from the *Official History* was a gross understatement. Reduction in mortality rates from 60 to 30 per cent meant that use of the splint was the second surgical discovery of the Great War. A modified Thomas Splint, with a T-piece, was invented for upper limb fractures.[7] Bone grafting began in the later part of the War, in base hospitals. Surgeons whose main skill was in orthopaedics also set up rehabilitation centres in the U.K. base, initiating a whole new field of care.

By 1916, military surgeons were operating on the abdomen, cranium, and major joints with equanimity, but were not opening the chest. Pierre Duval in the French Medical Service, and Colonels G. Gask and H.W.M. Gray of the RAMC, began to do so. According to their reports, they found it "perfectly practical", and, remarkably by late 20th century standards, "no special devices were needed for the maintenance of respiration, and the lung expanded rapidly after closure of the chest"(Gask). But the problem of sepsis, with pus in the pleural cavity (empyema), meant that 30 per cent of thoracotomies had to be drained. Because of the lack of specialist skill, and certainly because of the primitive anaesthetic procedures, mortality was only reduced from 30 per cent to 25 per cent

Plastic Surgery deserves a special mention. It is sometimes thought that the first major military plastic surgery was carried out by McIndoe in 1940. In fact, the Queen's Hospital at Sidcup, gifted personally by Queen Mary, was the location of work under Lieutenant Colonel Gillies (later Sir Harold Gillies). He worked with a team of surgeons from the three Dominion nations and repaired especially faces of soldiers. The basic plastic techniques were devised by trial and error; striking results were obtained.

ANAESTHESIA

The first general anaesthetic agent used was chloroform. There were no specialist anaesthetists with the B.E.F. — these arrived with the Territorials — and initially any MO gave a general anaesthetic. The skill of the nursing sisters who gave general anaesthetics has already been praised.

Ether was quickly used instead of chloroform, the latter being retained only for induction. Ether was administered as "warm ether vapour" irrespective of the condition of the patient or the nature of the operation. Air was passed through ether by means of a hand or foot bellows, an efferent tube passing through a thermos flask before delivering the anaesthetic gas to the patient. The very compact apparatus of Dr Francis Shipway was used after 1915 in CCSs. Ethyl Chloride was seldom used as an agent. Novocaine was commonly used as a local anaesthetic. It was employed in abdominal surgery, to infiltrate the abdominal wall — and to reduce the amount of gas agent required. This technique was believed by many, when (re)introduced in the later 20th century, to be a new idea! Spinal Anaesthesia was not favoured.

Captain Maynard Horne of 26 BGH gave over 1000 anaesthetics himself, of the 1530 administered in 1915–16. He ordered atropine as a premedication, adding morphia "if the patient was nervous." Being a specialist anaesthetist, he had experience of different induction methods; he believed that the Schimmelbusch mask with chloroform first then ether to follow, was safest. "Ether for septic cases" was his dictum. But he also induced anaesthesia with nitrous oxide and oxygen and used these as alternative agents. His personal favourite apparatus was Hewitt's gas and oxygen one; he gave some spinal anaesthetics, again because he was a specialist, trained outside the Army.

Captain Horne denied much post-operative trouble, apart from what he called "ether bronchitis", which he said was more prevalent in winter. He had two deaths on the table — "due to the operation not the General Anaesthetic", he wrote, in true anaesthetist's vein!

The anaesthetists had the same problems as they have today. Big fit men needed large amounts of anaesthetic. Heavy smokers had what was called "irritation." Because of the nature of the anaesthetic, men struggled during induction till the plane of surgical anaesthesia was reached. Shock and haemorrhage added to the difficulties. Pre-operative morphia was dangerous if given in large dosage, as happened not infrequently. An advance was "Hewitt's artificial airway for jaw spasm and stertor" — the first mechanical airway to be used.

Post-operative vomiting was common. It was treated by 2 per cent sodium bicarbonate, i/v.

RADIOLOGY

The 1915 Field Service pattern X-ray apparatus was a modification of the 1913 one. Alternating current was needed, so accumulators were used. At first they had to be sent to a French workshop to be re-charged, but very soon they were re-charged at the hospitals. There was the same difficulty as in the previous war — very long exposures were required for head and trunk films. Captain McDonald of 26 BGH used a 1 m.amp 5–7 B tube, with a small stereoscope, accumulating screen and cassette. The X-ray Tube was the MacAlister Wiggin; it "needed constant regulation but worked well."

X-rays were used routinely for fractures and foreign bodies. Two films were taken at right angles, for limbs and head examination. Stereoscopy was used for head, eyes, shoulders, pelvis, and chest. "With this is combined the measurement of displacement, and the depth is read off on a curve with displacement plotted against depth — a Mackenzie-Davidson method without his apparatus."

He also used the Hampson method of measuring displacement on the screen in chest examinations, where the body density was not too great. The parallax method was used for shoulders and thighs, when the patient could be put on the operating table.

Sometimes operations were done under X-ray control when for example a hand wound was being explored. X-rays were used to diagnose haemothorax, pneumothorax, pyopneumothorax, and gas gangrene, and for medical conditions. Lastly, they were used to treat some cases of skin disease, under the direction of the consultant physician. Radiology had progressed a long way in 10 years.

BASIC RESEARCH ON SURGICAL SHOCK

In the earlier part of the 1914–18 War, most research was in the bacteriology of the serious infections. By 1917, when resources of manpower were becoming progressively reduced, the AMS took on a new function — to explore ways of preserving the manpower of the nation. This included increased interest in rehabilitation, in measures to improve health in the younger men due for call-up (conscription having become necessary), and in research into known causes of disability and death. Surgical shock was now a problem to be tackled, as was blood transfusion. In 1917 a research centre was set up in Béthune, in 33 CCS, where Drs Bayliss and Starling undertook basic research into shock — not into clinical management, but into the underlying patho-physiological process which produced the condition. They had as a colleague Professor Cannon of Harvard, and Professor Crile, also from the USA, co-operated at the centre beside the Rémy siding with the staff of 10 and 17 CCSs. The British put their findings at the disposal of the U.S. medicals arriving in 1918.

The excellence of this work cannot be over-emphasised, especially when it is recalled that the research was being carried out in field conditions. It was one of the most profound pieces of research to come out of a war up to that date, and, as will be seen, several of the findings were forgotten until they were re-discovered in the next war and in civil surgery in the later 20th century.

Professor Bayliss gave a lecture on his team's findings which was published in the Corps Journal in 1920:[8]

In it he discussed the basic problem — "Where does the blood go?" for a soldier becomes shocked even if he does not lose blood. It was obvious that cardio-respiratory failure occurred — why? *"Is it the defective volume of the blood in circulation that is the main factor in acidosis?"*

"Lactic acid thought to be the cause of the cardio-respiratory failure — we crushed the thigh muscles of anaesthetised cats, and found a progressive fall in blood pressure with progressive acidosis (acidity of the tissues including blood)...the result was the same when any participation of the nerve centres was excluded by section of the spinal cord...it was due to some toxic product being absorbed from the injured tissue...acids thought to be innocuous, since the organism quickly neutralises their effect. The acidosis turned out to be merely the result of defective oxygen supply, due to failure of the circulation. Following the work of Dale, Laidlaw, and Richards on histamine,[9] we concluded that histamine itself was *one* of the causes of the patho-physiological changes...of course, it would be hasty to conclude that histamine itself is formed in injured tissues; there are probably related compounds with the same physiological action, such as those present in peptone and extracts of boiled tissues..."

They discovered a very great deal about the process of surgical shock — they were even aware of an initial rise in blood pressure in cases of gas gangrene — the equivalent of what was described as Type I septicaemic shock in the 1980s. They knew about dilation of arterioles and sensed what this meant. All this first-rate work was forgotten; researchers on shock over the last ten years of the 20th century would have done well to look back and to re-read the work done at Béthune in 1917.

Bayliss and Starling and their colleagues advocated the use of intravenous solutions to raise the blood pressure and restore the circulation — gum-saline solution, 6 per cent gum acacia in 0.9 per cent normal saline. They and the RAMC surgeons of the day realised that the effect of normal saline alone was only temporary, as was that of Ringer's solution. Blood transfusion was pioneered by Canadian surgeons in 1916 and 1917. Blood grouping was then a novelty, but was begun; stored blood was tried and found successful if kept under the right conditions. The Archibald and Bruce Robertson citrate method was used. Captain Oswald Robertson of the U.S. Medical Corps used an apparatus of his own in 1917. For actual transfusion, the paraffined glass tube of Kimpton Brown, also from the USA, was used. The writer recalls Major General Munro telling him in 1952 of how, as a junior officer, he remembered seeing this very tube used for one of the early blood transfusions.

POISON GAS

The Second Battle of Ypres began on 22nd April, 1915 at 5.30 p.m. with the release of Chlorine gas from cylinders by the Germans near Langemarck. This was a truly terrible battle. There had been warnings of the use of gas, but the Allies took no precautions. The green-yellow cloud was blown by a south-east wind towards a section of the line held by a French Colonial Division — which retreated very rapidly to beyond the Iser Canal. But the Canadians held on over the 24th to the 30th April; the British thought there should be a withdrawal, but General Foch was violently opposed — as happened on other occasions, the French obsession being as ever with attack. Over 60,000 British and Canadians died.

There were many accounts and vivid photographs of the first gas casualties. Pte Charles Campion of 1 CCS wrote in his diary: "We knew there was a big battle when there was a continuous bombardment…word came that gas had been used. We re-arranged the hospital…the 'gas' had affected the men on their eyes, their lungs, and their stomachs…it was a most distressing sight when the field ambulances arrived. The ambulance orderlies lifting out the most serious cases; these were placed in the courtyard for the removal of their gas contaminated uniforms.

More field ambulances were now arriving with the 'walking cases'. This was indeed a tragic sight. An ambulance orderly leading sightless men, the first man supporting himself with outstretched arm, his hand holding the orderly's shoulder, the second man with his hand outstretched to the first man, and so on."

Colonel Bowlby saw casualties on 2nd May after the gas attack at Bailleul and later Hazebrouck, "where the Dorset and Devons were affected... we saw about 50 in 2 and 8 CCSs. 10 died in 12 hours. Those we saw were fighting for breath. We found the best thing was to make them vomit, for in the straining and retching they cleared their bronchi...the men lie and gasp like fish out of water, and get blue in the face, and many die even after a week." 1300 cases came in over the next two days; Bowlby was angry at what he thought was lack of concern at home.

But the authorities acted quickly. Dr J.S. Haldane, the physiologist with special knowledge of the respiratory system, had actually arrived on April 26th, with another expert, Professor H.B. Baker.

Soon it was known that there were three types of gas — acute lung irritants, direct poisons of the nervous system, lachrymators; later the fourth, the blister agent mustard, was added. The scientists quickly confirmed that as well as chlorine, xylyl bromide had been used in the first attacks, as a lachrymator.

At first all the troops could do was to hold handkerchiefs soaked with sodium bicarbonate over their mouths and noses. The war diary of I/2 North Midland Field Ambulance tells how in early May their medical orderlies had to mix and supply the solution for dipping the next primitive respirators, a cotton waste pad for nose and mouth, in:

> Sodium Hyphophosphite, 10 lbs(45Kg)
> Sodium Bicarbonate, 2 lbs(900gms)
> Glycerine, 1 pint(500ml)
> Water, 1 gallon(4.5litres).

The respirator was soaked then squeezed nearly dry. If it had been exposed to gas, it was treated in a solution of half the above strength.

The field ambulance staff were also given 2 glass vacuum bottles for the RAMC to collect gas fumes — which obviously amused them!

The first method of releasing was compressed gas from cylinders. Since the effect depended entirely upon the wind, this had obvious disadvantages. So from April 1915 — July 1916 the Germans used shells to deliver the gas — this had many advantages. "T-shells" of xylyl bromide were used during this period, but from July 1916 — July 1917, the so-called "lethal shell period", phosgene, a toxic lung irritant, was used, and from

July 1917 till the end of the War gas shells containing the vesicant dichlor-ethyl-sulphide (mustard gas) were also employed. As soon as a new agent appeared, a specimen was sent urgently to the U.K. base, even as far as St Andrews, which had special chemistry skill; the Professor of Physiology there, P.T. Herring, burned his arms severely while testing mustard gas on himself.

Some agents, notably mustard, were called "persistent", because they were not dispersed by natural elements in the areas poisoned, and continued to produce their effects over a long period. The clothing of those affected had to be treated with great care.

The third stage in respirators was a fabric helmet, which was issued in December 1915, and called "P." It was succeeded by the "PH", then from August 1916 onwards the "large box respirator PHG." Small box respirators came out next again, and this type, probably the best respirator available, continued to be used; indeed, it was the standard until 50 years later when the NBC model replaced it.

The AMS worked hard to combat this new weapon. They had also to deal with carbon monoxide poisoning in mines and tanks. For the war gases, Captain Adrian Stokes devised an apparatus for distributing oxygen to a group of gassed men. Dr Haldane devised an oxygen apparatus of even better quality but it was not available till near the end of the War. Contaminated clothing was put in spirit followed by very hot water if mustard gas was the agent. Venesection was found useful for chlorine gas casualties.

The Allies naturally used gas agents in response, and gas was used then by both sides. Total casualties were 180,983 with over 6,000 deaths. Perhaps the most unhappy feature was late invalidism; sufferers continued to die of delayed respiratory failure till 1939, when poison gas was once more on the scene as a likely war weapon. This time, however, the civilian population was feared to be at greater risk than the military.[10]

The Soldier's Heart And Shell Shock

Two maladies were of special interest and frequency in the Great War and demand detailed comment. These were irregularity of heart action and the mental phenomena collectively called shell shock.

Cardiac symptoms were regarded with deep anxiety over the later 19th century, and the presence of a heart murmur was the recipe for invalidism and loss of employment. The pioneering work of Sir James Mackenzie, who showed that very many cardiac murmurs and symptoms were of no serious importance, and revolutionised the attitude of the medical profession towards them, had not been known generally and not by any means accepted. The later work of Sir Thomas Lewis, which told the same sort of story, was similarly not known by every doctor. Dr Da Costa had analysed 300 cases of the clinical picture which appeared in France during the U.S. Civil War — as long in the past as 1864–68 and 1876–96 — and called it "the soldier's heart." But, like so much of great value reported in that war, it had not been read widely in Europe.

Cardiac symptoms were first seen as a phenomenon after the Retreat from Mons. Physical exhaustion was followed by chest pain, palpitation on exertion, shortness of breath, and persistent tachycardia.

It has to be remembered that in these years the disease of acute rheumatism affecting the heart, rheumatic carditis, was extremely common. It regularly left cardiac murmurs of a type heard seldom in the later century. So rheumatic heart disease was a condition constantly in the background, and one of which all doctors were very aware. They had therefore to be careful in labelling anyone with cardiac symptoms and signs as having "functional disease."

Men in increasing numbers complained of pain felt at or below the apex of the heart, rarely radiating down the arms, and sometimes with tenderness over the praecordium, the area of the chest wall overlying the heart. They complained of giddiness, rapid heart action often with fluttering or heavy beating, fainting attacks, sleeplessness and headache, and were invariably easily tired out by activity which they had previously carried out without any trouble. When they were admitted to the medical division of a military hospital, they had persistent tachycardia, which fell to half the rate when they were asleep.

The dominant aetiological factor in the clinical histories of soldiers complaining of the "effort syndrome" was infection of one kind or another.[11] 32 per cent of men had this — 12 per cent rheumatic fever, and the range of respiratory diseases, dysentery and diarrhoea of unknown origin, between 5 and 3 per cent each.

Other precipitating causes were severe effort, and shelling. But "shell shock" from noise or burying coincided with D.A.H. in only 2 per cent of cases; the two war neuroses presented as cardiac effort syndrome or mental collapse but not both together. Trench fever was found to be a background factor when it appeared in the later part of the war. The syndrome came on also after gassing or wounding. Acute rheumatic fever was not common amongst soldiers in France, and although 50 per cent of young men joining the Army gave a history of previous rheumatic fever, true rheumatic valvular disease, where the heart valves had been distorted by it, was uncommon. If found, with no doubt about the diagnosis, the man was simply discharged from the Army.

This, where there was unequivocal evidence of true rheumatic valvular disease, was a straightforward enough problem. Such men did produce cardiac symptoms. The larger group, who had such symptoms but no evidence of organic disease, were described as having "D.A.H. or Disordered Action of the Heart."

Many young men, especially as the years passed and the less fit came to be called up, produced the rapid heart action with all the associated complaints during initial training. The size of the problem was shown by the numbers of men actually *discharged* on account of "heart disease" by the summer of 1918: nearly 37,000, and exceeded only by chest complaints and actual wounding(11). Overall, for every 3 cases of "mental" stress disorder there were 2 of "cardiac" stress disorder.

Of those liable to "D.A.H.", most were found to take great care of themselves, and to be introspective. A large proportion showed poor physique and took little exercise. Lewis and others stated that over 50 per cent were total abstainers, although the significance of this was doubtful. Perhaps of more significance, especially when medical science called for a change in smoking habits later in the century, was the finding that "excessive cigarette smoking was an important contributory factor in the breathlessness and praecordial pain of many with the effort syndrome."[12]

Management began with careful diagnosis, especially in special centres. By 1915, Sir Thomas Lewis had set up at the Military Heart Hospital in Hampstead a system of graded drills, and used these to grade soldiers sent there with supposed

"D.A.H." These were also used to improve the physique of recruits found to be more than usually unfit during basic training, and anticipated the similar centres set up in the Second World War.

Five special centres were set up in France, and probably saved 15,000 men from invaliding to the U.K. base. They were staffed by enthusiasts, but the general AMS were slow to utilise their expertise. It was not till the later War that their worth was realised; from March 1917 till November 1918 alone some 23,000 men passed through them.

Shell Shock And Mental Disorders

The fact that soldiers suffered mental distress during battle had been known for centuries. At the Battle of Marengo in 1800, for example, Napoleon is said to have considered that 20 per cent of his casualties were due to battle fatigue or stress. What made the 1914–18 War casualties notable was not the number of them — over 21,000 discharged and fewer than many believe — but the huge amount of concern and even mythology they produced among public and doctors.

The term "neurasthenia" was first used by Beard of New York in 1879: "a derangement of function resulting from exhaustion of nervous energy." Dr Guthrie Rankin, Physician to the Dreadnought Hospital at Greenwich in 1903, wrote that: "the increasing wear and tear of life at the present day probably plays the most important part in its aetiology."[13] He made the important point that had the disorder been prevalent in earlier periods of the world's history, "it could not have escaped detection at the hands of the many eminent clinical observers of ancient days."

The origin of the term "shell shock" remains unknown. It appeared in soldiers' letters in 1915, and could have been a soldiers' as distinct from a doctors' term: the very first RMOs' diaries talk of "spinal concussion" or "neurasthenia", but not "shell shock." Writers on the history of British Psychiatry[14] credit Elliott as the first to describe four cases of "transient paraplegia" (paralysis of the limbs and body) as early as December 1914, and the first to point out both that organic disease could be overlooked and that "functional disorders of the nervous system were common after a 'big shell explosion' ." Lieutenant Adolphe Abrahams also reported an early case of functional paraplegia and tremor.[15] Captain Croker also, as we remember, wrote of psychiatric cases in the very first weeks of the War.

Captain Charles S. Myers, a war-time medical officer, first used the term in medical literature in an article in the *Lancet* in February, 1915. What he described was regarded from the outset by MOs with special interest in psychiatry as a functional condition with a multitude of symptoms — paralyses of varying degree, tremors, blindness, deafness, mutism and other speech disorders. They differentiated it from the term neurasthenia, which was used from the very start of the War, and included patients presenting with anxiety and psychiatric symptoms. Again very quickly, RAMC officers noticed that the term neurasthenia did *not* apply to soldiers with severe exhaustion, even though this might be associated with crying, tremor, sleeplessness and agitation — the outstanding feature of this sort of nervous breakdown was the rapid improvement which followed rest and simple measures to reassure and restore confidence — the sort of panic attack the padres had dealt with successfully in the Boer War. In fact, in 1917 Captain W. Johnson preferred the term "exhaustion syndrome." While one of Captain Croker's patients filled the criteria of exhaustion, the other showed anxiety as soon as he came to the Front.

Simple exhaustion and neurasthenia with anxiety were the first two groups of war neurosis. The third was hysterical states, where there was evidence of true hysterical symptoms. The fourth included confusional states of all degrees, from mild to severe confusion, with at its most severe extent, the true major mental disorders.

Lieutenant Henry Yellowlees' account of his experience of psychiatric casualties over the summer of 1915, after 26 BGH was open and receiving in France, shows how quickly psychiatrists of his calibre created a specialist service. By September 1915 he had a separate hut built for psychiatric casualties, for soldiers; officers had their own ward within the hospital. Soon he had the bed complement doubled.

"The liberal views which one's previous experience has shown to be entertained by one's brother officers as what constitutes a 'mental case' have been amply demonstrated", he said. "Shock, neurasthenia, hysteria and malingering have all been received under this heading; a patient suffering from septicaemia and delirium due to a wound, and a Greek Canadian who preferred to talk in his own language. It is abundantly proved that a skilled alienist does most valuable work in such a situation as this, in preventing wastage from the Expeditionary Force."

That Lieutenant Yellowlees had a full range of mental disorder amongst his patients is shown by his breakdown of diagnoses:

Confusional Insanity	13	Delusional Insanity G.P.I.(Syphilis affecting the nervous system)	18
Stupor	3	Melancholia	16
Dementia	5 2	Circular Insanity	1
Mania	17	Other diagnoses(of these, 22 were cases of shock).	63
		Total	185

As with all cases in a military hospital, the chief difficulty was the need for rapid evacuation owing to the high admission rate and the limited accommodation. But, especially in mental disease, who to evacuate? "The difficulty", wrote Yellowlees, "was especially felt with regard to the confusional states, whether associated with shell shock or not, and the cases of suspected malingering.... Surprisingly few cases of shell shock showed symptoms which made their admission to a special mental ward really necessary, and of those who did, the majority were fit to be transferred to an ordinary ward in a few days. Of those cases of shell shock which showed symptoms of anything like a lasting nature justifying the use of the word 'insanity', there was a history of previous nervous illness in the patient or his family in over 90 per cent...once one was satisfied that a patient was undoubtedly insane, and unlikely to recover within a reasonably short period, one's chief concern was to evacuate him to England as speedily as possible. It was not practicable to do much in the way of treatment or enter into refinements of diagnosis."

He had unstinted praise for the RAMC TF trained orderlies, whose shrewdness and understanding made his work so much easier. Captain MacCormac, the general physician, held a more traditional view, and his remarks show so well the difference between his attitude and that of the specialist: "Shell shock admissions were frequent and did not respond readily to treatment…probably among the neuroses should be included various irregular and hastened actions of the heart, conditions giving most unsatisfactory results."

Lieutenant Yellowlees and the other emerging psychiatric specialists put their fingers on the prime diagnostic challenge — to differentiate the patients who were merely exhausted and who did not need more than sound rest and sensible reassurance, (the late 20th century term "counselling" had not flooded medical and media literature then) and who were *not* to be sent out of theatre, and those exhibiting mental disease and requiring continuing specialist care and treatment. The expression N.Y.D.(N) became used — Not Yet Diagnosed Nervous — for admissions before the diagnosis was clear.

The shell shock variety were as often as not helped, though by no means invariably or entirely, by hypnosis or suggestion under anaesthesia. Many with stubborn symptoms had to be evacuated to U.K., and of these, a large proportion showed themselves unable to serve except at the base or at home, or a recurrence of symptoms if returned to the front line.

A new difficulty arose for the AMS in their management of war neuroses which occurred during that greatest of all British battles, the Somme. Several thousand soldiers were evacuated in the first few weeks with shell shock, and many reached England. The expression "shell shock" became headline material, and as always was over-written by the media. It was, as the *Official History* recorded, "as if it were a new disease…certain members of the profession lectured and wrote on the subject as if it were some new and mysterious malady." It was not only the newspapers which were at fault. "Some patients with hysterical symptoms were pschyo- analysed…nearly all were treated on lines which could not fail to impress on the soldier's mind the mysteriousness of his malady…misguided public opinion had raised the psycho-neuroses to the dignity of a new war disease, before which doctors seemed well-nigh helpless. This view rapidly became widespread amongst the soldiers in France…even amongst some doctors. It wrought untold evil amongst patients, and undoubtedly precipitated breakdown in a certain type of man who might otherwise have held himself together…to the soldier's mind shell shock was as much an entity as scarlet fever, with the further addition that, being incurable, shell shock was more to be dreaded."

The problem was solved by the AMD with the institution of special centres — just as Lieutenant Yellowlees had done on his own initiative a year before. Lieutenant Colonels Gordon Holmes, the consulting neurologist, and C. S. Myers, were leaders in this enterprise. But the problem might have got out of hand, and the story is worth telling for this very reason. The same could happen in any war. The near 30,000 cases of shell shock in the 1914–18 War could have been many more.[16]

The relation of shell shock to cowardice and malingering requires comment. It is one of the myths that "shell shock patients who ran away were all shot anyway in the First War." This is certainly untrue. But the fact remains that many who deserted their post were shot for cowardice; Captain John Morgan, MC, told his students years later of how as an RMO he had to attend executions. His policy, approved by his C.O., was for the regimental officer concerned to give the firing party a judicious dram, march them to the firing line, order the execution, then order them to about turn, and march away at once, to be sent to bed down. "A number had their sentence overturned", he recalled, "but not if things were bad and morale not very good." He told also the story of Joffre, at the time of the Battle of the Aisne, coming upon a prospective firing party. The condemned was a young peasant lad. Joffre stopped, and asked to see him, explained the need for discipline gently and kindly — then ordered the execution to proceed!

Good Hygiene — A Success For The Medical Services
The so often atrocious conditions of the First World War could very easily have resulted in the breakdown of the hygiene of the army. That it did not, was one of the greatest of all the Corps' achievements.

The pre-war preparations laid the foundation for the success. The sanitary courses held at Aldershot ensured that a nucleus of experts existed, to train and supervise the rest of the army. When the Territorial Force came into being, civilian public health specialists were included in the consultation process, and the London Sanitary Companies of the TF RAMC were given the task of training the huge intake of war-time recruits in sanitation and hygiene.

A School of Army Sanitation was also created at Leeds — the northern centre where trainees, both soldiers and medical officers, from the north of England, Scotland, and later Northern Ireland, went when they joined. Specially enlisted personnel with civilian public health experience went to the TF divisions at the beginning of the War. At these schools, model grounds were built to show the recruits the range of urinals, latrines including native squat latrines, disposal pits and grease traps, field incinerators, disinfestors, water carts and waggons, washing and bathing equipment, food stores, and water sterilising equipment. The whole range of Army Health procedures were taught. Anti-fly measures were high on the list.

A sanitary section consisted of 1 officer (Captain or Lieutenant), 2 S/Sgts or Sgts, and 23 rank and file. A sanitary squad had 1 Sgt and 5 other ranks. They wore an "S" in red upon a yellow arm badge (which was unpopular), or, and this was significant, an RMP(police) badge. By 1917, trained sanitary personnel in France had increased to 25,000 officers and men, in 84 sanitary sections. In all theatres of the War, there were 215 sanitary sections.

Sanitation was now a matter of discipline; the responsibility for the health and hygiene of units was firmly that of the regimental officers. This was another major advance since the days of Lord Wolsley. Keogh's foresight had ensured that the health of the soldier would never again be neglected. The empirical figure of 0.3 per cent of strength was accepted as the permissible limit of inefficiency due to sickness in an army in the field, and, as the official hygiene regulations stated, "if this figure rose, the reason was usually some failure in the sanitary system or sanitary measures.... The responsible officer was the Commanding Officer."

He was required by Military Law to carry out the hygiene measures laid down.

Lieutenant Colonel H.K. Allport, RAMC, has a high place in the history of First World War hygiene. He produced the HEALTH MEMORANDA FOR SOLDIERS in 1910. As A.F. B51, it was issued to all men. This was an excellent book — sound, sensible, and above all, realistic. It was something the ordinary soldier could read easily.

Its subjects included personal cleanliness, clothing, hair, teeth, food, drink, smoking, spitting, the barrack room, chastity, service abroad (this meant India), marching, active service.

"WATER, the responsibility of all", had a chapter, and there were good notes on heat exhaustion, malaria, enteric fever, and the other diseases of war.

Some of the advice is dramatic and has continued to be part of the RAMC lecture course throughout the century: "latrines are the factories where the poisons of enteric fever and dysentery are produced (the filthy feet of the faecal feeding fly, as we were all told at Mytchett!)...from early times."...Colonel Allport cited Moses, "an able leader and sanitary officer." This book is so good it could be used today. The only omission would be references to cavalry. There was also a soldier's "small book", which contained advice on personal hygiene, field cooking, and recipes for messes of 60 men.

The great health and hygiene improvements of the War were prophylactic inoculation, purification of water, and disposal of waste.

While the Corps had been taken over by the Territorials and war-time doctors — all the clinical advances, the treatment programmes, the development of field units, the research, were powered by the part-timers who had become whole-timers, the organisation of the hygiene side remained largely the province of the Regular officers. And while Major General W.W.O. Beveridge was Director of Hygiene at the War Office, the outstanding figure was undoubtedly Colonel W.G. Horrocks, later Major General Sir William Horrocks.

The Medical History of the War, (Hygiene of the War, Vol 1), gives in its Appendix B the details of the water purification equipment and its use. The "Horrocks Box", the Standard Water Sterilization Test Case, which we all trained on for so long, appeared in 1915. The prototype for this was devised by Professor G. Sims Woodhead of Cambridge. The principles of water sterilization, however, were advanced and tested by Colonel Horrocks before the War in a notable series of experiments and proving trials. The final one of these had been planned to take place in September 1914; by then the British Army was in action in France.

Water sterilization now comprised four operations — coagulation of suspended matter by alum, filtration through sand, sterilization with chlorine gas or a chlorinating agent, and finally dechlorination to remove the unpleasant chlorine taste.[17]

With the new process went the now routine bacteriological testing of all water supplies.

Water carts were on a scale of 2 per bn or equivalent unit. Tanks and tank lorries carried larger amounts of water. There were also filtration units and filtration barge units. When poison gas began to be used, additional water testing procedures were added.

In Egypt and Palestine the water supply presented local problems. A Medical Advisory Committee of TF experts went out to Egypt and Salonica — and briefly to the Dardanelles. The sweet water canal was the only reliable source of drinking water, but water still had to be purified. A comprehensive water system was set up from late 1915 onwards — new branch canals were dug at Ferdan and Ballah, and 9 water purification points were built along the length of the canal, for troops east: Quarantine, El Shatt, El Kubri, Shallufa, Serapeum, Moascar, El Ferdan, El Ballah and Kantara. Later again, when the Jordan valley was taken, water was pumped by pipe towards the front.

All the above, and the discipline of disposal of excreta and refuse, meant hard work for the sanitary sections. Even during the Retreat from Mons, hygiene measures were never relaxed. When the lines became fixed, clearing ground of liquid and solid excreta was an enormous task, because of the enormous numbers of troops involved, and their concentration. The sanitary side learned that it was wasteful to retain their sections with a division on the move especially rearwards. The practical problem was that very large units passed in series through rear villages. Divisional sanitary sections were thus made extra- divisional troops and put under control of DsMS Armies — in practice, they became Corps troops. They could then remain in an area to clean up, and remain at railheads and in units and large camps behind the line.

RMOs remained responsible for their own unit areas. Some were more enthusiastic than others, and some very enthusiastic indeed. Captain J.W. Waite, RMO of the 14th Bn Royal Hampshire Regiment, was one such. "New latrines in HUNTER'S TRENCH", he wrote in his diary in 1916, "being dug deeper and made a respectable place. New timber framework with trap door in middle for covering refuse pits completely. Pioneers produced excellent large fly-proof pits with portable roof. Later officers' latrine refurbished."

All RMOs recorded in their diaries their very regular sanitation inspections. They chlorinated the water and toured the hygiene areas daily. They also described their own sanitation inspections by the sanitary officer from division, and their C.O.

So efficient did the sanitary service become that at the capture of Vimy Ridge in 1917 when three army corps were massed for the attack, within a week of the successful capture of the Ridge, "it was difficult to believe a number of troops had ever occupied the ground."

Army health includes many things other than water purification and adequate latrines. The AMS made a significant contribution to a wide range of health matters — clothing, and diet being the most important. Physiological demands of clothing in different climates were now recognized, and the doctors' advice sought. The soldier's boots were investigated by Lieutenant Colonel Kenwood, a member of the Army Sanitation Committee, and together with Mr Charles Heath, he suggested improvements. Diet, too, and nutrition, were regularly supervised by medical officers and advice given. All the items of the soldier's health of medical interest were for the first time written into the remit of the RAMC in the 1914–18 Great War. In these, as in so much else, the Corps had not just "arrived" — as had been so 15 years before. The RAMC was now respected and admired as an established part of the British Order of Battle.

Notes and references

CHAPTER 7

[1]By contrast the Germans had ten times as many killed as died from disease: 1,531,048 killed and 155,013 died from disease. They had 4,211,469 wounded. See German Official Medical History of the War, 1920, quoted J R Army Med Corps, Vol XXXIV, 554. The difference could have been attributed to the greater numbers of British troops in tropical and malarial regions.

[2]The "triple vaccine" (typhi, paratyphi A and paratyphi B) was introduced in January 1916. At that time typhoid and paratyphoid B infections were still endemic and relatively common in Britain whereas other forms of enteric were relatively rare. Paratyphoid A was however still endemic in India, Africa, and Turkey, all areas in which British troops might be called upon to serve. Re-inoculation was needed after 18 months to 2 years, as at present. While prevention was now certain, treatment did not change: fluids, jellies while fever was high, careful undisturbed nursing, haemorrhage treated by strict rest and morphine. A new line of treatment was chewing gum for care of the mouth. The British Union for the Abolition of Vivisection was the organization campaigning against anti-typhoid inoculation; amongst other things, they claimed that doctors carrying it out were doing so "on pecuniary grounds." See *BMJ* 1914; **11**: 1074.

See also *Punch*, 13/1/15, containing the advertisement by the British Union for Abolition of Vivisection, and the magazine's reply, 20/1/15.

[3]W.J. Tulloch's paper on meningococcal meningitis, J R Army Med Corps, 1917, Vol XXIX, 66–70, deals with the differentiation of types of meningococci. It was carried out during his service days and relates to a military epidemic. Tulloch regarded this work as a continuation of that of Gordon (of Gordon types I–IV) which was carried out while the latter was also an RAMC officer. See J R Army Med Corps, 1915, Vol XXV, 66–90.

[4]McNee, J.W., Renshaw, A, and Blunt, E.H., J R Army Med Corps, 1916, Vol XXVI, 490. A large number of war-time medical officers became famous in their various branches of the profession: J.W. McNee, Cuthbert Wallace, Gordon Gordon-Taylor, John Fraser (later Sir John Fraser of Edinburgh), Henry Wade (Sir Henry, also of Edinburgh), George Grey Turner, H.S. Souttar, Lord Moynihan (surely the fastest promotion in the history of the RAMC, he entered France as a Major in 1914 and was a Major General by 1917!), A.E. Webb-Johnson, Sir Robert Jones, Hey Groves, T.P.McMurray, orthopaedic surgeons, William Trotter and Sir Geoffrey Jefferson, neurosurgeons, H.D. Gillies, plastic surgeon, and B. Mendleson, dentist, T.J. Mackie and W.J. Tulloch, bacteriologists, Lord Adrian, Adrian Stokes, Sir Henry Dale, physiologists.

[5]Official History of the War. Medical Services — Surgery of the War, 1922, HMSO. This extract should be read and pondered over by every Director of Army Surgery on taking over his post.

[6]Op cit. The "tips for surgeons" covered the whole range of surgical specialties. Many are essential advice for the military surgeon: "Haemorrhage the cause of nearly all deaths in the first 12 hours... peritonitis occurs early in large gut wounds, but not for 6–8 hours in small bowel...if the entry wound is through the buttock, there is very often a dangerous compound fracture of the pelvic bones, and these wounds are especially liable to gas gangrene...site of entry of a missile very often at a distance from the abdominal wall, e.g. shoulder, chest, or buttock...entry wound may be minute — so small thought to be an abrasion, and still cause intestinal tears...intestine may be torn from blast injury even without the peritoneal cavity being opened...small intestine seldom wounded in one place alone...if kidney or spleen injured, colon often wounded also...if pt has a wound on back as well as abdomen, always treat back wound first; to turn pt on his face after an abdominal op results in much collapse", and much more.

[7]Hugh Owen Thomas (1834–1891) came from a family of Welsh bone setters. Sir Robert Jones was his nephew. He could be described as the Father of British orthopaedic surgery and was certainly the founder of the Liverpool School of the specialty. "His greatest contribution was the declaration of surgical principles which will survive long after his splints are forgotten", said Sir Reginald Watson-Jones (Hugh Owen Thomas — a Personal Study, 1934, London, O.U.P.). But it is his splint which the RAMC will always remember him for; with delayed primary suture, its success in reducing mortality of fracture of the femoral shaft was the greatest surgical event of the War. Mortality on the way to the CCS was 60 per cent initially; when the splint was applied at the RAP, it reduced to 20 per cent.

[7]It is of interest too that Thomas went to France in the later years of the nineteenth Century (one of the very few occasions he left Liverpool) to show his leg splint to the French medical service. They showed no interest whatever; it is not only the British who fail to appreciate a good thing when they see it. I am indebted to Mr Arthur J. Espley, senior consultant surgeon in the orthopaedic department in Perth Royal Infirmary, for this information.

[8]J R Army Med Corps, 1920, Vol XXXIV, 64–69. See also Special Report of the Medical Research Committee, Special Report Series,Nos 25, 26 and 27. London, HMSO, 1919–20.

[9]Sir Henry Dale, MD Cambridge 1909, FRS 1914, GBE 1943, OM 1944, joined the Wellcome Research laboratories after working for some years with Paul Ehrlich, and became the dominant figure in British research, especially in physiology and pharmacology.

In 1914 he was appointed director of the department of these subjects in the projected National Institute for Medical research, and during the War he worked on histamine and acetylcholine.

Acetylcholine is the body's most important neurotransmitter — a chemical substance liberated at nerve endings which transmits nerve impulses to muscle or other nerve cells. Histamine is a local hormone present in all body tissues. It increases the calibre and permeability of capillaries and the contraction of smooth muscle including that of blood vessels. Since increased permeability allows fluid to escape out of the blood vascular system ("Where has the blood gone?") and contraction of vessel walls regulates blood pressure, its importance in a condition like wound shock is obvious. See J R Army Med Corps, 1988, 134:138–145.

[10]For the full report of poison gas and its management, see op cit, Medical Services, Vol 2, chapters VII–XVI.

For earliest reports, see letter by J.M. McIntyre, Major RAMC from HQ 11th Army BEF, 2nd May 1915. He quotes April 23rd 1915, when gas first used — "2 kinds noted — heavy yellowish brown, from cylinders, 'believed to be chlorine'; the other, from shells — effects different — less asphyxiating — causes severe dyspnoea and temporary blindness with irritation of conjunctivae". J R Army Med Corps, 1915, Vol XXIV, 302. The first of use of gas was actually on 22nd April 1915. Total casualties were 185,000, with 9,000 fatal. I am indebted to Colonel Bob Joy, USMC, for correction on the first date of use of gas, which was not as stated by Major McIntyre. Also Lieutenants A.W. Hendry and E.C. Horsburgh, clinical description of early cases, ibid, 34 –376.

[11]Mackenzie, Sir J. "The Recruit's Heart", BMJ 1915; 2: 563. Also his "Principles of Diagnosis & Treatment of Heart Affections, Oxford Medical Publications, 1917. And see "The Soldier's Heart and The Effort Syndrome", Sir Thomas Lewis. London, Shaw and Sons, 1918, p 33ff. This book gives a full description and analysis of the war-time syndrome.

[12]"The immediate effect of cigarette smoking on healthy men and on cases of 'soldier's heart'." Parkinson and Koefod, *Lancet* 1917; **11**: 232.

[13]*BMJ* 1903; **1**: 1017.

[14]Elliott, quoted in "150 Years of British Psychiatry, 1841–1991", G.E. Berrios and H. Freeman, editors, London, 1991. See also Captain C.S. Myers, "A Contribution to the Study of Shell Shock." *Lancet* 1915; **1**: 316–320, and Lieutenant Colonel C.S. Myers, MD, ScD, FRS, J R Army Med Corps, 1916; Vol XXVI, 642–655, 782–797, 1561–582. Other useful articles are: "Arrangements for the care of cases of Nervous and Mental Shock coming from overseas", Lieutenant Colonel William Aldren Turner, MD, FRCP, ibid, 1916; Vol XXVII, 619–626; "A method of Treatment of 'Shell Shock'", Captain E.T.C. Milligan, MD, BS, Melbourne, ibid, 1917; Vol XXVIII, 272–273; "War Shock", by MD Elder, reviewed by General Macpherson, ibid, 1917; Vol XXVIII, 727–728; "Shell Shock, Stammering and other Affections of Voice & Speech" (paper at the Medical Society of London, 12/12/16), by Cortland Macmahon, BA, Instructor for speech defects at St Bartholomew's Hospital, ibid, 1917; Vol XIX, 192–201.

By 1915, the printed soldiers' letter forms contained sections relating to health. Lists of words were given, and the soldier had to strike out the items not required e.g.

The flies vile
rations are execrable
weather is much the same

I am suffering from a slight wound (shell
shock)(fright)
 severe
X or state disease: If the whole of this sentence is
struck out, the writer may be presumed to be well
or deceased.

How are the poultry(includes cows)
potatoes
children getting on?

I hope you are well
better
bearing up
not spending too much money
getting on better with mother

X insert here protestations of affection NOT TO
EXCEED TEN WORDS

ever_____(state what ever)

The staff officers who produced these would have profited in a
course in public relations! There is no doubt that in letters from
officers, the aspect of fear was often freely spoken of. A thesis on the
subject by Bruce F.J. Pandrich, submitted in 1988 to the University of
Dundee for the Degree of M Phil, describes the conscious efforts of
troops, soldiers and officers, to keep up morale. There was in addition
the 1914–18 war poetry, which mirrored in very personal ways the
feelings of servicemen. Of the many collections in existence, a 1988
selection is "The War Poets: My subject is War and the Pity of War",
the lives and writings of the 1914–18 War Poets, ed. Robert Gidding,
Great Britain, 1988, Bloomsbury Publishing Ltd.

RMOs were liable to be involved themselves if their unit failed to
carry out an attack or raid and enough men claimed they had shell
shock and would not leave their trenches. One RMO in 1915 was
court-martialled, being charged with failing to maintain morale and in
effect being too lenient with the soldiers. He was severely dealt with,
in spite of being defended strongly by General Sloggett.

[15]Lieutenant Adolphe Abrahams, RAMC, J R Army Med Corps,
1915, Vol XXIV, 471.

[16]Sir F.W. Mott, in his address to the War Neuroses Section at the
BMA meeting in April 1919, said that from his experience the most
serious cases of war neurosis occurred in 1915 and 1916, and that this
was due to the military conditions in those years. He considered the
improvement in 1917 and 1918 was largely due to the new N.Y.D.(N).
centres, (Not yet diagnosed Nervous) and to the special hospitals
where patients were treated before their mental upset became established.

[17]Horrocks decided that the first essential was not the sterilization
of water but rather its efficient filtration. He reasoned that when the
particulate matter was removed, sterilization would be much easier.
After experimenting with a succession of filter substances, he produced
an apparatus in which water was passed through a thick flannelette
wrapped round a perforated tin cylinder, with aluminium hydroxide
precipitated on the flannelette to increase its efficiency.

The next step was to sterilize the water. For this he used chlorine
derived from chloride of lime. Although previous tests by German and
Austrian chemists had not been successful, he used 1 part per million
of chlorine acting for half an hour on clarified water taken from sources
similar to those troops would use in war time. He treated water from

the upper reaches of the Thames, the Regent's Park Canal, and from the Basingstoke Canal in Aldershot. His tests showed that all waters were free from bacteria in 30 minutes, long enough for the water cart to return from the sterilizing point to the unit lines. Sodium Sulphite was used to remove the chlorine taste.

The "Standard Water Sterilization Test Case", contained cups, spoons, a container for the test solution, pipettes, stirrers, all in a partitioned box. This came to be known as the justly famous "Horrock's Box." See Hygiene of the War, op cit, appendix B, p 358.

Chapter 8

1920–1939. The Second World War — Europe and North Africa.

"Am fear nach gleidh na h-airm an àm na sìth, cha bhi iad aige an am a' chogaidgh."

(He that keeps not his arms in time of peace will have none in time of war).

Perspective.
The silent cemeteries of many nations bore evidence of the magnitude of the struggle that had ended. The terrible tiredness which followed the Great War was inevitable, and with this exhaustion and revulsion came active disinterest in all things military.

War exhaustion was soon followed by great financial depression in Europe, with major unemployment and poverty. To the west, financial exhaustion affected the USA also. In the east was the energy of socialism in Soviet Russia, where in spite of war-time losses, industry was said to be flourishing under the new system of Communism.

Communism had destroyed God, kings, princes, priests, and bourgeois culture, and now, its prophets declared, leaders would be elected by popular vote from the working classes and would be loved by all and entirely free from the vices of previous ruling classes. They and their comrades in equality would plan for the good of all men. The victory of Marxism over decadent Western Europe was inevitable.

Defeated Germany took harsh political punishment. The French enjoyed the Armistice meeting in the railway coach at

Compiègne; Sedan was now surely avenged. Few noticed, however, the remark of Erzberger to Marshal Foch that day: "A nation of 70 million suffers, but it does not die."

The foolish abdication of the Kaiser removed the only possible check in the way of a leader of dictatorial powers who might appear. The Versailles political measures, and the subsequent collapse of the currency, were bad enough to ensure that such a person would do so. The rising Nazi Party of the 1930's could point to them as indignities to be removed.

Military penalties of Versailles prohibited Germans from possessing any modern arms or equipment, and they were not allowed a single tank. In the 1920's, German soldiers were taught with wooden guns and dummy weapons. But the absence of arms did not prevent thought. By the end of the decade German military thinkers were already ahead of their French and British counterparts in their concept of armoured warfare; when Hitler called for German rearmament and got it, there was a powerful war strategy already in place. And there is no doubt that the development of the German Armoured Corps owed much to Adolf Hitler himself.[1]

By contrast the British Tank Corps was reduced from 18 battalions to a mere 4, and there was considerable pressure from backward-looking elements to get rid of it entirely. It lived in constant threat of disbandment until it received the Royal seal of approval on 18th October, 1923, when it became the Royal Tank Corps. It was fortunate that King George V had taken a keen interest in tanks since their inception and had more faith in the new arm than most of his generals.

As ever, Western politicians chose to ignore the increasing power and dedication of Nazi Germany. The three mediocrities of Mr Ramsay McDonald, the first British Labour Prime Minister, who had condemned Britain's entry into the 1914–18 War, and concentrated his foreign policy on the elimination of armaments; the Conservative Mr Stanley Baldwin, powerful in his 14 years of office, yet with no interest in the Continent of Europe; and "Good Old Neville" Chamberlain, were all passionately anti-war.

Adolf Hitler was the reverse. As early as 1930, he declared openly that once a National Socialist Government had been formed, he and his "Strassenkämper" (street fighters) would "tear the covenants signed at Versailles into shreds." Then they would rearm. 1918 would be avenged.[2]

One of the few men in Great Britain who saw the danger was Mr Winston Churchill. But his uncomfortable warnings were ignored. Even less excusable was the campaign to discredit and scorn his views, keep him out of office, and deny him space in the press. A particular enemy was Mr Geoffrey Dawson, editor of *The Times*. But others in the press supported him warmly, and called for his return to a place in government.[3]

Peace, financial recession, and appeasement towards the re-emergence of Germany again intent on domination — this was the background to the Second World War. In the Far East, Japan was making war on China.

Dispersal and Despair 1920–1935; Hurried Retrieval 1936–1939.
The RAMC had its 21st birthday in 1919. In July 1914 the still new Corps had 3,168 officers and 13,331 other ranks, Reserve and Regular, on its books. By 1919 it had 14,000 officers and 132,000 other ranks with no distinction between Regular and Reserve. It exceeded in numbers the original BEF.

In 1914 the AMS had 2000 patients in its hospitals; in 1919 it attended 577,000, and as early as July 1916 had admitted 48,000 patients to hospital in a single week. Instructors in "mass cas(casualty) management" of forty years later were surprisingly often ignorant of these facts.

Besides Martin-Leake and Chavasse there were six other V.C.s — H.S. Ranken, G.A. Maling, J.L. Green, W.S. Allen MC, H. Ackroyd MC, and J. Fox-Russell MC, not to mention a multitude of other decorations of all sorts.[4] These were added to Martin-Leake and H.E.M. Douglas, E.T.Inkson, and T.J. Crean, V.C.s of the Boer War.

Smooth casualty evacuation, delayed primary suture, Thomas splinting of limb fractures, flexible FSTs, lady anaesthetists, patho-physiology of wound shock, recognition of battle neuroses, were all innovations for the future. But perhaps the greatest of all advances was in Army Hygiene — the control of infectious disease by preventive measures. As one example, noted but worth repeating, there were 273 cases of tetanus associated with wounds between August and December 1914 on the Western Front, 12 cases in 1917, and 7 in 1918. Director General Goodwin wrote in 1919 that the War would have ended in six weeks if either side had relaxed its preventive hygiene measures. The Royal Army Medical Corps had reached manhood indeed.

On 8th June, 1920, a special commemorative dinner was held in London, chaired by the Rt Hon. the Earl of Midleton, K.P., deputising for the Marquess of Lansdowne. Lord Midleton was a good choice; he had begun reform of the Medical Reserves before Haldane. Toasts by Rt Hon. Winston Churchill and F.M. Earl Haig were made, the former praising Keogh in the eloquence only he could utter. Haig praised Generals Burtchaell and Sloggett.

Of the many words spoken on this occasion two quotations will suffice. General Keogh, the DGAMS of the Great War, told his audience that the Medical Services "had entered upon all campaigns in fear and trembling on account of the want of sympathy which existed in all previous wars", but "from the beginning of this campaign we saw that things had changed." He spoke frankly of the difficulties the Medical Corps had had with the War Office in earlier times. His words deserve comparison with the sadder evidence of his predecessor Jameson to the Royal Commission in 1901. Keogh's successor General Goodwin saw new understanding with the "Big Army" and "the vital need for ensuring the co-operation of the civilian medical profession." Time would tell how true those confident opinions would remain.

The years following this high point can be passed briefly. They marked the lowest point of the Corps' fortunes until the last years of the 20th century, when financial difficulties and political mediocrity once more coincided. The trends of those years illustrate well the attitudes of the political and populist mind which so constantly recur.

Treasury attention was first focussed on the fact that the ratio of medical personnel to the Army as a whole was much higher than it had been pre-war. This was an early reason for demanded reductions. The Treasury advisers did not understand that higher technical requirements and increased specialisation — the result of medical progress — both demanded this higher ratio.

Perhaps the worst thing about the various reductions in AMS manpower was their very uncertainty. Although General Goodwin in 1921 pursued a strong line of argument and consistency of proposal as his S.G.(Surgeon General) successor had to do 75 years later, he found himself constantly having to face what the *Official History* called "the most anxious and intractable problems."[5] Reduced numbers and repeated uncertainty meant disaffection, early retirement, and resulting increased workload for those remaining. Standards fell; even the paper on which précis for the Senior Course at Millbank was printed became as poor as lavatory paper. Eventually courses were cancelled and training accreditation lost, because no candidates came forward. From the early 1920s, the British Medical Association took an ever-increasing part in negotiating with the War Office on conditions in the RAMC. In 1924, after four years of argument, no progress was made. In 1925, the Warren-Fisher Committee was set up to look into the rising discontent among Defence Medical Services medical officers, most acute in the Army. In June of that year, Sir William Leishman, the DGAMS, reported that the state of the Corps was such that it was incompatible with military efficiency. At the same time, the BMA informed the War Office that it could no longer encourage doctors to join the RAMC nor agree to publish terms and conditions of service in the Journal until matters had been satisfactorily improved. Leishman's death in 1926 while in post as D.G. removed the last Director of world status the RAMC would have. Before his death, reductions to 982 officers and 4,279 other ranks were made by government.

Next, medical field units were abolished "because they would only be used on mobilization." How Regulars were to be trained for operations in the field was unclear. Although field units — ambulances, CCSs, and general hospitals — remained on the establishment of the TA, the Medical TA itself "endured a series of misfortunes so disruptive that as an effective force it simply did not exist at the time (the later 1930s) when its enlargement had become imperative."[5] By the late 1920s it had shrunk to 14 Fd Ambs, 1 cavalry Fd Ambs, 3 hospitals of cadre size only, and 4 hygiene coys. 1 field ambulance was considered sufficient, the government assured the AMD, to serve 1 division! And even in 1938, after two years of negotiation and increase of the TA hospitals to 29 on a Keogh-like pattern, the Minister of Health demanded, and obtained, a reduction. Beds were needed for possible civilian air raid casualties. It was apparently impossible to have beds for both civilians and soldiers. As the *Official History* again stated: "Much had already been accomplished towards the raising of these hospitals, including the appointment of officers and personnel, that could not be discarded without causing resentment and a sense of injustice among those affected. This, with the impression of vacillation on the part of higher authority, was not calculated to stimulate recruiting, nor to assist in co-operation with the medical profession in time of war."[6]

General Sir Alfred Keogh died on 30th July, 1936. He had all his records destroyed on his death, as he did not wish the outspoken comments he had made to Lord Kitchener in 1914 about the Medical Services, and some of his other opinions, to be made public. When Lady Keogh presented his banner to the College she told her audience: "Just before he died, he said: 'I loved the soldier — he is the best fellow in the world and I have done my best for him.'"

Over these inter-war years, the British Medical Association worked hard to resist the reductions, and the RAMC must be forever in its debt for the improvements in conditions and pay the BMA was able to win not only for them, but for the RN and RAF Medical Branches. It was largely due to its efforts that the TA hospitals were increased in number.[7] The Warren-Fisher Committee (in fact, a second committee) did not finally report until July 1933, when positive improvements were approved.

A few advances were made, however, outwith the Corps. In 1909 the first research was done into the nutritional requirements of the infantryman. Immediately after the 1914–18 War this was followed up by research into the energy expenditure of the soldier by Professor Cathcart in Glasgow. He had two Captains RAMC in his physiology department to help, D.T. Richardson and W. Campbell. Also, work on beri-beri and scurvy was done by Professor Starling (who became a Lieutenant Colonel and worked in the RAM College Hygiene laboratory).

Cooking and serving of soldiers' food was examined; in the early 1920's the first Inspector of Army Catering was appointed — Major R.G. Leggatt, a former RAMC officer.

The Pathology Directorate was founded in 1919 — the first Director was Sir William Leishman. Over the 1930's he superintended research on dysentery bacilli and the Salmonella group in India.

The threat of war was, as it will always be, the only real spur to increase in the provision of Army Medical Services. Once there was a realisation on the part of government and population that expansion could no longer be refused, a number of important innovations were made — in-trade training for RAMC soldiers,[8] specialist requirement for Regular officers, the acceptance of female MOs, anti-gas research and development, the study of lessons of the Spanish Civil War — especially relating to aerial bombardment and the use of plaster of paris for limb wounds. Medical cover for the entirely new Anti- Aircraft Command was set up.

Boyce Barracks, built in 1937 as a hutted camp for militia of the RASC, were named after General Boyce of that Corps. They became too small for the Service Corps on the outbreak of war, so they vacated them. Meanwhile the RAMC barracks at Haig Lines Crookham became too small for the RAMC, so they subsequently moved in. The RAMC thus acquired some extra real estate.

In 1936 a book "Organisation, Strategy and Tactics of the Army Medical Services in War" was written by Lieutenant Colonel T.B. Nicholls, M.B., with the commendation of the then D.G. It was *not* an official War Office publication !

This unusual book covered the entire range of AMS work — administrative matters, equipment scales, manpower establishments. It covered all field units from RAP to Base Depot of Medical Stores. It detailed all army forms referable to the Medical Services, estimates of casualties, field medical records (AF 3118 and its envelope AF 3118A; I.1220 case cards for hospitals, and so on), tables of vehicles, medical store requirements for resupply. It even included road space and load tables for field ambulances. Calculation of carrying time for evacuation was given by "G.W. Macpherson's Formula."[9] It must be unique in the history of Corps Training literature.

3rd September, 1939.

It looked like 1914 all over again. The twenty years of peace were as if they had not been. The B.E.F. was back in France. In some infantry divisions there was an unspoken suggestion that the sons now took up the war from where their fathers had laid it down. The January of 1940 was as the January of 1917. The frost was iron-hard round Le Havre as it had been iron-hard round Abbéville in 1917. Then came the thaw with mud and mist, bringing back further memories. The mademoiselles of yesterday were now the madames of today. A medical officer looking for billets for his unit near Doudainville opened an old door and read on the wall facing: "WIPE YOUR FEET PLEASE 1918."

The medical support followed the same lines. The panniers, the drugs, the tentage, the splints, the bandages, were all the same. But there was one new type of drug. It was called sulphonamide, and it had already been used to treat infections, from pneumonia to gonorrhoea.

The BEF was to follow the same pattern as before, too. It was to consist of two corps, with corps and army troops and LofC units. The Regular element was to provide in support RMOs for the teeth arm units — the combatant units — medical staff officers and clerical personnel for the medical branch of the staff of GHQ and the formations composing the BEF, two corps, five divisions, one LofC area, two LofC sub-areas, two base sub-areas and one medical base sub-area. It was also to provide 64 field medical units: 14 Fd Ambs, 10 Fd hygiene secs, 5 MACs, 7 CCSs, 13 BGHs, 3 convalescent depots, 6 amb trains, 3 mobile laboratories, and 3 medical stores depots.

These were put together from the RAMC companies scattered throughout the United Kingdom, from Shorncliffe and Netley on the south coast, the Royal Herbert at Woolwich, to York, Newcastle and Edinburgh in the north. Once again, the entire Regular element was cleared out; many units were made up to strength with Territorial soldiers.

Mobilization of the TA itself was subject to one or two different conditions from its Regular counterpart. The part converted into support for the new Anti-Aircraft Command was mobilized early, in June 1939. So this part of the TA was already functioning before the outbreak of war. Coastal defence was also supported medically by TA. But the field units were in a much higher state of readiness than the Regular ones; they had been training for many months in their home territories. The combatant element of the TA was not due to depart overseas earlier than 3 to 4 months after initial mobilization; its RMOs and Fd Ambs trained with their brigades and divisions so got to know one another. General hospitals opened, but there was certainly not the same scale of generous reserve support there had been in 1914. CCSs also mobilized, as did hygiene sections. And just as in 1914, it was not long before consultant staff were given individual postings to the hospitals theoretically staffed by Regulars. The regular staff had not the clinical capability of their civilian colleagues;[10] in this respect again history repeated itself.

The *Official History* described "confusion upon mobilization", especially where doctors with no TA training suddenly appeared in large numbers, and where these same doctors had to take over medical establishments empty of Regular staff or do many entrance medical examinations for the recruits flocking to join up. But this was the inevitable result of the longstanding shortage of funding, of history repeating itself; as the *Official History* again stated "there could be no alternative while the AMS remained at a strength which provided but little margin between field force requirements and total home establishments."[11]

Soldiers came in by different routes. Gordon Craik had been a bus conductor in Dundee but decided to join the Regular RAMC — on 12th December 1936 he had become 7263500 Pte Craik, G, at Crookham. The Depot was then in wooden huts, built 20 years before.

There were then 3 companies at Crookham. 'A' Company was for men returning from abroad and held the band and the buglers. Men returned from the world-wide stations: India, but also Kenya, Transjordan, Hong Kong and Singapore.

Recruit Craik was in C Coy, nearest the main road. Uniform was the service dress of 1918, RAMC collar dogs, box pleats and puttees, with a swagger cane when walking out, and a white buckskin leather belt. The armlet with the Red Cross was not worn. Webbing was of the same vintage; the ammunition pouches of the infantryman were replaced by the plain straps of the medical orderly.

The peaked cap was also the 1918 pattern. "Headdress was seldom removed", Craik remembered — "only for church and going to bed...oh, and in the dining hall. The officer asked for complaints but he walked round so fast he was gone before you'd time to make any."

Basic training took six months — 3 of "soldiering" — drill, P.T., shooting, education. Pte Craik recalled the realistic training of the gas chamber. This was followed by 3 months of basic medical training, which he thought was "useless because it was nothing like reality." After one year of satisfactory service and after passing the exams, the basic trade of N.O.3 — nursing orderly class 3 — was awarded. In 1937 they had one field ambulance type training day, with casualty collection, "but no others."

Officers were dimly remembered. Major Tweedy was in charge of the drill square; Major King was his O.C. He could not recall the Colonel apart from seeing him riding on a horse !

He remembered mobilization clearly. He was recalled from a detachment of a sergeant and several other RAMC soldiers working at Porton Barracks, Brighton. The Fd Amb he joined at the Royal Herbert Hospital Woolwich was a newly-created one, from 12 Coy RAMC and numbered No 3. "There was no such thing as a field ambulance in the Regular RAMC — only the TA had them, and they knew how they worked. We knew nothing. We had only one spell of serious training for war — that was in May 1939, at Tweseldown Camp Race Course, where we set up an ADS. And the officers didn't help. They were still in the olden days."

They sailed over the Channel in heavy rain, after leaving Southampton on Sunday 17th September. In 3 Bde were the King's Shropshire Light Infantry, the Duke of Wellington's Regiment, and the Sherwood Foresters. They were part of I Div, commanded by Major General The Hon. H.L. Alexander. Landing at Dieppe, where all their transport had gone separately, they had only a bus to transport the officers and 3 furniture vans to take the soldiers. "The numbers were made up by reservists", Pte Craik recalled, "but mainly by Territorials who knew something about it. Our first location was Mons-en-Pavele, near Douai and Lille, in the B.E.F. sector."

Mr Ken Lewison, from the other end of the country, was a TA soldier. He had been articled to an accountant in Swindon in 1935, and joined the Wiltshire Yeomanry, TA "It was a social club." When the unit moved to Devizes for training, he joined the local Fd Amb — the 145 North Wiltshire Fd Amb, (in fact called 145 South Midland) because he had done a first-aid course with the St John Ambulance. "But when I was interviewed, the C.O. said we needed a clerk. So as I did accountancy, I became a clerk."

"The NO3 (Nursing orderly class 3) training was boring — I'd done it with St John. But the field training was excellent —

realistic, with mock bomb attacks and that sort of thing." Camouflage of the unit from aircraft was practised. But at Annual Camp there was plenty of free time given for sport and recreation; TA C.O.s were well aware that for many of their soldiers Camp was the only holiday they had and planned accordingly.

7283199 Pte Lewison was embodied, with the whole of his Fd Amb, on 1st August, 1939. They went at once to Salisbury, for a month of training. Now a Corporal, he was posted to Boyce Barracks on 23rd December. Boyce Barracks was full of intakes, of soldiers from all over including India and the Middle East, and of young officers, "newly joined direct from civvy life."

Then Cpl Lewison was taken out of his unit and sent to France as part of a reinforcement draft. They arrived at St Pol, where they joined a field hospital. "We had 2 officers and 3 ORS (other ranks), 5 ambulance cars and a 10 tonner converted into a sort of operating theatre. Captain "G", a Regular, was an alcoholic dead beat, and supposed to be a surgeon, but Lieutenant Adam, an Edinburgh graduate, was 28 and a very good doctor. He had done only 6 weeks at Boyce Barracks. The radiologist was a Major Blair and he got me to help him with the officers' mess account!"

Lieutenant Colonel J.R. McDonald, MC, TD, came in another way — with his whole unit. He was from Durham, had served as a regimental officer in the 11th Bn The Border Regiment, of 97 Bde, in the earlier War, been wounded at Passchendale, and awarded the MC in 1918. He had then completed his medical studies, and been a keen Territorial. He had raised his unit, No 8 CCS, at Chester-le-Street, and was proud that "We were the first Territorial unit to go to France. We were attached to I Corps — all Regulars." Territorials always wanted to show themselves well in the eyes of the Regulars. 9 CCS, the other high quality TA medical unit, went to 2 Corps.

From North England, too, came 151 (Sunderland) Fd Amb. It had been formed as a "light" Fd Amb in 1937, when the government began to resurrect the Territorial Army. It was "light" because it had more transport than a "heavy" one, and so could move more easily. R.S.M. Richardson and Jack Menham, both Geordies from Newcastle, came from 149 (Newcastle) Fd Amb. Then came the hold-up already referred to, from government indecisions. A nucleus was formed, but "We were not allowed to recruit till March 1939 when other new TA units were being re-formed and conscription introduced. 151 was recruited in *one week* at Hutton Drill Hall, Newcastle."

Jack Menham, now S/Sgt, told the mobilization story: "On 2 Aug 1939 telegram coded 'Hastings' arrived. R.S.M. Richardson 'phoned the C.O., & 2I.C. — Bob Forsyth. The C.O. was Major Swindale — he had been a brigadier in Signals in WW1. We mobilized. Then on 23/8/39 all leave was cancelled but members could still live at home. Soldiers were officially warned against writing to Ireland. At 1920hrs on 24/8 telegram 'Plummer' called out the Main Party — S/Sgt Menham, (me), L/Sgts Scott & Trotter, A/L/Cpl Robinson, Ptes Armstrong, Bennett, Collin, Compton, Hamble, & the C.O., 2I.C., Adjt & Q.M. Lieutenant Williams. We did a lot of anti-gas training — the C.O. had been in WW1." The mobilization of 151 was better organized than that of the next down the line: Ronald Hunt, orderly room clerk of 152 — so posted because he had done a course in Pitman's shorthand — had to drive around Dundee delivering call-up papers in his motor car !

Captain John Matheson had joined the TA in 1936 after being in Edinburgh University O.T.C. His unit was 11/2 Scottish General Hospital. "We did no RAMC training as such", he said. "we never went to Millbank, for example. The main work was training medical orderlies and I gave many Red Cross lectures. I went to Netley in 1938 and was impressed by the quality of the RAMC N.O.1 Sergeants. I was impressed as well by the pyramid of authority — everything was so orderly."

"In May 1939 — sudden expansion to 1200 beds and we became 23rd Scottish General. A radiotherapy consultant from Glasgow came to take over as C.O. and was promoted full Colonel. I sat a promotion exam Capt to Major at Edinburgh Castle, then had a field exam. We read the Field Surgery Pocket Book. Oh, and then there was a book by a man called T.B. Nicholson.... No nursing sisters appeared till we mobilized — the Matron had to make them join the TA — 80 came from hospitals throughout Scotland...Miss Laing had been decorated in the First War...." From Major Matheson's account, there is no doubt that the mobilization system which General Keogh had set up 25 years before was superior.

From Ireland came Martin Fallon. Persecuted as a little boy during the First War because his father was in the Royal Irish Constabulary, his family had actually left to live in the north of England, but had returned. Now a medical graduate of Trinity and with his FRCS, and with one brother a Regular officer, he went to Belfast to enlist. He was turned down because sugar was found in his urine. Angry and baffled, he went back to Dublin and after special tests found he had a congenital complaint which produced this, renal glycosuria, but which did not prevent him from serving. So back he went, was accepted, and found himself at the RAMC Training Centre in Leeds.

10th May, 1940. The Battle of France.
The first winter was called "The Phoney War", because nothing happened beyond some First War type patrolling. There were the usual training exercises. Casualties arose from accidents. It was not till early December that the BEF suffered its first deaths from enemy action, and 3 Fd Amb, Pte Craik's section, was involved. "I remember it well", he said in 1993. "The King had visited on December 8th. Next day the KSLI put out a recce — orders were not to open fire unless the French did — we were under command of the French, you see — the CSM did not know this. They let off. All the others then did. There was deep snow. A L/Cpl was brought in dead and several wounded to our MDS we had just set up. This was the night of 8/12/39."

Gordon Craik was not issued with the new battledress till late November 1939. "We got a second issue which was impregnated with some stuff that smelled like lime — it was supposed to be an antidote to mustard gas. The men washed it to get rid of the smell."

It was the Norwegian Campaign in April which preceded the major German attack. RAMC units went and returned with the task Force sent to Norway. 23 Scottish GH, now in Peebles, had to prepare to receive returned wounded. "It made me realise this was the start", said Major Matheson.[12]

Yet from mobilization day the AMS had put in place a worthwhile support for the 1939 BEF. Over the cold winter and cold spring they had thought hard about what needed to be done. The question of wound infection was a high priority. A Medical Society was formed in the Dieppe area, and Colonel L. Colebrook, now promoted to the necessary level in the Army to be listened to by senior officers, spoke of the streptococcal infections of the earlier war, referred to the joint work of the Medical Research Council (M.R.C.) and the RAMC, and the hopes for the new drug sulphanilamide and its even newer first cousin sulphapyridine (M&B 693).[13] He pointed out — and this view was repeated by Sir Max Page — that the technique of wound excision discovered in the Great War was still essential. Colebrook made the historic comments, when he spoke to the RAMC officers in late 1939 at Dieppe: "It may well be that by their early administration (sulphonamides and drugs given systemically for infection) soon after a man is wounded, it may be possible to prevent many of these infections from developing, or, failing complete success in that, may render them non-invasive, and therefore much less dangerous to life. The war is likely to give us a far better chance of finding out what is possible in that direction than we should have in many years of peace.... Sir Edward Mellanby recently remarked that if such a preventive method of these chemotherapeutic agents could be clearly demonstrated, it would be almost a more important happening than the war itself."

There had of course been other advances since 1920. Major General Priest, Consultant Physician to the BEF, spoke at the Dieppe Medical Society of the electrocardiograph, X-Rays, test meals, the gastroscope, and chemical testing of the stools for occult blood — all for the new disease of duodenal ulcer. Civilians who thought men with diabetes could now serve if they used insulin were quietly warned of the error of their idea. This capable and experienced Regular physician warned his audience of the "New RAMC" of dysentery, trench fever, relapsing fever, and typhus — the "old diseases" of war.

Army Health units were set up and working. Being Regular ones, their numbers were low — No 1 Advanced Depot of Medical Stores (Major Martin), No 1 Mobile Laboratory (Major Francis), No 1 Mobile Hygiene Laboratory (Major Berry).

During the quiet months the Fd Ambs held, at their MDSs, all uncomplicated and V.D. cases. An outbreak of scabies brought in 280 patients, which were sent to No 8 CCS as the Fd Ambs were too full to keep them.

General sanitation would become more of a problem for the BEF than was realised. A serious weakness in the training of

TA units was failure to practise it and its detailed application. Hygiene was a major element of Service medical care where the Regulars were invariably superior. Many RMOs had no field experience. The *Official History* put it bluntly: "It has to be recorded that one cause, and by no means a minor one, of the low sanitary standards was the ignorance or indifference of officers commanding units."[14]

There were dental colleagues, too, working alongside, But because the Dental Corps had only 32 Army dentists with the BEF of 158,000 men instead of the recommended ratio of one to 1500 men, many suffering with dental diseases went untreated. It was not only the doctors whose numbers had been dangerously cut by the politicians prior to the War.

Trained nurses were in the same position. When the War began, the Matron-in-Chief, Miss Roy, had only 700 Regular nursing sisters. As with the men, the numbers were quickly made up by call-out of reservists and mobilization of the TANS. As with the men, they all merged into the QAIMNS, and well over 1000 would later be evacuated via Dunkirk.

The medicals were as always in the hands of the Generals who commanded generally. After the long-awaited German attack of 10th May, 1940 began, the Battle of France was over in six weeks. Years of pretence and appeasement had softened the French as well as the British. The French, claiming as in 1914 to be the experts in war, were found out by the speed and novelty of the German offensive.

The Allies had 3,142 tanks and the Germans 2,580. But the Allied armoured vehicles were spread out uniformly along the front; the Germans were concentrated against the French 9th Army which Lieutenant-General Sir Alan Brooke, the G.O.C. 2 Br Corps, had found distinctly unimpressive when he visited. The crossing of the Ardennes by armoured formations was regarded as an impossibility — Captain Liddell Hart had said it was feasible before the War, but his suggestion had been dismissed as "an excitable imagination."

OPERATION SICKLE, as the German attack was codenamed, did just that on 10th May 1940; the French High Command was utterly bewildered when the full impact of the crossing of the Meuse became clear on 14th May, three short days later. The massive air attacks by conventional bombers and the

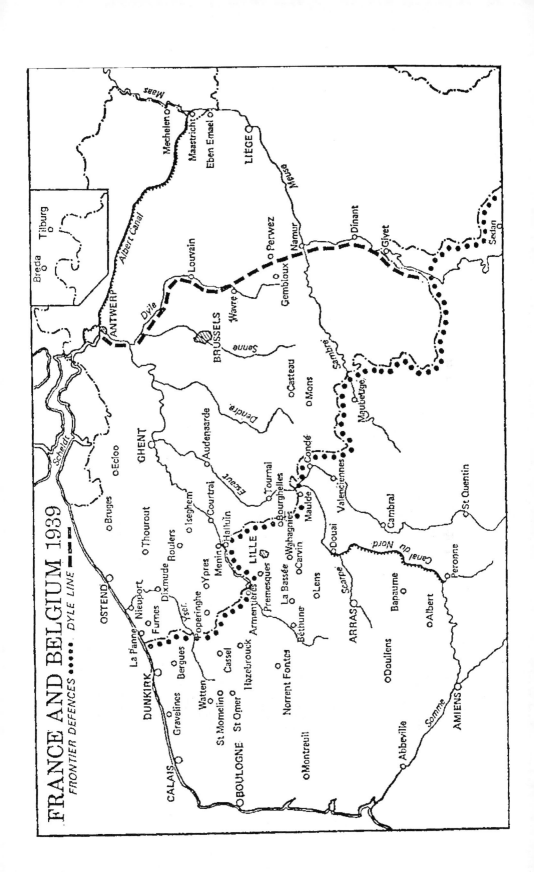

FRANCE AND BELGIUM 1939
FRONTIER DEFENCES •••• DYLE LINE ▬▬▬

new terror weapon, the dive bomber, destroyed French weapons and French morale. Major General Erwin Rommel took personal command of the 7th Grenadier Regiment at the German bridgehead over the Meuse at Dinant. On 16th May Churchill met the French War Cabinet at the Quai d'Orsay and found them completed dejected. General Ismay, who accompanied him, remembered saying to himself that the French were beaten already.[15] By 20th May the German 2nd Panzer Division reached the mouth of the Seine.

The collapse of Belgian resistance was even more swift. On 10th May an assault group of German gliders landed at 0530hrs on the roof of the neutral Belgium fortress of Eben Emael, in a new way of waging war. The fortress fell at 1200hrs the next day; the Belgium commander committed suicide. It was a brilliant exploit.

The BEF had initially been deployed along part of the Belgian frontier with a French Army north and another south. The British area extended roughly from Lille in the north to Douai in the south. 1 Br Corps was on the right, 2 Br Corps was on the left. Plans D and E, referring to the rivers Dyle and Escaut, tributaries of the Scheldt and where the British were to advance, would be initiated as soon as the Germans invaded Belgium.

On May 25th the enemy pressure on the Belgian front had increased to such proportions that the British, who had advanced into Belgium when the attack commenced, moved to try to close the gap through which the Germans had advanced to the sea. But the Belgian Armistice left a 20 mile(32Km) gap which could not be closed. On May 27th King Leopold of the Belgians asked the Nazis for an Armistice; he did not match his great father Albert for bravery.

One other strategic surprise occurred, this time a negative one by the otherwise immaculate German High Command: on 24th May Hitler himself countermanded the order of General von Brauchitsch to advance on Dunkirk. The attack was not resumed till the 26th, and allowed the fighting withdrawal to the Dunkirk beaches.[16]

The Medical units followed their teeth arm formations during the retreat. Lieutenant Colonel McDonald of 8 CCS wrote in his personal diary: "Sunday 12/5/40. Rouvroy. The ordinary calendar is out of date, as are all events prior to

Friday…. I imagine W.S.C. gritting his teeth at No 10 Downing Street…I cannot help feeling annoyed that Britain did not tackle the situation more seriously in the early days. I heard the Queen of Holland on the radio…the Dutch have flooded their land…." For neutral Holland had also been invaded. As Warsaw had been destroyed by the Luftwaffe, now had Rotterdam, and soon it would be London's turn. Those angry persons who would later repeatedly instance the bombing of Dresden by the Allies were curiously unaware of these events of the Second World War where the pattern of destroying an open city was set by the Nazis.

For the BEF the force and speed of the German advance destroyed all hope of containment. Pte Gordon Craik heard the guns begin to fire at 0500 hrs on the 10th. His 3 Bde had been dug in but now moved to Louvain, and their Fd Ambs went with them. "But they had to clear out as soon as they arrived", said Craik. "The Germans broke through on the 12th and from then, it was a highly disorganized withdrawal." He had been sent to an Ordnance Recovery Section as their medical orderly, a unit of about 40 in all, and went back with them to Dunkirk. "We went back every way we could. I arrived at the Mole at Dunkirk on the 25th. I went to the fish dock to help with wounded. We drew lots for getting away. No 3 Fd Ambs retreated with their Bde — I never came across them till I got back to Leeds."

"I never saw the ADMS, let alone the DDMS", said Pte Craik. But Colonel C.M. Finny, his ADMS, was certainly there, and his experiences during this so-short war were fraught with anxiety and fear. He travelled night and day, visiting his Fd Ambs, going ahead to recce sites for MDSs and ADSs for them, begging for transport for RAMC personnel, avoiding German bombers. His concern was constantly for his medical units and for the casualties they were passing back:

"May 14th. Last night the enemy began to attack… the cavalry withdrew and the bridges were blown up… the country seems to be a mass of spies. Among other activities they indicate the position of bde or bn HQs by whitewashing their houses in a special way, or by ploughing arrows in the ground, not easily seen from the ground, but obvious from the air…I was visiting the HQ of an Infantry Brigade when a message came in to say the enemy had broken through… it turned out to be untrue, but I could not risk the chance of the ADS being left without transport at a time when a quick get-away might be called for.

I visited the O.C.s of all three Fd Ambs, who were in the Savanthem area, explained the position and gave instructions for the hour of withdrawal of ADSs and the locations to which the units are to proceed. The main bodies of the Fd Ambs were to move as soon as possible, so as to leave the roads as clear as possible for the fighting troops." Colonel Finny had a clear grasp of the needs of the teeth arms. But he did not forget things like the need for baths for the troops: "Advantage has been taken of a lull in our movements to get the men a bath. The Mobile Bath unit started to function in Bodues, and also sent forward sets of sprays in Roubaix and Toueriong, near enough to the fighting line for the men to walk and have a bath when opportunity offers."

He went with his division on the inevitable road to Dunkirk, never losing sight of the priorities and needs of those his Corps was there to serve. Like all doctors — at least almost all — he kept his sense of humour: "The sea at La Panne is a sort of military Harley Street." And he never lost sight of his responsibility: "I then returned to my Fd Ambs. Z had already left, but I gave orders for the transference of such patients as remained in X and Y to the Casino, and for the rear parties to be detailed — by drawing lots if necessary — except that C.O.s were forbidden to remain…they were ordered as soon as this was completed to send all available ambulances and drivers to join the MAC behind the Casino, and to march to Dunkirk… as disposition of motor ambs had been made, and all Fd Ambs less rear parties had left, there appeared to be no object in remaining. I therefore disposed of my kit, drove to the report centre and had my car put out of action. After a somewhat tedious journey along the soft sand to Bray Dunes, a jetty of small planks led to some small boats."….[17]

Colonel Finny returned to England in a destroyer. Cpl Lewison, who like Pte Craik had got lost from his unit, drove in a truck with an officer and others, dive-bombed all the way. "I was evacuated on the 2nd day of the evacuation. Walked along a causeway to the sea…got on a small yacht — 12 all told — and ferried back to Dover. Harry Bates owned and sailed the yacht. His wife was a QA (nursing sister). He was a London stockbroker."

Not all the medical units were passing casualties back. Some were treating them to the highest degree of care possible; these were the CCSs.[18]

The story of No 8 CCS in retreat is perhaps the best to tell for this time of defeat in the Corps' history. The Clearing Station was the largest RAMC unit to undertake definitive surgery during the Battle of France in 1940; the battle was over before casualties could go any farther.

On March 16th, 1940, 8 CCS was attached to 1 Corps and relieved No 2 CCS at Rouvroy. Later, it was linked with Nos 1 and 7 CCSs.

From 16th March till 10th May, No 8 received all sick from 1 Br Corps. They were set up in a good site, in a church hall, beside a trotting track for horses. In these 8 weeks, they had *no* battle casualties. But they had had 3000 admissions — acute cases as in a civil hospital. Evacuation to the rear was by a daily ambulance train.

Colonel Dawson, DDMS 1 Corps, visited 8 CCS regularly, as did Major General Scott, the DMS. Lieut-General Sir Alan Brooke also inspected. The C.O. liked General Scott, and another DDMS, Colonel Hood.[19] The role of No 8 CCS in Plan D had been carefully studied and preparations made. It was to advance into Belgium with 1 Corps to Ninove, 10 miles(16Km) east of Brussels.

No 8 CCS was supplemented by an FST from 7 CCS at the start of the real war. But on May 15th their FST was transferred to 1 CCS — "Cox, Hammond, Sister Ward, and 2 men." Colonel McDonald's own diary and the unit war diary together told a medical account of the retreat to the sea:

"23/5 WORMHOUDT PREVENTORIUM, 8 miles (13km) S of Dunkirk.[20]

The events of the last few days will, I suppose, be writ large upon the pages of history. These last few days have been the most hectic in my life. It is a fairly unique experience to be in command of a hospital unit during a rout — for this is no orderly retreat. Only those of us who have been through it can appreciate that this is the worst vicissitude of war."

He spoke with sorrow of their French Liaison Officer — who was such a gentleman — and of his dismay at the failure of the French Army, especially of the troops opposite the Ardennes mountains who had mutinied. He spoke of the lack of insight of some of the nursing sisters of his own unit, of the increasing realisation of the others of how bad things were, of the stopping of the Postal Service, of their feelings towards the French ("It's funny how we dislike the French, even though we're sorry for them").

And being a First War officer, he mused, on May 27th:

"Casino, Bray Dunes: Extraordinary fact that I am now revisiting Bray Dunes. It was the rest area for the British troops in the Nieuport section of the front…(Major Glyn Hughes was on the very ground he had been on in 1916–18. "All our scraps were over the ground I knew inside out from the last contest…my ADS at Vimy was actually at the exact spot where I was in trenches then, and all the Belgian bit I'd been in for ages.") It is obvious that, unless the tide turns very soon, we as an army are finished. There is no doubt that we underestimated the power of armoured divisions and an overwhelming air force. We have seen a lot of the latter… perhaps the aeroplanes do not effect much material destruction or cause casualties, but they do have an intense demoralising effect. To be dive-bombed, as we were on the road today, is the nearest approach to the tortures of Hell that I have ever known.

The tale of WORMHOUDT is one of stench and filth and gore. And superhuman efforts on our part to succour the wounded as best we could. We remained three days from Thursday until yesterday (Sunday). We admitted about 900 wounded, we fed them, operated upon a hundred men and buried nearly fifty. Then we evac all our pts to a hospital ship at Dunkirk. Let us hope that they are all back in Blighty by this time and that they will soon forget the horrors of the last few days. What calls most for remark was the courage and endurance of the men. I never heard a word of complaint. Perhaps the most distressing sight for me was the long queue of ambulances waiting to come in. Many of the plastered limbs were swarming with maggots and the stench was dreadful."

Colonel McDonald then described the screw being turned as more and more wounded arrived. By then there were no nursing sisters — they had all been sent off. But "cooking, beds and mattresses — still available." The exhaustion of the wounded, and the occasional neglected tourniquet with its devastating result, remained in his mind.

Perhaps the most moving part of Colonel McDonald's account is the way he almost soliloquises on what he saw, he, not a raw recruit nor yet a Regular. He had known, like Major Glyn Hughes, the guns of the earlier Great War; both thanked God (McDonald, born a Scot, was an elder in the Presbyterian Church in Durham) that "the Germans haven't brought up their big guns to Dunkirk." They were experienced enough soldiers to be aware of the difference between bombs of the comparatively light dive-bombers and the monstrous bombardment of heavy artillery.

"Still, I suppose this is the biggest challenge of army military medicine", wrote McDonald. "We must be prepared to function under any circumstances and to improvise…water supply failed on Saturday (2 days before) so no more operating." He expressed yet once more the truth of one of the factors we saw at the beginning of this history — that the RAMC has to serve as members of a learned profession assisting fighting troops; no matter how skilled professionally the medicals (and the nurses) are, they are finally totally dependent upon the professional skill of their generals.

Finally, he described sending off his men and junior officers — being in the rain all one day, the next in the water to the waist ("the water was warm") and having to come ashore again, before being finally embarked. He saw "the multitude of ships"; he, too, marvelled at the sheer professionalism of the Royal Navy — the officers with their white collars and neat ties, the gentle, cheerful sailors.

On June 1st, at Bradbury Lines, Hereford, after sending a telegram to his wife, he thought back: "Now, as I sit in this well-furnished mess, it all seems like a dream or a bad nightmare…No 10 CCS captured to a man…most medical units seem to have got away intact…the French Armistice will be ingeniously brutal."[21] He reflected, too, on the losses of friends. But compared to the other conflict he had known, the British losses were slight: in the Battle of France they had lost only 68,111 killed, wounded, missing or POW, and 599 who died of disease or injury.

Captain Martin Fallon found himself on a train bound for Dover that June. "When we arrived", he recalled, "we found 350,000 men coming the other way. I remember one who shouted at us — Jesus Christ get back the other way! So our train shunted, and back we all went." And Major John Matheson was embarking with his hospital to the Middle East when the Dunkirk evacuation was in progress. "What were we coming back to ?" they all asked.

The Aftermath. The War in the Middle East.

Perspective.
"In our fight against the Western Powers England has shown herself to be the animator of the fighting spirit of the enemy and the leading enemy power. The defeat of England is essential to final victory."
Hitler's War Directive No 9, 29ᵗʰ November, 1939.

"Since England, in spite of her hopeless military situation, shows no sign of being ready to come to an understanding, I have decided to prepare a landing operation against England, and, if necessary, to carry it out. The aim of this operation will be to eliminate the English homeland as a base for the prosecution of the war against Germany and, if necessary, to occupy it completely."
Hitler's War Directive No 16, 16ᵗʰ July, 1940.

The extent of the peril for Western Europe and indeed for the world was barely appreciated at the time. The greatness of Mr Churchill was however soon realised by the British, who united as not since Napoleonic times. Those who heard his speeches and were moved by them could find it hard to understand the few who many years later refused to sign his retiral presentation in the House of Commons, or who boasted of "having got rid of Churchill."

Britain became a nation under siege. Schoolboys built anti-tank concrete barriers all around the coast; men worked in munition factories till they dropped from fatigue. The Local Defence Volunteers stood guard with the returned serving soldiers. Most of the Empire rallied; at home men and women worked day and night to produce all that was asked for to wage war. Lord Beaverbrook, owner of the Daily Express, was appointed Minister of Aircraft production in the new National Government made up from all parties.[22]

The south was an armed camp, awaiting invasion. No 1 Div was re-formed in Lincolnshire, for example, to guard that coast. Cpl Lewison, who had stayed on in Dover to look after wounded as they arrived, now found himself based at the RAMC Depot, in charge of a squad of RAMC recruits, all navvies. Their job was to dig anti-tank ditches in southern England.

The Battle of Britain, one of the most vital battles in history, was won by the R.A.F., whose reputation was assured for all time as a result. The scientists whose radar led the fighter planes to the German bombers, and Churchill, whose flash of inspiration in ordering an air raid on Berlin drew the response on London and so gave the fighter stations a respite and time to re-group and repair, have their due place also. As well as British, there were Polish pilots — 1 in 10 of all, and those from other European countries plus a few from the USA.

The Desert War.
Once the Battle of Britain had been won, the Middle East became the vital strategic theatre. The entry of Fascist Italy into the War in 1940 made it essential that the Italian bases in Africa be neutralised and the British presence in Egypt and Palestine, to safeguard oil supplies, be secured. The Suez canal zone also guarded the route eastwards to India and beyond. Mr Churchill and his cabinet — with advice from the Chiefs of Staff, of whom the great soldier Sir Alan Brooke soon became pre-eminent, decided to send the only available British armoured division to North Africa at once.

So the focus moved away from Britain, to the Middle East. Here the medicals were presented with a new series of problems as they supported the teeth arms. The campaign in France had given no opportunity for success or new advance. But now in this very different terrain, the Corps *would* have every opportunity. By late 1940 the original Regular members had made *their* contribution — they had been the first in place. The Territorials had made their contribution — they had been second in place. Both of these elements, trained in their differing roles, were now, as in 1915, taken over by the flood of temporary war-time officers and men. The best brains in British medicine were there, at every level and in every single specialty.

War in the desert was essentially a war of movement and dispersion. The terrain determined this — huge expanses of sand

and rock, limited on the north by the Mediterranean and in the south by the sand lake of the Qatarra Depression, making a rather narrow but extremely long battle ground of over 1000 miles(1600km) from the base hospitals in Alexandria. These featureless miles were under the proven power of the Air Arm — from now onwards for ever more, all land units had to learn to hide from the bomber or if not possible as here, to disperse widely.

Egypt was thought of as a tropical country, but the nights were cold — often bitterly cold. There was plenty of pneumonia and influenza. "Men arriving were better to go back into warm serge after 1600 hrs", as one ADMS put it. Dysentery was the endemic disease which mattered; everyone was at risk. Troops had to be warned against eating any vegetables or fruit not disinfected: "an inspection of the local methods of cultivation and irrigation will show why these precautions are necessary," said a health briefing.

Water supply was from the Nile, and 20 gallons (90 litres) per man per day was the generous allowance. But only treated water was safe. Disposal was difficult, because the sand was often no more than a foot (30 cms) deep and below was impervious rock. Soakage pits were not effective, so porous pipes had to be sunk.

Because of the flies and the constant risk of infection, latrine construction and discipline were a major concern of the hygiene sections. Disposal, too, had to be burning of solid faeces from the pails — and the contractors who emptied these latrine buckets required the closest supervision.

Drafts as they arrived had to be warned against tetanus, typhus, small pox, and heat stroke. There was Yellow Fever in the Sudan and Malaria in the Canal Zone though not in the Western Desert. In the cities of Cairo and Alexandria there was abundant V.D. where prostitution had become "mechanised", the women being taken around in taxis or horse carriages. Care of the feet was important; feet had to be hardened for marching on the rough ground, especially after they had become soft during the sea voyage from Britain.

The first medical appreciation by the DDMS of the needs of what was called B.T.E., or British Troops Egypt, was a small pencil-written document in October 1939. By the next year, things were different. On 12th November, 1940, Brigadier O.W.

McSheey, the DDGAMS, was writing of the large forces being put in place. These included troops from New Zealand and Australia, and the greatest care was taken to cater for the wishes of them and their governments, especially as regards casualty evacuation to their homes. There were also Indian troops, and some French and others. The AMS had 340,000 British personnel alone as their medical responsibility, and with a bed requirement of 8 per cent, had to find 2400 beds for the Army, 2400 beds for the RAF, now a major service with 40,000 Officers and airmen in the Middle East Force, and 600 beds for the R.N. They also had a commitment for the large number of Italian POW taken after the first campaign of General Wavell.

As the Middle East campaign progressed, with advances followed by defeats and retreats along the North African coast, the medical ORBAT became very large indeed.[23] The DMS, Major General Percy Tomlinson, was a Regular officer who fulfilled a major role. Of all the multitude of medical cares he was responsible for, two were both new and peculiar to the campaign — first the new armoured fighting vehicles and their medical support, with the long carry from the front line — which lengthened and shortened and was complicated by the need to support the Tobruk garrison while under siege — and second the development of the blood transfusion service. These were the principal achievements of the Corps in this period of its history.

The armoured division fought faster, farther, and longer than the old cavalry. The RMO could not have a dug-in RAP beside Regimental Headquarters, or if he did, it was likely to be 50 miles (80km) behind the forward operating tanks. RHQ, and the RAP, were a moving vehicle. Evacuation in an armoured formation was from before backwards — the reverse of traditional rules. He collected casualties in his ambulance car and evacuated them to the nearest ADS, in practice near his bde H.Q. There was no time or opportunity for field ambulance cars to come and collect. Wireless was essential.

Captain J.D.P. Graham was a typical example. He had graduated at Glasgow in 1937 and graduated MD in 1939 with High Commendation. Obviously a 'flier',[24] he was doing research in London in 1940 and got away from this with great difficulty to join up. He in fact applied to join the RAF Medical Branch, but like Martin Fallon had renal glycosuria and was turned down. So he fasted for 24 hours before his medical for the RAMC to ensure he would pass.

He had no previous military experience or interest — apart from being in the Local Defence Volunteers, the precursor of the Home Guard, which he went into after the fall of France. Posted to the 3rd County of London Yeomanry Regiment, a TA unit, he was suspicious of them at first and recorded in his wartime account that he was, like so many RMOs before and after in such a Regiment, "with them but not entirely of them." His suspicions were enhanced when on embarkation with the rest of 22 Armoured Bde, the others being 2nd County of London Yeomanry, a battalion of the Gloucester Regiment, and brigade troops, a member of the ship's crew was bitten on the leg by his C.O.'s dog, which that officer had smuggled on board with the intention of taking it to Africa !

No special training was available for RMOs with tanks. The tropical disease briefing, given as always by Regular RAMC whose abilities to produce such briefings was immeasurably greater than anyone else — impressed him. But being posted into the 7th Armoured Division meant that Captain Graham and his fellow- RMOs had to learn fast.

From the first he was in some awe of the German "flak mobile 88 gun" as he called it. "This gun, a work of power and ingenuity, could function as a high-reaching anti-aircraft weapon or be stretched horizontally when it made a devastating anti-tank weapon. The Afrika Corps had 2 heavy armd divs, 15 and 21 Panzer, and their motorised division, the 90th Light — plus all support necessary.... We were to learn the cardinal lesson of warfare in this area that campaigns need more than valour and determination but also a massive organisation to succeed...the Germans had eqpt sent from Marseilles, Pétain fully co-operated..."

His descriptions are vivid and demand to be included in a history of the Corps in this campaign: ... "Resupply was at night. The armourers worked flat out as this was the most vulnerable time; a stray shell in the midst and we all might have gone up in flames...I had to ensure that my replacement medical stocks had arrived including the splendid item called 'medicinal brandy'...my chief anxiety was that I would find myself with a load of wounded men and no 'blood waggon' (ambulance car).

It did happen but some sort of lorry was turned over for the purpose with everyone's consent…consideration for the wounded on both sides was a characteristic of the sldr in the desert.

A tank cannot readily be fought with corpses or bits thereof in it but one hesitates to tip a friend out into the unfeeling sand for the jackals to vandalise, and it was not uncommon for me to have to hold a gravedigging session after food and before sleep. The padre was a good chap but his place was at the main echelon which could be at bulkhead store some 50 miles(80km) behind.

(After burials) I would go round and hold a peripatetic surgery with the crews and with the echelon drivers before they withdrew and an uneasy silence fell on our slumbering strength…the Regt went into a 'leaguer' every night — soft skinned vehs in the centre and armd outside — like the Boer laager. The leaguer facilitated safe liaison with the echelon, our umbilical cord. Failure to meet up with it and we were immobile, vulnerable, and most unhappy.

At this 'sick parade' I had to make crucial decisions as to who might have to be sent back. Nothing upset a tank crew more than a break in the close links which enchained those men, the merest breath of suspicion of defection before a battle (once joined there was no looking back) depressed them dreadfully and many a man soldiered on despite numerous desert sores on his hands or feeling like hell with jaundice. My job was to protect the others from infection or from the consequences of physical failure and to retain the confidence of the whole body of men so that they knew that I was in no way a 'soft mark' and a comrade sent back was in dire need of attention."

Captain Graham, very much the war-time doctor with no fear of the military hierarchy, could be somewhat cynical on occasion about his medical superiors. Of his DDMS he wrote: "I never saw him except when things were stable on the front and perhaps the Corps Commander decided to display an interest in the welfare of his troops which was best achieved by inspecting the medical services, or the DDMS felt it wise to anticipate enquiry by doing likewise." And of the DMS : "I never encountered such a person or even knew his name or rank."

The original establishment of two cavalry field ambulances to an armd division was replaced by that of three light field ambulances, each with 14 ambulance cars. Ambulance cars were the essential feature of the "light" Fd Ambs, and their number was supplemented by a divisional pool if the ADMS had managed to create one. Because the carry back to the CCS was so long, the ADS had to hold casualties, and placed at bde H.Q., it was the focal point for collection. Triage was done here.

The Main Dressing Station (MDS) was at divisional level and could be made into an Advanced Surgical Centre (ASC) if conditions required, by the addition of an FST. Behind these units, distances to the subsequent stages in the evacuation process were frighteningly long.[25]

The actual removal of casualties from tanks was a new skill to be learned. An early 1941 method using long web straps was devised at the RAMC Depot by Major S. Elliott, but did not work in practice. Next, a special suit of overalls was experimented with early in 1942, with strengthening by straps, loops or handles at the back of the neck and inside vest. But the medical personnel found that casualties, except in tank commanders who were exposed, did not occur unless the vehicle was penetrated. If it were, it was almost certainly put out of action, and the crew abandoned it before it went on fire or "brewed up." So there was no time for elaborate apparatus. "Slings and webbing were useless in the Middle East Force (M.E.F.)", was the experience of the medicals: "every wounded man, unless completely incapacitated, got out unaided or pulled by the collar", wrote the DMS, Percy Tomlinson, in a note of 29th January, 1943. "Slings were only for morale. A white scout car, converted to carry two stretchers, was used in 1942 for each armd unit. This was *not* marked by the Red Cross, is driven to the disabled tk by a driver accompanied by the RMO's orderly, to bring cas back…."

Light stretchers were also a necessity. The Neil-Robertson, an old naval type, with its external wrappings removed, was tried; it could immobilise the body and limbs of the casualty and so allow him to be withdrawn through the driver's door. Each light tank had one fixed outside it. The Smith-Duval, of stout canvas, was similar, but could be carried inside the vehicle. But the same principles as above applied. There was seldom time for the application of a stretcher. Because of the long carry, each division had at least 1000 standard stretchers; the medical authorities pressed for each new division arriving in the desert to have an extra thousand.

Field ambulances had to learn quickly and to a high level of efficiency if they were to survive in the desert. As well as the immediate need to find their way, they had to learn to be self-supporting for resupply of rations and stores. They had to be capable of closing, moving, and setting up fast — always the needs of their type of field unit — but because of the rapidity of armoured warfare, their skill had to be even higher. Also, because of the type of warfare, they had to be prepared to hold up to 100 patients.

151 (Sunderland) Field Ambulance, whom we remember mobilizing, arrived on 20th April, 1941 at El Quassasin camp. The soldiers found the place "desolate, natives stinking and always pleading for money." At first many went to hospital with diseases acquired while bathing, from flies, and from sun exposure. They learned fast.

On 13th May they were put under command of 7th Armoured Division, the Desert Rats. By the 23rd of May they had learned desert navigation, how to pull casualties out of tanks, and most important of all, how to dig proper slit trenches and how to dive into them when the air sentry blew his whistle. "The ADS was set up behind the Piccadilly battle and had to scatter at the rapid German advance", recorded the War Diary. One RASC driver wrote on the 24th of November: "4 stretcher cases and moved over to the Surgical Centre for more. Shell hit surgical cart, killing driver Harrol. I moved off, most of our stuff is on the move, whining and screaming of enemy ammo, puffs of dust and blue smoke all around, vehs in all directions. I have no idea which way to go. We stop about 10 miles away after passing through a South African leaguer who know nothing of us. 2 of the patients have another wound — both in the thigh thank goodness…I find 9 bullet holes in the amb one through the door next me…a number of our boys wounded and a good number missing. Move farther on and stop for orders, feeling the do was one of bewilderment, feel weak afterwards and very hungry. I am told to take my amb and 4 others to a MDS somewhere then Major Forsyth has to lead us, thank goodness… dentist Robertson and padre Gordon captured at Sidi Rezegh…"

While most field ambulances suffered casualties, a few were surprisingly lucky. Sgt Ronald Hunt, who had been taken away from 152 to find himself in its successor 174 (temporarily commanded while in U.K. by Lieutenant Colonel A.H. Macklin who had been with Shackleton in the Antartic), recalled that only two men were killed in the North African Campaign. One was his close friend, S/Sgt Brogan, who was killed by a shell while in charge of stretcher bearers at En Fidaville in April, 1942. "As he fell, he shouted 'So long, boys'. The only other casualty was Pte Currie, a quiet and likeable lad whom it was difficult to believe was a promising boxer before the war." As 174 was part of 51(H) Div, this was indeed unusual.

An emergency commissioned officer, James Baird, found himself posted to the successor of 51(H) Div, the 9th Scottish. For a time in one of its Fd Ambs, 174, he volunteered to join the newly formed 11 Commando of 600 men called 11 Cdo (Scottish). This had started life as four independent companies for Norway, before he joined. They were part of a commando brigade, one of the others of 600 men being the Guards Commando. Their first engagement is worth recording as it was against the former ally, the French.

Carried by a fast merchant ship of the Glen class from Cyprus, they were tasked with an attack on Vichy French in Lebanon. The target for 11 Cdo was a bridge on the Litani river between Tyre and Sidon. In error the commando landed in two places, and were decimated by the French 75mm field guns, ranged exactly on key points above the landing. Captain Baird was impressed at the number of buttock and pelvic wounds, and the malignant malaria which infected the troops. The brigade was disbanded and soon replaced by the commandos led and trained by one of the Highland Chieftains, Lord Lovat.

Posted to No 1 Mobile Military Hospital (MMH), he found himself part of 30 Corps, an armoured one. He recalled the light Fd Ambs evacuating to the heavy Fd Ambs, and next to the CCS some 50–100 miles(80–160km) back. He took part in the Sidi Rezegh battle to relieve Tobruk: Nos 14 and 15 British CCSs were in support, then NZ and SA CCSs, i.e. 2 clearing stations brigaded together. "Of the pair, one was kept nearly empty, the other working; 2 in front, 2 behind, and for mobile warfare they leapfrogged. At Sidi Rezegh, we got cas from literally all over — German, Italian, British. For news of how things were going, we listened to the long-range radio from London... we aimed to get a cas wounded in the morning to the CCS by afternoon, trying to apply the 6-hour rule for abdominal cas."

"Although light Fd Ambs had FSTs attached, FSTs tended to be put with heavy Fd Ambs. A noteworthy heavy Fd Amb C.O. was Bill Scrivin, a pre-war Regular who became Consulting Advisor in Anaesthetics later."

"In our CCS, we had the very best mix of TA and Regular — the senior surgeon was R.A. Stephen, who had joined the Corps in the 1930's — from Aberdeen University; and Territorials: the senior anaesthetist was J.W.L. (Johnny) Bain, also from Aberdeen, John Swinney, who became a urologist in Newcastle — he was a **brilliant** surgeon; Vivian Jenkins from Wales, very confident of his ability; Noel Bonnin, seconded from the Australian Medical Corps — they had no CCS at this time (Tobruk 1941). I was the 'odd job man'."[26]

"The Commanding officer was Charles Croft, a TA St Thomas' graduate, and physician from the Devon and Exeter Hospital. He fell heir to a complete mobile hospital equipment from the USA, said to have been sent over to Britain, in fact to Bristol, for air raid casualties. But it went to the Middle East by mistake. Its vehicles had been built by the International Harvester Firm, which usually made tractors. Its three 10 ton desert worthy trucks held all the major surgical equipment, they went at 70 mph, and the troops called it 'Croft's Circus'!"[27]

Just as the British CCSs took German casualties, so the German opposite numbers took British. The stories of them setting up in the desert quite close to each other are true, and are a tribute to the bond of care which the best doctors share. It is another reason why the medicals ask to be placed in a different category from all other members of the combatant forces. The story to be told as example is that of the British FST, attached to a CCS well on the German side of operations, where a newly arrived young surgeon from England, a graduate from Edinburgh, had a German General brought in dangerously wounded. The surgeon operated on him, working as anxiously as those of us who have known the burden of surgery share and which others who are not surgeons cannot. General Rommel visited the unit and talked to the young surgeon, who explained to him what he had done and what he thought the outlook would be. He was called Ian Aird.[28] Rommel, the gentleman he was, answered courteously. Later he directed that food and water be kept for the CCS. His kind action was spoiled by Italians who stole some of it.

Blood Transfusion Service begins.

Captain Jimmy Baird was full of praise for the blood transfusion service the AMS was providing. This second new and vital advance in casualty care had, like everything else, been started in France but there was no time for it to be developed. The Blood Transfusion and Surgical Research laboratory of the BEF in France had Field Transfusion Units (FTUs), and there was a base unit, the Army Blood Supply Depot, in Bristol. This Depot sent 990 bottles of blood and 116 of plasma to the BEF between May 10th and May 31st 1940. It was the first supply of its kind for the British Army. Each FTU in France was more or less permanently attached to a CCS, there a most immobile unit. It is clear that the FTU officers all did well; they acted as resuscitation officers within their unit. The transfusion apparatus was satisfactory; the Type "A" refrigerator worked well but was too big. It was found very soon that transfusion had to be adequate and rapid, to be effective.

The *Official History* recorded an age-long difficulty: "The Transfusion Officer should have been recognised as a specialist and given appropriate rank. Officers of the rank of Lieutenant found great difficulty in seeing that their recommendations were followed, and lacked the authority which would have attended a higher rank or designation as a specialist."[29]

In the Middle East Force, the Army Director of Pathology was Guy Pulvertaft, but the transfusion service was the responsibility of the Deputy Director at G.H.Q., Cairo, Colonel John Boyd. It consisted of a BTU (Base Transfusion Unit) and several FTUs. In addition, each BGH had a small transfusion section within the hospital.

The BTU prepared and issued all transfusion fluids, including blood, plasma, saline solution, blood grouping solutions. It also prepared sulphonamide drugs for injection. Volunteer blood donors came from troops stationed either temporarily or permanently at the base areas. As demands increased at the time of the El Alamein battle, it became necessary to form a mobile bleeding section of 1 officer and 17 O.R.s. This worked near the Infantry Depot at Geneifa, where one of the General Hospitals was (No 19), and where 70,000 troops were stationed. Only Group "O" blood was used as it was found impracticable to use the other groups.

The officer who did the actual provision was G.E. Buttle. He was a biochemist and biologist who had been trained by Professor, now Brigadier, L.G. Whitby. He was a dominant person, perhaps *the* dominant person, in transfusion at this time. "Buttle's Bottled Blood" was sent in crates by returning empty ambulances or trains, in refrigerators. Each FST and CCS had its own refrigerator. "There was no time to group in battle", said Captain Baird. "Because of the heat, its life was less than six weeks. (In practice the period was less than this). If it wasn't used, it was sent back and the serum extracted. Sometimes a bottle of whisky came up in one of the bottle crates if things were quiet."

Notes and references

CHAPTER 8

[1]Panzer Leader. General Heinz Guderian, London, Michael Joseph, 1952, p 24.

[2]Munchen Suddeutsche Zeitung, 26th September, 1930; Frankfurter Zeitung, same date.

[3]See, for example, *Daily Mail*, 11th May, 1936, after Hitler's seizure of the Rhineland.

[4]A new Order was introduced late in the 1914–18 War, the Order of the British Empire. This was for distinguished service and for gallantry apart from an isolated action of the battlefield. The "levels" of this new decoration did not at first relate to rank; in the early lists a Captain could be awarded a CBE if his performance earned it and a Lieutnant Colonel an MBE. It was not till much later that the levels were tied to rank and a Captain or Major, no matter how distinguished his contribution, was never awarded more than an "M." The same had applied to other orders at the time of the Boer War, as already seen.

[5]Medical History of the Second World War, Army Medical Services, Vol 1, HMSO, 1952, pp 5, 22. (For a short account of the almost unbelievable reduction in the British Army in general, see "Against All Odds — the British Army of 1939–40", a National Army Museum publication, 1989). Army estimates were reduced every year from 1923 to 1932, during which the Navy received an annual allocation of £17M, the RAF £7M, while the Army received only £2M).

[6]Op cit, p 30.

[7]Op cit, p 63ff.

[8]In 1924 the RAMC was divided into various technical trades which the recruit could enter after completing his 6 months' basic training: nursing orderly, mental nursing orderly, special treatment orderly, operating room assistant, trained nurse, pharmacist, dispenser, masseur, laboratory assistant, radiographer, clerk, hospital cook, sanitary

assistant, optician, packer and storeman, and surgical instrument maker. Later the trade of chiropodist was added. There were 3 grades of each of these e.g. N.O.3 (nursing orderly class 3), N.O.2, and most advanced, N.O.1. Each trade and class carried a specific rate of pay.

[9]Macpherson's Formula was to estimate time to calculate a round trip for ambulance evacuation.

T = time allowed W = no of sick/wounded t = time taken by tpt for 1 journey and return M = units of tpt available n = no of pts each unit of tpt carries

$$\text{Time required} = \frac{1}{M} \times \frac{W \times t}{n}$$

[10]An exception to this was Major General Priest, Consulting Physician to the BEF at the beginning of the War. He had been a foundation scholar at Gonville and Caius College, Cambridge in 1904, M.B. 1908, and served in India and Mesopotamia in 1915 and 1916. He was MD Cambridge in 1933 and FRCP(London). After the French Campaign, however, he was sent to Western Command in England, where he remained for the rest of the War. Another was Lieutenant Colonel D.C. Monro, who became Consulting Surgeon, Middle East Command.

[11]Op cit, pp 113–114. In 1950 an official book of 100 pages on Mobilization was published by the War Office. It was one of a series, "to preserve the experience gained during the Second World War, 1939–45". This is a comprehensive account of procedures and lessons and should be remembered in any future transition to war. But in the nature of things, historical books like this are ignored, and much more work needs to be done and more mistakes made, than are necessary. I am grateful to Major "Doc" Holliday, RAMC, for the sight of this publication.

[12]For a well-researched book on the Norwegian campaign, see Norway 1940, by François Kersaudy, Collins, 1990. Its account of the blunderings and ditherings of the politicians is very frightening. A short military account is in chapter 3 of "The Saturday Night Soldiers", by A.V. Sellwood, Wolfe, London, 1966. Medical details are in the Official History, and a personal field ambulance account is "Soldier, Sailor, or Ruddy doctor", by Major W.M. Evans, MC, J R Army Med Corps, 1942, Vol LXXVII, 111–121.

[13]Leonard Colebrook was Consulting Bacteriologist to the BEF. As in 1914, civilians of experience quickly came into post. Another was Max Page, who became (Clinical) Consulting Surgeon. Colonel John Weddell, a Regular officer who went out as the original Surgeon, continued to give only administrative and equipment advice. Sir

Edward Mellanby FRS, physiologist and pharmacologist, the secretary of the Medical Research Council, was another senior civilain employed.

[14]"Finest Hour", Winston S. Churchill, 1939–41. Martin Gilbert. p 349. General Ismay, who accompanied Churchill, wrote later:

"I have never forgotten the look of complete dejection on the faces of Reynaud, Daladier and Gamelin as we entered the room at the Quai d'Orsay. I remember saying to myself 'The French are beaten already.' M. Raynaud cheered up under your (Churchill's) influence, but Daladier and Gamelin remained the picture of misery and despair throughout."

[15]The best accounts of the German armoured attack in 1940 are, not surprisingly, German. See Panzer Battles, Major General E.W. von Mellenthin, Cassell & Co, Ltd, 1955, and Panzer Leader, General Heinz Guderian, Michael Joseph, 1952. In the first of these, General von Mellenthin sums up the French campaign: "The Battle of France was won by the German Wermacht because it reintroduced into warfare the decisive factor of mobility. It achieved mobility by the combination of firepower, concentration, and surprise, together with expert handling of the latest modern arms — Luftwaffe, parachutists, and armour. The series of disasters in subsequent years must not be allowed to obscure the fact that in 1940 the German General Staff achieved a military masterpiece, worthy to rank beside the greatest campaigns of the greatest generals of history. It was not our fault that the fruits of this tremendous triumph were wantonly thrown away."

[16]J R Army Med Corps, 1941, Vol LXVI, 67–85. The ADMS emphasised the following points which he believed were particularly important in a retreat:

a) Evac of RAPs — this was always done by motor ambulances, because "one of the few advantages of a retirement is that heavy artillery has not had time to come into action, and particularly in urban areas ambulances can easily reach the RAPs."

b) Cas in a column *en route* — when time permitted, motor ambulances were always distributed throughout the column to deal with air raid casualties. Even when roads were severely congested, the results of dive bombing and machine gunning from the air were surprisingly mild.

c) Amb transport of fd ambs — It is impossible to attach motor ambulances to units and at the same time leave the fd ambs enough for their own needs. When the position was stabilised the MACs worked well, but during retirement it is not easy to locate the HQ of a MAC and ambs which have gone to a CCS may be unable to return. In these circumstances, holding a section of a MAC under control of the ADMS proved most valuable.

d) Handling of fd ambs — experience proved the importance of never opening more DSs than were required. One fd amb was always kept "on wheels" and able to move at very short notice. It was found useful to get at least one fd amb away as early as possible, so that it could form an MDS in the new area in plenty time. The hour for withdrawing an ADS is often difficult. If withdrawn too soon, there is nothing to deal with wounded, often at a critical time. If allowed to remain too long, it may be captured or at least get in the way of the fighting troops, who may require all available space. The most satisfactory method was to "hang it" on to the nearest Bde HQ.

Colonel Charles Morgan Finny was a Dublin graduate who had joined the RAMC on 17th January, 1911. He served in India during the First War, had been in Malta in the 1920s where in 1927 he was awarded the OBE, and in India again in the 1930s. He had been a surgical specialist, taking his FRCS of England in 1921. He was promoted brevet colonel in January 1937 and substantive in 1938. As ADMS in 1939 he was 53 years old — evidence of the slowness of peace-time promotion. He was promoted Major General in 1941 and retired finally in 1946.

[17]There were of course general hospitals. At La Baule, beside St Nazaire, the surgical staff were all Territorials who in later years became well-known surgical names: Lieutnant Colonel A.E. Porrit, Majors A.L. d'Abreu, R.S. Handley, J.S. Jeffrey. Major E.S. Rowbotham was one of the anaesthetists. Major B.M. Dick invented a new dressings system. They continued operating till 18th June, 1940, the final evacuation day of the BEF.

[18]Op cit, Campaigns, Vol 1, p 17. "In every subequent campaign, in varying degrees, the same factors, ignorance concerning sanitation and lack of disciplinary control, made their appearance. Good standards of hygiene were not achieved until senior combatant officers had themselves received training and had come to recognise their responsibilities."

[19]Colonel Alexander Hood was born in Leith, by Edinburgh, in 1888, and graduated in Edinburgh in 1910. Joining the RAMC in 1912, he gained many prizes as a young officer. He served with the Indian Expeditionary Force in 1914–16 and returned to India from 1916 to 1921. He became a pathological specialist in 1923 as a Captain, and took his Edinburgh MD in 1931. But he had made his name in Egypt and Palestine, being promoted quickly to ADMS and then DDMS. In France he was holding his position at a rank lower than usual.

[20]A preventorium was a French hospital for the care of children thought to have been exposed to infection by Tuberculosis.

[21]On 1st June the staff of 12 CCS drew lots for three officers and 30 men to remain with their wounded and so become POW. 12 CCS was the last organised RAMC unit to remain functioning in France that summer.

[22]New Zealand and Canada were solid in their support. In South Africa, the Boer Prime Minister Hertzog had to be dismissed by the Governor-General, as he was clearly pro-German, and replaced by General Smuts. Significantly, the Australian High Commissoner in London suggested that Britain make peace approaches to Germany. The Irish Free State politicians were of course determined to give no help.

[23]Apart altogether from RMOs and fd ambs attached to forward units, there were 2x200 bed, 2x600 bed, 2x1200 bed British General Hospitals(BGHs), 1 convalescent depot, 7 hospital ships, 3 hospital carriers, 2 advanced depots of medical stores, 2 ambulance trains, 2 port detachments RAMC. There were 3 corps fd ambs, 4 mobile CCSs, 6 FSUs, 4 FTUs,(surgical, transfusion, units) and 1 Canadian CCS supporting a British division.

In Alexandria, Nos 8 and 64 BGHs were several miles apart. In Cairo, No 9 took skin, chest, and maxillo-facial; 15(Scottish) was described by General Tomlinson as "the Millbank of the M.E.,(Middle East) and was reserved for serious cases"; it held specialist orthopaedic and neurosurgical patients.

For details of medical units at the base alone at the end of 1942, see Medical History of the Second World War, Campaigns, Vol 1, p 393, appendix XV.

Senior Consultant staff included: W.H. Ogilvie, Philip Wiles, D. Evan Bedford, Sydney Smith, J.A. Sinton, V.C., G.W.B. James, R.F. Barbour, G.I. Scott, R. Patterson, R. Lees, G. Kersley. Some M.R.C. staff were attached.

(By the end of the War there were 93 British consultants, medical and dental, who were serving or had served at home and abroad. Two had died on service. There were 9 Australian, mainly from Melbourne, 8 Canadian, 2 New Zealanders, and 3 British South African. Their names and specialties are to be seen in the mess at Millbank).

[24]J.D.P. Graham's later career was distinguished. He became Professor of Pharmacology in the Welsh National School of Medicine, and a Fellow of the Royal Society of Edinburgh.

[25]Distances were difficult to quantify on account of the fluctuating nature of armoured battles in particular. Figures produced from the RAMC Depot suggested:

RAP to ADS 8–12 miles(15–20km); ADS to Advanced MDS 12–15 miles(20–25km); Advanced MDS to Rear MDS 46 miles

(75km), but could be 50 miles(80km) or even over 100 miles(160km); to CCS the distance could be 80 miles(125km). To the General Hospital was as much as a farther 80 miles. Thus there was no option but to develop the Advanced Surgical Centre.

[26]Lieutnant General Sir James Baird, personal communication, October, 1993.

[27]Croft's Circus was not held in as much esteem by other officers. R.G. Atkins, DDMS Rear HQ 30 Corps, described it as "more useful at a fixed CCS rather than a light section, as when he arrives at the scene of the action it takes 1 3/4 hours to erect his 'circus'. It is much too big and cumbersome, is not light proof for night work. It is not firmly enough fixed and in trials up here is tearing already." He called in the Ordnance to try and make it more servicable.

[28]Ian Aird, then a Major, commanded No 1 FSU of 1 BGH. The incident occurred at the Battle of Sidi Rezegh. After the War, he became Professor of Surgery at the Hammersmith Hospital. His text-book was a classic for aspiring FRCS candidates for at least a generation. No 2 FSU was commanded by Major Dermid Bingham, and also did first-class work.

[29]Medical History of the Second World War, Vol 1 op cit, p 100. The original design for the Army Transfusion Service was drawn up by the Royal College of Surgeons of England soon after the Munich crisis in 1938. Key staff were ear-marked for an overseas Transfusion and Surgical Research Laboratory. After Dunkirk the laboratory was disbanded. Between 1929 and 1930, much research in haematology had been done by L. Whitby, H. L. Marriott, S. R. M. Bushby, A. Kekwick and Janet Vaughan (p. 418). Before the war, civilian blood transfusion organisation was local and voluntary, but a National Transfusion Service was set up in 1939, and in 1940 a regional service was begun under the Emergency Medical Services. Conspicuous service was given by Sir Lionel Whitby and Dr Janet Vaughan (pp. 419–420).

Chapter 9

Victory in Africa. The Return to Europe.

There were events dependent upon the passage of time and unrelated to the War which affected the Corps; deaths of great figures, promotions and retirals. Three major ones occurred in the 1941–42 period — the death of Major General Sir William Horrocks, the appointment of a new Director-General, and the appointment of HM Queen Elizabeth as Colonel-in-Chief.

Sir William Horrocks died in 1941. His field had been that of Army Health, and he had made an immense contribution. This field was dominated by the life-career Regular officer in the RAMC; while the Corps looked to the Reserve and war-time specialists to provide the experience, and the high skill, in clinical medicine, there is no doubt that the Regulars had the monopoly of ability in Army Health. From Parkes onwards, the infectious disease briefings, the design and development of every sort of hygiene measure, was done better by them than by anyone else. The production of superb bulletins and pamphlets continues to the present day.[1] Sir William Horrocks' two biggest services were in the provision of safe water and, less well known, in the protective measures against poison gas in the 1914–18 War.

Lieutenant General Sir Alexander Hood was appointed D.G. in the August of 1941. He had begun the War as a Colonel, and like Keogh, had been promoted over the heads of his seniors. From being acting Brigadier in July 1940, he became Major General and Lieutenant General on the same day, 1st August, 1941. He was the largest figure the Corps had had since Leishman, although Sir Maurice Fell had been Director General of the newly-formed RAF Medical Branch before being appointed DGAMS.[2]

In 1942 the Duke of Connaught, Colonel-in-Chief since 1919, died. His successor was a happy choice for the RAMC — the most wonderful person who all her life had the ability to make the person she was talking to feel they were the only person in the world — Queen Elizabeth.

El Alamein and Tunis.

It is sometimes said that El Alamein was the last major battle of this War, and perhaps the last major battle ever, to be fought by Great Britain and her Empire alone. But this is untrue; in Burma the Battle of Imphal was of greater significance. Had the Japanese won, the fall of India could have followed, with all the too calculable consequences. And the Burma battle was also fought by Great Britain and her Empire alone. Yet Alamein has its place as a major turning point which cannot be discounted.

After the reverses inflicted by the seemingly invincible General Rommel, the new leadership of General B.L. Montgomery, the 8th Army Commander, and General H.L. Alexander the CinC, who had once written so kindly to Captain Hugh Shields' parents, introduced a new drive and purpose. These two generals and their armies would remove the Axis Powers from Africa and later from Italy.

The El Alamein Battle, or more strictly, perhaps, the second El Alamein Battle, was planned by Montgomery to be a set-piece infantry attack, on First War principles. The infantry would, by attrition, wear down the enemy, "like a crow-bar moved this way and that", as he himself said. Once the enemy front was breached, and only then, would the now greatly strengthened armoured divisions sweep through. Casualties were likely to be high. Buttle and his staff worked unceasingly to build up a sure system for taking blood to the desert.

"We are all looking forward to a good party", wrote the confident, perhaps rather flamboyant Brigadier "Rats" Atkins, OBE, MC, MD, a Trinity Dublin graduate and DDMS of 30 Corps:

"we hope so. It may be difficult; but I think the RAMC will do well, and I believe myself that we have the chance, which has never happened before, of bringing surgery up to such an extent, that lives and limbs will be saved, that we never dreamed of before." There was no doubt that at every level the AMS were confident and determined.[3]

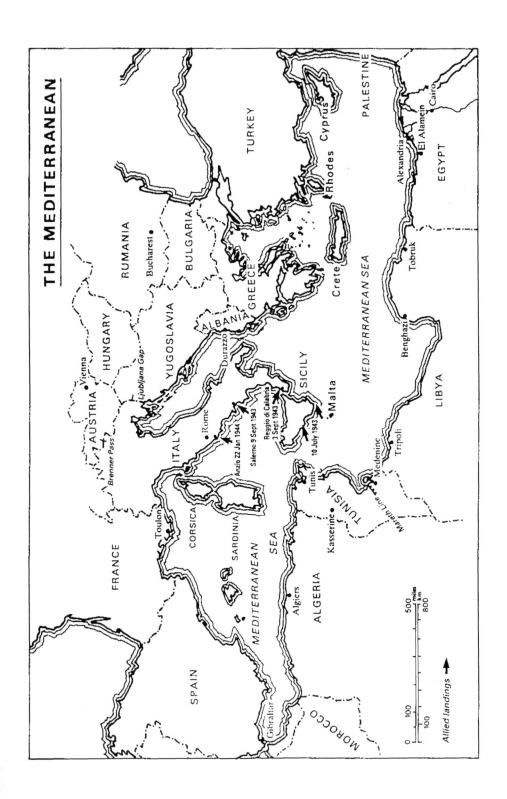

THE MEDITERRANEAN

FRANCE

SPAIN

MOROCCO

Gibraltar

ALGERIA

Algiers

MEDITERRANEAN SEA

SARDINIA

CORSICA

Toulon

ITALY

Rome

AUSTRIA

Brenner Pass

Vienna

HUNGARY

Ljubljana Gap

YUGOSLAVIA

Durazzo

ALBANIA

GREECE

RUMANIA

Bucharest

BULGARIA

TURKEY

Anzio 22 Jan 1944

Salerno 9 Sept 1943

Reggio di Calabria
3 Sept 1943

SICILY

Malta

10 July 1943

TUNISIA

Tunis

Kasserine

Mareth Line

Medenine

Tripoli

LIBYA

Benghazi

Tobruk

MEDITERRANEAN SEA

Crete

Rhodes

Cyprus

PALESTINE

Alexandria

El Alamein

Cairo

EGYPT

500 miles
800 km

100

100

0

Allied landings ↑

Montgomery's Order of the Day's second paragraph was famous: "We are ready NOW. The battle which is now about to begin will be one of the decisive battles of history. It will be the turning point of the war. The eyes of the world will be on us, watching which way the battle will swing…it will swing our way."

He spoke of "Hitting the enemy for six out of Africa" and asked that "The Lord mighty in battle will give us victory."

Captain Graham, who had had years in the sand, was his usual rather cynical but amusing self: "On October 22nd", he wrote in his diary, "was issued the famous battle order from General M which lacked the succinct quality of its predecessor by Nelson and is therefore less quotable. It included a somewhat puerile phrase that we were about to 'knock the en for six' out of N. Africa…all things considered, it was a well enough chosen message; it was directed most appositely at those who had to do the actual fighting, particularly junior officers who had to lead infantry into well defended minefields reminiscent of FWW…those of us old hands in 7th Armd Div thought cricket a less than happy simile for the battle of attrition."

He was in 13 Corps. Well away from the first infantry attack, he was nevertheless highly impressed by the intensity of the artillery barrage: "We had no ear muffs and I had to stuff my ears with cotton wool…the pulse of the concussions went right through one's body and jarred inside one's skull."

With his corps was 50 (Tyne-Tees) Infantry Division, one of the proudest in the Army. 186 Fd Ambs were amongst them. In 30 Corps were 51(H) Div,[4] with 174, 175, and 176 Fd Ambs. South of them marched their good friends, the 2nd New Zealand Division, and north of them their other friends, the bold, assertive 9th Australian Division, who had the hardest fighting of all.

One of those infantry officers who had led his men into the minefields was Major Hew Blair-Imrie. He was wounded in a mine blast, suffering what turned out to be nerve damage in his right arm. Although the RAMC was sometimes called unkindly "Rob All My Comrades", and this did happen, almost all the tales of the wounded on the way back were of kindness. Major Blair was impressed by the attitude of the RAMC, orderly in the ambulance taking him to the ADS, which carried a wounded

German and a wounded Italian as well as him: "The orderly fussed over these two like an old hen and gave them sips of water — cigarettes and so on,[5] just as if they were British…I got my stimulant in the form of hot sweet tea. It was a life saver…there were some pretty bad cases."

(At the ADS) "The RAMC all ranks were grand and had been at it for 14 hrs non-stop before I arrived. It wasn't that they just did their job, but they were so kind and so eager to help and do all they possibly could for the wounded. I was most impressed. At the same time I didn't see how they were going to get themselves clear as there were wounded still coming in and wounded waiting to be evacuated…I was to be evac to the MDS."

"The MDS was a much larger and more elaborate establishment ... and was all underground…we landed up at a CCS which was crowded out…I think this is the nearest to the front they allow women."

Eventually after a very bumpy journey, he found himself in a hospital in Cairo: "had my boots, my T.O.S.(Tam-O'Shanter), binoculars, taken by an orderly. About this hospital, one got the impression that we were really rather a nuisance arriving at this unearthly hour (3 a.m !) but that we'd better be put somewhere. We were told to get ourselves cleaned up and a very indifferent orderly was eventually routed out to take me to a sort of bathroom where he tried to clean off the clotted blood with stone cold water (there was no hot). I found my way to my bed — the orderly had vanished — and some time later a cup of stone cold tea was brought. The chap knew it was cold but it didn't seem to worry him. All this is rather rotten, I'm afraid and I've really put my impressions as they were at the time — had been 36 hours on the way back and only had 2 of sleep (induced by morphia)."

"Nevertheless the difference in attitude between the chaps at the front and at this hospital stuck out a mile. In one case it was the casualties that mattered, in the other hospital routine. The only good thing about the place was Lt-Col Boyd, who was at Barts and who decided the treatment. He was grand."

"I used to wonder often how people, and especially myself, would behave under fire for the first time — now I know — and it's very comforting for the next time."

The victory was won; the pursuit, for pursuit it was, of the German and Italian forces westwards to Tripoli and beyond followed fast. "This time", said Montgomery, "we are not going back."

It was as if the previous years were years of training for this major success. A new factor was air supply; by December 1942 and January 1943, blood and plasma were regularly sent by air to the Advanced Air Transport Centre (attached to a FTU) at a series of airfields from Benina onwards to Buerat and finally Tripoli.[6]

From the western side, from Britain and the USA, came the 1st Army, a joint British-U.S. Force, to clear Algeria of the enemy. Most of the men had not seen action till then.

Pte Frank Seabrook, a bank clerk from Lowestoft, became company clerk in the HQ of 159(Welsh) Fd Amb. Called up as long before as 18th January, 1940, he was first with 198 Fd Amb, whom we shall hear of again later, and was transferred to 159 in 1941.

"159", he recalled, "was a TA unit — very proud — they had a Welsh hat on their sleeves. They had St David's Day parades. They had been in France and returned via Dunkirk. But they were friendly to outsiders. R.S.M. Rees was telling us what a privilege it was to be with them. Alf Ball was their bugler, and Sgt Glyn Jones of the QM dept ran the choir. The Welshmen had to welcome a new C.O., a Scot called by all Johnny Trotter, and a new 2I/C Major Turner, also a Scot." 159(Welsh) Fd Amb embarked in October 1942 on the Clyde, and practised landing from a Landing Craft Tank(LCT). First practices were spoiled by Welshmen singing; Major Turner had to give them a hard time. When they did set sail, half the unit was on the Awatea and half on the Otranto. Approaching Algiers in the early morning of 8th November, they saw the lights of the town. Then they watched the assault troops, their faces blackened, leave in their LCTs.

"We could not help admiring the coolness and courage of the Navy at all times, but especially now and during the landings. There was complete silence after the LCTs left. It was a moment I shall never forget."

Then followed what Pte Seabrook called "The long struggle for Tunis." His account of the landing at Algiers contrasts vividly with those of the Gallipoli Campaign. But once ashore, things were very different this time. "I remember so well the marvellous work done by our doctors — in difficult conditions and under considerable stress...they may have differed in their personalities — from the rather impetuous Captain Wilson to the very gentle Captain Guild — but all were filled with the same care and devotion...and also the nursing orderlies who did their utmost to carry out their instructions."

As the advancing 8th Army entered the succession of towns along the Libyan coast, the ever-present hygiene sections found yet another job to do. This was the organisation of hygiene services as soon as the town was captured. It was a measure of the high state of efficiency that lists were prepared, in advance, of reconnaissance parties to follow immediately after the fighting troops. Other Heads of Services as well as RAMC were of course included.[7]

The advancing 1st Army in Tunisia had its own problems to solve, different from those of the Desert Army. In the Allied attack on Sedjenane in March and April 1943 by 5 Corps, the ADMS of 4 Div had to use 20 mules with cacolets — Boer War style — and litters, and employ relays of stretcher bearers to carry casualties for 4 miles(7km) to an ADS, because the country was so mountainous and had no roads whatever.

Again, the principle of bringing the surgeon as near as could be to the wounded was planned and successfully carried out. In the medical plan for an Allied attack on Toukabeur (near the hill known later as Long Stop Hill) the corps Fd Ambs and 3 CCS were used, plus the Motor Ambulance Company, now an RASC unit. Bren gun carriers with 2 stretchers, flying Red Cross flags, did the initial carry to the divisional MDS. The 3 CCSs were grouped together, and only wounded were admitted. Sick all went to the corps Fd Ambs.

Although, as Pte Seabrook had prophesied, it was a full 6 months before the fighting was over and Tunis was captured, the fall of that city did indeed close a chapter in the 1939–45 War. The next would be the assault on the continent of Europe, beginning with Sicily, progressing up Italy, but the great challenge would be the move over the English Channel to re-take France, Belgium and Holland, and enter the Homeland of Germany itself.

Medical problems of the Middle East Force.
Of the North African diseases, bacillary dysentery was the most constant threat, and "diarrhoea" was the commonest symptom

needing medical treatment. Diseases of the digestive system, which had been prevalent from the first months of the War, continued to be important. Thus in the worst months of 1942, in hard desert warfare, digestive disease accounted for 65 per 1000 strength, Dysentery for 33, V.D. for 31, Malaria (in the Canal Zone, not in the desert, though India served troops continued to have relapses) 30, and skin diseases, 16/1000. This contrasted with accidental injuries — many due to burns, when soldiers set fire to the sand beside their slit trench; these were so frequent that when Lieutenant Colonel John Matheson sent his MD thesis for approval to GHQ, the numbers were removed by a censor.[8] They were 48 per 1000 strength compared to 31/1000 for battle casualties.

In 1941, sick rates per thousand were 555 to battle casualties 35, a ratio of 16 to 1, and in 1942, virtually identical. Disease rates overall in 1942, again in the worst months of summer, were 2.39/1000 in July, 2.42 in August, and 1.96/1000 in September. The previous best average was 3/1000. By contrast in Egypt and Palestine in the 1914–18 War, the ratios were 100 sick to 61 battle casualties in 1917 and 100 sick to 56 casualties in 1918.

Other diseases occurred; around Bardia was tick-borne Relapsing Fever, and Tick Typhus in Tunisia. Diphtheria was relatively common in the desert. It responded to anti-toxin, but large doses for prolonged periods were often needed. Faucial and cutaneous types were both seen (the cutaneous type being the desert sore of Boer War days), but cardiac failure, not uncommon in civil practice, was not seen. This was probably due to the age and fitness of the patients. In the latter part of the Tunisian Campaign, skin disease became a serious problem. In 5 Corps alone, for example, there were 516 cases of scabies, 315 of impetigo, 180 of boils, and 1414 men infested with lice of various sorts, during the course of the final battle. Very soon after the fighting was over, however, and the men could wash and swim in the Mediterranean, the incidence fell.

Major D.M.F. Batty was an assistant physician in Edinburgh Royal Infirmary in 1939. Volunteering in 1939, he had the amazing experience of not being called up until April 1940 and then posted to 22 BGH, the Liverpool TA Hospital, going overseas the next day. Because the unit was alerted to go to Norway, "I arrived in civilian clothes, was given my TAB (typhoid) and tetanus injections with the advice that I had to have my rigor and be ready to move to the troop ship on the Clyde in 12 hours!" He just had time to get a suit of battledress, without any badges of rank, have his rigor, and board the train for Govan. Now in the Middle East as a specialist physician, his account of infective hepatitis, a virus infection which created much concern and which was in many ways a "new disease", is an excellent one.[9]

Infective Hepatitis was an important disease. In the last four months of 1942 the outbreak was explosive; 10,000 cases occurred. The outbreak started during September 1942 among the New Zealand and Australian divisions holding positions on the "Alamein Line" west of Alexandria. It spread rapidly, some units losing 9 per cent of their strength, and soon covered the whole of the Middle East. It receded after the four epidemic months of October to January, but flared up again in the autumn of 1943, with epidemic intensity not only in North Africa but also in Sicily and Italy. The fact that the large majority of those affected had symptoms which did not demand hospital treatment in the way that the old Typhoid fever had, caused many to stay in the line and not seek evacuation. Indeed, in the Afrika Corps, many units just did not remove those affected from duty.

"Infective hepatitis", recalled Major General John Matheson many years later, "was an important and puzzling disease. It should be remembered that routine and mass inoculation was suspected as a significant cause—large numbers of reinforcements were inoculated en masse, and infected needles might have been the cause in large units which developed an outbreak soon after arrival in the desert."(8)

"Exhaustion cases"—the current term for mental breakdown or inability to continue to fight following the stress of battle — were a different problem from those of 30 years before in the thunderous barrages of Flanders. There had undoubtedly been many men breaking down in the desert, but the symptoms had never been in any way as severe as those in shell-shock times. As Lieutenant Colonel John Matheson put it: "In Tobruk there was heavy shelling, and troops were hemmed in as they had been in the line in Flanders, but they did not develop mutism, aphonia, blindness, deafness, limb palsies. Collapse with tremor *did* occur, anxiety manifested itself, one C.O. took a pathological hatred against one of his officers and sprayed his dugout with a light machine gun, but there were no hysterias as above. Even at Bir Hachim, where the Germans pounded the Free French and the British in the line beside them, these hysterias did not occur." He wondered whether the conversion hysterias might not be a 1914–18 phenomenon.[8]

In these early months of the Tunisian Campaign, the diagnosis of N.Y.D.(N) was given to all cases who showed nervous symptoms. Later the policy was changed as it was found that this diagnosis was often misleading. Patients were classified into 1) those affected by explosions, 2) genuine exhaustion from long continued front line duty, and 3) N.Y.D.(N). A special proforma was issued for this last group. "It was considered that the diagnosis 3) was a stigma to be avoided where possible", wrote a DDMS who had not had an opportunity to read his First War History. (The same applied to Delayed Primary Suture, described in the 8th Army medical reports as *that* Army's invention !).

Also as in 1916, it was found that as the fighting continued, the number of cases who filtered direct to the ADS, avoiding their own RMO, increased. Cantlie, DDMS of 5 Corps, noted the story of a division promised relief as soon as they had taken a range of hills. They fought well. Then they were retained against stiffening opposition. The number of exhaustion cases increased, but not the number of battle casualties otherwise. "Hope deferred maketh the heart sick" was the comment.

"New" psychiatrists appeared in the corps area from January, 1943. The DDMS commented: "The first reaction of the psychiatrist's presence in the area was that he would down-grade every man who came before him...decided that the P was only adviser to DDMS and that his decisions could be over-ruled by him…P sent into battle, so that he could see what men had to put up with." Once again appeared the difference of view between the "soldier" medical officer and the specialist psychiatrist, which still continues.

Medical Airborne Forces.
Parachute troops had played a large part in the success of German victories in France, Greece and Crete. Britain had none until 1942, when the 1st Airborne Division was formed and began to train in England. As training in the new type of warfare was

undertaken and close study of the needs of the Airborne Force made, the first medical unit to be formed was, not surprisingly, the field ambulance — soon called the Para Field Ambulance. Its first analysis of objectives was written in May, 1942, by its C.O., Lieutenant Colonel M. McEwen, DFC, TD. As his decorations reveal, he had served in the First War, been a pilot, and between the wars, a keen Territorial after graduating in medicine at Glasgow in 1924. He wrote in a memorandum:

"Previous conceptions of the Fd Amb with land forces do not hold in the case of a para unit. There is a fundamental difference affecting the tactical handling, in that the former is primarily concerned with collection and evac of cas, while the latter is concerned with the collection and treatment, and is faced with the probability of holding serious cases, with no hope of evac for up to 6 days. Further, a land Fd Amb has adequate transport, while the para unit has to rely on hand carriage, with a possibility under certain circumstances of captured vehs."

The tasks he saw as:

1) care of cas on the Dropping Zone (DZ),
2) care on the approach march in to or out of the assembly area,
3) collection of cas in the bn area and their immediate treatment,
4) transport of cas to a DS and treatment there,
5) holding and after treatment at the DS for up to 6 days,
6) later, evac to captured hospitals/ medical units of land forces.

"In certain types of operation e.g. destruction of a coast battery, enemy H.Q., a rapid withdrawal will be effected as soon as task is completed. Any seriously injured cas will have to be left behind with 1 or more bn orderlies to look after them. The greater part of the bn medical resources, including the RMO, may still be required for another task."

The new PFA (Para Fd Amb) was organised as an H.Q. plus 4 sections. Each section of 1 MO and 19 O.R.s, with their equipment carried on the men, was enough to set up a DS for the immediate treatment of 50 casualties. Each section had to be self-supporting. 2 Whitley bombers, the first British airborne troop carrying aircraft, or 1 C47, the Dakota, flew the section into action. Other "jumping personnel", including cooks, drivers, the carpenter, transport officer, with their heavier kit, needed

6 Whitleys. In one lift, 14 Whitleys carried the whole PFA. But in practice, the number to be dropped was always less — it depended upon the task or the tactical situation.

Surgical teams, with all their necessary equipment, were normally attached to a section, or 1 team to 2 sections.

While the first airborne tasks were small raids or attacks on strategic targets, with quick withdrawal, the aim was to produce a major airborne unit. On 23rd May, 1942, Major General F.A.M. Browning, DSO, commanding 1 Airborne Division, in his second training instruction, noted that " many details of ground usage by tps needs to be improved."...also "the general object of trg was not for small raids, but for a big operation of the whole division."

The medicals shared the severe parachute training. The jumping was in many ways the least of it — the hard work was to fit the men for the gruelling fighting on the ground after they had landed. Fitness training, and first-aid and resuscitative training beyond the standard usually required for RAMC orderlies, to which was added infantry skills, formed the basis. The new "battle drill" was included. And to the ordinary individual and collective Fd Ambs training was added practice in clearing loads from the Dropping or Landing Zones to the RV. As duties had to be interchangeable, men and officers were taught the whole range. Finally, the use of smoke — as cover for the evacuation of casualties — was practised.

The ADMS of 1 Airborne Div was Colonel A. Austin Eagger. Arthur Eagger, called "The Boss" by his officers and men, was born in Northern China in 1898. He was the son of Scottish missionaries. In the First War he had served in the Gordon Highlanders, and was wounded in 1918. In 1922 he completed his medical training at Aberdeen University, the first university in Britain to have a "mediciner", or professor of medicine, on its staff. Between the wars he had been in the Territorial Army.

Exercise "MERLIN" on 15th September, 1942, was a major preparatory exercise for the first airborne landing of the war as part of what General Browning had called a "big operation"; soon after, 1st Para Brigade was part of the force which was to assault the enemy in Algeria. The G.O.C. wrote on 28th October:

"To all ranks of the 1st Para Bde. You are the first troops of the Airborne Division to go overseas to take your part in the final defeat of the enemy.

As such a great responsibility rests upon each one of you…the thoughts of all your comrades in the Division go with you.

A great future awaits the Airborne Forces, and in your hands that future rests."

This was the attack which preceded the sea assault. 1 Para Bn was dropped at Souk. El Arba at 1315 hrs on 16th October, 1942, and 2 Bn with 503 Regt, Parachute Royal Engineers, were dropped at Tebessa at 1030 hrs on 15th October, to occupy the airfield, called Maison Blanche.

Many things were inevitably quite hazardous, in this very first major operation. Not least was the fact that there were no large-scale maps, tourist size — 1:200,000 — were all that was available. Colonel McEwen, commanding 16 PFA, noticed that their landing area was just a cross on a very vague part of the map! But the attack was successful.

As SMO of the 1st Para Bde, Lieutenant Colonel McEwen, went into army health action at once:

FIELD 17 Nov 1942.

To H.Q. 1 Para Bde. Subject: Aerodrome Maison Blanche.

From SMO 1 Para Bde.

I have inspected the sanitary arrangements at the above aerodrome and find them most unsatisfactory. The following remedial measures are urgently required.

a) The aerodrome and an area of 100 yds(110m) surrounding it to be immediately cleared of all papers, tins, bottles, scraps of food, etc, and also of *human faeces*. Personnel are defaecating anywhere and everywhere…

He then went on to require the digging of a deep trench latrine behind each hanger, with fly-proof seating and toilet paper; one trough urinal beside each; one ablution bench at the water point in front of each hanger — all to have correct run-off soakage pit via grease traps in case of ablutions; one wash up bench for exclusive use of cooks in front of each hanger; Six shower baths; "numerous fly-proof receptacles"; two incinerators in front of each hanger; all rubbish to be collected twice daily and incinerated; surface drains to be kept clear of rubbish, sprayed with PARIS GREEN (anti-mosquito). He next put out MAIs (medical administrative instructions), requiring returns of disease, scabies and lice, casualties of bns and Fd Ambs, self-inflicted injuries, and of the "designated diseases of anthrax, poliomyelitis, typhus, cerebro-spinal fever", and others. He made the need for hygiene the priority issue it had to be, no matter how awkward his measures may have seemed to some non-medicals.

The land battle after the initial landing provided plenty of mistakes and plenty of problems for all arms, and not least for the RAMC. In the initial drop, it had been at once apparent that dispersal of Fd Ambs personnel amongst the rest of the unit was unhelpful, as it did no more than delay the assembling of the medical section. Although the obvious risk of losing a section entire if a plane was shot down existed, it was considered later, on balance, better to put the section "stick" to jump together.

A special concern was how the French near Algiers would react; Major W.R. de B. des Voeux, the Brigade Major of 1 Para Bde, who was one of the solitary three casualties in the drop, twisting his ankle, found General Barre, commanding the French troops in Tunisia, at his headquarters hidden in the hills. He found the French typically cold and insistent that all speech be in French and that the Major keep the British troops hidden! Fortunately General Pequin, commanding the French aviation, was more friendly, and after Major des Voeux had explained politely in his fluent French that the British had come to fight the Germans and not to hide themselves, a comprise was worked out.

2 Para were forced back into the hills by German tanks. Later they were split up and surrounded, and had to fight their way out. In the confusion, Lieutenant McGavin and the 17 soldiers of his section were captured. During the battle, much of the ADS was lost, apparently because it was not within the perimeter of the defence.

Equipment being used for the first time stood the test — apart from the inevitable losses of containers during the drop and later. Each man carried basic pouches with field dressings. Each parachute rifle company had its quota of medical equipment; 1 airborne haversack, 1 medical water bottle, 1 airborne stretcher, and so on.

The airborne FST did exceptionally well in this first ever action. The ADMS in his report afterwards wrote: "Lieutenant C.G. Rob[10] commanded a FST which did exceptionally well.... I was impressed by the efficient way compound fractures had been put in POP by the Surgical Team."... of Lieutenant Rob he said: "an officer of great initiative and exceptional professional ability, and that equally good results cannot always be expected." For when the ground medical units collected the treated casualties, the high standard of care was quickly reported around the RAMC. It was a happy first start for the newly formed "para-medics."[11]

The Return to Europe. Sicily and Italy.

Attacks onto the toe of Italy soon followed the victory parade in Tunis. Both King George VI and Winston Churchill were present, as they had been earlier in Tripoli. The first Allied landfall — for U.S. troops were now heavily involved, and the Canadians re-appeared — was on the Island of Sicily.

For the invasion, it was decided to put extra FSTs on the hospital ships accompanying the assault. The team from 58 GH consisted of "Dad" Hawthorne the anaesthetist, who had been a sergeant in the Essex Regiment in the First War, James Ross the surgeon, and Messrs Evans and Wagstaffe, the theatre orderlies. The sister was not posted in till later; she would be a Canadian.

Cpl Evans was a Regular soldier, called back from the Reserve. He had been at Dunkirk and Crete.[12] Wagstaffe was the youngest, English and unmarried. The medical officers were amazed at the white sheets in their comfortable cabin, "where the sheets and towels showed a striking contrast to our begrimed and sand-impregnated clothes."

They sailed on H.M.S. *Amra*, staffed by South Africans. Their initial sense of things being easy was rudely shattered when the hospital ship *Talamba* was bombed — in spite of her white paint, red crosses, and lights. Their first hours were taken up, anchored off the beach at Avola, dealing with badly burned casualties from the ships which had been hit, and listening to the noise of the bombs falling too near them for comfort. The worst burns came from the Timothy Pickering, which had been carrying petrol and ammunition. For the first time the FST encountered coloured American soldiers, and they were impressed by their fortitude.

"We entered the main harbour and anchored among the main vessels of the invasion fleet, the unloading of which was in full swing", wrote Major Ross in his diary. "Everybody looked out eagerly...the landscape was quite strange to us after the monotonous sands of the Western Desert. Here were hedgerows and trees, orchards and glades — how green — we were back in a world we knew...our road went up the valley of the Anapo; in the fields alongside, under the big olive-trees, were tents, bivouacs, and vehicles of the numerous units which had arrived before us. The sunburnt soldiers, obviously all the old desert crowd, brewing up or washing in their roadside camp, shouted greetings to our fellows speeding by."

"Some miles inland we reached the little town of Florida. The streets were packed with the inhabitants, every window balcony being full as well. Extraordinary sensation to see women again with their faces exposed and dressed in a civilised way, after years of looking at swathed-up walking Arabians...Did these Sicilians hiss or cat-call ? Not a bit of it. Smiles on all sides, waving of hands, laughter at the antics of our fellows crammed on the lorries...'Oh boy, look at that one there! Hullo, darling!'"

"The hospital tents went up quickly, and the personnel also went under canvas. We still messed in the open — our mess table piled with grapes and figs, lemons and tomatoes... after the short commons of Tripoli, we gorged ourselves on the delicious fresh fruit."

"When the sisters came, a few days later, they had their mess a couple of hundred yards away under an immense locust-bean tree... we could watch them, and they us; we would occasionally exchange mess visits, exchanging the shade of the olive for the shade of the locust-tree, all rather delightful in the warm Sicilian evenings." Major Ross, romanticising at the climate and the new-found absence of glare from sun, was brought to earth by his C.O., however, who pointed out, the first evening walk they had together, that the pools Ross thought so pretty were full of mosquito larvae. And in no time malaria was the enemy the medicals had to combat. It became a high priority.[13]

There was a long struggle up the length of Italy. Losses were heavy, especially in the succession of set-piece battles, some in country whose geography favoured the enemy, especially an enemy as skilled and resourceful as the Germans. Sea landings were opposed, especially at Salerno and Anzio, and the Monte Cassino and Gothic Line Battles have gone into British military history.

The British Medical Area on the Anzio beachead lay on slightly sloping fields, about 300 yds(274m) off the right-hand side of the main Anzio-Rome road and 3 miles(5km) from the coast. Below it and to the north, and only about 200yds(183m) away, was the reinforcement/reception area for British troops on the beachead, hidden in a dense tangle of brushwood. On the right, across a field, lay ammunition dumps, and behind, to the south, the cemetery and more ammunition dumps. Across the main road some barns housed part of an FDS. Later, a Bath Unit moved in there.

14 CCS arrived on February 8th. Its tents were erected rapidly by the staff, all desert veterans: reception tent at the entry, then the pre-operation and resuscitation ward, with the theatre tents leading off from it by a corridor of tent walls. Next came the ward tents, and farther away were the Medical Officers' and RAMC WOs' and soldiers' lines. None of these were dug down at first. The CCS opened at 1800 hrs on the 8th and the reception and pre-op wards were filled immediately. The first operating session began at 1930hrs, and 14 major cases were done through the night, including 4 penetrating abdominal wounds. The men had all been wounded that day, the average time between wounding and operation being about 7 hours. Machine-gun, shell, and mortar had caused the majority, and most of the men had not one but many wounds. The night shift fell into their beds on a bitterly cold morning; they would re-start again at 1400hrs the next afternoon.

The weather now utterly broke down and furious icy winds howled over the dismal flat beach area. The rain and gale slowed down the fighting, too, and made flying impossible. All air attack ceased on the next three days. The evacuation of wounded had to stop also, and both 14 CCS and its neighbour 21 became absolutely full. Another FSU came in and set up their big operating tent alongside. The surgeons and sisters and anaesthetists and the operating theatre assistants had budgeted to work 12-hour shifts, but the three shifts had to overlap, so great was the load of work.

The contrast with the heat and dryness of Africa could not have been greater. Figures in great-coats, tin helmets, and gas cape waterproofs, dripping and mud-stained, stumbled through the doorway to the ward, kicking aside the sodden blanket curtains, as they carried in their stretchers. (US troops, who had been told Italy was a hot country and issued with tropical kit, begged for British greatcoats). The theatre stretcher bearers were continually coming in from the theatre corridor, carrying patients just operated on. The transfusion orderlies hurried about, carrying the transfusion stands, bottles of blood and plasma, and the giving sets for administering them. The doctors of the CCS were constantly bending over the men, fixing the transfusion needles in place. The FTU arrived and took over this hard work; at this time the transfusion needles were not the sophisticated variety of the 1980's but thick needles which could all too easily come out of the vein, leaving a large haematoma at the site. The atmosphere, the kit, and the certainty of aerial attack were different from 1918, but the European weather was not.

Although the Anzio beachead was overlooked to such an extent that the German enemy said it was "the biggest POW cage in the world", the Allies made progress in this fierce battle and captured prisoners themselves. The doctors felt as they always did towards these: "The Jerries were an ordinary crowd, well behaved, wandering off to the latrines and returning quietly...apart from their uniforms, many very like our own lads — not really strangers."[14] And the medical officers as always knew that the nurses got the patients better in the way only they could: "On the 19th a great event occurred. Reinforcements arrived for the CCS, and with them our QAIMNS sisters...they had been most disappointed at being left behind till now (the Americans had had sisters on the beachead since D-Day)...now they were here — our pretty Matron and her nine sisters...they were in great form...Miss Campbell took over as theatre and Miss Payne the pre-op ward...they took over the wards again."

For these amphibious operations, from the attack on North-West Africa onwards, modifications in the usual medical field disposal was planned and tested.[15] Inevitably, there were mistakes in the early operations. Brigadier Robert Atkins criticised "Operation HUSKY's" (Sicily) failure of the beach planning staff to cater for the needs of medical units especially as regards stretchers and blankets, as well as medical stores, to provide a medical pool of reserves — since RAMC losses of personnel were not insignificant. He was also critical of the failure of Naval officers in charge to include medicals when issuing orders, and of having no hoist arrangements for returning casualties. These last were so poor, he reported, that in future the medical authorities must have the right to inspect all ships to ensure that equipment was satisfactory. As far as the Army was concerned, he was also critical of the calibre of the SMO(Beach); several were just not good enough for what soon proved to be a key job during the landing.

Medical and Surgical success. Penicillin.

The campaigns in North Africa and Italy saw no new major surgical technical change — delayed primary suture was established everywhere. As noted, those with no knowledge of history believed it to be a new invention. There was a phase of packing wounds with vaseline gauze after excision, and enveloping the limb in Plaster-of-Paris, but this was found unsatisfactory and was soon discarded.

Trueta, in the Spanish Civil War, had excised wounds and then encased the limb in POP, to await suture sometime later. But the appearance of the sulphonamides raised again the notion that this new drug would do away with the necessity of immediate excision, and that Plaster plus sulphonamide was enough. The first U.S. Army surgeons were enthusiastic supporters of this method, until their very bad results taught them otherwise. They became the latest group to learn quickly that d.p.s. (delayed primary suture) was the procedure of choice.[16]

The "Tobruk Plaster" was devised because of the very long carry of desert warfare, and was so-called because it was used during the siege of Tobruk. The Thomas Splint of the 1914–18 War had saved many lives of those with femoral shaft fractures, but on the long LofC in North Africa was insufficient in itself to immobilise the bone comfortably. So the splinted limb was wrapped in shell dressings and wool, and then encased in a cylinder of Plaster-of-Paris. With this absolute fixation, the patient could travel along the uneven desert tracks in comfort. It was largely in 62 G.H, by Colonel Wilson Smith and his colleagues in the Tobruk garrison, that the method was developed.

Use of Penicillin was going to be the major advance, however, along with blood transfusion, of Second World War surgery. And because the major early work in the clinical use of what was the first antibiotic and hence a revolution in medicine was largely done by the RAMC, its story requires to be recorded *in extenso*.

Penicillin was discovered in 1929 by Fleming. It was introduced into the Army in April, 1942, when at a meeting of the War Wounds Committee of the MRC, Professor H. Florey offered a small quantity of it which had been prepared at the Sir William Dunn School of Pathology in Oxford (and where Trueta had worked) to the War Office. He asked that it be tried out in the Middle East.

The strength of this new drug was expressed in units — Oxford units — and the very first of these preparations were only 30–40 units in strength. But by July 1944, because of the speed of its development, its strength was 1600 units per mg. The first batches were sent out by air, and after 15 patients had been treated, its obvious benefit in controlling wound infection was reported by R.J.V. Pulvertaft.[17]

A team was then sent to Africa — Lieutenant Colonel Ian Fraser, surgeon; Major Scott Thomson, anaesthetist, and an RAMC technician. They sailed for Algiers with 10 million units in May, 1943. Lieutenant Colonel John Matheson, then an ADMS in GHQ, remembered "This jolly chap (Fraser, a Northern Irishman, with their delightful fun and wit) came in", and remembered, laughingly, the DDMS Jock Macfie, saying "Never heard anything so ridiculous!" Fraser and his team went at once to Tripoli to begin their clinical trial.

But because major operations had ended before they arrived, Fraser's team's first use for the new drug was on septic wounds already weeks old. Professor Florey arrived almost immediately after. He very quickly decided that the real place for penicillin was in the early stages of wound infection and before chronic sepsis had developed. Soon Brigadier Hugh Cairns, the neurosurgeon, came out and joined the team, and the preliminary report was sent to the MRC in October 1943.

Lessons were quickly learned and the results made widely known. Indications, dosage, treatment schedules, were all worked out. Lectures and demonstrations were given, in England courses were begun at the Royal Herbert Hospital Woolwich, and then Sir Howard Florey had a film made. Later again Naval officers, civilians, and Allied Forces Medical Services were taught. It was clear that penicillin, by reducing the overall stay of wounded in hospital, was a great saver of the precious commodity of manpower, then as through the centuries the great limiter of Britain's armies. It had been also made clear that many other diseases responded dramatically.[18]

Colonel Ian Fraser, having acquired a DSO for gallantry in the field, became ill and was replaced by Lieutenant Colonel J.S. Jeffrey. By now the intramuscular route was standard; because 15 minutes after an injection of 15,000 units the level of penicillin in the blood was no longer bacteriostatic, the drug had to be given 3-hourly. Pain at the time and after was a problem; skin irritation and other toxic effects in a few cases became recognised. The appearance of resistant organisms had been noticed.

In the British Army in Italy, at first operations at the CCS, the routine became to insufflate penicillin/sulphamonide powder, 5,000 units per gm, through the wound on completion of wound excision. The instruction of the day went on: "wound left open, insufflated with powder to form a thick 'hoar frost' (average 2–4 gm i.e. 10,000–20,000 units), covered with vaseline gauze, and immobilized for the journey. Primary suture of wounds in the forward areas, where the patient cannot be retained, is always dangerous."

This notice, to the RAMC surgeon of 1943, has brought us up-to-date: those of us who have done just the same to a war wound we have just excised, feel at once that these are our colleagues in a way that the previous war surgeons somehow are not. We are doing "the same thing."

Objective results, too, were striking. Lieutenant Colonel Fraser and his colleagues showed that out of 100 wounds so treated at a CCS in Sicily, the average time after wounding being 10 hours, and not disturbed till they reached a base hospital in Tripoli 5 days later, 50 per cent showed no growth on bacterial culture when unveiled. 100 wounds treated with sulphonamide showed only 17 per cent with no bacterial growth. The result was significant.

The medical officers treated flesh wounds, femoral fractures, gas gangrene cases, and marvelled at what were to them miraculous cures. Penicillin was something which would change the face of sepsis, and they realised this; for the first time ever, infection was treatable by systemic means.[19]

As we read the accounts of the surgeons of the Italian Campaign, as distinct from the North African Campaign, we cannot but feel that an advance had occurred. Report after report tells of a higher level of attainment. "To make the wound safe for life is not enough", said Major H.W. Burge at the Congress of Central Mediterranean Force surgeons in Rome on 12th–19th February, 1945.

"We must make it, too, safe for successful suture" — and he and the other "galaxy of talent"[20] stressed that now RAMC surgeons were looking to the minimum of post-operative complication. "In Africa the Advanced Surgical Centres had dressed patients placed on the table; now we have the patient stripped, examined, recorded, X-rayed — all done. The skin is prepared in pre-op..."

At the same Congress the DMS was Major General W.C. Hartgill, CB, OBE, MC, KHS, a New Zealander who had joined the RAMC. "A great chap", remembered General Matheson, "a great smoker." He had chaired a committee which recommended changes in the structure of field medical units, which would have implications for many years in the future.

The change in the RMO's equipment of most importance was the use of the stretcher jeep; although the bren gun carrier had been useful in Africa, in Italy the jeep had advantages. The terrain meant that a 4-wheel drive ambulance was best for field ambulances carrying.

In Africa and in Italy, the ASC, made up of an FDS and a FSU, had taken away from the status of the field ambulances; it had, according to Hartgill's committee, become an almost unnecessary stage between the RMO and the units behind. He therefore proposed a larger field ambulance, of 310 all ranks. It should have 3 companies, 1 to each brigade, of 70 personnel, and a H.Q. of 100 all ranks. This would form the divisional light sick reception Station. One FDS would remain with each division; it needed a mobile steriliser and X-ray, and should have 60 beds and not 40.

Hartgill had special comment on armoured divisions: "Evacuation from an armoured formation is regarded as being much more difficult than it is, it is probably the easiest formation of all from where to evac wounded. The cas are always comparatively light and vehicles are plentiful." What Captain J.P.D. Graham would have said to this might have been worth recording.

His greatest change was proposed for the CCS. He regarded the CCS as having had its functions taken over by the ASC, and looked forward to a 200 bed field hospital being substituted instead.

He also had proposals for the Medical Branch at Divisional HQ. "The ADMS Branch must become an attached HQ and the ADMS be designated Commander AMS (CAMS)." But these two changes would be many years in the future.[21]

These, and many other advances of the Middle East and earlier Mediterranian Campaign, would be carried forward into the next phase of the Return to Europe.

OVERLORD.
"If they attack in the West, the attack will decide the War." (Adolf Hitler, December, 1943).

(In 1944) "Germany's sole conceivable chance of escaping catastrophe lay in the destruction of OVERLORD": Op cit, Max Hastings, 1984, Pan Books, p 70.

Our Corps had been asked to give the fighting arms medical support in landings from the sea before. Those in NW Africa, Sicily and Italy had taught lessons and revealed shortcomings. But this assault, across the narrow English Channel, had somehow a special significance for the British. The Americans had no qualms; the British had. It was perhaps their history of involvement in Continental Europe which, however much it allured in days of the Plantagenets, had gone wrong and turned them away to seek their fortune over the wider world. The story of Napoleon's intended invasion they knew well. Most of all was the recollection of the so-recent expectation of invasion of England herself, following the defeat of France, four years earlier. For the older generation there were the memories of the Great War.

Their successors as a world power would provide the majority of the Force; the ever likeable Canadians were there, as were the French — for them this was their homeland they were going back to. Then there were Polish and some Dutch soldiers. The British were back to their traditional role of being the smaller army, under command of the General whose nation was to provide the largest contingent. There were to be four phases in the Battle for Western Europe.[22] The first, the landing on the Normandy beaches, was clearly the most critical. General

Eisenhower, who had not commanded anything larger than a battalion before coming over the Atlantic, wrote an Order of the Day, which was to be broadcast if the attack failed.

For this initial landing, the AMS task was to provide medical cover almost as soon as the first infantry and armour had landed, and inside a beachead which would be small and packed with every conceivable sort of military hardware.

Planning and training must leave nothing to chance. The motoring maps of Algeria would not do this time. But for at least the previous year, His Majesty's Government had encouraged British citizens to look out every holiday photograph, map, and item of local information, about France, Holland and Germany, however small and apparently insignificant, and send them in to those planning the invasion so that they could create the most detailed picture for the attackers.

OVERLORD was perhaps the first time highly detailed loading tables, as they came to be called, were used in medical planning on a large scale. They had been used, especially by the US military, before Operation TORCH, the invasion of Tunisia. But this era marked the end of the previous practice of transporting all a medical unit's kit in a bulk move. For the medicals — as well as for others — particular attention was paid to "assault" and "light" scales of equipment so that the units landing early would not take up shipping space unnecessarily. "Tactical packing", a similar term, had at once been seen essential for airborne operations, so that all bandages did not find themselves in one canister. Here, because of the astronomical volume of stores having to be transported in small vessels and in the correct tactical and logistical sequence, it was even more vital.

The "block system" was the expression used for the tactical packing of hospitals, and followed similar principles.

Details of the recovery of casualties back to England had also to be planned with the same care. Experience in the Mediterranean had shown that the Landing Ship Tank (LST) had much to offer close in-shore; hospital carriers had to stand off and were large enough to present big targets for bombers. The appearance of the DUKW (dual drive $2^{1/2}$ ton (2.55 tonnes) amphibious truck) was a benefit not previously available.

Of the multitude of other policy and other items, setting aside of MOs and RAMC soldiers to be attached, in the first few weeks, to the Agency looking after Civilian Affairs, to assist with civilian casualties; the date for nursing sisters to arrive (agreed to be not earlier than D+8; till then RAMC orderlies from units crossing later in the procession had to be temporarily employed); maintenance of supply of stretchers, blankets, pyjamas, pre-sterilised surgical instruments and dressings, medical comforts of all sorts from self-heating cocoa and urinals to transfusion fluid and penicillin; water — 2 gallons(9 litres) allowed for each casualty during the first 48 hrs; increase in holding capacity of hospitals and CCSs; extra FDSs for exhaustion cases; a labour force from the Royal Pioneer Corps; depots of medical stores — all had to be planned and organized. It was the province of the Quartermaster's side — as vital a part of the Corps as the doctors — to do most of this. Lastly, and important from both a medical and political point of view, was regular liaison with the US Medical Services on the whole range of shared interest and information. The Age of Technology had arrived earlier, but by now most people were aware of it.[23]

By May 1944, Southern England was packed with troops. 224 PFA, who were to be dropped at the start of the assault, were "literally prisoners in our own country…for us the operation had already begun", their men remembered. "certainly we did our best to enjoy those last few days, for few of us had ever felt so conscious of being alive. But at the same time we were aware of another emotion, a sense of our collective importance." This was almost another generation of war-time soldiers — they had spent all their time since being called up training in the U.K. base for D-Day. And they were also younger. The writer remembers as a schoolboy army cadet on his way that month to a course at the Army Physical Training Corps Depot in Aldershot, having passed his preliminary course in Redford barracks, being offered his seat by a lovely elderly lady in the bus on his way through London. "Don't they look so young", she said to her friend. At $15^{1/2}$ he was only one year off service age.

"We knew we were to be the spearhead of the invasion for which the world was waiting with baited breath." This was true, and the men of the invasion army talked and recalled that time in a unique way. It was different from anything in First War diaries or letters.

"Few of us will ever forget our feelings when we ourselves set eyes on the huge important maps marked OPERATION

OVERLORD and saw for the first time place names like VARAVILLE, OUSTREHAM and CAEN. The thoroughness of this plan, illustrated with a wealth of aerial photographs and models, astonished us by the completeness of the information it was based on and filled us with confidence. As one unit followed another through the briefing tents, we found it difficult to tear ourselves away…we wanted to make ourselves word perfect in our part." It was feared that the Germans might bomb the South Coast and disrupt the troop concentrations.

"By midday on 4th June we heard that the invasion had been postponed. Next day it was all on again though the sky was overcast, but weather reports were favourable…three hours before dusk we paraded, fantastically upholstered, every pocket bulging through festoons of webbing; we stuffed ourselves into our jumping jackets and waddled to the waiting lorries.

Then we smoked our last cigarette in England while we chatted to the RAF crew.

Even the most insensate among us were hardly immune from a slight shiver as the engines roared for the take off."

90 per cent of the field ambulances who were dropped in Normandy had never been in action before. Well used to the machine-gun and tracer fired at them during the realistic battle drills while training (where a casualty rate of up to 1 per cent was the accepted norm), they had not known yet the reality of war. So the effect of heavy flak from the anti-aircraft batteries, which forced the pilots to take violent evasive action and made their jump different from anything they had experienced during training exercises, was upsetting. The well-practised sticks came apart; their DZ at Varaville they found to be a marsh, because the enemy had flooded it. This was not in the previous training. But the attack was successful.

Lieutenant A.C. Holliday was Q.M. of 20 FDS. The unit task was to land on Queen Red Beach and set up a Beach DS as part of the Beach Group. Holliday had joined the unit as recently as late May, while it was in Waterville Camp in Hampshire. He thought the unit members, while having no real fear of the approaching battle, were curiously lacking in plans for after the War. This was some thing he had not met before.

He went with three other officers and 40 other ranks to Newhaven on the Monday, after getting up at 0500 hrs. Their

LCI had 200 troops on board from various units. Everyone had full marching order and one blanket. The medicals carried their haversacks full of dressings. The rest of 20 FDS was in other LCIs; they had a total of 3 MOs, a Dental officer, and 1 non-medical officer apart from himself. There were 90 ORs including RASC. 20 FDS had no attached FSU or FTU, but instead 1 surgeon, 1 anaesthetist, and 2 extra MOs.

When they set sail at 2000 hrs, the sea got very rough. As always, it got rougher as soon as they met the open Channel. "The sea was full of craft, all zig-zagging… about midnight we saw hundreds of planes, many towing gliders, Airborne to secure the bridges over the Orne and the canal…unforgettable sight was the naval bombardment — we were lifted to see the enemy getting it after so many Luftwaffe raids. We cheered the Navy."

They approached the shore at 0830 next morning. Almost everyone had been sick. No-one had slept. But because of the good air cover, there had been no interference by the enemy.

Their much-practised exit from the LSI wasn't possible. One side door was hit by a rock when it was opened, the other was smashed by an abandoned craft. Mortar and shell-fire was falling around. The flail tanks had cleared a way through the minefields[24] and this was marked as ever by white tape. Lieutenant Holliday admired the M.P. who was directing traffic "as if he was at the Aldershot Tattoo."

They found their site was in a minefield, so had to have the C.O. pick another in an orchard. The surgeon, anaesthetist, and several men were missing, so the Q.M went to search for them and bring them back.

"Mitting, the young surgeon, had been violently sick but did a wonderful job… he started operating at once under a tarpaulin stretched over a lorry and kept going till he was completely exhausted. He should have been relieved by a FSU coming with the next tide but they did not appear and he worked on. He should have got a medal."[25]

As QM, Holliday was responsible for the rations, supply of stretchers and blankets, and everything else besides. The unit had only biscuits, but "gallons of tea." Like all good quartermasters, he managed to produce what was needed, and cigarettes and even some whisky as well. "How we stayed on our feet I have never fathomed. But the combatant troops were tireder than we were. They fought determinedly, though they were so sea-sick."

Another FDS, No 2, was commanded by Lieutenant Colonel I.S. Campbell, RAMC His dental officer, Captain Alex Blair, was the unit anaesthetist and resuscitation officer. 2 FDS was also a Beach DS; "the criteria were ?fit to travel — estimated by physical signs." Penicillin was given in doses of 100,000 units — by now the preferred dose. It was laid down that it was to be used only for battle casualties, not accidental wounds and certainly not for gonorrhoea. (This last might seem superfluous, but Colonel Campbell remembered a group of entrepreneurial young ladies who arrived and set up another sort of service for the troops — they even brought some protective screening ! The Military Police arrived, sent them away, but not before relieving them of their financial takings which they handed over to one unit's benevolent fund).

Colonel Campbell recalled in a few sentences the whole story of the beachhead — the storm of wet weather, the Mulberry harbour being begun, the amazing possibility of buying picture postcards of the locality, the priorities of evacuation. As at Bloemfontein, when stores of higher military importance had to have priority, Normandy casualties had to be held on the beach until needs of war had been supplied and passed onwards. He enunciated the clear finding of the landing soldiers, as far as casualty evacuation was concerned: "The LSTs saved the situation."[26]

Captains Begbie and Smith were on the strength of 105 General Hospital, and their story is worth telling. Two weeks before D-Day they and other RAMC officers were posted to "help man a hospital on the south coast", said Captain Begbie. "I joined the Queen Alexandra Hospital at Cosham, Portsmouth, with a mixed staff of Services and staff from the London Hospital. The roads and woods were packed with army…. The medical civilian staff were under a senior civilian and they seemed to us clueless…on D-Day, having seen the vessels moving, I found myself the only MO posted to Reception and some theatre equipment was not even unpacked.

My first casualty arrived at 6 p.m. on 6th June — a young rating off a destroyer — the troops had been issued with special D-Day money and he gave me one of these as a memento…very soon we became hectically busy as a CCS. The front-line MOs had attached the labels with diagnosis and clinical notes —

ambulances poured in — after emergency treatment was given as necessary they went off by hospital trains for surgery. Penicillin was very scarce — we had to plead for this drug from the MO in charge, a naval officer we called Penicillin Pete.

French casualties and POWs came in as well as our own men. Some of the Germans were very young — one lad aged 19 told me he had been in the army for three years. Nights were very lively with German bombers making for London and Spitfires chasing them and the sky alive with tracer bullets. On 12th June an unusual noise wakened me in the dawn — in the sky was a strange, aircraft shape with fire issuing from its tail — the first of the V1s had arrived. They were to become a frequent sight.

Recalled to our unit in July we found ourselves in the shooting down area of V1s and when the engine cut out everyone dived for cover and we had some nasty cas when they were shot down."

The hospital crossed over in the first week of August, and before they sailed, the unit had a visit from Brigadier Arthur Porrit, Consulting Surgeon to 21 Army Group ("we were all proudly wearing our 21 Army Group badges" recalled Captain Begbie) and Brigadier Bulmer, formerly a much loved O.C. Medical Division now promoted.

"We landed at Arromanches and thence by truck through inches of dust through the French lanes amid much cheering to a transit camp with polluted water and very primitive facilities…our troops greeted us with 'Time you people turned up' ."

Soon 105 prepared to take over a large tented hospital from another unit. "We were within hearing of the battle zone and the sky lit up at nights with tracer bullets. Living quarters were in lines in the orchards of Normandy, our mobile kitchen organized feeding for our own mess tent and our hygiene was pretty good with canvas basins and baths. Work was very brisk", went on Captain Begbie, "with our own casualties and POW, many of whom had to be de-loused. Fighting was not far away in Caen and St Lo…we were at Ranché near Bayeux. One tragic incident followed the Battle of the Falaise Gap. These cas came in with various diagnostic labels from the field ambulances and were scattered in various wards before it was realised that we had a typhoid epidemic on our hands…quite a number died in spite of up-to-date inoculations."

The Break-out, pursuit, and on to Victory in Europe.

The British were given the task of holding the solid German defence at Caen in July. "It was pretty unpleasant", said Captain Watty Yellowlees, MC, who had first reached Africa with the 1st Army but now found himself with the Cameron Highlanders. A relative of the Lieutenant Yellowlees who had been an early psychiatrist in the First War, he achieved the rare distinction of being described by Major General Wimberley of 51(H) Div. as the "epitome of the Regimental Medical Officer." While the British pinned down large enemy forces, the U.S. Forces broke through in great strength at Avranches, raced behind German positions at Argentan, and the Canadians advanced south from Caen towards Falaise. The capture of the German Army in what was called the Falaise Gap ensured that the end of the Normandy phase was certain.

Captain Begbie takes up the story: "With the offensive moving forward we got orders to move also. Our C.O. with an advance party departed — destination unknown to us. The tremendous job of packing — even by full light of hurricane lamps — got into the swing and by 0400 on the 8th of October 1944 we were on the road — quite a spectacle as the O.C, Surgical Div left in charge decided to move in one fell swoop.

Unfortunately all the food was packed in one huge lorry which broke down. (Tactical packing was not the O.C. Surgical Div's strong point). The cunning sergeants had managed to stock up with hard boiled eggs and apples and kindly offered some of their hoard to us.

We passed through towns of sheer ruin and desolation — Caen, Amiens, Major, etc, and staged overnight at Amiens. The local town mayor knew nothing of our arrival but managed to get some beds and tents but no food...NAAFI tea and hard tack biscuits kept us going...NAAFI tea was foul — a mixed powder of dusty tea, sugar and dried milk. Roused at 0400 and so into Belgium which was so neat and tidy in stark contrast to France. We sped through Ostend and then heard gunfire and saw smoke ahead and the Military Police chased after us to tell us the Germans had only just retreated and we had to turn about.

We passed the Belgian Military Hospital where we should have taken over but the Germans had smashed it all up and booby-trapped the whole place...the Belgians meantime were occupied searching for collaborators…young women had their heads shorn and shopkeepers had their premises gutted and contents thrown into the gutter.

Word would come of urgent evacuations and fleets of ambulances would arrive…my largest ward had 70 beds all full…at the Walchern tragedy to our troops and an old friend John Forfar[27] brought in many of his men badly wounded…"

But Captains Begbie and Smith had an unexpected find in Bruges (which the Germans had not devastated) — "we found a bottle of Chanel perfume." For Isma Begbie and Beryl Smith were women RAMC officers, sharing with their fellow officers all the dangers of the Normandy campaign. They were among the first women MOs to go over to the continent.

To reduce the account of the rest of the Normandy Campaign to a few sentences does not in any way detract from the immense achievement which it was. But as far as the Medical Services were concerned, all that could be said has been said already; all the units of the AMS simply did again what has been described before. They do not need to be repeated. This time there was a victorious army to support. The evacuation became almost straightforward, and was made easier because the U.K. base was so near.[28] As the Allied Forces moved through France, the British and Americans entered Holland, whose citizens had had such a hard time during the Nazi occupation, and Belgium, so fought over through the centuries; they were met with joy everywhere. "The terrific crowds and the welcome we got will never be forgotten by those who were there", said a soldier of 128(Wessex) Fd Amb of the liberation of Brussels: "so the night need not, and perhaps better not, be recorded here."

The final round was as hard as any. All roads were badly cratered and impassable until bridges had been built. Air bombs and sea mines exploded under vehicles frequently hours after the leading troops had passed. The verges were heavily mined and road blocks and booby traps abounded… defence at all times stubborn — this was the verdict of Lieutenant Colonel J.M. Scott, OBE commanding the Wessex Fd Amb as it supported the Guards Armoured Division to the end of the War.

The Arnhem Battle, code-named MARKET GARDEN, the bold attempt to hasten victory by securing a succession of bridges between the Dutch frontier and the Neder Rijn, was a glorious failure. It has been written about most fully. The contribution of the AMS was especially that of the "para fd ambs" — 16 PFA with the first lift of paratroops and 133 PFA with the second lift. After the nine days of battle, from 17th till 26th September, 1944, the RAMC had had their full share of action. The general military accounts make little mention of them, as happens not infrequently — Christopher Hibbert's book making one only, naming "the RMOs J. Logan and D. Wright, working constantly and tirelessly, their forearms covered with blood." [29]

Major General R.E. Urquhart's account, however, tells of the wounded singing as they marched into captivity: "they sang on the march, and the Dutch civilians looked and marvelled, and the Germans were awed." The General spoke of "Warrack (Colonel Graeme Warrack, DSO, TD, ADMS of 1st Airborne Division), with his 24 medical officers at the hospital and 180 medical orderlies and Sbs as well as a number of Dutch nurses who had been working in the dressing station...it was a cold and unfriendly place and the conditions were primitive." Our Corps shared the Arnhem Battle with the rest of the Army. [29]

The daily news of the advance through Germany was interrupted by the pictures of the Belsen extermination camp when it was liberated on 15th April 1945. The horror of the photographs of the "pit of Belsen" and the living skeletons there was perhaps unequalled in the Western World, for the later pictures of the atomic bomb burst would show no more than a cloud in the sky and a number of casualties in figures. People did not really understand the significance of the bomb at first, but they shuddered at the implications of Belsen immediately. No one who went to Belsen — and RAMC units were at once on the scene — ever forgot it. [30]

One personal story can perhaps close the chapter. It concerned Lieutenant Colonel Martin Fallon, who had such difficulty in getting into the RAMC from Eire at the beginning of the War.

He had served in the Middle East, in Syria and Palestine first, then in Alexandria. Promoted Lieutenant Colonel he returned to U.K. by way of Malta and Naples. He was specially selected and promoted quickly, such was his reputation as a fearless, tireless surgeon.

"So much happened from D-Day onwards", was his recollection. Two events out of a multitude we will record — the first his contribution to the Arnhem Battle. He was O.C. surgical division in 39 General Hospital, placed in a Brussels hospital — "a huge place, with acres of grounds" immediately after the liberation. "After we had all been kissed on both cheeks, d'ye see, we got on with Montgomery's plan to win the war all on his own."

His account of the Arnhem Battle is a fascinating one, told from the aspect of one in medical support in the rear. His own contribution was told almost dismissively.[31] "Two hospitals took casualties on alternate days — ours took 5825 in 13 days. So did my opposite number in the nearby general hospital. So we were both busy…we both got the OBE. Most of the cas were from the forces trying to link up with the paras — I remember the Irish Guards were the lead regiment in the Guards Armoured Division. They were told by Monty to drive along the road two a-breast, as it was so wide. The German 88s knocked them off the road like ninepins — two at a time."

The second was Colonel Fallon's most famous patient of the War — William Joyce, Lord Haw-Haw. With his cheerful Irish humour, Martin enjoyed cocking a snook at authority if he felt like it.

On the evening of 28th May, 1945, Joyce was walking through a wood which overlooked the harbour at Flensberg. He saw two British officers gathering wood and for some unbelievable reason called out helpfully in English "there are a few more pieces over here", and was recognised by one of them, Lieutenant Perry. Perry, thinking Joyce was going to draw a revolver, shot him first. The bullets fired at close range passed through Joyce's right thigh, through his perineum, and out of his left thigh. Taken prisoner, Joyce was brought to 71 BGH at Flensberg Heath, beside British Second Army Headquarters. The O.C. surgical division was Lieutenant Colonel Martin Fallon, the anaesthetist, Major W.H. Scriven.

"Joyce had five holes in his arse when he was brought in to me", recalled Martin with his usual style of wit. "When he left he had the four extra ones closed." Fallon was put under severe pressure from the military police to hand over Joyce at once, but he refused. Pressurised again, he sought and obtained help from his DDMS, Brigadier Glyn Hughes, to have the patient kept in his care until his wounds were healed. Then, and only then, did Colonel Fallon agree to his removal.

Notes and references

CHAPTER 9

[1]cf, for example, Parkes' "Practical Hygiene", briefings for troops before the Boer War, pre-1914 work at the School of Hygiene, Sanitary Strategies (secret papers) 1939–45, Wellcome Archives 740, "Medical Diseases in Tropical and Sub-Tropical Areas" 1946, etc. Few people in Britain will know that no less a person than von Moltke wrote, on Parkes' death: "Every regiment in Europe ought to parade on the day of his funeral and lower their standards in honour of one of the greatest friends a soldier ever had." (M.E.M. Walker, "Pioneers of public health" Oliver and Boyd, Edinburgh and London, 1930, p 136.

[2]The status of the Army Medical Services probably never stood higher than in the 1939–45 War, especially in 1945 and during his time as D.G. He was not stood down at the end of hostilities, but continued in post until 1948. His major long-term contributions were to set up an excellent research facility and to inaugurate the military psychiatric service. Blood transfusion was in fact begun before 1941, and the credit for forward surgery must go to Sir Anthony Bowlby rather than to Hood. He was Governor of Bermuda from 1949–1955 — again evidence of his distinguished career. To Scots his winning of the Queen Victoria Jubilee Vase (the "Jug", as St Andreans call it) at the Royal and Ancient Autumn Meeting in 1953, "having an allowance of eight strokes", gave particular pleasure. He died in 1980.

[3]The medical units were handled differently in the mainly infantry battle of El Alamein compared to earlier in the North African Campaign. Because of the nature of the attack, they were phased in 3 stages — concentration, approach march, and deployment as the attack commenced. Field Dressing Stations had their role enhanced; there were now two to each infantry division. CCSs were to be as far forwards as possible. 10 miles(16km) behind the start line was actually achieved for 15 CCS; Brigadier Atkins' hopes were fulfilled.

For an armoured division of 13,000 men, infantry divisions of 16,000 each, plus 11,000 corps troops, 500 wounded were expected from the armoured division (5 per cent cas rate), 600 for one infantry division and 900 from the other (2.5 and 7.5 per cent rates respectively), and 2.5 per cent for corps troops — 250 casualties. This would give an estimated number of 2250 — 1000 lying and 1500 sitting. For the 1000 lying, 250 amb car journeys, using 84 cars, would be required; for the 1500 sitting, 24 amb car journeys carrying 270 cas and the remainder by Troop Carrying Vehicle (TCV). The medical planners asked for an extra 3-ton lorries in addition, as they considered there would be a shortfall.

[4]There was no doubt that certain TA divisions were of higher calibre than others in 1939. So there was a grading system between first and second status units. The same grading occurred with medical units; the best were those sent early to France to complete the BEF ORBAT.

[5]In the anti-cigarette era of the late 20th Century, it has to be remembered that one of the vital supplies for troops in this War was cigarettes. A few commanding officers who were non-smokers were in serious trouble when they forgot this need of their men.

[6]In the hard Mareth Line Battle, 1393 casualties passed through medical units. There were 17 transfusions for every 100 casualties. and 65 pints for every 100 casualties, 45 of whole blood and 20 of plasma. This included advanced and main dressing stations and CCSs. The report of Colonel Boyd remarked drily: "The more expensive units (e.g. NZ) were not in action at this time. About 500 pints (250 litres) used in this 10 day period. Increase probably due to increased no of mine cas." In his notes written later, Colonel Boyd wrote: "The BT service has again proved its worth and been instrumental in saving many lives. All ranks deserve high commendation."

[7]See "Medical Aspects of the Occupation of captured enemy towns and ports", by Colonel W.L. Spencer-Cox, MC, J R Army Med Corps, 1944, Vol LXXXII, 150–156.

[8]Major General John Matheson, OBE, personal communication. For a personal diary of an NCO who developed symptoms of mental exhaustion and who was well-known as an entertainer after the War, see "Mussolini his part in my downfall" by Mr Spike Milligan, Michael Joseph, London, 1978. Whatever the reader may think of the humour of this biography, the accounts of the writer's nervous symptoms, p 278ff — and of his in-patient spell with sandfly fever, p 32ff, are of interest as showing an unusual soldier's attitude to war in North Africa and Italy.

[9]Major (later Lieutenant Colonel) D.M.F. Batty, wrote: "The low incidence of fatal issue taken with the very mild constitutional upset

made me wonder if a man should go off sick with it and if he did how long he should remain off duty. However the jaundice was often prolonged, the liver function tests abnormal for even longer periods and it would seem better to play safe and put the man off duty until things had returned to normal. It was noteworthy that the incidence of cirrhosis following hepatitis of that era was extremely low." This sums up the view taken by RAMC physicians of the time. (Dr D.M.F. Batty, personal communication, 1993). For details of the disease, see Van Rooyen, C.E. and Rhodes, A.J., Textbook of Virology.

An amusing sideline to the infective hepatitis epidemic was the unusually high incidence among British Army officers compared to soldiers. This different incidence was not repeated in other nations' figures. Reasons given were 1) British officers drank more spirits than their men; 2) They wore pyjamas in bed, and so got chilled; 3) officers (especially in Italy) rode in open jeeps and so caught cold; and 4) officers did not have their personal "kfs and plate" (knife, fork, spoon) but used eating utensils in a mess and therefore shared. This last was thought to be the most possible of reasons.

[10]Lieutenant Rob had graduated MB, BChir, in 1938 and taken his English FRCS the next year — clear evidence of his ability. In due course he became Professor of Surgery at St Mary's Hospital Medical School and Consultant in Vascular Surgery to the Army. His Mitchiner lecture, given in 1986, is worth reading (J R Army Med Corps, 1986, Vol CXXXVI, 11–15).

[11]A large literature exists on the history of the Airborne Forces. The definitive work on the Medical Units is: "On Wings of Healing: the Story of the Army Medical Services 1940–1960", by Lieutenant Colonel Howard N. Cole, OBE, TD, FRHist.S, William Blackwood and Sons, Edinburgh, 1963. The officers who were members of the history committee of the Airborne Medical Society were: Brigadier A. Austin Eagger, CBE, Colonels Graeme Warrack, DSO, TD, M. McEwen, DSO, DFC, TD, Guy Rigby-Jones, MD, TD, and Lieutenant Colonel J.S. Binning, RAMC, (TA). Three other officers who were prominent in the production of the History were: Colonel P.R. Wheatly, DSO, and Lieutenant Colonels A.D. Young, DSO and D.C.G. Whyte, DSO.

[12]Cpl Evans had been an operating room attendant in 7 BGH in Crete and been captured by Nazi paratroops. He recalled: "The Jerries made us walk in front of them as they attacked the New Zealanders. They made the walking wounded as well as RAMC do this — some of us got killed...I escaped, though." The paratroops were prone to this sort of behaviour, but the German soldiers in the less fanatical units were not.

On the other hand, 7 BGH in Crete set up a 600 bed hospital and Captain Robert (later Colonel) Murlis said many years afterwards that he was not entirely surprised the Germans were suspicious that it seemed too large for the number of troops on the Island. Their HQ ordered them to camouflage several white tents, which he said the Germans must have seen from the air, and "added to this we had a row of 70/72 gallon fire extinguishers which, on wheels, must have looked like howitzers, and we had two wells, one on each side of our site, the water raised by donkeys at the end of a long pole which must have looked like an A-A site." He felt the enemy had grounds for believing the British were breaking the Geneva Convention by using a hospital to shelter military installations (personal communication, 1991).

[13] Malaria was of course present in the Canal Zone, the Sudan, and North Africa. But it was endemic in Southern Italy; 5 Corps alone had 600 cases almost at once. Sappers suffered especially as they had to bridge streams during the night. Affected soldiers were returned to unit after 3 days' Quinine and 5 days' Mepacrine — the new anti-malarial drug. Brigadier Cantlie, the DDMS, thought this too short: "No one is really fit for duty after malaria for 3 weeks", he complained to his clinical officers. At the British Society for the History of Medicine in Bristol in in September 1997, Professor J.P. Mitchell, who had served in Italy, remarked on how not enough warning had been given to troops, emphasising as he did so the paramount need for Army Health advice. In prevention of typhus, too, as in Naples, great credit has to be given to the Hygiene sections.

[14] For an excellent account of an FST in the Anzio beachead, see James Ross, "Memoirs of an Army Surgeon", William Blackwood and Sons, 1948, Edinburgh. In later years James Ross became President of the Royal College of Surgeons of Edinburgh.

For details of ration scales, see Medical History of the Second World War, op cit, Vol II, pp. 253, 372.

[15] Op cit, Vol II, p 279–285.

[16] Russian surgeons claim that N.I. Pirgov was the first military surgeon to use P.O.P. in war, in the siege of Sebastopol in the late 19th Century. Though used to a slight degree in 1914–18, it was Trueta who first developed its systematic scientific application for wounds and fractures.

[17] Pulvertaft, R.J.V., Local Therapy of War Wounds with Penicillin, Lancet 1943; 2: 341.

[18] Florey H.W, Jennings M.A, Sir William Shaw Dunn School of Pathology, Oxford. BJS, 1944; 32: 112–116. This volume of the British Journal of Surgery was devoted to Penicillin.

[19] Surgeons and bacteriologists were: A.L. d'Abreu, R.L. Button, I. Fraser, J.S. Jeffrey, D.W. Jolly, P. Clarkson, K.C. Eden, W.E. Hamilton,

J.D. Maclennan, W.H.D. Priest, J. Johnstone, Scott Thompson, H.L. de Waal, A. Pirie, and G.K. Tutton.

[20]The "galaxy of talent" — the phrase was General Hartgill's — included: H.W. Burge, Harold C. Edwards, C.J.B. Murray; Patrick B. Clarkson of No 4 Maxillo-facial Unit; F.J. Gillingham, neurosurgeon and later PRCSEd; A.L. d'Abreu and W.F. Nicholson, chest surgeons; R. Furlong and Barbara Stimson from No 16 Ortho Centre at Cassino, R.L. Bristow and T.B. McMurray, orthopaedic surgeons: general surgeons C.G. Rob, H.G. Eastcourt, G. Blackburn, C. Parish, G.Y. Fegetter, R.W. Raven, F.A.R. Stammers, W.D.F. Lytle and Lieutenant Colonel Bennet from New Zealand; R.V. Battle — burns; D.S. Poole-Wilson and Thomas Moore, urologists; J.J. Mason-Browne, who was then a vascular surgeon. Major General Munro, then Consultant Surgeon at the War Office, who had travelled to Rome for the Conference, said: "You are all miles ahead of a fellow in my position, and I would not dare to speak except on general principles." Also present were Major General Philip Mitchiner from 8th Army and Naunton Morgan, Consultant Surgeon, P.A.I.Force.

For an analysis of medical disease in the theatre, see "Health of the Middle East Force 1942–43", by Colonel A.E. Richmond RAMC and Lieutenant Colonel H.S. Gear (South African Medical Corps), J R Army Med Corps, 1945, Vol LXXXV, 1–32, and "Military Medicine in Italy, analysis of one year's work in a medical division (Rome), Lieutenant Colonel G.M. Komrower, MB Victoria, MRCP, ibid, July, 1946.

[21]See History of 2nd World War Medical Services, Administration, op cit, Vol 1, p 465–477.

[22]Phase 1. Assault, Battle of Caen, build-up for break-out from the beachead. 6th June — 25th July, 1944. Phase 2. Break-out, pursuit across Seine to Meuse-Escault Canal, capture of Antwerp and its port, airborne operation to force crossings of Maas and Rhine. July — September, 1944. Phase 3. Advance to Belgium, and set up of advanced base for operations into Germany. To mid- January, 1945. Phase 4. Battle of Reichswald Forest (OP VERITABLE) and Rhine Crossing (OP PLUNDER)) which took British 2nd Army to the Baltic, 1st Canadian Army to West Holland, with finally German surrender to 21st Army Group on 5th May, 1945.

[23]There was 1 Beach Sub-Area to each of the assaulting divisions. This Area controlled Beach Groups, each of which had 2 FDSs, 2 FSUs, and a detachment of a Fd Hygiene Section, plus 2 FTUs, 1 RPC (Royal Pioneer Corps) Coy of stretcher bearers, 1 pl of DUKWS, and half the Corps FDS as Casualty Embarcation Point (CEP). All these were to land on D-Day. It was planned that one CCS would land in

each Sub-Area on D-Day, but bad weather delayed their landing till D+1. Hospitals followed in sequence, and all the medical ORBAT supplies. It was a vast undertaking.

[24]The British had a range of devices to aid the attack, called in general "funnies." Among them was the flail tank, whose rotating chains flailed in front of the vehicle and struck the ground ahead, thus detonating any mines under the beach. The Americans eschewed these "funnies", but British inventiveness came in very useful in this machine and the others.

[25]Alison Kennard Mitting was a Liverpool graduate of 1940, and had taken his Edinburgh Fellowship in 1943. He was a temporary commissioned medical officer, as were all the others coming into the RAMC now. He ended the war as a Major and surgical specialist. After the War, he became a consultant orthopaedic surgeon in the Birmingham Region.

[26]The first wounded to reach Great Britain from the invasion arrived on the evening of D+1. During the first few days they were divided into organised and unorganised parties. The first category arrived by medically equipped LSTs (landing ship tank) for the first 4 days, then by Hospital Carriers and by LSTs. Gradually most were evacuated by Hospital Carriers. The second arrived by any type of craft and usually in small unannounced parties.

At Southampton, the policy was for all wounded stretcher cases to be examined by a surgeon for allocation to a) Port Hospitals — those urgent and unable to travel, b) Road Transit Hospitals, and c) transit Hospitals supplied by Casualty Evacuation trains (CET).

In the early days, casualties arrived frequently and in small parties at various points in the docks. This was the period when the LSTs were vital for quick return of the wounded. They were taken from the docks to the ADS of 199 Fd Amb in the Deanery Schools in Southampton for sorting. Later, when craft were bringing larger numbers of cas at less frequent intervals, it was found quicker and more convenient to classify them at the point of disembarkation.

It became clear that Hospital Carriers brought casualties over the Channel in 12–24 hours, but LSTs in 30–72 hours. This great difference was not realised at CEPs in France, and many seriously wounded lay unnecessarily long on stretchers. Also, the uncertainty of the duration of the voyage by LSTs made it difficult for MOs to decide their treatment policy. The Mulberry Harbour, the artificial harbour built on the Normandy beach, made it possible for larger ships to come in to shore.

In the first fortnight, 6–19 June, casualties had not passed through a General Hospital; this began from June 20th onwards. In the first

month, at Southampton, 12,327 cas were received and passed on. In
the first fortnight, 65 per cent were lying and 35 per cent sitting, and
in the second, 20 June-6 July, 52 per cent lying and 48 per cent sitting.
Their disposal on disembarkation was:

To Port Hospitals 1,133 (9.2 per cent), to Road Transport
Hospitals 904 (7.3 per cent), and by rail 10,290 (83.5 per cent). The
increase in the proportion of the last category was due to minor sick —
who were conspicuous by their absence in the earliest stages of the
campaign. The MOs at Southampton noticed that although there was
a high incidence of infection in the first days' wounded, "such was the
mental exaltation of all ranks that their general condition was surprisingly
good." In the second fortnight, more cas arrived 4–7 days after
wounding, with only their first field dressings on, and their general
condition was correspondingly worse. The heavy rain had not helped.

During this second fortnight, penicillin had been given regularly,
and to minor wounds. Pain from the injections was often worse than
from the original wound. 199 Fd Amb noted the tendency to give
penicillin as a priority in treatment and to neglect surgical toilet.

[27]Captain J.O. Forfar, MC, was a class-mate of Isma Begbie's at
St Andrews. He later became Professor of Child Health at Edinburgh
and an internationally famous paediatrician. He described his
experiences as an RMO to a Royal Marine Commando in two
excellent and fascinating booklets, "The Battle for Port-en-Bassin
6–8 June 1944: A Medical Officer to a Royal Marine Commando",
Proceedings of the Royal College of Physicians of Edinburgh 1994;
Vol 24: pp 218–246, and "Towards Victory in Europe: The Battle of
Walcheren", ibid, 1995; Vol 25: pp 451–475, 623–638. He remarked
humorously: "The Naval MO s didn't like the dirt of land warfare, so
the RAMC had to look after their marines !" and "My wartime
comrades who had a bad time recovered as they did not have to
undergo counselling." (personal communication, St Andrew's Day
OTC Regimental Association dinner, 1995).

[28]Professor J.R. Learmonth of Edinburgh wrote in the spring of
1945 of a visit to a CCS in Holland "about 3 miles(5km) from the
line.". A civilian surgeon with obviously no knowledge of the RAMC,
he was amazed at the level of treatment he saw: "housed in a brick-built
school, lit by electricity, and manned by three surgical teams with their
complement of nurses. On his arrival, the wounded man was taken to
a resuscitation ward, carefully examined, and if necessary given a
transfusion, during which a medical officer was in almost constant
attendance to determine the optimum time for operation, a decision
of vital importance for the subsequent welfare of the patient. When the
time for operation came, I found that the members of the surgical team

on duty were waiting in white operating clothes; the anaesthetic was carefully chosen and expertly administered; and the operation itself was conducted with a smooth competence and finished technique. Thereafter the wounded man was transferred to a roomy ward, to a real bed with real sheets, where he was tended by highly trained nursing staff…the arrangements could hardly have been bettered in a teaching hospital in Britain."

For details of the Army Transfusion Service up to the end of the War, see *Medical History of the Second World War: Medical Services in War*, editors Sir Arthur McNalty and W. F. Mellor, London, HMSO, 1968, pp 423. I am grateful to Professor L. G. Whitby, son of Sir Lionel Whitby, for information.

Although the nurses have their own historical records, their contribution was well described by a former teeth arm officer in: "Front-line Nurse : British Nurses in World War II", by Eric Taylor, Hale, London, January, 1997.

[29]The Battle of Arnhem, Christopher Hibbert, B.T. Batsford, Ltd, London, 1962, chapter 6, p 106. Arnhem, Major General R.E. Urquhart, Cassell, London, 1958.

[30]In April 1945, under a flag of truce two German officers warned the advancing 8 Corps of a danger of disease ahead. As a director of hygiene, Lieutenant Colonel Alexander (Sandy) Michie was sent to investigate. He found the 80,000 inmates at Belsen. They had had no running water for six days, and were dying at the rate of 1000 a day. "As the officer leading the initial relief his fast and cool planning must have saved thousands from certain death…for 45 years he could hardly bring himself to relate the experience: it was so indescribable that people could not begin to imagine the scale of inhumanity and suffering…" (obituary, *BMJ* 27th January 1966,). And Major John Sheather, RASC, in charge of a team responsible for checking the maintenance of B vehicles in the Corps, recalled: "I can not really still think about it…I took some photographs, took them home and showed them to my wife…we burned them…there were plenty guards about…our chaps just shot them if they showed any cheek." (personal communication, 1997).

[31]Personal Communication, 1990.

Chapter 10

The Far East. Achievements of the 1939–45 War.

Perspective.

On 7th December, 1941, the Japanese Air Force attacked the U.S. base at Pearl Harbour, the Philippines, and the British Crown Colony of Hong Kong. Japanese troops landed on the coast of Eastern Malaya. All these attacks were unannounced and unexpected. Britain, Holland, and the USA declared war on Japan and on December 11th, Germany declared war on the USA. As the result, the 1939–45 War became truly a World one — more so than the 1914–18 Great War.

Japan had begun an expansionist policy as long ago as 1915. In 1931 she had invaded Manchuria; in 1937 had occupied five northern Chinese provinces and in 1941 was still involved in what she called "The China Incident." The other territories now attacked represented sources of raw material and bases for further expansion: Japan was to set up a "Greater East Asia Co-prosperity Sphere" in which Japan would be dominant.[1] Thus the invasion in 1941 was an event as significant in world history as any since the Reformation and the discovery of America — it represented a conscious attempt by an Eastern Power to defeat the Western World. In spite of Japan's ultimate defeat, she would again set out to dominate the world, this time by trade, from the 1960's onward, until checked again at the century's end.

From the British and Australian points of view, the defeats were swift and catastrophic: Hong Kong, where the Canadians had sent a full brigade, fell on Christmas Day 1941. Singapore fell on 15th February 1942, after a disastrous defeat in Malaya. The rape and murder of QA nurses in Hong Kong, and the early treatment of wounded in Malaya and Singapore, gave notice of what was to come. "Never in their history were the Army Medical Services called upon to discharge their functions in circumstances more difficult than those that obtained in the Island and City of Singapore", said the *Official History*.[2]

General Wavell was rushed to Malaya to try to salvage the tactical situation, and General H.L.Alexander was similarly sent to Burma, where the British and Indian Armies were as rapidly sent into retreat. In Burma was the added strategic possibility of a Japanese invasion of India and all that that implied.

From the Japanese point of view, there were two strategic aims — to conquer Australia in the S.W. Pacific, and India in S.E. Asia. The successes of the U.S. Forces in Guadacanal and Guam, where the naval battles of the Coral Sea on 7–8 May, 1942, and even more so, of Midway on 4–7th June, were the beginning of the counter-attack, of and the bravery of the Australian comrades in New Guinea, held one of two Allied hinges. The other hinge was the holding operation and then re-conquest of Burma — this was the British, Indian and African responsibility. Although to those in the U.K. base now experiencing air attacks from the German V1s and the first surface-to-surface missiles, the V2s, these seemed totally different wars, they were all part of the one world-wide struggle.

The Campaign in Burma.

It remains true that the Burma War was all-too-forgotten when compared to the nearness of the European Campaign, and it deserves, in this account of the RAMC, a large place of its own.[3] For the conditions were truly worse than anything experienced in the West, the military and medical problems were totally different, but the results comparable. In fact, in relative terms, they were superior.

In the Far East also were the soldiers captured at Hong Kong and Singapore — the fall of the latter of incalculable importance to the whole subsequent status of Britain, whose fall-out continued until the end of the century. The bravery of these — in the British and Australian Holocaust — became a unique part of British military history and created a descriptive term as evocative as any of the century: "the Jap POW."

In Burma, the sheer size of the front is not generally appreciated. Japanese held territory in S.E. Asia extended 2,500 miles

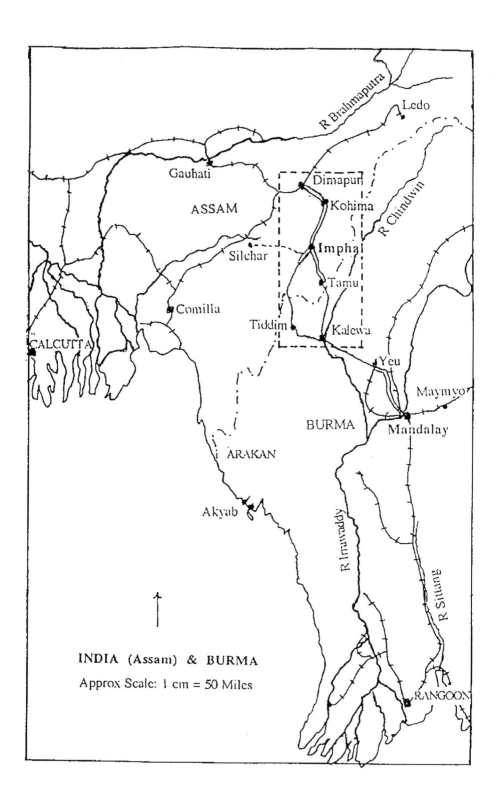

INDIA (Assam) & BURMA

Approx Scale: 1 cm = 50 Miles

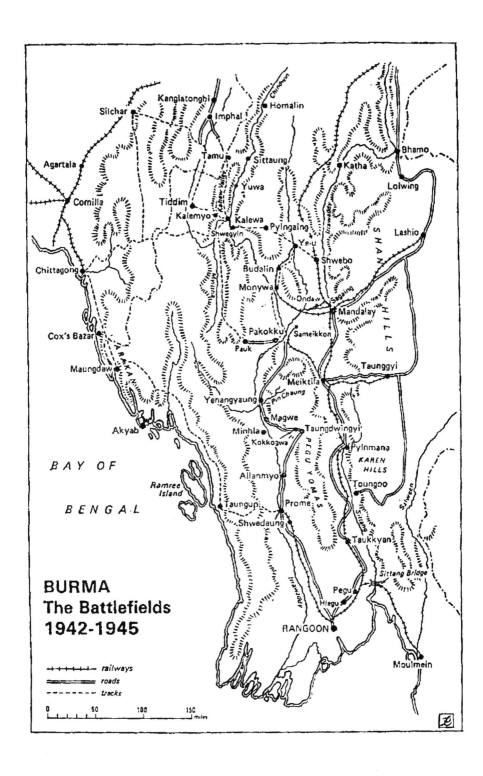

BURMA
The Battlefields
1942-1945

railways
roads
tracks

0   50   100   150
                 miles

(4,000km) from the north of Burma. The Burmese Front alone was 700 miles(1100km), second only in length to the Russian Front. The Japanese were fighting from interior lines. They controlled Burma's rivers, railways, and roads, and since they were a rice-eating army, they lived off what Lord Louis Mountbatten, the Supreme Allied Commander in the Theatre, called humorously "the fat of the land."[4]

The British, on the other hand, were fighting from the most difficult LofC imaginable, against the steep, jungle-clad mountains and fast-flowing rivers. Any advance had to be carried out along the single axis of the supply route. On the credit side was the fact that by late 1943 the Allies had virtual mastery of the air, and the Royal Navy commanded the Indian Ocean.

The Japanese had poured into Burma from the south, up to the head of the Burmese mountain valleys, and their forward units were on the eastern banks of the Upper Chindwin (map, p). Laterally and across their rear they had the river and road communication and Burma's main railway. The British also had a railway which ran roughly parallel to the front, but so far away that it could only be tapped effectively at one point, Dimapur. Dimapur was itself 100 miles(160km) from the combat zone. From this point to their advanced outposts on the India-Burma border, the British had to build metalled roads through virgin forests, around precipices, winding literally into the clouds and continuing along the full length of the Central Front. They remain marvels of military engineering. But no roads ran backwards towards India from this front. Even if the Supreme Commander had not already been skilled in three-dimensional warfare, and eager to make use of all its possibilities, the development of air transport for supply, reinforcement, and, for the sick, evacuation, would have been forced upon him.

This was the Central Front. The Japanese had also made their way from Rangoon up the coastal belt to Arakan, and had set up a line north of Akyab. Again there was a LofC gap over which only mules, ox-waggons, and infantry were the carriers.

From the Allied point of view, the greatest disease in the world remained the chief enemy. In early May 1942 the exhausted remnants of General Alexander's army crossed the Chindwin after retreating along the length of Burma, through one of the most intensely malarial areas in the world. The rains had broken and the troops, with no mosquito nets and no blankets or tents, were exposed to the full rigours of climate and disease. As Field Marshal Slim said later: "Our lack of preparation in Burma, military, administrative, and political, made it difficult for our commanders even to bid for the initiative."[5]

At Imphal no hospital accommodation was available and the only medical units were 8 CCS, which had marched out with 17 Indian Division, the rearguard division of the retreat, and the divisional field ambulances. Scarcely a man remained uninfected, and all had a desperate defence to make. The defenders of Imphal were among the bravest of the brave in the 2nd World War. Both medical units were full to overflowing — the CCS had 2000 patients, the Fd Ambs 600 — even RAPs held 60–70. The nearest military hospital was 150 miles(240km) away in Manipur Road, the roads between constantly blocked by landfalls and floods, and very many men at all stages of illness (and with Malaria complicated by unrecognised scrub typhus), died in the packed ambulances. It was the old story — the sudden and of course always unexpected attack from a place the politicians did not contemplate, with the inevitable British reverse and unnecessary loss of life because of inadequate resources. The crawling ambulance cars on the LofC in Burma in 1942 mirrored the boats on the Euphrates in 1916.

Recovery was much faster and more effective in the Second War, and no junior officer was harassed for daring to make errors public. The isolation of 4 Corps holding Imphal proved a blessing in disguise for the Medical Services, because Lord Mountbatten realised at once that *air* evacuation of casualties — hitherto only used in grave emergency — must be the normal means of evacuation. It was accepted at once that light aircraft would have to be made available to carry to CCS level. The Supreme Allied Commander who commanded in Burma confirmed one of the basic maxims of the AMS; by his action at the highest level he decreed what they would have to do. On this occasion his wise decision opened a splendid new chapter in the medical evacuation process.[6]

The third sector of the Burma Front was the Northern, based on the town of Ledo. This was the area of General "Uncle Joe" Stilwell, who in spite of his rather pathetic hatred of the British, sucessfully co-operated with them, and kept his army of Chinese in the War. With the British and Chinese he supervised the building of a chain of airfields over the Ledo mountains to China.

One major aim of those British Allies was to cut the communications of the Japanese 18th Div on the Ledo Front. This was to be done by a Long Range Penetration Force commanded by Brigadier, later Major General Orde Wingate. The second was to engage the greater number of Japanese divisions elsewhere in Burma. Medical support for both these was the responsibility of the AMS.

By January 1944 the Japanese High Command decided they must attack India without delay, largely to forestall the base from which powerful armies were being assembled for an Allied assault on their Homeland. Lieutenant General W. Slim, the 14th Army Commander, was ordered to clear the Akayab peninsula and as far south as possible. The available troops were 15 Indian Corps under command of Lieutenant General Sir Philip Christison. This Arakan Campaign was dominated by the Mayu Ridge, which the Japanese in turn intended to use to split the Allied Front. In 1943, when the Japanese had occupied Arakan originally, they had struck up the Kalapanzin Valley and cut the British LofC. General Slim therefore proposed to advance not only down the Kalapanzin as well as the coast, but also to throw a flank screen in the valley *beyond* the next mass of hills, the Kaladan Valley. 81 (West African) Division were given this important task, and the appearance of these magnificent looking warriors from Africa in the Arakan encouraged friend and frightened foe.

To link the main forces in the coastal belt and Kalapanzin Valley, two passes through the hills were developed, the Goppe pass, and the Ngakyedauk pass — which entered the immortality of British soldiers' language as the OKEYDOKE PASS.

Lieutenant General Hanaya, the Japanese GOC in Arakan, placed Colonel Tanahashi in command of a force which was to split the British-Indian Force by capturing these passes. This would not only divide the British Force but also its LofC.

The initial attack succeeded in isolating the Divisional Administrative Area of 13 Corps — supplying 7 Div and a brigade of 5 Div, which came to be known as the "Admin Box." In this box were 8000 administrative troops — pioneers, sappers, ordnance, signallers, and medicals; mule companies, native road builders. There were also Royal Artillery units and anti-aircraft guns. Protection had been no more than enough to resist an armed raid. Now it was surrounded by thousands of Japanese assault troops. But Colonel Tanahashi had been unaware of the air as the source of supply; Major General F.W. Messervy, CB, DSO, had flown in a West Yorks Bn, a Punjabi Bn, a company of KOSB, and some tanks and more guns. The box was surrounded by barbed wire; a vital battle of the whole campaign was about to begin.

The Japanese press and radio "went to town on the news." They shouted of Victory and that the way to India was open. Tanahashi would be in Chittagong within a week. Indian traitors drew up proclamations for parades at the Red Fort in Delhi. "Tokio Rose", the Jap singer, crooned "Why not go home? It's all over in Burma."

The Allied victory in the battle of the "Box" made the rest of the advance possible and removed the threat to India; as long as India and the British garrison there was secure, the world-wide power of Britain would survive. Air supply saved the day, and this was highly significant as a happening which changed the history of warfare and indeed of nations: the Age of Naval power as the supplier or blockader was over. Its success confirmed Brigadier Wingate's view; "The vulnerable artery is the LofC winding through the jungle floor. Have no LofC on the jungle floor. Bring in the goods, like Father Christmas, down the chimney." The Americans were making the same discovery in the Pacific.

"The Box" was a battle where the RAMC gained one of their battle honours. "The casualty stations overflowed while a depleted medical staff worked like demons (or like angels, as the writer thought would read better!)...the devotion of the doctors and their orderlies was truly moving. Some of them paid the final terrible price of duty...It was impossible to hold every point in strength, and one night in pitch darkness the enemy over-ran the MDS on the edge of the box. They burst in upon the place shouting and howling like dervishes. But their savagery was not that engendered by battle. 48 hours after occupying the MDS a senior Jap officer entered and ordered all wounded to be massacred. Orderlies and patients tried to escape by crawling on their bellies in the darkness through a deep nullah(ditch). Some of the patients were too weak, and others too severely wounded, even to move from their stretchers. The Japanese went from bed to bed bayonetting every man who showed the least sign of life. Their heart-rending cries and groans were heard by their comrades beyond the nullah, helpless to rescue them.

The doctors fared no better. The Japanese lined up six and in cold blood shot every one dead with a bullet through his ear. One MO survived as he was working away from the captured area. Another faked death when he saw what was happening by falling flat on his face and daubing himself with blood. Over 80 casualties were butchered. It was said that whenever the incident was mentioned in the Box, a hush fell over everyone.

But the "Box" held; General Christison destroyed Tanahashi's bold enterprise. The Admin Box Battle ended when Major Ferguson Hoey of the Lincolnshire Regiment led their assault on Point 315 which dominated it, dying as the feature was captured and winning the V.C. By the time the monsoon broke in June, the fortress of Razabil was captured and all the tunnels through the Mayu Range were in British hands.

The Chindit campaign of 1943 had its critics, but General Wingate prepared to send five brigades 150 miles(240km) behind the Japanese lines where they would be in striking distance of the Mandalay-Mytkynia railway and road system. He acted on a dictum of General Sherman: "The enemy's rear is there to play hell with."

One part of the force was to march from the north, under Brigadier Bernard Fergusson, parallel with Stilwell's advance. The major part, in OPERATION THURSDAY, involved troop-carrying gliders landing in areas code-named Broadway, Chowringee, Piccadilly and later Aberdeen. The operation was hazardous; many troops had not flown before; there were no escorting fighters. Of 54 gliders setting off, 46 landed. A total of 12,000 men, 1200 animals, were put in place with the loss of only 121 men. The success gave useful information for OVERLORD. And one name to be recorded is that of Major General Alf Snelling, the "grocer of the 14th Army", who was responsible for supply.

The later Burma Campaign made constant use of airfields. In the fierce battle for Meiktila, the temporary loss of the airstrip was serious. 16 CCS was set up here. 33 Corps pushed down towards Mandalay.[7]

Medical planning became therefore dependent on the new fact of air evacuation and re-supply. This was the new element in medical thinking. 27,000 were wounded, but ten times that number sick with Malaria and dysentery. No attempt was made to move in general hospitals or convalescent depots during the re-conquest of Burma. There were no BGHs because of the time required to move and set up such heavily equipped units. Instead the AMD used CCSs and Indian Malarial Forward Treatment Units (IMFTUs); the latter were the only hospital cover to accompany the Army. These units had been designed earlier in the campaign, to hold and treat malaria cases as far forward as possible, and allow quicker return to unit. But they did in effect become FDSs, and their Malarial treatment function was less used.

The 14th Army had Corps Medical Centres — 1 or 2 CCSs together, or 1 or 2 IMFTUs plus ancillary medical units, X-ray, field laboratories, FTUs, dental, ophthalmic and neuro, and a psychiatry centre. There were 2 CCSs and 2 IMFTUs to each corps; the remainder were held back at army level. As the battle moved forward, and with increasing momentum, and centres became outside the range of light aircraft, the major medical units were leap-frogged in the usual way. If a CCS had to move suddenly, its held cases could remain in the IMFTU (FDS).

4 Corps had 24 CCS and 16 IMFTU; 33 Corps had 13 and 8. Later in the advance, 16 CCS was brought up, and again 10 IMFTU and 8 CCS. Being lower priority units, their moves were by lower priority transport. Once, for example, 10 MFTU was moved 30 miles(48km) by 150 bullock carts. In Burma, there was a chronic shortage of transport for medicals. This was partly because the war establishment of an Indian CCS was only 22- three ton lorries, and in fact not one CCS had more than a third of its establishment — 4 or 5 lorries was the average. There was never the profusion of materials found in Normandy.

Kan was the first fully developed corps airhead, and the first experience the RAMC had of light planes close to a CCS.[8]

MEDICINE AND SURGERY IN THE 14TH ARMY.
There were the usual diseases of war in Burma — Scrub Typhus, Infective Hepatitis, Amoebic Hepatitis, Smallpox (which was endemic in the civil population), Cholera. These occurred in

small amount: in the last six months of the campaign, for example, there were only 629 cases of Hepatitis, 69 of Cholera, and 198 of Smallpox. V.D. incidence was very low; 0.04/1000/day while in the jungle, but as always, higher while the division was resting or men on leave. The East African Division, which had the highest incidence, had in total only 1,364 cases. Dysentery and diarrhoea fell from 0.23/1000/day in November 1944 to 0.07 or so from February 1945.

The achievement of this campaign was the improvement in managing the greatest disease in the world. Personnel and means available for reducing wastage from Malaria were better then ever before. Even during the monsoon, though Malaria casualties were still severe, they were not crippling. And as well as prevention and treatment, research was carried out,[9] in the Malaria Field Laboratory.

The range of measures included individual protection — the new Di-Methyl-Phthalate, a mosquito repellant used after 1944, and mosquito nets. Dress regulations were still a disciplinary requirement. A new type of net was used from the Meiktila Battle onwards. Next was anti-malarial units (AMUs), one to each division and corps HQ, one to army HQ. The AMUs taught the use of DDT as an anti-mosquito agent instead of the previous Paris green, developing the indications for it and methods of spraying. Co-operation with the hygiene sections already in place had to be worked out. New sprayers were developed, until every platoon had its own. Established methods had still to be insisted upon, such as drainage of swamps. The AMUs had to explain the limitations of the new chemical on ground and as airspray — as always, troops and commanders at once thought the new marvel did away with basic anti-malarial disciplines.

The new drug was Mepacrine.[10] At first it was given to only a proportion of the troops of the 14th Army. But by 1st March, 1945, all troops east of the Bramaputra River were given Mepacrine. Before that, in the January, Supply and Transport Units had taken over distribution from medicals; supply was by air. In Brigadier Ian Milne's opinion "It was really mecaprine, along with sulphaguanidine, which won us the medical war in Burma."

The main logistic problem was the distribution of stocks to cater for changes in tactical position of units. It was surprising how long it took the planners of the day to realise that the man's ration pack was the place to put it. It soon became evident that men needed a reserve supply of the 1–2 tablets they needed every day. 11(East African) Division had the good idea of using a .303 cartridge case with a watertight plug as a container.

Results were striking. This was an advance comparable to the introduction of inoculation against typhoid fever years before. In a comparison of two areas in 1944, one of which had Mepacrine and the other not, the incidence of malaria cases in the non-protected area rose and fell with each transmission, while those in the protected area remained on a steady level in spite of more chances of infection. In 2 Div in October 1944, weekly casualty rates fell from 250–400 to below 50 in six weeks after the drug was taken, without any diminution in the intensity of transmission. In the whole 14th Army in the first 5 months of 1945, the incidence was *one-fifth* that for the same period on 1944.

It remained difficult to convince the soldiers that they take the drug. The ADMS 2 Div, Colonel W.J. Officer, wrote: "The chief cause lies in the attitude and lack of experience among the senior officers in formations…many have yet to appreciate the tactical effect of a first-class outbreak of Malaria during operations." How often could that remark have been made during the 20th century. And as so often, it was the *officers* who failed to check, leaving it to the senior NCOs. Fifth column propaganda did have a role; it was put about that Mepacrine made men sterile and impotent, and a severe attack would occur after they had got home. Men feared that "bottled-up" Malaria would break out and be untreatable.

The very fact that the Allies had this new medical discovery led to an assessment of what came to be called Tactics of Malaria Warfare. Because they could reduce the incidence of Malaria, and the Japanese could not, the British could fight in conditions where Malaria was prevalent. Air photographs showed mosquito breeding areas. From March 1945, all Jap POW were questioned about Malaria and the state of their quinine supplies. Blood slides were also examined in prisoners. Thus it was possible to choose to fight the enemy during a period of maximum prevalence of Malaria, especially Malignant Tertian, since his drug was quinine. Thus fighting was begun in the monsoon. It was also possible to manoeuvre the enemy into a malarious area. Again, it was then easy to block his supply route for quinine re-supply, and expect a breakdown in his troops 4–6 weeks later.

The Consultant Physician to 14th Army, Brigadier I.G.W. Hill,[11] as well as reporting upon disease, laid stress on the peculiar logistic difficulties of the campaign — the supply of water, which taxed even the skill of the Royal Engineers, and the supply of medical stores. Such went by air, like all else and were delivered by air drops, air landings, but also had to arrive by vehicles which, like everything else in the Forgotten Army, were old and in short supply. The excellence of the system was shown by the fact that fortnightly demands, from depots of medical stores, were found sufficient unless in emergency or in the case of transfusion fluid.

As far as provision of medical specialists was concerned, the Brigadier stated that his very best young men were sent forward into the jungle. One or two who remained in India and years later became professors of medicine might have pondered that statement!

Overall, the average sickness rate was 1.2/1000/day but fell to 1.0 in the last few weeks of the campaign. Although this was in part due to the fact that fighting was by then taking place in the healthier Central Burma plain and in the South Burma area, it still represents a great medical achievement. And although the work potential of surgeons and of their soldier operating assistants was substantially less, owing to the climatic conditions, than that in temperate regions, their survival rate of wounded was 95 per cent as against 92.8 per cent in the British Liberation Army of Europe and 95 per cent in the star-studded Central Mediterranean Force.

RATIONS.

Part of the AMD responsibility in war was the provision of suitable food for the armies. In the 14th Army, there was a good deal of comment on newer types of ration, and of the need for special ration. This was because of the special needs of soldiers in the theatre, and because of the wide range of diets requiring to be provided for the various tribes of the British Empire who made up the Army of Burma.

The Medical Services were on the whole critical of the food supplied. At the end of the campaign, the Army Health medical officers wrote that not enough had been done to bring the current ration issue to a standard commensurate with modern dietary principles and needs of modern warfare. In early 1945, the 2 Div report on rations commented: "In this sixth year of war rations suitable for our particular type of warfare are not yet available and still will not become so before the beginning of the next campaigning season…if it had not been for the "K" ration (a U.S. product) the modern ration would have differed in no way from that of the last war… in spite of the Napoleonic dictum, little effort has been made by those responsible to produce a good ration for the fighting soldier."

A number of "Ration Scales" had been available in India and in Burma. There was a "Rehabilitation Ration", used during the final period of training in India in an attempt to maintain men's strength at a peak and prevent them using their reserve while in the jungle. It was about one and a half times the normal ration scale, but produced a degree of avitaminosis as it consisted largely of tinned meat and biscuits. The soldiers were quickly dissatisfied when they went back on to "normal" rations.

There was also a "Delhi Light Scale", which was a total failure; the soldiers did not like the meats in it, and the tea, biscuits and cheese were often decomposed by the time they opened their boxes. The army health officers were extremely critical of the Delhi Ration and even wrote that one brigade, 16, showed premature fatigue at the time they reached their active area of war because they had had it and nothing else.

The American "K" ration was regarded as better than the British scale. It "showed an attempt at variety, which none of the others did, and after living on it for 5 months men still spoke well of it…the fact that the Americans managed to substitute three new types of biscuit (at British Soldiers' request) for the very sweet sort initially supplied made the troops feel that there was someone sufficiently interested in their welfare to take action." The packing of the K ration was thought excellent by soldiers; it was waterproof enough to withstand most dampness.

Finally, the "Jungle Ration, Mark 1" was a great disappointment. For a start it was too heavy. It was packed in Britain, but in packages of many shapes and sizes, and it could not be easily carried in a soldier's kit in one piece. The tin opener for the big food tin broke — in contrast with that of the K ration — and a big knife or bayonet had to be used to prize it open. The cheese and jam containers had to be more or less smashed open, so that these popular items were lost. There was much too little sugar, and far too many salt tablets — 32 in each pack. The doctors commented: "If this number was reduced to 6–7 and Mepacrine and water sterilising tablets, as well as sugar, packed instead, it would be an advantage."

One ration which was praised, however, was the Special Force Re-habilitation Ration, for those returning from service with the Special Force, the Chindits. Its only reported problem was that it could not be tolerated suddenly by men who had been on K Rations for long periods.

SPECIAL FORCE MEDICAL PROBLEMS.

The Chindits' campaign was of considerable value. But the AMS officers had real doubts about how satisfactory their contribution was allowed to be. It was one of the basic features which were seen in the first chapter of this account, the feeling of the RAMC that they were not treated fairly by the "Big Army" — only this time it was the "little army" of Brigadier, later Major General, Orde Wingate, which was involved. The "Big Army" of General Slim they had no qualms about.

Both at DDMS level and below there was disquiet. It was known that at least one Staff officer posted in had reservations about Wingate's mentality and fitness to command,[12] and it was said that reservations by some medical officers had been quashed at as high a level as Mountbatten and Churchill himself. But since much of this is hearsay, it cannot be more than mentioned as such. Nevertheless, the formal reports of Colonel W.J. Officer, ADMS of 2 Div, are critical of the way his predecessor had been excluded from giving advice and even from being allowed to visit his medical officers, and the attitude he himself had experienced.

Certainly the de-briefs of soldiers and officers were less than happy as far as military and medical care were concerned. Psychiatric reports on men from three of the major units making up the force in July, August and September, 1944, make unhappy reading. Although they were interviewed soon after they had come out of the jungle, in 69 Indian Rest Camp, when they would still be exhausted, this was taken into account.

Members of the three brigades had similar grievances. Strongest were broken promises by the commanders about when they would get out. They were especially bitter over the conditions at the "Blackpool" position. Many reinforcements were inadequate and untrained. The campaign was much too long — had it terminated before the monsoon many deaths from disease would not have occurred. K rations were "almost unbearable after 3 months."

Medical failings concerned the lack of medical inspection before troops were sent into the jungle. Some had none at all. Others were actually checked for fitness by a Sergeant-Major consulting their pay-books. Despite the admirable efforts of the MOs, (with two exceptions) treatment was described as "inadequate to ridiculous to call it treatment at all…men were turned away with the apology from their RMO that he had nothing to give them." Column 16 of the Honeymooners[13] had no MO at all for 6 weeks. "One RAMC Corporal was giving intravenous quinine, pentothal for general anaesthesia, and doing minor operations, as there was no MO available." Many men said they were afraid to report sick, both for fear of being declared scroungers, and because they might be left behind. Few had confidence of being evacuated if sick; by contrast, wounded men who needed surgery praised their surgeons. (In the first long range patrol campaign, casualties were either carried out from the jungle, or even left behind. Some were put out of their suffering).

What men called "unknown fever" (which was Scrub Typhus, transmitted by jungle mites) affected morale badly. They saw friends "dying like flies" and were afraid to visit a sick mate with the disease. Men who were older, and those who were underweight — and had to carry a pack over half to three-quarters of their own weight — had great sympathy. So had those wearing glasses, who constantly feared losing them; glasses were useless in rain and sweaty conditions.

Public flogging of British Other Ranks caused deep resentment. A few syphilitics were interviewed by the psychiatrist, but dismissed as "being of such a mental make-up as to spread dissension through *any* unit."

The medical officers of one brigade themselves criticised their DDMS and ADMS and were angry that the DDMS had stated that too many fit men were being evacuated. They claimed that this showed a lack of appreciation of the true state of affairs and reflected upon the senior officer's judgement. In reply, the DDMS said that he had visited whenever he could, when within marching distance of an airstrip, but that columns were usually too far away.[14]

The unit which had the lowest incidence of disease and especially of mental breakdown was the 1st Queen's Own Cameron Highlanders. They are mentioned specifically in the formal medical reports of the Burma Campaign. Their RMO was Captain John Lawson, RAMC, who first served in a FMTU and then was in 6 Fd Ambulance. When Captain Peter Baikie, the Camerons' RMO, was killed by a sniper's bullet while crossing the Irrawaddy River, John Lawson was transferred to the Scottish unit. So often in military reports the tale is told by a senior officer, frequently the commander, and as frequently the tale told by the juniors reads more convincingly.

So it was in Captain Lawson's case. An able war-time doctor who later became a superlative general practitioner, the G.P. assessor of Army General Practice 35 years later on behalf of the Royal College of General Practitioners, whose President he later again became, his account is full of detail which sometimes confirms the official one and sometimes does not.

He was at Kohima with 1st Camerons, then part of 6 Bde, the other regiments being 2nd Dorsets and 1 Royal Welch Fusiliers. He remembered Brigadier Hill arriving in late 1944 and asking "Where's my tent"? to be given a jungle knife and told "Cut your own!" And he remembered Colonel Officer, the ADMS, arriving at his RAP when things were hectic and complaining that a bottle was unlabelled. "Do you want this like Harley Street"? said the temporary commissioned medical officer to his Commander. "But", laughed Captain Lawson, "he just said 'yes'!"

From this RMO's point of view, what made evacuation possible was the aeroplane — especially the U.S. L5 jeep plane. It could hedge-hop, and the U.S. pilots were "amazing." The speed of the later campaign was one of his strong memories, especially to Shwebo and on to Mandalay.

Captain Lawson recalled an item not mentioned in the formal reports. This was the "prefabricated MDS, made of wooden walls and transportable by 3-ton lorry. It was remarkably quick to put up and take down." This remarkable piece of kit was the brain-child of R.S.M. Danny Kaye, of 6 Fd Amb. Lieutenant Colonel Gordon Fagg, in the 1980s the Corps Regimental Secretary, remembered the R.S.M. seeing a large pile of suitable boards, collecting them, and having them made into a series of interlocking sections. Carried on lorries, they were locked together, covered with tarpaulin, mosquito netting added, and hey presto, a field hospital ! Colonel Fagg recalled how these were used particularly at Indaw. The R.S.M. also put a water tank up a tree, with a drip and fan, to cool the tents. "Lady Mountbatten was impressed when she visited."

Official reports stressed the need for dress discipline against insect bites. "But we went about stripped to the waist most of the day", he recalled — and photographs in the history of 6 Fd Amb bear this out. Those who wore shirts all day suffered badly from prickly heat, and the worst sufferers were the Warrant Officers who "not only wore thick shirts but Sam Browne belts as well."

"Many more men than the authorities admitted didn't take their Mepacrine", Captain Lawson said. "I was never very keen on the idea of putting it in the ration, because we had a Mepacrine parade every morning, to make sure that the men at least were issued it. The propaganda against it was very strong…in any event, I think the scrub typhus was as bad as any disease we had — the men I saw, at unit level, weren't as ill as they got later, by the time they were back at the AMTU."

"One of the reasons the Camerons did so well was that we had a wonderful padre. I shared a 40 pounder tent(20kg) tent with him. So much of my work was helped by him — he wasn't much of a preacher, but there was no-one in the unit the soldiers would have done more for than Padre Frank McLauchlin…he won the MC and bar…when we got to Japan after the War he was a help with the V.D. problem (the Camerons had by far the lowest incidence of venereal disease in the occupying units; much of the credit for this undoubtedly went to Captain Lawson's own insistence on E.T.(emergency treatment) units for men returning to barracks after a night out). For the Japs were clever little buggers — they put brothels in the areas where the occupying troop units were, and filled them with highly infected women — it was deliberately done."

"But what the men got at the end of the war and after was depression — but only because they had been away from their highland homes for a long time. After all, 2 Div was away in 1939 and they had served longer than anyone else."

Like all his medical colleagues, he had immense respect for the RASC drivers of the field ambulances. He quoted Captain R.E. Johnson, Admin officer of 6 Fd Amb, as saying "One always forgets the RASC, and this is probably the highest compliment one can pay them. Under Mr McAdie, CSM White and Sgt Gibson, they drove across India and settled down to run on the nightmare road Imphal to Dimapur — a series of hairpin bends and sheer drops — as if they had been brought up to it…patience of a very high order was needed to crawl down that road with serious cases aboard, but they produced it. They were always missing meals and sleep."

Forward of the MDS, armoured and jeep ambulances were principally used, staging to soft cars later as the distances grew longer. The armoured ambs were confined to roads, but were often the only means of getting up to a coy of Dorsets stuck near the tennis court of the District Commissioner's bungalow. These armd vehicles were the only wheeled vehs that visited them regularly every few hours and, if nothing more, prevented the frightful fear of being hopelessly cut off. Drivers Wilson and Nimmo, with Mussel White and Leadbetter as medical orderlies, put in some sterling work on these vehs.

"The jeep ambs did not normally carry orderlies, so the driver had to take his place…the RASC are notoriously bad walkers but they make up for this by pushing their vehs up to incredible places to save the RAMC carrying the patients farther than necessary. This habit plus that of always carrying tea, sugar and milk made them universally popular." From the start of this story, comradeship with the "waggoners" has been real and lasting.[15]

The British and Australian Holocaust.

In all their history, no British soldiers suffered the degree of deliberate deprivation and calculated brutality as did the Japanese POW. And because there were many Australian comrades with them, and some Canadians, as well as many Gurkhas, they suffered also. The story is a terrible one, and for the doctors presented conditions no training could possibly prepare them.

The term holocaust is justified by the fact that the Japanese deliberately set out to humiliate, starve, and work their POW to death. As Lieutenant Colonel C.Dee Shapland put it: "This (the fall of Singapore) was indeed (quoting the Prime Minister) 'the greatest disaster to British Arms which our history records' and disastrous, too, it was for the unfortunate prisoners who for the ensuing three and a half years were to be kept in filthy prison camps widely dispersed throughout the Far East on a starvation or semi-starvation diet and to be riddled with malaria, dysentery, beri-beri, pellagra, and other tropical diseases from which countless thousands were to die."

Malaya and Singapore were the source of almost all these POW. A few lucky ones were rescued from the sinking *Prince of Wales* and *Repulse*; the bulk were machine-gunned to death by the Jap Air Force.[16] It was Churchill himself who had over-ruled the Admiralty's wish that the force, commanded by Admiral Sir Tom Phillips, be balanced by the addition of fighter air support; their sinking was perhaps the moment which ended a century of Royal Naval supremacy in world affairs. From now it would be air power which would be triumphant, and new nations would take over Britain's World Role.

British commanders, too, in the usual British tradition, were powerless to prevent the Japanese taking control of the air base in Thailand, Singora, from which they launched their earliest attack on Malaya — as this would have been "provocation!" The Malayan Campaign was marked by every sort of unhappy failure. While the action at Jitra was a disgrace to British Arms, the subsequent confusion in Singapore did not justify the breakdown of discipline by some Australians.[17]

General Yamashita, the victor, was asked by General Percival, the loser; "What about the lives of the civilians and the British and Australian troops? Will you guarantee them?"

Yamashita replied: "Yes, you may be easy about that. I can guarantee that absolutely." Yamashita was executed for war crimes on 23rd February, 1946.[18]

British and Australian killed and wounded were 9,000; 130,000 were captured, including 198 Fd Amb, which Pte Seabrook had briefly served with in 1940. Part of 18 Division, they had landed just in time for the surrender.

The first major outrage was on 13th February, 1942, when the Japanese captured the BMH in Singapore. They ran amok and bayonetted patients without mercy, entering the operating theatre and killing the anaesthetised patient and then the surgeon,

Captain Allardyce. "About 400 were left and these were tied in groups of four or five and taken to a bungalow in Alexandra Park. There they were herded into rooms, 50 to 70 men to a room, the sizes of which varied from 9 by 9 feet(270cm) to 12 by 12 feet (360cm). Bodies, which were now covered with dirt, sweat, and in many cases blood, were crammed against one another and mostly it was a problem to raise a hand above the head. The stench of exhausted and ill bodies was increased by the fact that the men were forced to urinate and defecate against each other. The physical effects of not knowing what was to happen to them must have been worse.... Their fears were fully justified because many men died from thirst and general exhaustion, and the Japanese took absolutely no notice. Indeed, a survivor reported that when dawn came, some Jap soldiers could be seen devouring tinned fruit. Water was promised to the dying and injured, but none came." The men were taken out and shot in twos and threes. On the 15th February, the RAMC were allowed to go about their usual duties: General Yamashita appeared and expressed regret at the incident. He said the hospital was between two important military objectives, complimented the Commanding Officer on the way the patients were being looked after and told him to regard himself as a direct Representative of the Emperor and that no higher honour could be paid to the hospital.

This "Alexandra Incident" typifies the extraordinary behaviour of the Japanese. As John Leckie remembered, "If one of us went into a part of the camp forbidden, he was tied to a pole and beaten every now and then. If a pig went into the same part, it was tied up for an hour or two and beaten just the same."

At all camps it was obvious that the Japanese were guilty of the most bestial cruelty. Many of the individual acts passed all comprehension in sheer beastliness. Savage punishment was meted out without rhyme or reason to all and sundry at times, and punishments were savage and severe, completely beyond the ends of any real or fancied crime. Deliberate murder was certainly carried out and deliberate murder by starvation was clearly shown by the ration scale promulgated on May 26th 1945, which gave a total day's ration of 150 gm of rice, plus a few meagre extras which were usually denied to the sick. The caloric value of such is around 500 and physically impossible to maintain life.

Certain sorts of cruelty merit recording. At the main camp at Palembang, in the middle of the camp in front of the guard room, was a small barbed-wire enclosure about 10 by 8 feet (300 by 240 cm) with a lean-to roof, no sanitary arrangements, no shelter, and the floor bare mud. Into this, as punishment, specially selected men were thrown and left for periods of from 3 days to 3 weeks. Once there were 16 men in this hell-cage for 5 continuous days. A number of men went temporarily insane.

Nursing Sisters were of course also treated abominably, both QA and Australian, in the first place by deliberate murder on the beach and later by cruelty and starvation.

Needless to say the Japanese deliberately withheld letters, Red Cross supplies and medicines, although they were in stores just outside the camps. Many of these were produced as soon as capitulation was announced. In a few instances things were better; in Hong Kong small amounts of medicine, totally inadequate, were issued monthly. These were iodine, aspirin, Mag. sulph, Soda bic, small amounts of sulphonamides, and Vitamin B. Dr Selwyn Clarke, DMS Hong Kong, helped by sending drugs in 1942. Internees fared better than soldiers overall. In Hong Kong, according to Captain Warrack, the POW bribed guards to obtain Vitamin B tablets.

In Hong Kong transfer of acute surgical cases to hospital was invariably refused. Patients had to be carried to the Indian soldiers' camp by the surgeon, assistant, and anaesthetist on a stretcher for 500m, where there was a theatre. Four perforated peptic ulcers and four appendicectomies were done; all recovered.

But in the majority of camps there was a deliberate policy of complete, or almost complete, withholding of all medical supplies, equipment, and facilities. Occasionally the Japanese did issue a small amount of anaesthetic agent and preventive inoculations for dysentery, cholera and typhoid. There was constant interference with the work of the RAMC MOs and NCOs, both by Japanese guards, and, worse, by Japanese medical personnel. A quota of work would be set, stating that a certain number of prisoners would be available on a given day. If this quota was not met, the camp guards, *backed by their medical officers*, would rout out the sick and unfit without regard to protest by RAMC officers. If the MOs protested too strongly they were beaten so badly that fractures resulted, and in some instances senior medical officers were sent into solitary confinement for 6–8 weeks.

The Thailand-Burma railway was the most horrific of all. Many accounts remain to give at least some inkling of what it must have been like, and the drawings of Ronald Searle depict the visible degradation. "Every morning those who could walk went out to work, under continuous blows and slashings by the screaming Japanese: 'All men shigoto ! (work). Speedo, speedo, hurryupo !' At night, blood-stained, these half-naked, starving men returned with an astonishing range of oddments hidden under their loincloths or under their various hats, to tend their wounds and to dream of food."

"The work was exceedingly heavy and would have taxed the strength of a fully fit labourer. The Jap other ranks, and the North Koreans who assisted them and were as often as not even more sadistic than even their own Japanese masters, drove the prisoners on with blows from fists, boots, sticks and wire whips. The working day was 14 hours long, sustained by 3 pints (1400ml) of boiled rice.".[19]

One party of survivors told of how in a working party of 1,000, 400 died. In this group, some of the men, weak as they were, had been used to pull bullock carts. When the bullocks died the Japanese replaced them with POW. 2 bullocks were used to pull 6 large bags of rice, and 6 men were used to pull 10 bags. These were sick men who had been taken from hospital to do this work. There are various estimates of the death rates; perhaps on the railway, 10,000 men out of the 60,000 who had been sent there died.[20]

The POW morale remained high, to the wonder of those who looked at them, like Professor Girdwood, from the outside. The Japanese insisted upon the prisoners bowing low before the sons of heaven. But in one camp, the prisoners used to bow at morning roll-call and boom out "Good morning, Mr Churchill, Good morning, President Roosevelt, Good morning, Comrade Stalin." "Goon baiting" was enjoyed, but judiciously lest it provoked a slap.

Being struck on the face was commonplace, one or more times. One had to stand to attention for hours. If a prisoner was caught stealing food, he had to kneel to attention for a whole day. Roll call was in Japanese, and POW learned to count in Japanese and officers give orders. The tune "Miya Sama" of Gilbert and Sullivan was found to be a real Japanese one. Tall stories were told about other parts of the world, to have a laugh at the guards. John Leckie told of how a Chinese peasant brought his daughter to a Jap officer for his pleasure and offered her to a group of POW "Two of our lads had a go", he laughed; "the old peasant then said: 'Jap officer number three!'"

(The Japanese systematically enslaved hundreds of Korean girls as "pleasure girls" for their soldiers. They refused to apologise for their actions later in 1995 when asked to do so).

At a camp in Formosa, where the prisoners worked in an underground mine, they would sing:

> "Doon the mine, bonnie laddie,
> doon the mine you'll go,
> Though you're feeling tired and weary,
> You dare not answer no."

At this mine, the heat would exhaust the men, and they would collapse at the pit head. The Japanese would throw a bucket of water over them, and when they had recovered, send them down again. Yet they still could sing their song. The guards could not understand. POW also became excellent thieves — just like the inmates of Belsen on the other side of the world, where the liberators found the same thing.

Preservation of morale was a function of all officers. In Japanese camps, unlike German, the officers insisted upon staying with their soldiers. But the medical officers, and the padres, had a special skill to offer. Most padres were excellent and worked with their doctor colleagues; an exception was in Formosa where a Roman Catholic refused to carry out burial services upon Protestant prisoners.

The Sunday service became not only a day allowed for rest, but almost a political force in the resistance against the oppressor.

Yet worship provided symbols of love and hope which shone through into that dark world, a world where the wonderful virtue of the special charity which is Christian had never been part of its culture. The prisoners could certainly relate to someone who, too, had endured humiliation and beating, and who had triumphed in the end. They were in the spirit on the Lord's day. The North Koreans and the Chinese were similar to the Japanese; their world too was a world without charity.[21]

Captain George Blair arrived in Malaya in November 1941 with 9th Indian Division. They had come from Nowshera, where his unit, 5 Field Regiment, RA, had enjoyed the atmosphere of British India. They were a Regular unit of the RHA. When he left India for Malaya, he asked his bearer: "What's Malaya like?" His bearer replied: "Bad place, Sahib. Many men die. But *you* will come back, and if ever Blair Sahib returns to India, I will be here to meet you." This RMO had a remarkable capacity to earn respect and affection which would make his story as a doctor in a Japanese camp worth recording.

Captain Blair is interesting because of the excellence of his clinical records, which he kept at the risk of his life in Taihoku Camp, Formosa. He in fact submitted an MD thesis on his return; it was returned to him as "not scientific enough" and he was advised to alter it and re-submit. But he never did so. The restraint and dignity with which he describes his life as a camp doctor is especially remarkable when it is realised that the camp staff were all executed for war crimes after the War.

He spent the first eight months of captivity in Changi and the remaining three years in Formosa. He describes the work of the RAMC in constructing adequate latrines, at first deep trench and later bore-hole. "The small amount of cookhouse waste was disposed of in an Otway pit." As ever, traditional Army hygiene measures were successful.

He describes the difficulty British and Australians had to get used to eating rice — the initial feeling of distension followed soon by hunger. During all the time he was in Changi, it was possible to supplement the Japanese rations by buying on the local Chinese black market. The Japanese did however allow a canteen to sell nuts, fruit, and tinned fish. Early diseases were dysentery, and the malaria which men had not reported during the fighting and which was now relapsing.

After four months dysentery and Malaria cases fell, but in July 1942 occurred a severe outbreak of stomatitis, glossitis, and scrotitis, followed by the condition known as Changi feet.[22] This was the first evidence of the deficiency diseases which were to be the main part of his thesis.

There was a lighter side to life in Changi — "A notable feature was the rugby pitch in the area. Here, football and hockey, as well as rugby were played, and it was hard, at times, to realise that one was a prisoner. There was a barbed fence and Japanese patrols passed two or three times a day, but roll calls were infrequent. Each area made its 'local rules', and provided a working party could be produced when demanded by the Japanese little attention was paid to the prisoners."[23]

"Conditions in Formosa were quite different from those in Singapore," recorded Captain Blair briefly. He described the sick parade — following the lines already given, when the Japanese medical Lance-Corporal was in charge of disposal, giving tallies with Japanese characters on them relating to what he considered the severity of illness. "Unfortunately, the Japanese view of severity of sickness did not coincide with mine." About once a fortnight the Jap doctor, who was nominally in charge of all the prisoners on the island, arrived at the camp, and the medical orderly produced the sick list for his inspection… "he was, on the whole, singularly unco-operative."

Description of the frustrations of having no drugs, or inadequate drugs (for the Japanese did supply some for perhaps three days at a time); of the monthly consignment of cotton wool, bandages, gauze, ointment, which had to be washed again and again until they rotted, of sterilising his syringe and one or two instruments over the steam from the rice being boiled in the cook-house, is calmly made: "I am well aware that many of my colleagues worked in very much worse conditions and with even less equipment."[24]

In his analysis of deficiency diseases, where his thesis was that the conditions he saw occurring were not those of straightforward vitamin B deficiency, but due in part to lack of protein, he estimated that the maximum calorific value of their diet was about 1,600 calories but throughout 1945 fell to 1,200. He describes his own symptoms of disease, and the value of American Red Cross drugs and multiple vitamin tablets, when they arrived, in reducing symptoms.

The end of the War came to his practice of 300 men of 5 Field Regiment and about 250 other officers and men from various other British units near Kirun, just in time. As in all camps, rations were being reduced. "We knew, of course, that something big was to happen — from the radio.[25] And we knew that if any landing occurred, we were all to be massacred — we formed ourselves into resistance groups."

The Japanese Order for disposal of POW in Camp 6, Formosa, was probably a standard one; this extract was read at the war crimes trial.

Appendix D

The official Diary of the Taiwan POW Camp was captured intact. The following is a copy of the official translations of part of the entry dated 1st August, 1944.

The following answer about the extreme measures for POW was sent to the Chief of Staff of the 11th Unit (Formosa POW Security No 10).

(Referring to an Allied attack): "Under the present situation, if there were a mere explosion or fire, a shelter for the time being could be held in nearby buildings such as the school, a warehouse, or the like. However, at such time as the situation became urgent and it be extremely important, the POWs will be concentrated and confined in their present location and, under heavy guard, the preparation for the final disposition will be made.

The time and method of this disposition is as follows:

1. The Time

Although the basic aim is to act under superior orders, individual disposition may be made in the following circumstances:

a. When an uprising of large numbers cannot be suppressed without the use of firearms.

b. When escapes from the camp may turn into a hostile fighting force.

2. The Methods

a. Whether they are destroyed individually or in groups, or however it is done, with mass bombing, poisonous smoke, poison, drowning, decapitation or whatever, dispose of them as the situation dictates.

b. In any case, it is the aim not to allow the escape of a single one, to annihilate them all, and not to leave any trace.

3. To: The Commanding General.

The Commanding Military Police.

Reported matters conferred on with the 11th unit, the Kirun Fortified Area H.Q. and each prefecture concerning the extreme security in Taiwan POW Camps.

I hereby certify that this is a true translation from the Journal of the Taiwan POW H.Q. in Taiwan, entry 1st August, 1944. (signed) Stephen H. Green

This is Exhibit marked 'O', referred to in the affidavit of James Nehemiah Cross. Sworn before me this 19th day of September 1946. (signed) P.A.L. Vine, Major, R.M.

certified as exhibit 'O' in Doc no. 2687."

And yet, survivors of this camp remember the now freed British troops giving their former captors cigarettes ! A similar story is told by Major Ian Stonor, MBE, of their release in their camp in Manchuria: "The Russians were all for stringing the whole camp staff up — but we went all 'British' and said they mustn't, as they would have to have a fair trial!" But Major Stonor, who as a junior officer had been ADC to General Percival, and remembered him as "a very nice man — perhaps too nice", summed up what is the feeling of all former POW: "If they have any sort of celebration of V.J. Day in 1995, I don't want to go to London and share a bowl of rice with a Japanese."(17)

Captain Blair serves as the example of an RAMC RMO who upheld the highest traditions of his Corps. The feeling for him by his fellows was remarkable — when he was ill with bacillary dysentery and his life hanging in the balance, hardened regular soldiers prayed for his recovery.[26] His birthday card, miraculously adorned with a sprig of heather and a piece of tartan, was signed by all 500 men in the camp. Decorated for gallantry as camp doctor, he was very surprised when the Major who processed his demobilization stood up and saluted him. By now he was feeling well, but his sister recalled to the writer many years after his death that at this time he still had nightmares when he remembered the occasion the Japanese had threatened to cut off his right hand. He presented his medical records, which he had hidden under the floor, 30 years later to the Corps muniment collection at Millbank; he was always sad that he received no note of acknowledgement from the curator of the day — Major General Alastair MacLennan. With his great friend Thomas Jenkins Pugh, the padre whose nationality is not hard to identify, and who, full of life and fun, became the chief chaplain after the war to Butlin's Holiday camps, he wrote to the relatives of the men who had died when they both eventually reached the United Kingdom. With their names must also go that of Sgt Edwards,

RAMC, who had been with the Regiment and its RMO throughout. "He was a tower of strength." All these men had seen through the veil. There were many like these three in the Far East; these three serve as their representatives.

It is perhaps worth noting that had the atomic bomb not brought the War in the Far East to a swift conclusion, the end would have been protracted with the probable loss of a million men on the Allied side alone. (It is now known that Emperor Hirohito's was the decision to surrender, and that between 26th July and 15th August, 1945, his life was in danger from some of his hard-line warlords). All the prisoners would, of course, have been massacred. This fact should perhaps be pondered not once but several times by the quickly-appearing anti-nuclear protesters who upbraided the British and Americans for using the new weapon, and by their successors, some of whom were undoubtedly most sincere. In later years the "revisionist historians" claimed that Japan was beaten in the early summer of 1945 and that there was no need to use the weapon. Probably the best reply to them was made by Mr Alastair Cooke in his "letter from America" on BBC 4 on Sunday, 13th August, 1995. In it he told of the note sent by Einstein to Roosevelt in 1939 referring to the possibility of setting up a "chain reaction" in a heavy metal like uranium and producing a huge explosion — with his fears that Nazi Germany could develop such a technique — the later making of the bomb and its eventual sanctioning as a weapon. He corrected the assertions of the revisionists with their axes to grind: the Japanese were in no mood to sue for peace; they dismissed the Potsdam ultimatum; they had, contrary to the statements of the revisionists, 5 million men holding islands over an enormous extent of the Far East as well as on the mainland of China, Indo-China, Formosa, Borneo which could not have been easily taken; the estimates of Mr Stimson and General George Marshall, both men of honour and sensitivity, that Allied casualties would be 1–2 million and Japanese double that over a war lasting probably 18 months. It was in view of these casualty estimates that they decided the death of some 40,000 Japanese in two air strikes the more merciful option.

Although Michio Watanabe, the Japanese Foreign Minister, expressed deep remorse about his country's "reckless decision to start a war with the United States" on 6th December, 1991, at no time have the Japanese apologised for their treatment of their Western nations' prisoners; the apology given by their Prime Minister in August 1995 and again in 1997 was grudging and did not impress former prisoners, nor the Royal British Legion.

RAMC in German POW camps.

There were RAMC, soldiers and doctors and dentists, in prison camps of the Germans. Their contribution, though very different from those in the Far East because of German acceptance of the Geneva Convention, has a necessary place in this history.

Captain Hunter Annan was captured in Crete at the end of May 1941. His first experiences were upsetting — the German MO who arrived at the caves where wounded and sick were, suggested that they shoot the seriously wounded. Next, his forced march of three days to Salonika, carrying two heavy haversacks of medical equipment as well as his own kit, was "the hardest time of my captivity."

They travelled through Yugoslavia and into Germany to Berlin. His next camp was Dabenbdorf Stalag 111D, which held 250 men. He was the only officer as MO and was not permitted to have anything to do with the running of the camp. This was done by the senior ranks (Senior NCOs) from the two regiments in the camp — The Welch Regiment and the Argyll and Sutherland Highlanders. Their Commandant had been himself a POW of the British in the First War, in a camp in South West Africa. He was very helpful in every way.

Captain Annan's account of his dealings with the routine medical care is worth quoting, as it shows the contrast with those in the hands of the Japanese:

"I held daily sick parades and certified those unfit for work to the German Feldwebel. As long as the number was reasonable that was not disputed. At first there was a high proportion of sick and we had a lot of arguments about numbers, but when Red Cross parcels came regularly each month, men were much more fit and sick parades got smaller. By this time we had a fair idea of the percentage the Germans would accept and we developed a rota system of days off work to make up the acceptable limit! In my opinion all sides were happy with the arrangement, and few problems arose. In many ways the men on working parties accepted they were better doing something than nothing and they were mostly able to take care of themselves, and some even fraternised with the local girls."

Later he was in Saxony in the Lazarett Konigswartha, 40Km from Dresden. This was a proper hospital, and he was able to undertake surgery, as he hoped to train as a surgeon after the War. His description of the conditions showed that all that was necessary in the way of drugs, dressings, and theatre equipment was provided.

His only real anxiety was when he protested strongly about the beating of a Cypriot prisoner in the nearby punishment camp, and wrote to the Swiss that the man should not have suffered such injuries in a civilised country. He found himself before a visiting German general, had to explain himself, and feared he might be sent to a punishment camp himself. But his explanation was accepted. He mentioned several times the fear of the Germans of visits from the SS.[27]

Medical Achievements of the 1939–45 War.
Many basic assumptions remained unchallenged. The AMS was in service to save life, prevent suffering, and preserve function. The causes of death and disablement were still haemorrhage, shock, and infection, as far as the wounded man was concerned.

The most important advances on the surgical side were in what could be called accessory methods by other specialists than surgeons themselves, real advances in surgical technique, and improvements due to altered conditions in warfare. Much of the smooth evacuation in the British Liberation Army, as the Force in Western Europe was called, was because the army itself was a victorious one, moving from one success to the next with sure lines of communication behind it, and the U.K. base very near.

The last of these advances can be recorded first. One was the excellent physical condition of the troops themselves. Hard basic training had produced fit and extremely toughened soldiers, who withstood wounding and were especially resistant to disease. The numbers of those with the disabling medical conditions of previous wars — from rheumatic heart disease to bad teeth — were by 1944–45 much lower than 25 years earlier.

Removal of wounded from the battlefield had improved enormously. The small, eager jeep could go almost anywhere to remove casualties. The small planes in Burma made the difference between life and death for hundreds of wounded, and the Dakota did the next leg of the carry. Even Sunderland flying boats were used to carry casualties from the Indawigi Lake, west of Mytkyina, to bases in north-east Assam from May to July of 1944. There were of course the traditional slower routes of evacuation by river steamer down the Brahmaputra to Sirajungi and then by train to Calcutta or directly to India from Chittagong by sea.

Probably the most outstanding advance of the War was blood transfusion. In 1939 Sir Lionel Whitby, the first Director, found resuscitation much as it had been in 1920. The person who made probably the greatest contribution to the actual functioning of the service was Lieutenant Colonel G.H. Buttle, who set it up in North Africa and then went on to Normandy. The influence of the service he set up on the history of surgery in warfare cannot be exaggerated. The Field Transfusion Officer developed from the uncertain, low-ranking man of May 1940 to become a key person of the forward surgical group. The "pre-op" ward became all-important; all surgeons who had experience of the later War were in agreement about this. Whole blood was soon found to be better than plasma. The amount surgeons and anaesthetists in 1945 considered correct was 30 pints of blood(60 litres) and 20 (40 litres) in forward operating units for every 100 casualties.

Chemotherapy in 1945 was "still under trial"; it must be remembered that it was entirely new and relatively unknown. 21 Army Group, including the British invasion Army, went into Normandy by November 1944 with a special "Penicillin service", with a "Penicillin officer" (like the one Isma Begbie and Beryl Smith had to deal with) to supervise its management. Penicillin had by then been known to be better in every way than sulphonamides. In complicated wounds — those first receiving attention many hours after injury and when complete excision might not be possible, or in wounds where bone was involved, chemotherapy (i.e. penicillin as distinct from sulphonamides) increased the scope and safety of surgery and allowed earlier closure. The secondary suture of compound GSW fractures within 10 days of wounding, converting them from open to closed fractures, was one of the outstanding advances of the War.

Use of Penicillin in head and spinal surgery, and in thoracic surgery, where delayed primary suture does not apply as in limb wounds, was also a huge advance. Even in Burma, where No 3 Neuro-Surgical Team of Major Frank Nicholson's had to put up with insects from the forest falling into the cranium, results were improved significantly.

Head wounds were treated increasingly in special units from 1943 onwards, and to these NSTs were added Ophthalmic Teams, and Maxillo-Facial Teams where dental colleagues were included. In Normandy, Ear, Nose, and Throat Teams appeared. The specialist skills of all these brought about improvement in results which had not existed previously. It was not in survival alone, but in clean healing, control of infection by surgical procedure, and preservation or restoration of function, that the wounded soldiers benefited.

In head injury, the death rate from penetrating missiles, which was 45 per cent in the only fully recorded series of the First War, that of the U.S. surgeon Harvey Cushing, fell to 20–25 per cent in North Africa, Italy and Normandy, and to only 10 per cent in the last stages of the fighting in Europe. Deaths from late infection, 25 per cent in Cushing's series, were 11 per cent in earlier North African fighting, 4 per cent in Tunisia and 6 per cent in Western Europe. Because of the addition of penicillin, the percentage of head wounds healing by first intention rose from 70 per cent to 90 per cent.[28]

Burns had been a new injury in the Royal Air Force, which civilian surgeons had made great progress in treating by grafting and repair. In granulating wounds of amputation stumps, infected compound fractures of the leg, and infected burns with delayed healing, the Bunyan-Stannard envelope, the invention of a Naval surgeon, was regarded as "better than anything previously available."

There was experimentation with the closed plaster method of treatment of limb wounds in bad conditions, but "never at the expense of delayed primary suture." No real progress was made in the treatment of vascular injuries.

The use of the naso-gastric tube in post-operative abdominal cases, to reduce post-operative distension, was pioneered in the desert by Major T. Giblin of the Australian Medical Corps.

Orthopaedics had emerged as a specialty in the 1914–18 War under the leadership of Sir Robert Jones. With the usual peace-time parsimony and the lack of clinical material for the full-time

RAMC, it had completely disappeared by 1939. It developed once more in North Africa, as did the other specialties. The most outstanding advances were in treatment of open femoral fractures and penetrating wounds of the knee-joint. Once more, it was the advent of penicillin which was the non-surgical factor. The Tobruk plaster remained popular till the end of the War.

Major General Heneage Ogilvie wrote however in December 1945: "It cannot be foreseen that the Ritz-Carlton conditions of West Europe on the Allied side enjoyed during the closing phases of this War will ever be repeated; in a later war a return to simpler methods may be the truest form of advance."[29]

The Psychiatric service had been officially recognised as a specialty during the War; its principles of management learned in the Great War had been re-learned by the civilians who filled its ranks from 1941 onwards. Some of these psychiatrists had to learn by hard experience, and at times conflicts arose between the "new experts" and their military superiors. The causes of what was presently called "nervous exhaustion" were confirmed as continuous hard fighting, heavy mortar fire, the loss of friends, respected officers and NCOs, the horrors of the mutilating effects of high explosive, war weariness especially amongst desert and Far East veterans. New factors were the effect of known bombing of the home base, with death and danger to families — this was new from 1914–18 — and, in the later months of the War, shortage of good junior leaders because of the selective demands of the RAF and to some extent of the RN, for potential aircrew and others filtered from the more intelligent Service intake.

All these causes were listed. Exhaustion centres on 1914–18 lines were set up in the corps area. Treatment was by the same measures too — rest and quiet, soluble barbitone (Medinal), sodium pentothal, and phenobarbitone, sometimes with hyoscine; these were the drugs used, both orally and by injection.

The greatest medical advance was certainly the control and improved treatment of Malaria. Sulphaguanidine in bacillary dysentery was a lesser but dramatic advance. While chemotherapy was beginning to show its worth, and over the whole range of medical disease, it would not prove this fully until some time later, as clinical reports began to be published. Several RAMC reports were noteworthy for their caution in 1945.

Although there were slight variations in treatment in various areas in Burma, quinine, pamaquin and mepacrine in combination was the standard. In one paper by Brigadier I.G.W. Hill and others, a "new routine treatment" was described, of mepacrine only. The régime was: 2 days of 0.9Gm, then 5 days of 0.3Gm., followed by a suppressive dose of 0.1Gm a day for 6 weeks, or longer if in an area where suppressive mepacrine was being taken.[30]

Hygiene and Sanitation were as before. Captain Watty Yellowlees could complain in Tunisia and Italy that his C.O. found it easy to have slit trenches dug, but did not seem to realise that latrines were equally important. The MO's remarks in the Burma Campaign have already been quoted. Over and over again hygiene staff — senior NCOs who were often the most important members of the sanitation system — complained that field hygiene seemed regarded by some as more of a hindrance than a help! Major J.H. Lawrence, O.C. of No 2 Fd Hy Sec, wrote three truths readers might remember: "It is during the battle and immediately afterwards that unit hygiene tends to slacken off, and stimulation is required; areas must be systematically cleared and cleansed; and there must be load-carrying vehicles to bring up sanitary stores from base."

The biggest acute hygiene problem the RAMC had to face was the clearance of the Belsen death camp. This was undertaken and solved with a remarkable level of efficiency — the "human laundry", the physical clearing of the site, the rapid setting up of food, clothing and all necessities in a short space of time, even the management of the Germans in the camps and the civilians brought in to do the hard labour, all was mainly an AMS task. It was a battle honour of the Army Health component of the Corps.

The Army health measure which excelled all others was without doubt the introduction of DDT. Indeed, it can be said that its use was as important an advance as the introduction of antibiotics, with respect to the amount of infectious disease it prevented, from Belsen and Italy in the West to Burma in the East.

The tactical use of field units had shown some, but not many, changes. The field ambulances had stood the test of time and remained a key unit. Jeeps had made it possible to do with fewer

SBs. The "light" field ambulances were retained for armoured brigades if, and only if, such were operating in an entirely independent role. An ASC based on a FDS was "definitely second best" to one based on a CCS. But an FDS had to be attached to a CCS to increase its capacity for filtering off lightly wounded and sick.

As ever, nursing officers were vital — their numbers were reduced for a short time to 3–10 from a pool in a CCS, but were soon restored to their previous 14. Better transport by road vehicle, and, of course, air evacuation, were set to bring permanent change to "the road back."

The 1939–45 War brought the AMS to another high peak of achievement. All the elements of the professions — nursing, including the nursing care of the RAMC soldiers, the NO3s, 2s, and 1s as well as the QAs — medical, dental, padres, and hygienists, quartermasters, radiographers and all sorts of laboratory staff, and by no means least, the soldiers of the medical equipment depots. Field Marshal Montgomery wrote warmly of the "Royal Army Medical Corps, whose contribution to Victory has been beyond all calculation."[31]

Notes and references

CHAPTER 10

[1]The extent of the proposed Greater East Asia Co-Prosperity Scheme, in particular its "Land Disposal Plan", issued by the Japanese Ministry of War in December 1941, is described in detail in "Fascism for Beginners" by S. Hood and L. Jansz, Icon Books Ltd, Cambridge, 1993, p 84ff. ISBN 1 874105 08 0. Not only Hong Kong, Burma, and Malaya, but Australia, New Zealand, The Dutch East Indies, Hawaii, States along the western seaboard of the USA and Canada, and even Jamaica and the Bahamas, were to come under Japanese control. At the other end of this scale, and from the immediate point of view of the treatment of malaria the occupation of Java by the Japanese in February 1942 was important, because this was the main source of cinchona bark, from which quinine was manufactured.

[2]Medical History of the Second World War, Campaigns, Vol 2, p 98. For details of the medical cover in the battles for Hong Kong and Malaya, see chapters 1 and 2.

On April 23rd, 1942, at a secret session of Parliament, Mr Churchill described the capitulation of Singapore as…"after 5 or 6 days of confused but not very severe fighting the Army and Fortress surrendered. The Japanese have not stated the numbers of prisoners they have taken but it does not seem there was much bloodshed. This episode and all that led up to it seems to be out of harmony with anything we have experienced or performed in the present War."

[3]Two members of 6 Fd Amb were aboard a transport ship, the *Varosova*, *en route* to Rangoon for the final battle there. (The ship) "was literally infested with rats and cockroaches; they scrambled over your body as you tried to sleep, especially if you slept on the deck as 80 per cent of us had to…on 'V.E.' night each man was given a bottle of beer…we listened to the wireless commentary on the Royal procession to St Paul's Cathedral; those of us with sufficient interest listened to the 'Thanksgiving Service' and not once were the men or the war out here mentioned by the Archbishop of Canterbury in his address. 'The Forgotten Army', how true!"

[4]Mountbatten was a grandson of Queen Victoria. He was born in Frogmore House, Windsor Castle, in 1900. At his baptism, he was said to have knocked off the Queen's spectacles. He had a distinguished career in the Royal Navy; the usual snide parliamentary question about his promotion being due to his Royal connections was easily refuted. In the War he came into prominence as Chief of Combined Operations, and was associated with two famous remarks: he said to Mr Hugh Dalton that he found very little difference between De Gaulle and the Vichy generals, and he provoked the remark of De Gaulle "Je connais la guerre" when he sought to limit the number of persons having access to information about commando raids.

As well as being an Admiral of the Fleet and Supreme Commander in the Far East, he was the last Viceroy of India. He was murdered by the I.R.A. on 27th August, 1979 when an old man with his grandson; the event, hailed as a great act by some nationalist Irish, ("We will tear out their sentimental, imperialist heart. The execution was a way of bringing home to the English ruling class and their working class slaves that their government's war with us is going to cost them as well") coincided with the murder of 18 paratroopers at Warren Point. The world-wide flood of telegrams, the book in Rangoon which a multitude signed, and the week-long State mourning in India perhaps put the Irish boastings into perspective.

[5]The 14th Army later included the greatest span of Empire soldiers of all time. As well as British and Old Commonwealth troops, there were "Chins, Kachins, Karens and Burmese, men from the U.S.A., and the greatest numbers by far, the men of the Indian Army, the largest volunteer army the world has ever known…Sikhs, Dogras, Pathans, Madrassis, Mahrattas, Rajputs, Assamese, Kumaonis, Punjabis, Garwhalls, Nagas… Africans from East Africa and more heavily built from West Africa, with the tribal slits slashed deep into their cheeks — a division of each." The Royal West African Field Force had many outstanding medical officers. See account by E. C. Lanning, MBE, in BMA file. Z. Lett, after the war, actually published a paper "Chloroform and Ether Anaesthesia in War-time Burma" in the University of Hong Kong — also in BMA file. There were also the marvellous Gurkhas, over the century the most consistent and loyal ally Britain has had. (Lieutenant Colonel John Masters DSO, The Road Past Mandalay, 1961, London, Michael Joseph. See also Defeat into Victory, by Field-Marshal Viscount Slim, 1956, London, Cassell and Co, Ltd, for the definitive story of the 14th Army).

[6]It was the siege of Imphal which put an end to the policy of siting large hospitals forward and at the same time established the necessity for air evacuation. Medical officers who were most aware of the new need and whose names merit recording were Brigadier G.R. Macalevy, DDMS 4 Corps and Major General T.O. Thompson, DDMS Eastern

Army. These officers pressed the Staff from the beginning of the Burma Campaign to provide aircraft. Due to their pressure, aircraft, with some limitations, were used first on an organized plan in the Arakan in 1943. It is of interest that, by contrast, the RAF in the desert were very unwilling to accept the use of aircraft for casualty evacuation for a long time.

Air evacuation was planned to take place in two phases:

a) Evacuation from divisional fd units in the most forward centres to the corps medical areas in the corps areas. Divisional fd units were often under shell and mortar fire and even within range of small arms. Jap snipers were particularly dangerous and efficient.

b) Evacuation from corps medical centres to advanced base hospitals.

[7]The 2nd British Division War Memorial at Kohima was designed and built by men of the Division. The principal feature is a great monolith brought from the hills and placed in position by 200 of the local Naga tribesmen, who would accept no payment for the work. Behind the massive pillar runs a semi-circular wall of grey dressed stone into which copper plates are set engraved with the Roll of Honour. The wall is carried on into wings on both sides and the whole is paved with stone and approached by a sweep of shallow semi-circular steps. On the face of the central stone is engraved a cross with underneath the translation of an old Greek epigram:

"When you go home tell them of us and say,

For your tomorrow we gave our today."

Below the verse is a copper plate of dedication, and on the plinth's reverse is another plaque which tells the story of the Battle of Kohima and the opening of the Road.

[8]Evacuation from div fd units was by two types of light aircraft: L5 — called the "flying jeep" or "Stensen." This was an American aircraft, a high wing single-engined plane with a low landing speed, capable of carrying 1 sitting casualty. Some of them were modified to take 1 lying casualty. The L1, the "Vultee Vigilant", was similar; some larger versions could take more. For details of these, see "Air Evac of Cas in S-E Asia", Brigadier J.T. Robinson, OBE, MD, J R Army Med Corps, 1946, Vol LXXXVII, p 181–190. For the best general account, see "The Burma Campaign — 1942–1945, A History of Cas Evac, ibid, 1948, Vol LXC1, 101–124.

[9]No 1 Malaria Field laboratory was at Comilla and sent out mobile sections. They had five lines of study: 1) they showed the presence of hitherto unsuspected Anopheline vectors — Anopheles jeyporiensis, first found in the Arakan foothills from mid February till the onset of the rains, and Anopheles leucisphyrus in the jungle just before the rains. The former was largely responsible for the failure of the

operations in Arakan in early 1943; 2) they estimated urinary mepacrine concentrations with a fluorimeter, using sunlight as the source of U/V rays. Thus they discovered a means of checking the degree of care with which mepacrine was being taken by a unit; 3) they worked on methods of proofing wide-meshed nets with Di-Methyl-Phthalate and other substances so as to be protective even when in contact with the skin; 4,5) they studied effects of outdoor DDT spraying on land and by aircraft.

[10]Mepacrine. For an idea of how far things had changed, see e.g. "Prevention of Malaria on Field Service" from GHQ New Delhi, India, ref GIPD-38-1274 Army-18-4-42, signed by W.H.G Baker, Lieutenant General, Adjutant-General,. India. There is a certain naivete in his statement, when listing avoidance of villages, spraying with "flit", and clothing measures: "From practical experience in this war, the following precautions have been found to be invariably successful when carried out in full." He had not been in Burma. He compares with the brigadier of 9 Ind Div who told his men in Malaya that the Japs couldn't see in the dark so would be easy to beat !

For an account of the very different conditions existing in the jungle, I am indebted to Professor Ronald Girdwood, CBE, MD, PPRCPEdin, who served in India: "In Burma the two main forms of malaria were benign tertian and malignant tertian, due respectively to *Plasmodium vivax* and *Plasmodium falciparum*. Sometimes both were present. Quartan fever, due to *Plasmodium malariae*, was less common, and *Plasmodium ovale* was not found. In Burma the chief carriers were *Anopheles minimus* and *A. jeyporiensis var candidensis* in hilly regions, with *A. sundaicus* along the eastern coast adjoining the Arakan and probably *A. annularis* in the inland plains. The symptoms varied a great deal and sometimes the infection was discovered when the patient had been sent to hospital with an other condition. The temperature was nearly always raised, sometimes as high as 106°Fahrenheit (41°Celsius). Fortunately the measures taken ensured that the mortality was very low. It was not unusual for the spleen not to be palpable and quite often the liver could be felt, even in a first attack. Usually there was a feeling of chill with headache, weakness, and malaise. Sometimes there was nausea and vomiting and occasionally abdominal pain. When M.T. Malaria was suspected, it was important to start treatment as soon a blood smear was taken, without waiting for it to be examined."

The official "War Office Memorandum on Medical Diseases in Tropical and Sub-Tropical Areas" notified in Army Orders of November 1942 gave quinine as the best prophylactic drug, but already the seizure of Java by the Japanese had made this unrealistic.

Mepacrine is an acridine derivative which was synthesised in 1930 by I.G. Farbenindustrie. The tablets were of mepacrine hydrochloride. It was advised that it be given on a full stomach. It was thought to be a better drug for those suffering from Blackwater fever. It acted on the asexual parasites within the red cells but had little action on the gametocytes and none on the sporozoites. Another new drug, pamaquin (plasmoquine), a synthetic quinolone derivative, was found to destroy gametocytes.

In Eastern India and Burma (it was not used at first in Western India) it was to be taken for the first seven days in a dose of two 0.1Gm tablets daily after the evening meal, and thereafter in the dose of 0.1Gm daily. It was soon found that mepacrine induced gastritis and sometimes psychosis, and that it stained the skin yellow. However at the time it was such an effective preventative drug that it became an offence for troops to develop Malaria in the fighting area.

In some areas the incidence of Malaria was seasonal and the seasons were known and published in District Orders. Suppressive treatment was to be taken if possible for 7 days before entry to a malarious area and from 28 days after leaving. The drug reduced the occurrences of clinical attacks without actually preventing infection. Benign tertian Malaria sometimes might relapse a few weeks later but this was rarely so with malignant tertian. Wingate's men were said not to receive their food until they had taken their mepacrine and their Malaria rate stayed low until June and July 1944 when their general condition was so bad that even those with mild attacks of Malaria had no reserves of strength and collapsed from exhaustion, exposure and strain. In 1943, for every man evacuated with wounds, 120 were evacuated for sickness, especially Malaria. Following the institution of Malaria Forward Treatment Units, preventative measures of all kinds, the ratio of medical to battle casualties fell to 19 to 1 in 1944 and 3.4 to 1 in 1945. See Marriot, H.L., Hill, I.G.W., Bomford, R.R., 1946, Trans R. Soc. trop. Med Hyg. 39,461.

[11]The consultant physician and surgeon to 14th Army were both Edinburgh graduates — I.G.W. Hill, who became a distinguished cardiologist, Professor of Medicine at St Andrews University and Physician to H.M. The Queen in Scotland, and John Bruce, who became Regius Professor of Surgery in Edinburgh, Surgeon to the Queen, and a world-famous figure; both were knighted.

[12]Captain John Lawson said: "All the doctors thought Wingate was mentally unstable. We couldn't write it down, of course, but we all agreed amongst ourselves. We couldn't understand why he was kept on." (Personal Communication, 1994).

[13]The Bedfordshire and Hertfordshire Regiment was known by the soldiers as the "Beds and Hearts" — hence the "Honeymooners!"

[14]For full detail, see RAMC archives, box 184, Wellcome Institute. The ADMS's complaint about failure of the General Staff to inform the medical commander repeats what had to be said so many times: "so often one finds that (plans) are known to a junior "G" officer but are not told to the Med. Service until it is too late to be of use in the making of an efficient medical plan...the habit of looking upon the doctor as a fifth columnist, liable to blab, is all too common...the doctors probably hold more personal and confidential secrets than any other individual." For General Slim's opinion on the Special Force's exhaustion, see Defeat into Victory, op cit, p 280. For a short account of *medical* disease among Chindits, see the report by Lieutenant Colonel J.N. Morris, J R Army Med Corps, 1944, Vol LXXXV, 123–132.

[15]The determination of the RAMC to overcome the difficulties at the battle of the "Box" can be gauged by this description of the MDS of 6 Fd Amb in the Jotsoma area: "There can be few MDSs so compact as this one was. The area covered, excluding unit personnel, was less than 70 yds by 20 yds (60m by 18m), and yet everything was present.

"At road level there was a pull-in for 3 ambulances from which a ramp led up to Cpl. Watkin's reception, M.I.(medical inspection) and triage room; through that on to the main terrace where the theatre block, minor treatment and evac departments were laid out.

The pre-op, post-op, and theatre rooms varied in size from 9 feet by 9 feet to 12 feet by 12 feet (270cm and 360cm) with a head-room of 6 1/2 feet (195cm). Walls ranged from 2 1/2 feet (75cm) to infinity. Roofs were splinter proof. Inside white sheets hid the virgin earth or sand-bags and increased illumination. Mosquito nets covered the openings left for doors and electric light was generously laid on. By driving angle irons into the walls stretchers could be slipped in like triple bunks so that patients could be easily watched and treated or fed as required.

The theatre was a masterpiece as laid out by Major Thomas. Although so small that even a Manx cat would have been hopelessly concussed in one swing round, there was floor space for the table, the surgeon and his assistant, and the anaesthetist. Instrument trays, etc, were all fixed to the walls where they were in easy reach of the surgeon. While the other rooms became delightfully warm when in use, the theatre became oppressively hot until the RASC rallied round and fitted up two electric fans. When they were at it they also improvised a suction apparatus from the induction manifold of the generator engine.

The evac and minor treatment dept was in a large tarpaulin 'cut-and-fill' construction with sand-bag walls on two sides. Here also the increased number of cas forced quadruple bunking.

On the next terrace up was the detention ward for about 30 minor sick, the Q.M. store, and Sgt Watson's dispensary. Above this were the Indian gunners with their little 3.7s which barked away at all hours of the day and night, but, like pie dogs, we soon got used to them.

The unit personnel lived or existed down the khud on the other side of the road where the slope was about 1 in 2, but by levelling off small areas they soon built themselves snug little 'prefabs'. (Prefabs were houses built of prefabricated sections and put together quickly; they were used in the U.K. base during the War for house building).

In the hub of this colony was the cookhouse from where Sgt Jarvis and his men worked wonders.

For 3 weeks the MDS under Major Smalley's and Sgt-Major Kay's organization worked like clockwork, but the pre-monsoon rains started and eventually made a move vital. Poets write lovingly of springs bubbling up and of cheerfully chatting running water, but the men of 6th Fd Amb wrote no lyrics when a spring suddenly appeared in the back wall of their apartment and the water ran silently through their beds."

[16]POW testified to the different attitude of the Japanese Navy towards them, compared to that of the Japanese Army. This some supposed to have been because the Jap Navy had been trained by the Royal Navy; they believed this was the reason for their kinder manner.

[17]Personal Communication, Sister Margaret Mcpherson, QARANC, 1965, who was on a ship which got away from Singapore. She recalled clearly the behaviour of Australians at the time: "The Aussies were throwing people off the ships to get on themselves." Lieutenant Ian Stonor, who was ADC to General Percival, confirmed that such acts of indiscipline took place. In a letter from Rear-Admiral E.J. Spooner, who was hidden on Tjebia island with him, to Captain Cazalet, RN, on a naval message pad, was the remark: "The present state of affairs was started by the A.I.F. (Australian Imperial Forces) who just turned tail and let the Japs walk in" ("Course for Disaster — from Scapa Flow to the River Kwai" by Lieutenant Richard Pool, 1987, Leo Cooper Ltd, Appendix II, p 195). And Major General Gordon Bennett, the Australian General, "flew off in a long-range Australian flying boat, leaving his Brigadier in charge, without saying anything", recalled Ian Stonor; "I wonder what happened to him when he got home." But his successor, promoted by Percival in Changi, Major General C.A. Callaghan, was a splendid man in every way.

There was also the story of the British traitor, Captain Patrick Heanan, an Indian Army officer, born in New Zealand but educated in England. He was thought to have sent many photographs of military sites to the Japanese, taken while he was in Malaya before the invasion,

and sent to the enemy. His story is told in a book, "Odd Man Out —
the story of the Singapore traitor", by Patrick Elphick and Michael
Smith, 1993, Hodder and Stoughton. In it they debate the fate of
Heanan. But Lieutenant Ian Stonor remembered the officer clearly;
"Heanan had been most unpopular in the Indian Army, and finished
in the Rice Corps (Indian Army Service Corps). He was arrested
during the campaign and put in Changi. He got more obnoxious as the
Japs got nearer. The M.P.s got fed up with him and one day they just
took him out and shot him. There were plenty bangs, so no-one
noticed." Lieutenant Stonor was also hiding on Tjebia island, along
with the Admiral and several of the military police. (Personal
communication, May, 1994).

[18]The Conquest of Malaya, Arthur Swinson, Purnell's History of
the 2nd World War, Vol 7, p 721.

[19]Official History, op cit, Vol 2, Campaigns, p 141–167.

[20]Fifty years after; some experiences of the medical care of prisoners
of war, R.H. Girdwood, Scot Med J 1993; 38: 120–124.

[21]Two late 20th century books about the way of life of the Chinese
which detail the attitude of their and the Japanese races are: "Behind
the Wall", Colin Thubron, 1987, William Heinemann, and "Wild
Swans — Three daughters of China", Jung Chang, 1991, Harper/
Collins. The latter tells of the hideous cruelty and behaviour alien to
western minds found in recent Communist China.

[22]Eric Cruickshank, 1946; **11**: 369

[23]"Camp Pie" was the medical magazine of Changi Camp. No 11,
"produced by kind permission of O.C. Roberts Hospital, Changi
POW Camp, Singapore, Colonel J.W. Craven MC, TD, had a
drawing of two girls in sarongs on a tropical island on its front cover.

Its editorial read: "Christmas is rapidly approaching and already we
are busy on schemes to publish a bumper Christmas number. One
which will be long remembered. It will be our first, and unlike most
publishers, we hope our last. To produce this special number we need
seasonal articles and poems, jokes, etc. Why not try your hand."

The 11th number had a section called "pie crumbs", with "questions",
"believe it or not", "it's a fact" parts. There was a large sports section: "We
congratulate those who entered the 18th Divisional sports, and who won
four events, were third in another, and walked off with the
championship…Capt Clarkson was the most successful winning both
the high jump (4'11" – 1.5m) and the 120 yds (132m) hurdles. Lieut
Glancy won the long jump (17'11" – 5.4m) and Sgt Sercombe was third
in the 100 yds (110m) and Padre O'Mahoney fifth. The relay team Capt
Clarkson, Capt Wallace, Padre O'Mahoney and Sgt Sercombe won the
relay after a very exciting finish…once again we say 'well done medics'."

[24]In spite of the conditions, a wonderful range of equipment was constructed for patients. For transfusions (where there was no shortage of volunteers), stethoscope tubing and old needles were used. Bamboo was actually used also. Needles were fashioned from old bicycle spokes. Suction pumps of bamboo with a metal handle made from a Sam Browne belt; artificial limbs, a dental drill made from a cheap Jap grindstone with its small handle, a length of Bowden cable from an old motor bicycle attached to the spindle, a slide valve made from a car tappet and guide, and then a right-angle hand piece and drill. On the other hand, John Leckie remembered vividly, while on the railway, having the remains of a septic tooth removed by a dental officer with a hammer and chisel. "I couldn't eat for three days", he laughed later; "and those three days we had better food than for months !"

Some of the medical equipment and procedures were portrayed by not only British, but also their comrades the Australian prisoners. It must be remembered that Australians shared the hard times, and that memory continued ever after. Murray Griffin, an Australian Official War artist, produced some remarkable paintings of the construction of prostheses; see "Murray Griffin and his Changi clinical paintings", by Colonel John Pearn (who remained proud to be styled Royal Australian Medical Corps), The Medical Journal of Australia, 1991, Vol 155, December 2/16, p 775–777.

[25]Radios were a huge means of keeping up morale. There were as always a small number of Japanese speakers amongst the POW as well. Radios were hidden behind a sink, in a broom-head, in a concertina played regularly and carried by guards, in water bottles and in artificial limbs. And as in all good novels, in the Jap commandant's kit !

[26]See obituary in "Gunner" July 1979; personal communication, E. Leeson. For a horrifying account of life in the Formosa camps, with details of the work in the copper mines, beatings — especially of officers, murder of sick by deliberate neglect, letters of complaint by the prisoner officers, and the change in behaviour of the guards at the Japanese surrender, see Major J.F. Crossley, MBE, TD, RA, in RAMC archives no.1016 in Wellcome collection.

[27]He achieved his ambition. He became a distinguished orthopaedic surgeon in Bradford, and later a member of the Court of Examiners of the Royal College of Surgeons of Edinburgh. In later years again, he became a strong member of the RAMC(Scotland) golf team.

[28]See. e.g., Major F.J. Gillingham, *Brit J Surg*, War Supplement No 1, 1947; 80–87, and Sir Hugh Cairns, Penicillin in Head and Spinal Wounds, ibid, 1947; **32**: 199–207.

[29]The best description of the role of the AMS in the Second British Army's Campaign in North-West Europe is by Lieutenant Colonel R.

Gwyn Evans. MBE, MB, MRCP, — like Lieutenant Colonel John Matheson, a Territorial who became an ADMS (Ops and Plans).

See J R Army Med Corps, 1947, Vol LXXXXVII. This excellent and very full account covers the whole range of Corps activities, both medical and military. It should be read again on the prospect of a further European war.

[30]Marriott, H.L., Hill, I.G.W., Hawksley, J.C., Bomford, R.R. 1946, Medical Experiences of the War in South-East Asia Command, *Trans. Royal Soc. Trop. Med. Hyg.*, **39**, 462–484; Fairley, N. Hamilton, 1945, Chemotherapeutic suppression and prophylaxis in Malaria, ibid, **38**, 311–365. I am grateful to Professor R. Girdwood for these references.

The best paper on scrub typhus is probably that of Sayers, M.H.P. and Hill, J R Army Med Corps 1948, Vol XC, 6–22. It was written in 1945.

Wartime advances in medicine which could be translated into civil practice were detailed in a Honeyman Gillespie lecture in Edinburgh on 13th June, 1946 by Major General Sir Alexander Biggam. He described the use of pamaquin in addition to mepacrine in Malaria and also the even newer drug paludrine, marketed by I.C.I. He described the use of the newest sulphonamides in bacillary dysentery, and of penicillin followed by emetine and emetine bismuth iodide in acute and chronic amoebic dysentery. This régime was valuable for the many sufferers evacuated from the Far East; the addition of intramuscular penicillin made many previously refractory cases become amenable to the drugs specific against *Entamoeba histolytica*.

[31]The only V.C. awarded to an RAMC soldier in the War was to L/Cpl Eric Harden, for bravery in collecting casualties under fire at Roermund in Holland in 1945. Serving with 'A' troop, 45 R.M. Commando, on the Maasbracht-Linne Road, on 23rd January 1945, he carried back four or six wounded over the snow-covered ground, being fired at the whole time by Germans. Eventually he was shot in the head and killed.

Describing his chest wound suffered on 13/10/14 Montgomery wrote in 1967: "My platoon first, then regimental stretcher bearers, took charge of me. Once I got to the ADS, I was taken over by the RAMC and their organization and care was superb; I was in the Herbert Hospital Woolwich before I really knew what had happened. Since those days I have always had a great admiration for the RAMC and the nursing sisters and orderlies, and in the desert war and later in Europe always did what I could for them."

Chapter 11

The National Service Era, 1948–1963. The Cold War and the Peace-time RAMC

Perspective.
"In war, the practitioners and consultants from civil life become the principal experts of diagnostic and therapeutic medicine...as do the pathologists." Brigadier J. Bennett, Director of Army Medicine, 1948.

"In all the peace years, the surgeon is merely holding the fort, preparing for war, organising according to the lessons learnt in the last war, against the day when the alarm will sound and the civilian surgeons return." Brigadier D. Fettes, OBE, Director of Army Surgery, 1948.

The end of the Second World War saw the beginning of the decline of Great Britain as a world power. Even before its end, it was clear that Churchill's voice no longer had the same command and authority. The United States, builder of the atom bomb (though Britain had one also), and the huge USSR — whose German scientists, quickly collected, would put it ahead in space and rocket technology — were now two large land masses with their own resources of population, raw material, and food. It was said by some that the US favoured the USSR against the "colonial power"; if so, it was a mistake it soon surely regretted. They both looked to dominate; the US industrially, the USSR politically. The progressive detachment of the overseas possessions of the British Empire, at its height the largest the world had seen, was carried out with much dignity and endeavour; in the few instances where some rancour existed, the hope of those leaving was that if the newly independent countries thereafter became failures, their political and economic ills could no longer be blamed on colonial exploitation by the British. It was the loss of the Indian sub-continent in 1947 which was the biggest strategic loss. As Field Marshal Lord Alanbrooke wrote; "Now anyone could twist the lion's tail with impunity."

The defeat of Nazi Germany removed, at least for a time, the fear of German domination in Europe. With the end of the War, the true scale of Nazi atrocity became clear. The European nations were free again; some had suffered more than others, especially Norway and Holland. These would soon become staunch allies in the soon formed North Atlantic Treaty Alliance (NATO). Brave French had hidden and preserved British escaped prisoners. The Poles, for whom Britain and France had gone to war in 1939, were now prisoners of the Russians.

Yet not everywhere was the defeat of Nazi Germany a joy. On V.E. night, a Union Jack was burned in the grounds of Trinity College Dublin. Perhaps those young who burned it had been so blinded by their hatred of Britain that they did not see the pictures of Belsen, Auschwitz and Dachau.[1]

It quickly became apparent that the move of the Soviets west was posing the biggest threat to Western Europe since the time of Charlemagne, when the Saracens were at their most militant, or perhaps the time of the Mongols, who, in 1241, reached Legnica (Liegnitz) in Poland, only a weeks's march from Dresden, and penetrated into north-east Italy. The Soviet western boundary extended to the eastern zone of the divided Germany. All the Eastern European countries behind were subject. Berlin was an isolated island within — the Berlin airlift, another of the battle honours of the RAF, saved the city from incorporation.

Soviets had almost reached Denmark and the North Sea, but were foiled by Allied intervention. Their Communist creed, however, now finding open favour in all countries, made no secret of its intention to take over the corrupt world of the West. "We will bury you", said Mr Kruschev.

In all parts of the world its agents were at work. The Universities of Oxford and Cambridge, always hotbeds of revolution, had their open Communist Party cells, and secret traitors already in post. The latter would not be exposed until many years later. In the Far East, Communism was victor in China, where the later horrors of the cultural revolution were also to become public in due course. The March of Communism was irreversible, its proponents declared. Many Western socialists were sympathetic.

This new world order was called by Sir Winston Churchill "The Cold War", and its continuance over the next 40 years would determine all military strategy during that time. Fears were most immediate in Europe and in Malaya, where Chinese Communist guerrillas looked likely to take over the peninsula and beyond. Open warfare broke out in 1950 in Korea.[2]

All this led to a unique period in British history — a period when conscription would be called for in time of peace. This was the National Service Era. It would last for 15 years. One Army would be needed to go to Germany as more than a mere post-war garrison: it would have to guard the eastern boundary with the Soviet bloc. In the Far East, active operations would also require many troops — the errors of 1941 dared not be repeated.

The National Service Act and the National Servicemen.

The Reserve and Auxiliary Forces Act of 25th May, 1939, was concerned with the call out for service of those already in the TA and other Reserves including Regular reservists, "for the defence of the nation against any external danger."[3] Later in the War conscription called up for service those who had not volunteered for any military service.

In times past, such Acts had come to an end with the cessation of hostilities. But in 1947, though the major War was over, the external threat was regarded as so great that a further Act, the National Service Act, 10 and 11 Geo 6, was brought before parliament by the then Labour Government which had been voted into power the previous summer by a huge majority. The debates of 1947 deserve study; they reflect the political consensus and divergence of the day.[4]

The final outcome in 1948 was that National Service was to be 2 years, and the National Servicemen (NSM) were in effect 2-year Regulars. After their 2 years with the Colours they had still 5 years of Reserve service, during when they could be recalled. It was expected, particularly by Field-Marshal Montgomery, now CIGS, that they would go into the TA after completing their full-time service. The Territorial Army itself, merged with the Regular Army in 1939 at the outbreak of hostilities, was re-constituted as a separate Army in 1947. NSM were to serve in the

Regular Army anywhere in the world, with any unit including those normally open to volunteers only like paratroops. They were in fact and in law 2 year Regulars. Their rates of pay, however, were different.[5] For the NSM — there were no conscripted women — the notice of call-up came by post. After a medical examination near his home, as a rule by civilian medical practitioners and according to the new PULHEEMS system,[6] he would, if passed fit, receive his joining instructions, and a 3rd class railway warrant to his training depot. For RAMC soldiers and medical officers this was Aldershot. The day and time of arrival, a Thursday, was stated on the orders; the recruits were collected by lorry and taken to Keogh Barracks, Ash Vale, for soldiers, and Queen Elizabeth Barracks, Crookham, for officers. Intakes were twice monthly, 200 being the number for soldiers and 20 to 200 for officers — the largest numbers of them being in February and July, coinciding with the twice-yearly cycle of ending of house posts.

Assembled at "B" (Reception) Company, Keogh, the NSMs' recruit course was of 6 weeks' basic training in drill, weapon training, education, and all things military. After passing out on the "Big Square" before the Commandant of the Depot and Training Establishment, a further 6 weeks of special-to-arm training followed.

At the end of this 3-month period, identical for NSM and Regulars, the now trained RAMC soldier was posted to a unit anywhere from Korea to the Caribbean, for the remaining 18 months of his time. He was, it is worth re-stating, in all respects other than pay and status, "a 2-year Regular soldier."

Officers had a 6-week course, called rather unfortunately "LOFAs" (Lieutenant on First Appointment). Again, everyone including the few Regulars went through this. On arrival at Crookham, to live in the "spiders" (as the hutted living quarters were called), the recruit Lieutenant was issued with two sets of battle-dress, two pairs of black boots, gaiters and a web belt, which had to be blancoed and the brasses polished, a steel helmet and a 1914–18 pattern respirator. The rest of his clothing was bought from his uniform allowance of some £40 — the most expensive item being the officer's hat at £5.

Instead of a greatcoat, all MOs bought an officer-type raincoat from whichever of the military tailors they used. This raincoat made them easily identifiable.

After leading the passing-out parade on the "Big Square", they stopped drill. Recruit officers were first drilled in private seclusion by the famous Q.M.S. Donegan until he became Depot R.S.M. in 1953.[7] The Lieutenants had one special period of drill on the main square before passing out, under instruction by the Depot R.S.M. "When that man (R.S.M. Bullough) came up to us, I thought he was a friend", lamented Norman Bradford from Belfast in October 1952 as his squad marched off at the end of the drill period. Yet it was remarkable how a group of often initially unwilling doctors was transformed into a smart and proud squad at Crookham.

The recruit MOs had also to take part in a training mess dinner at the Depot Mess proper, Redfields Officers' Mess.[8] Some cynics felt that this was a means of officer selection !

Two weeks of professional training within the gracious atmosphere of Millbank followed. Here lounge suits were worn, the NSMOs lived 3 to a room and shared a pitcher of hot water to wash and shave with. The quality of instruction was high, and for the first time the new men began to understand the excellence of military medicine.

Lastly, a further 2 weeks were carried out, this time in the military surroundings of Keogh Officers' Mess, one week at the Army School of Health and the second at the Field Training Centre. Here hygiene and RAMC skills were taught, the dangers of "the filthy feet of the faecal-feeding fly" emphasised at the School of Health, and some preparation for war training carried out at the Field School. One Army School of Health Commandant was H.E. Knott, later to become D.G.

Finally, each was posted — to three sorts of area: home postings (this included BAOR, the British Army of the Rhine in Germany), the Middle East, or the Far East, including Korea. While many who went to Korea volunteered to go, this was not always so. The writer, returning from leave in spring of 1953, discovered he had been on a draft for Korea as a Field Transfusion Officer (perhaps because he had done extra obstetrics and gynaecology) but had been taken off as he had at that date a single-figure handicap at golf and was required for the Corps golf team.[9]

The bulk of NSM enjoyed their time as 2-year Regulars. How they fared depended upon their own attitude and that of the unit they served with. A few were resentful and ungracious. But by and large, the RAMC looked after their National Servicemen well — unlike some other branches of the Army, which did not; in a few officers' messes, the NS officers had to sit at a separate table.

There was another side, however. Virtually the whole of British medical graduates did their period of conscription — a very few avoided doing so.[10] But most remained birds of passage, with no intention of continuing a service connection on leaving.[11] The image they would carry back with them to civilian life was more important than later Regular RAMC officers realised. Several, a few of whom rose to become high-quality officers, elected to convert, or to take a permanent commission at the end of their 2 years. Had there been no National Service, at least one or two of these would have been denied to the Corps.

As always, many, while quickly aware of the tradition and the excellent administrative ability they met, were critical of the standard of medical and especially surgical clinical technical ability they saw in Regular specialists with whom they came into contact.[12]

Lecturers, who taught them, were not equally regarded. Many found Army Health lecturing uninspiring, some were puzzled at answers given to medical questions, and others frankly critical of surgical advice offered. Such lecturers did not give a good impression, even military professors, and this was unfortunate. Amongst the NSM were, inevitably, a large number of men of considerable ability who in due course rose high in the profession. On the other hand, a number of lecturers were clear and interesting — one was Lieutenant Colonel J. Baird and, perhaps as much as any, Mr Grundy the entomologist.

The last NSM left in 1963 as the last groups had to sign on for $2^{1/2}$ years. A number extended their full-time service, as they were allowed to do with Commanding Officer's consent. It was the successful end of the Malayan emergency on 31st July, 1962, which was the reason why no more were needed, as this large commitment was over. In the 15 years of the NS Era, the British Army was large — training depots were abundant in many parts of the United Kingdom — and particularly in the large garrisons of Aldershot, Catterick, Tidworth and Salisbury Plain, Colchester, Chester, London. Other historic garrisons were in Dover and

Portsmouth. Infantry depots were in the tribal areas. Because of the very large needs of the NS Army, war-time camps such as Blandford, Ripon, Barnard Castle, Oswestry, Rhyl, Barton Stacey, Hindhead and Yeovil were retained — none of which had been military areas in peace time. For the British Army, still of considerable strength, was deployed over the world. It was in Armies of occupation in Germany, Austria and Japan. Internal strife with serious security problems in India, Palestine, and the Far East, and on the borders of East Germany and Yugoslavia, needed an operational level of troops.

By 1949, although Britain had withdrawn from India, Ceylon, and Burma following the granting of independence, and from Palestine following the setting up of the State of Israel, there were still garrisons in Malta, Cyprus, Aden, Egypt, Malaya, the Sudan, Hong Kong, the West Indies, and in both East and West Africa. The Trieste British element remained. There were troops in France, Belgium, Holland, Eritrea, Cyrenaica, Tripolitania, and Somaliland. The British Army was dispersed, in fact, more widely than it had been between the 1920 and 1939. All these garrisons required medical cover in varying degree.

The largest number of NS MOs were RMOs (90 per cent of RMOs in the 1950s were NS) and the largest number of RAMC soldiers were in hospitals around the world, or in field ambulances of the home and BAOR ORBAT. As well as orderlies there were pharmacists (ranked Sergeant), radiographers, and laboratory and hygiene technicians. Most had a busy but not exhausting work load — ample time for recreation, following the peace-time Service pattern, and opportunity to serve in the overseas countries they would not otherwise had the chance to visit. At this date, the choice was certainly wide!

The group of MOs who had the hardest time were those in the training depots, especially those of the larger Corps like RE, RASC and R. Signals. At its peak, National Service meant the arrival of thousands of youths every two weeks throughout the year. (The exception was December, when there was only one intake).These young Lieutenants had to medically examine, inoculate, educate, and doctor the often hundreds strong intakes of recruits twice every month for almost 2 years. They often had anxious decisions to make; the bulk of recruits who ran into medical or psychological trouble did so during their 6-week basic training. Sadly, it was from this group came those whose resentment and anti-army jibes persisted throughout their lives.

There were even punishment postings for NS MOs. One Glasgow RMO, angered at the refusal of any officer in a Guards' Regiment to speak to him at breakfast, lit the adjutant's newspaper one morning. He was removed next day to an unglamorous destination. Another was the Welshman of high principle who, having reached the dizzy height of acting Major's rank as Officer in Medical Charge of Troops on a troopship bound for Singapore, had been told to issue contraceptives to the soldiers when the ship docked in Malta. He emptied the entire stock of french letters into the Grand Harbour. He spent the rest of his time in No 2 Trg Regt RASC at Willems' Barracks, Wellington Lines, Aldershot, a gloomy and uninspiring, as well as a very hard, place to be. When he asked if he could live in the McGrigor Mess up Gun Hill, he was refused.

It was not only in Guards and some Cavalry officers' messes that NS medicals were not accepted. Two medical and dental officers who spent periods of over a year in Queen's Barracks, Perth, were not once allowed "to put a foot over the doorway", as one recalled, of the Black Watch mess. One of these, 40 years later, was much amused at being invited to the Regimental cocktail party. He had become a Dental Major General in the interval.

The National Servicemen held the fort for 15 important years in the 20th century. They swelled the ranks of the British Army at a time when our nation, because of its tiny population, could not otherwise have produced the numbers to garrison the West and deter the East. They did everything asked of them and merit acknowledgement; they were in no way a collection of the disaffected and unhelpful. They had their share of decorations in all active theatres. By the end of the century they were dying out, but this was their legacy.

Malaya Emergency.

The Malayan emergency began in May 1948, with serious attacks on life and property by well-organised gangs of Chinese, whose support came from mainland Communist China. They followed standard terrorist patterns; European planters or tin miners were, with their families, taken out of their houses and shot. The gang then disappeared into the jungle.

An emergency was officially declared the next month. The war would continue for 15 years, but would be eventually won by the British. It was a rare example of such a victory against a determined terrorist enemy.

The medical services were well prepared on this occasion. Colonel D. Bluett, the ADMS Malaya District, was for once in the position of having both adequate hospital provision and adequate equipment — his predecessors had insisted these be available after the end of the Japanese War.

There were British Military Hospitals at Singapore, Kluang, Kuala Lumpur (BMH Kinrara), and Taiping (BMH Kamunting), and a convalescent one in the Cameron Highlands. There were Medical Reception Stations at Johore Bahru, just across the causeway from Singapore, Seremban, Ipoh, Penang and Sungei Patani. Later there was another MRS at Malacca. The RAF had a hospital at RAF Butterworth, on the mainland near Penang Island. 16 Field Ambulance was outside Kuala Lumpur in the earlier 1950s and 19 Field Ambulance was in Taiping from 1955. Though these may seem many, it should be remembered that Malaya is about the size of England without Wales, and most of it is humid jungle.

The first priority was to find RMOs for the British and Gurkha battalions arriving — these came quickly from the Singapore Garrison — and to make the field ambulances up to strength. Liaison with the civil medical services was important. Special light stretchers and Dakotas and Auster planes were next priority — the "ferret groups" of specialised jungle fighters needed trained RAMC orderlies with carefully designed and stocked jungle packs. Captain John Heber, a NS officer, designed a special light weight anaesthetic pack which was excellent for jungle use.

Men had to be very fit to go on jungle patrol, so medical examinations had to be even more thorough than usual. The greatest difficulty was the removal of casualties from deep inside the jungle — it could take two weeks to get a stretcher through dense foliage. Road ambushes, where casualties inevitably occurred, were difficult to cover medically. On one occasion, a trained elephant was used to smash its way through the jungle, to bring out stretcher cases. After some time, helicopters became available.

Another job for the medicals, as indeed for all troops, was the constant help given to the civilian Malay population. So began what came to be known as the " hearts and minds" policy; it paid dividends after the emergency was over, and carried on until British forces finally left some 10 years later. It was something the troops did well, and something they enjoyed doing.[13]

Korea.

This shorter-lived but true shooting war began in the early hours of 25th June, 1950, when Communist North Korea attacked South. Because the Russians took offence and did not attend the subsequent Security Council Meeting, they were unable to veto the call for the United Nations to respond.

The response was United States led, and as had happened before, began with high hopes of a quick victory once the marines arrived. But the North Koreans proved a determined enemy, and the eventual success of the Allies against them was reduced to nothing by the appearance of the Chinese.

As always, the AMS had to provide support to the Army where the conflict occurred. The first health shock was the severity of the winter of 1950–51, when our troops found their boots and their clothing totally insufficient. The cold was severe; –20–30°C. During the greater part of the winter, the two Commonwealth Brigades — following the usual pattern — were fighting rearguard actions or holding defensive positions. Forward troops were either standing-to or sleeping in the open, and the lighting of fires was of course not possible. 152 cases of frostbite were sustained among Commonwealth troops, out of some 800 battle casualties.[14]

Medically directed investigators got quickly to work. By the next winter they had devised the boot CWW (for cold, wet, weather), the layered system of clothing, and the parka outer garment. "We went to the Americans for their food", recalled Captain Morrison Dorward, a NS MO, "but they came to us to scrounge our kit and boots".[15]

The Korean countryside over which the war was fought, though monotonous, was by no means unattractive. In the west, where the British Commonwealth Division was, it was a succession of small round-topped hills 150–300m high, separated by narrow valleys. At one time it had been wooded, but most trees

had been felled during the Japanese occupation. In the east the hills rose to 2000m, with dry water-courses which became fast-flowing streams in the hot wet summer season.

The Commonwealth ORBAT was three independent brigades — 25 Canadian Infantry, 28 British Commonwealth Infantry, and 29 British Infantry. 25 Cdn Fd Amb had its FST and FTT attached, but these worked in a US Mobile Army Surgical Hospital (MASH — to be heard of regularly from now on, especially by the TA Medical Services). It was however no more than the equivalent of a British ASC. 60 Indian Para Fd Amb had its full establishment, including 2 FSTs. 26 Fd Amb originally had 22 FST and 9 FTT attached, but the FST was detached to 29 GH with the British Commonwealth Occupation Forces.

From 1950 26 Fd Amb was the only major RAMC unit deployed. After the fierce battles of 1951 the division held a static position for the year, north of the 38th parallel and the River Imjim, and 30 miles(45km) from the west coast. Casualty evacuation followed traditional lines — by hand carry to the RAP, Fd Amb transport for 1–2 miles(1500–3000m) to ADS, MAC from the bde ADS to a MASH some 10 miles(16Km) down the MSR (main supply route), thence by rail to Seoul, a farther 30 miles(50Km) back, and thence by RAAF Dakota to Kure and the general hospital. When helicopter evacuation became more rapid, there was a danger of casualties arriving at the operating theatre too deeply morphinised.

Medical cover in the Korean war was very much a Commonwealth affair, and in general relations were very good. The U.S. were friendly and helpful. Some of their medical and nursing officers took their orders so seriously that they clumped around the hospital in Seoul in heavy boots and steel helmets. Captain Jimmy Henderson, who was on the staff of that hospital, perhaps because he had done his post-graduate year in the USA before returning to do his NS, had an arrangement with a class-mate chum, David Alexander, RMO of the 1st Royal Warwicks, to tease newly-arrived American doctors. James would invite them to the front line — very much the front line, on 1915–17 principles — and give David a message to expect them. Very new Americans would be brought to the Warwicks officers' mess tent, where a waiter, immaculate in a white jacket and bearing a silver salver, would enquire of them: "Would you care for a drink, Sir?"

Because of the nature of the fighting, with patrolling, attacks and defence over open countryside, the chance of casualties being unattended in view of the enemy was not infrequent. RMOs and RAMC soldiers had to collect and bring wounded in from the company or battalion area, as in early 1914, and this, as then, required great bravery in face of fire. It was evident from the start that the eastern mind had not absorbed the ethos which produced the Geneva Convention.

Sgt Bernard Baker was awarded the MM for his bravery on the morning of 25th April, 1951, when ordered to join Y Coy, 1st Bn Royal Northumberland Fusiliers (the Fighting Fifth) with a party of SBs, in a counter attack on a feature called Hill 261, to relieve Z Coy of the battalion and evacuate its wounded. He made five separate journeys along a ridge, under continuous small arms and light automatic fire. In all, he rescued 15 wounded men "with great coolness and regardless of his personal safety."

The most famous infantry engagement of the war was in the same battle, when A Coy of the Gloucestershire Regiment, the left forward company of the battalion, was attacked by Chinese in great force on the night of 22nd–23rd April. On the next day, the remnants of the Gloster Bn were concentrated on Hill 235. For his bravery then and earlier in the year, Captain Robert Hickey was awarded the MC and Captain Douglas Patchett, RMO of the 8th King's Royal Irish Hussars, the same decoration. The Black Watch were also involved in this battle, and again in the Battle of the Hook, which became for them a battle honour. Their RMO was Sam Jilkes and their padre Tom Nicholl (who had been decorated with the MC in North Africa). The two always drove about together, and were known by the Jocks as "Body and Soul"!

Of disease prevention, Lieutenant Colonel R.L. Marks, C.O. of 26 Fd Ambs, wrote: "I think that in instituting preventive measures to be carried out by the individual, we must remember the private soldier's point of view. In winter he had to take all the precautions against cold injury — change and dry his socks, powder his feet dry, dry his boots, do his washing, DDT his bedding and air it. In an isolated position he had to think about water purification and rubbish disposal. In the haemorrhagic fever season he had to smear all his outer clothing with DDT once a fortnight. In summer he had to take anti-malarial precautions and possibly extra salt if on heavy work. He had to work stripped to avoid tinea (skin rash) and wear long trousers, boots and puttees against the haemorrhagic fever mite. In fact, if he was really medically conscientious he would have little time left for his normal duties."

Some of the Glosters, and others, were captured by the Chinese. Like the prisoners in 1941, they found at once the Chinese degraded them, ill-treated them and punished them in an irrational way. In 1966, the writer, at the Field Training School fortnight at the end of the Senior Course, heard Major (later Major General) Sandy Ferrie give a talk on how to resist ill-treatment as a POW. The adjutant of the Glosters, Captain (later Lieutenant-General Sir Anthony) Farrar-Hockley had a film made to describe the sort of behaviour to expect, and how to try to stand up to it.[16]

The account of Harry Griffiths' period of service in Korea is of special interest in placing the National Service Era in historical context. He was called up in September, 1952, and was posted to a large training depot, No 5 Trg Bn, RASC, at Hammersley Barracks, North Camp, Aldershot. During the next winter, Lieutenant Griffiths was busy dealing with the influenza epidemic which affected hundreds of recruits.

Then one morning in the Spring of 1953, he was rung up by the ADMS, Colonel P.F. ("pedlar") Palmer, and told he was to go to Korea as a blood transfusion officer in place of another medical officer whose name had been taken off the draft. "After 6 weeks of training in blood transfusion work, I embarked in the *Empire Pride* at Liverpool, on a dark, rainy night."..

He had the widest of experiences after arrival and the boredom of the 5 week voyage ("with no air conditioning, fairly squalid conditions in the troop decks, 4 officers to a cabin") was over. First he was in the Commonwealth General Hospital in Japan, at Kure, where he took over No 11 Field Transfusion Unit ("my staff consisted of two Corporals — NS — one was a diesel engineer and the other a glazier. Later we had a QA posted to us"), and, because he wanted to become a surgeon in due course, helped with the d.p.s.(delayed primary sutures) on casualties flown in from the front line. Their busiest time was after the Battle of the Hook.

"We got on well with the others", he remembered; "the Canadians were sometimes a bit touchy…the d.p.s. sessions were the day after admission, all surgical staff helping under the watchful eye of Colonel David Wright who moved amongst the 6 tables accommodated in 2 large theatres. It was significant that all the junior medical officers were NSM, the Regulars providing the consultant staff and some middle grades only."

Next, on 19th November, 1953, he went to 26 Fd Amb. His journey was by ship, train, and finally by jeep "in the dark, cold, biting wind." He went at once to the CCP, "where we were looked after by Major Stone, a Regular officer, who was 2i/c of the Fd Amb. His team were 2 NSMOs, 1 NSDO…the ground was so hard (-20°C) we could not drive tent pegs in so could not move our tents…we were about 1 mile(1500m) south of the Imjim River, in the Brigade area. On our left were the U.S. 1st Marine Division, to our rear was the 1st Royal Staffs camp and close to that the 1st Royal Tank Regiment with their Centurion tanks."

Next Captain Griffiths went back to No 11 FTU for a spell, but returned to the front soon when he was offered "an appointment as coy commander of the Fd Amb." To do this, he agreed to extend his NS time by 4 months. This time he was with 29 Fd Amb. — "A somewhat unusual move for a NS officer but a very welcome advance of military career and pay!"

Next again he was posted from the Fd Amb to the 1st Commonwealth Division HQ as Deputy Assistant Director of Army Health(DADAH), replacing an Australian who was returning home. "It was occurring to me that serving in this theatre, still with wartime accounting (though not for much longer), was an experience which NS medical officers could look back on with considerable astonishment and not a little pride. The work in the Hygiene Department was not difficult and one became very familiar with the procedures laid down for the construction of kitchens, disposal of waste water, storage of food and maintenance of rubbish dumps, to name but a few. It was a great opportunity to see the whole of the Divisional area, visiting units of 28 Bde, which was combined British and Commonwealth, and 25 Bde, which was purely Canadian…. The ADMS of the Div was Colonel E.J. Young, late of the Royal Canadian Army Medical Corps, and under him a happy, mixed band of Commonwealth soldiers worked well."

Finally, after combining his DADAH post with that of DADMS, Major Griffiths returned home: "In an Airwork Hermes from Singapore which took us in short hops home stopping at Bankok, Calcutta, Delhi, Karachi, Bahrain, Nicosia, Rome, and finally Blackbush Airport in Hampshire. When we arrived in England it was cold, with rain falling."…

"Thus ended my military career with the Regular Army the remainder of the time being spent with leave and demobilization procedures. However, military service is a disease and I was sufficiently affected to continue for a further thirty years with the Territorial Army."[17]

Suez, 1956.
This, an attempt by the British and French to mount a major attack on their own, was planned as a much bigger affair than the Korean; it was to involve an Army Corps. The reason was the nationalisation of the Suez Canal by Colonel Nasser, who had seized power in Egypt, and occupied the Canal Zone in defiance of a previous undertaking not to do so.

The Operation, code-named MUSKETEER, continued, including planning, from 6th August till 27th December, 1956, and was a failure. The DDMS of 2 Corps, Major General Willie Officer, made a forthright report of the operation from the medical point of view. As in his Burma days, he was not afraid to criticise.

The initial plan was to seize Alexandria. The DDMS recorded the political manoeuvrings, the dithering, the constant changes of requirement, the demands for action at once when not logistically possible — all the clinical features of a weak political will. The same will be seen again in subsequent "bush fire" wars later in the century.

In the planning, General Officer noticed that the French were much quicker and cleverer at having landing platforms on their ships constructed than the now hesitant British. The plan was modified; Port Said was now the objective. The code-name was changed to MUSKETEER REVISED.

The immediate task was to take Gamil Airport. 3 Para was to undertake the airborne assault. Medical para units were trained in anti-terrorist actions in Cyprus, where the Greek Cypriots had a terrorist campaign against the British of their own in progress. At this date, medical personnel had to be blood grouped and have the information stamped on the reverse of their ID discs — a novelty.

For an operation of this projected scale, there was a shortage of trained RAMC. The idea of calling upon the medical TA had not yet been thought of. The only ready source was Regular Reservists; many of these were recalled. Some were decidedly unwilling. The same problem applied to other Arms.

The para assault was made at 0730 hrs on 5th November, 1956. It was opposed quite heavily but the enemy fire was inaccurate. Five hours after the initial drop, 3 killed and 31 wounded had been brought in to the surgical post the FST had set up. Of the total, 2 were parachuting injuries, 12 due to small arms, and 17 to shell and mortar splinters — mainly the latter. The total was 5 per cent of the Force and inside the 9 per cent planned for. The RMO of 3 Para was one of the casualties in the descent, but stayed at his post for several hours. A further 7 casualties occurred in street fighting the next day. Captain John Malcolm Elliott, a 2-year Regular anaesthetist attached to the FST, won the MC for personally collecting casualties under fire.

By P+1 hr (an hour after the drop) all equipment had been gathered, and half-an-hour later the FST was able to begin operating. By P+3 hrs, in answer to a request by wireless (as the term then was), a Naval Helicopter brought in 30 stretchers and evacuated 5 wounded. From then on RN helicopters maintained a casevac service to the off-shore carrier.

The rather sad end to the Suez operation is not the concern of this history. The AMS system worked well, although the DDMS was critical of many errors.

One fact which would have repercussions in operations much later in the century where the Naval Medical Service was involved alongside the Army, was the clear ignorance of Naval surgeons of basics of military surgery. In the Royal Marine Commando Brigade, the Naval MOs sutured wounds; they went septic and one marine developed gas gangrene. "Their training should have taught them", said General Officer, "what to do at RAP level — not to try too much." It was evident that the policy on-board could not be applied to land war conditions.

Medical officers to commandos were sadly unaware of the Army evacuation system and the surgical support the Army routinely provided in such a Force. As well as wrongly doing primary suture, the Naval doctors had attempted intravenous therapy at an unwise stage in the evacuation process. "Previous RN training was unsuitable", was the DDMS' final conclusion.

The other recipient of criticism by the DDMS was the Regular Reserve element — they too "would not appear to have had the principle of d.p.s. sufficiently stressed in training." But he considered that many Reservists had worked well.

The Suez venture showed serious flaws in the mobilization procedure. Units were "made up" for the occasion; the soldiers were unfamiliar not only with the equipment, but with one another. The calibre of certain officers and Senior NCOs was poor — "Eight Army Emergency Reserve officers were 'only doctors'; one Admin officer was described by his C.O. as a psycho-neurotic; an RSM was inadequate; one Chief Clerk was 'a private'" — wrote General Officer in his Secret Report on Operation Musketeer. He criticised 15 Fd Amb for poor discipline. In summary, and of historical interest when the next phase of thinking about reinforcement of the Regular Army came along, he suggested the Army Medical Service follow the example of the TA and its principles of training for mobilization.

Perhaps the last point of all to be recorded about the Suez operation is the traditional one: the Medical side were given no information by the General Staff side.

The Borneo Operation, January 1963–June 1965.

No sooner was the Malayan emergency over than a Communist inspired rebellion broke out in Brunei, less that 500 miles(800Km) from Singapore. Brunei is a small independent Sultanate under British protection, with a valuable oilfield.

Royal Marine commandos and Gurkhas, rushed in and put down the main rebellion in a fortnight; a FST from Singapore under Brigadier R.S. Hunt treated only 30 casualties. But the threat of attack from Sukarno's Indonesia over Brunei's southern frontier needed a force of Malaysian, New Zealand and Australian troops, as well as the British and Gurkhas, to overcome it.

As in Malaya, soldiers were in patrols deep in jungle, fought at close range with the new self-loading rifle (SLR), sub-machine guns, and grenades. Again as in Malaya, there was the need for all ranks to be trained in extended first-aid, and also as in Malaya, there was the difficulty of evacuation if helicopters were not immediately available.

New medical features were the use of an oral antibiotic, oxytetracycline (Terramycin), for prophylactic chemotherapy. Tetracycline was used because as well as being absorbed by mouth it was not affected by the hot moist climate. Immediate use of helicopters meant wounded were taken from wounding site direct to hospital.

Though the campaign was a small one — only 119 wounded with 3 deaths, the old recurring faults in surgery recurred — plating of a badly comminuted femoral shaft fracture, and inadequate d.p.s; in the local conditions of the Far East, "delayed primary suture" meant closure later than the standard 3rd to 5th day.

The other new feature was the effect of the new considerably higher velocity rifles. The wounds they produced had much greater tissue damage, sometimes with actual shattering of the limb. Not by coincidence, a re-run of ballistic studies was in progress at the Department of Surgery at Millbank and at Porton Down, both at the same time.[18]

During the post-1945 War years, the background major weapon was the atom bomb and later its hydrogen successor. One site of research was in Maralinga, in Australia.

Maralinga Range Support Unit, as it was called, occupied several thousand square miles in the far west of South Australia. The name Maralinga was coined specially and meant "The place of thunder." From 1950 onwards it was used as the site for testing British nuclear and thermo-nuclear weapons. The unit was staffed by members of the three Services from U.K. and Australia, and it was usual for the RAMC to provide the MO.

Captain (later Major General) George Cowan, who held the post in the 1960s, found he had to deal with fractures in kangaroos, anorexia in pet parrots, and ill-health in pet lizards, as well as the usual range of medical, dental, and hygiene problems. Because of the isolation and the boredom, psychological upsets were not infrequent.

The MO was relieved every 8 weeks by a colleague from the Australian equivalent of the medical TA, the Citizen Military Force Reservists. The last RAMC officer left the range in December 1965 and the unit closed soon afterwards. It was the sort of posting, far away but with great responsibility, which the Corps would lose progressively from now on.[19]

There were many other large actions in the first decade after the end of the Second World War. Operations against the Mau Mau in Kenya went on during 1952–56. This was a long and often hard campaign and disposed of the hope of establishing an African base to take the place of India. The Cyprus emergency filled the years from 1955 till 1959. Gradually the Empire shrank; West Africa, Eritrea and the Sudan, Jamaica and British Honduras (though a garrison remained here till the 1990s), British Guiana, Swaziland, the Persian Gulf, Aquaba on the Red Sea, the Western desert remnants, all disappeared during the National Service Era.

Peace-Time Activities after 1945.

It is now forgotten just how exhausted the British were after this War. They had sold almost all of their overseas financial wealth to keep the war effort going. The children and adults who were in the home base had suffered bombing, (66,000 civilians had been killed alone) and learned the meaning of blackout, clothes and food rationing, so that those in that age range never got over the feeling that they must always leave a clean plate.

Rationing continued until the mid-fifties — food in fact became scarcer after the War was over because the U.S. had stopped their lease-lend and the British were short of money to buy it.[20] Industry was slow to pick up, in spite of the efforts of the post-war Labour Government. It was the tiredness of a nation which had held the ring for a century, and by the inexorable law of history, was now to feel that retirement had much to recommend it.

The RAMC War Memorial Fund was launched in 1946, just after the War. "The Memorial to the dead of the Royal Army Medical Corps in the War of 1939–45 will consist of a fund to be known as 'The Royal Army Medical Corps Memorial Fund'. This will be devoted first to the welfare of families of all ranks of the RAMC who died on the War of 1939–45; also of all ranks of the Corps who served in that War and of their families who may be in need of help through sickness or misfortune; secondly, to the provision of a permanent Memorial part of which shall incorporate the names of those who died."

The Queen gave her good wishes. At the inauguration, in November 1946, representatives of Regular, Territorial Army, and War Engagements took part.

At the same time, the Hymn for the Fallen of the Royal Army Medical Corps was written by Brigadier Price.[21] To be sung to the tune of St Clements (Hymns Ancient and Modern in the Church of England hymnal No 477), its two middle verses were the most moving:

> They faced the worst that cruel war meant
> Brought mercy to the ruthless strife,
> Relieved the wounds, assuaged the torment,
> And dying, gave their comrades life.

> Unarmed they bore an equal burden,
>   Shared each adventure undismayed,
> Not less they earned the Victor's guerdon,
> Not least were these in the crusade.

The next year, 1949, The Memorial Book of Remembrance 1939–45, containing the names of 2,463 all ranks of the Corps was placed below the memorial window in Westminster Abbey. A page is still turned formally by RAMC representatives every month.

1948 saw the Jubilee year of the RAMC. For us, this was a special event. Sadly, there was very poor coverage of the Jubilee by the BBC, in spite of a letter to the Director General of the BBC on 6th January of 1948, giving details of the forthcoming celebration. On 9th April RAMC were informed there were not likely to be any "takers" in the programmes department. The media kindly said there was "the possibility of a 'flash' on the Light Programme. AMS wrote twice more, but was finally told on June 9th "there is no possibility of a broadcast." It was a real and unnecessary slight.

Corps Day however went splendidly well. That Royal Superstar, the Queen, was there at her barracks at Crookham.

She watched four companies of NS recruits, who had served between 3 and 10 weeks, march past. In her speech, Queen Elizabeth said, expressing her congratulations, that the RAMC had now the responsibility of the care of the health of the new National Service army: "The future reputation of the Corps will largely depend on the efficiency and sympathy with which this service is carried out." How significant and far-seeing her words were. And after, she walked among the troops, with her amazing ability of making whoever she talked with feel he was the most important person in the world.

Not only at Crookham were there celebrations. There were parades in Edinburgh at HQ Scotland, Stirling, Dundee, Glasgow, York, Catterick, Lincoln, Sheffield, Chester, Hereford, Manchester, Burton-on-Trent, Swansea, Horley, Maidstone, Eastbourne, Netley, Tidworth, Wheatley, Plymouth, Exeter, Waringford Northern Ireland.

There was a parade in London, where Field-Marshal Viscount Slim made a great speech of praise in Central Hall Westminster on June 26th.

In Scotland the then G.O.C. and Keeper of Edinburgh Castle, General Sir Philip Christison, reminded his audience that his grandfather had been in the IMS — and we remember his service to one Wolseley as a young man, the same officer who so pathetically forgot his debt to the Army Medicals in his later years as the Army Commander.

And there were parades in Berlin, Austria, Trieste, Gibraltar, British Troops in Egypt, Eritrea, West Africa, Kuala Lumpur, the Caribbean — marking the world wide British sphere of influence still existing.

The Adjutant General, General Sir James Steele, said at the Jubilee parade at the Depot: "Perhaps some of you young soldiers here tonight, as you approach your seventies, will hear "Retreat" blown at another Corps Rally to mark a hundred years of our history, and the events of this evening will come crowding back in your memory." As this is written, his words are fulfilled. As with the medical officers, the RAMC soldiers who served as 2-year Regulars remembered their service with pride and affection.

Other things happened. In autumn 1947 the Commandant of the Depot and Training Establishment felt that the Regimental March, "Bonnie Nell" (Corps members sang to its tune: "We're hard up, we're hard up, we're always bloody well hard up") seemed to lack "something of the swing and rhythm required for a Regimental March." (The Regimental March of Boer War days, "Washington Post", was not inspired either). So he arranged a competition, open to serving Directors of Music and Bandmasters of the Army, and offered a prize of £100 for the winner.

The conditions specified that "The March should bear a title suitable to the RAMC and it should be founded on one or more suitable national folk songs or popular airs."

24 entries were sent in — Sir George Dyson, Director of the Royal College of Music, and in conjunction with the Royal Military School of Music, gave the prize to Major J.A. Thornburrow, Director of Music, the Royal Horse Guards. Unfortunately he died suddenly before the result was announced.

"Here's a Health unto His Majesty" — an old song, was given a pleasant and dignified melody and well arranged. It was played before H.M. The Queen, who gave it her "unqualified approval."

At this time, too, was a change in the official toasts. "The King", followed by the National Anthem, was now to be followed by "Our Colonel-in-Chief — The Queen." Following this toast, 8 bars of "The Eriskay Love Lilt", in E flat, was to be played by the band.

In 1946 The War Office, in one of their regular odd requests, asked for the description of the RAMC flag. No information was forthcoming from the archives, so a description was made up ! The result was the description of a "Flag of Dull Cherry, (Royal) Blue, Old Gold — stripes all of equal width and the flag is twice as long as it is wide. Normal size is 6x3 feet(180x90cm)."

In October 1948, following the Jubilee, the Army Medical Services Magazine began. Price 1 shilling(5p) it incorporated the "News and Gazette" of the RAMC, RADC, (the dentists had now their "Royal Army Dental Corps") and Army Nursing Services. It became a forum for news of all Corps doings, of the three Corps involved. For on 1st February, 1949, the Queen Alexandra's Royal Army Nursing Corps was instituted. Initially, ranks and titles similar to those of the new Womens' Royal Army Corps were used; the titles "Sister" and "Matron" were to be retained, as they were still retained after the unhappy Salmon Committee Report of 20 years later abolished them in the NHS.

This change coincided with the Service Nurses' own Jubilee. Their Corps had its own celebrations, fitting for their own glorious contributions over the years. The notion of male nurses being "QAs" had not then arrived.

For the inauguration of the QARANC, a parade was held under the command of Colonel H.S. Gillespie at the Depot at Hindhead. 200 officers and other ranks, all wearing the new No 1 Dress, were inspected by the then Adjutant-General, General Sir John Crocker. The march past was to the new March "Grey and Scarlet", played by the RAMC band. Finally there was a tableau of the growth of the Military Nursing Service. Soon after, the QAIMNS mess in John Islip Street, along the road from Millbank, was declared the Headquarter Mess of the new Corps.

The AMS magazine was a success from the start. Each issue carried a wide range of news from the still-widespread AMS world. There were Territorial Notes in each issue, with reports of the various sports and military competitions.

King George VI died in 1952. He had come to the throne following the Abdication crisis of 1937, and with the enormous help of Queen Elizabeth, had overcome all the misgivings of that unhappy time. Now his daughter Elizabeth became Queen, and her coronation in June 1953 was a bright event in the sombre days of post-war Britain.

1963 saw the discharge of the last NSM. For the first time since July 1939, the Regular Army became an all volunteer Force. From the first call up of the "Militiamen" in July 1939 until the call up of NSM ended in late 1960, over 3,800,000 men were enlisted into the British Army.

In the peak year of the Era, there were 223,000 National Servicemen in the Army compared with 181,000 soldiers on a Regular engagement. By 1960, there were 79,000 NSM left in the Army. The decision to end National Service gave the Army a major task. It had to reorganize and recruit to increase its strength to the required figure of 165,000 by the end of 1962.

The problem was not only one of reaching the numerical strength. The ending of National Service meant a very large shortage in the Technical Arms, and the RAMC is one of these. For a time, there was a serious lack. The NSM had brought in all the medical graduates of the Nation and many of them had cleverness and skill which was suddenly lacking. There was the inevitable backlash of loss of interest, too, which meant that joining the Army Medical Department became unfashionable. On the other hand, enough NSM of ability and drive had decided "to stay on" that there was a good nucleus available for the next few years and longer.

Well before the end of the NS Era, however, the man whom many considered the greatest post-war D.G., Lieutenant General Sir Alexander Drummond,[22] began to realise that to maintain the Regular element in the Corps at a high clinical level, a new sort of training for specialists was vital. If it was not, the RAMC would become divorced from what was now the standard demanded by the NHS. By 1958, the Diamond Jubilee year, and when a special commemorative First Day Cover was issued, he was openly talking of "austerity" as the Regular Forces were about to run down. The TA was well supplied with consultants — though poorly recruited for other ranks — and they had gone through the National Service system.

The old grade of specialist, such as General Cantlie had been designated in general surgery and he himself in oto-rhino-laryngology, was now unacceptable in the eyes of the committees of the Royal Colleges and the major specialty Associations. The NHS progression through registrar, senior registrar, and lastly, full consultant status by accreditation and open competition, would have to be available to the RAMC to give the Regular equivalent standing.

General Drummond also saw that the continuing diminution in the range of postings for career medical and dental officers — India was already a fading memory — was going to lessen the attractions of a Regular career. His second task was to produce a series of measures which would encourage new entrants.

Finally, soldier training would have to be provided in newer and better surroundings; this would mean upgradings and improvements at Mytchett.

Negotiations with the major post-graduate bodies inevitably took time. Several of the changes were not finalised until after General Drummond's six years as D.G. were over — the longest period of office since General Hood's. But the credit for their initiation and their eventual acceptance by the Colleges and Associations was his. Clear and accurate briefing — Drummond as D.G. would never go into an important meeting with the

Adjutant-General having forgotten his brief — as a successor did in the 1990s — firm negotiation, and above all, great determination, were the hall-marks of his character and personality.

The training of consultants was to follow exactly the NHS pattern — specialists and senior specialists corresponded to registrars and senior registrars, and earned increased rates of pay. Because Army hospitals could not provide the range and difficulty of clinical material the NHS could, attachments to selected Teaching Hospitals had to be negotiated. If the officer was judged at the end of his higher professional training as fit to be a consultant, he went before the Army Specialist and Consultant Board. When passed, he achieved consultant status and the pay that went with it. The difference with his civilian colleague was that his consultancy was not won in open competition. The recognition of Army specialists as fully comparable with NHS ones was sealed in 1961 by agreements with the Royal College of Surgeons of England and the Royal College of Physicians of London for joint chairs of surgery and medicine. Their remit was not to spend their time on clinical duty, but rather to undertake research and development in their specialty.

In 1962 the two schemes to encourage young doctors to join the Corps were introduced — the medical cadetship scheme and the "New Deal", announced in the House of Commons on 8th March, 1962 by the Secretary of State for War, Mr John Profumo.[23] Basically, these two packages allowed undergraduates, if accepted for a commission, to have the last 3 or 4 years of their university fees paid, and themselves paid as Second Lieutenants on probation. When they graduated, they became Short Service or Regular officers; the majority chose Short Service. They had to serve at least 5 years.

As far as graduate entry was concerned, medical and dental officers (aged 25) were Captains on entry; could expect promotion to Major after 5 years (had previously been 7; and remained 7 for TA) (aged 30); and to Lieutenant Colonel after 13 years (aged 38). Most, it was stated, would be promoted to full Colonel's rank after 23 years (aged 48).[24]

The "Peace time Footing" had of course come about years before the end of National Service. Wartime hospitals in Lincoln, Shaftesbury, Chepstow and 101 Military Convalescent Depot at

Bedford, had closed in 1949, and the "Established" Military hospitals, the old "permanent" hospitals, were then used.

It was in the early 1950s that the AMS reverted to its pre-war hospital establishment. Each hospital, as before the 1939–45 War, had an RAMC company based on it at Aldershot (1 Coy), Bovington (2 Coy), Hindhead (3 Coy), Netley (4 Coy), Catterick (7 Coy), York (8 Coy), Colchester (9 Coy), Shorncliffe (10 Coy), Woolwich (12 Coy), Cowglen (13 Coy), Northern Ireland (15 Coy), Millbank (18 Coy), Chester (19 Coy), Tidworth (20 Coy) and overseas at Gibraltar (28 Coy), Malta (30 Coy), Hong Kong (27 Coy), Singapore (32 Coy), Jamaica (29 Coy), and Bermuda (25 Coy). In addition, BGHs, still war-numbered, were in Germany at 94 in Hamburg, 29 in Hanover, Iserlohn, Wuppertal and 84 in Berlin; 31 in Klagenfurt, 83 in Trieste. Every station had its hospital. Field ambulances formed part of each division at home and overseas.

For basic training, the third part of the D.G.'s plan, significant changes were also envisaged. Since the War the Depot and Training Establishment had been at Crookham. The Army School of Hygiene, renamed the Army School of Health, was at Keogh Barracks, Mytchett.

In 1949 the Field Training School had opened at Mytchett, next door to the Army School of Health, to train personnel for war. In 1949 also a Field Ambulance Training Centre was opened beside the BMH at Iserlohn, to provide the same field training facility for men in hospitals and static units of the BAOR.

The move of the Depot and TE from Crookham to Mytchett began in 1962 and was not finally completed until 1964. In Keogh, the new Training Establishment was to consist of the Depot Training Wing and the RAMC Apprentice School, (from Crookham) and the Field Training School Wing and First Aid Training Wing (to Mytchett Place). Also in Mytchett were the Army School of Health, the Technical Training Officer, H.Q. Army Emergency Reserve (AER), the RAMC Staff Band and the RAMC museum.

All troops were to be in Sandhurst blocks. New messes were built. New sports fields were in the parkland by the lake. New W.O.s and Sergeants' architect designed messes were completed by 1963.

The 47 married quarters were to be increased by 72 and 15 new officers' married quarters to be built. It was a large and impressive development.

The Territorial Army, too, did not get the quota of ex-National Servicemen the post-war Generals hoped for. But enough of these did remain to provide another nucleus as the war-time members retired — this time for the support the Regular RAMC was going to demand during the Cold War for a further 25 years.

The TA had been reconstituted on 1st January 1947. It too was big — its medical element alone was 69 units strong. There were 33 Fd Ambs, 7 FDSs, 5 CCSs, 15 G.H.s, 2 beach medical units, 1 hygiene coy and 6 F.S.T.s. Of these, 39 were re-formed from pre-war units, some re-organized, and new units raised to fulfil the current TA ORBAT. At this date the Territorial Army was indeed a separate Army, with divisions in all the tribal areas of the U.K., and needed the appropriate medical units to support it.

The amount of TA medical presence can be gauged by describing Manchester as a typical large English town: the drill hall in King's Road had 125, 126, and 127 Fd Ambs of 42 Div, 7(Western) General Hospital, and 12 CCS. There was a divisional medical headquarters, TA, with a TA ADMS and a regular DADMS. In 1953 the City of Manchester honoured the hospital, and it was allowed to wear the distinctive badge with the eagle on blue background, part of the City's arms. It was re-named 7(M) GH,TA.

In 1950, the first of many re-organisations took place. This led to quite marked changes in the medical ORBAT; but units disbanded were put in suspended animation in a reconstituted Supplementary Reserve which was soon referred to as the Army Emergency Reserve. Now there were 61 units — 32 Fd Ambs, 9 FDSs, 6 CCSs, 9 GHs, 4 FSTs and 1 hygiene coy.

There was an initial vagueness about exactly what was the role of not only the AMS TA, but perhaps also the full-time arm of the Corps. This was remedied as a series of exercises, beginning in 1948 with Exercise MEDICAL BAMBOO, following the CIGS's Ex BAMBOO. It was set in Northern Malaya and Thailand.

Exercise BRITANNIA followed in 1949. Its theme was defence against a nuclear attack. These exercises would continue in various form throughout the Cold War. The medical equivalent, Ex MED BRITANNIA, was held at Mytchett over 12–15 December that year.

Clinical and military reports from the Hiroshima raid were given. The theme was military medical support of Civil Defence. The ADS (not surprisingly!) was to be the initial filter. In later phases, the use of divisional Fd Ambs was discussed, and the use to be made of the DADAH and his sanitary staff. Evacuation of casualties was complicated by the new element of irradiation by gamma rays; the lack of what was soon to be called Nuclear (and later still, Biological and Chemical) training was very evident.

In 1960 was Ex MEDICAL CANALETTO. It was set five years in the future — based on a defensive battle fought in a European setting by a United Kingdom Corps, part of NATO. Nuclear weapons of low yield were used by both sides. FSTs and FTTs were deployed with the use of Whirlwind helicopters. There was much talk of the need to lighten medical equipment and make it airportable. A new feature was a demonstration by the Durham Light Infantry of protection of troops against nuclear warfare. Lieutenant Colonel E.M. Turner, QARANC, talked on "The Will to Live", based on her Far Eastern POW experiences. From 1962 the D.G.'s Exercise was down-graded to a Study Period, because of a reduction in the activity of the Field Training School. This was an early portent of things to come.

This element, the training for war, was one side of the Corps' education. The other was the professional training which went on at the College at Millbank.

In the NS Era, there was a basic course twice a month. But there was the need to train officers and laboratory staff in all skills and more than a basic course was essential for the full career RAMC members. Long-serving teachers were Major Stanley Elliot, OBE, TD, FRIC, who was in post from the War till 1965, and Mr John Grundy. Major Elliot's subject was hygiene, especially water supply and purification. Mr Grundy taught entomology and was an outstanding figure. The Grundy Lecture was established after his retiral.

The professional teaching staff at Millbank changed as did all Regulars, as a man moved from posting to posting. There was however a permanent staff, both of mess staff and of teaching staff in the entomology department. Civil consultants and civilian experts taught their specialist subjects; if they had served in the recent War or were Territorials, so much the better.

Between 1960 and 1970, after the end of the NS courses, there were 31 Junior Courses. Three numbered courses were cancelled. These were now all for Regular officers, full career or Short Service. The number of officers passing through on these courses (nos 85–115 inclusive) was 559. But even as late as 1964 the Junior Courses were very short, consisting of 6 weeks at Mytchett alone. However, there were now Senior Courses, lasting 5 or 6 months, and including the taking of the Diploma in Tropical Health and Hygiene (DTM&H). Medical officers took the Senior Course some 4 years into their service. This pattern continued.

At the end of these courses, prizes and medals were presented, and the Corps had its share, as do all academic institutions, of several of high worth. Many doctors in the peace years were of high quality, well worth their prestigious awards.[25]

The mess staff fulfilled the requirements of the Headquarter Mess. They looked after the permanent staff, the officers on courses, and the staff of the Queen Alexandra Hospital just along the road. They had to officiate at formal functions. Sometimes they had to discipline over-exuberant junior officers. The Corps was fortunate in having a succession of staff of personality and usually of distinction.

The first and longest serving was universally known as "Mr Pomfret." Born in 1883, he was taken by the first C.O. of the Queen Alexandra Military Hospital to the Hotel Belgravia in 1902, then to St Ermins in 1903, and to the H.Q. Mess Millbank in 1907 when it opened. There he remained, except for war service with the British Red Cross in Alexandria between 1914 and 1918, until he retired in 1949. Mr H. Williams came in 1928 and remained till he had a major operation in 1949 and died soon after. Mr Pomfret was head porter and Mr Williams mess steward. The mess steward from 1945 till 1966 was Mr H.J.F. Barnett; he was awarded the Imperial Service Medal.

In the dining room was Jim Grey, from 1950. "He was brilliant", remembered Mr Matthew Dooley, who arrived as a

NSM and stayed on till nearly the end of the century; "he knew everyone's name and even initials." Also a well-kent face in the dining room was Johnny Burgess — stooped, balding, with the "Racing Times" sticking out of his pocket. Later again, Peter Giuste arrived as waiter and barman in 1970. He was from Dominica. In 1971 came Mrs Agatha Hope, also from Jamaica. She, too, stayed till the 1990s.

In the post-war years, the only permanent senior staff were the Commandant, Assistant Commandant, Mess steward, and Treasurer or Accountant. Major Rufus Still was Treasurer till the mid-1970s, when Mr T. Graves was appointed Mess Manager. At this time the mess was being less well used, because of the closure of the Queen Alexandra Hospital. His business acumen improved usage and financial return till his resignation in 1985. Mrs Mary Kerslake then took over the Mess Manager's post. Her husband had been steward from 1973, when Major General J. Baird, then Commandant, appointed him from his previous post in the officers' section.

The peace-time RAMC comprised much more than medical training and training for war. The RAMC Association's activity increased throughout the 50's. Its welfare work in the country was reported in the Army Medical Services magazine, begun after the war and including Dental and Nursing items from both Reserve and Regular units world-wide.[26]

The four Colonels Commandant, the two Dental Colonels and the single QA Colonel Commandant, one of their number being changed annually, were responsible for "the domestic affairs of a Regiment or Corps." Appointed for five years, their remit covered esprit de corps, tradition, liaison with the civilian community, controlling charitable funds, especially the War Memorial Fund, and maintaining close links with all elements of their Corps at home and abroad. As well as arranging the various Honour church services, they arranged, in 1957, the Jubilee of the TA and of the College and H.Q. mess at Millbank.

Sport encompassed a wide range, with many trophies to be played for. These included the Bostock Cup for cricket, the Harwood and Irvine Cups for football, and the largest number of trophies, the RAMC Challenge Cup, Pindi Goli, Irvine Challenge, Veterans' Cup, Vesey Holt and Alexander Hood Cup — for golf.

The Corps Band flourished. A Medical Staff Band began in 1894 when a bugle Sergeant and 7 boys with string and wind instruments played at the Medical Staff Corps Officers' Mess at Aldershot. In the early years, Surgeon Major H. Grier was the leading figure — he began boy musician training.

After a gap of some years, the Band was re-formed in 1915. By 1939, the Band was officially taken over by the Army Council. Many well-known civilian musicians, including the majority of Jack Hylton's band, joined at this time. Isaac Vanpick (better known as Lee Sheriden from Henry Hall's band) sang with them as a guest on occasions. All members were demobilized in 1945, but after re-forming again in 1947, it became a foremost Army Band. Major L.D. Brown MBE, LRAM, was Director of Music from the early 1950s and was a well-known figure.

In 1962 the first lady officer was granted a Regular Commission: Major Mary M. Munro. Lady Medical officers had been commissioned on a wartime basis from 1939 — two early ones were Mrs Ethel Whitby and Miss Muriel Boycott. They were appointed on 4th November, 1939, "with the relative rank of Lieutenant RAMC." Mrs Whitby served throughout the War, becoming acting Major in 1945. Her husband was Sir Lionel Whitby. The lady officers coming soon after, Isma Begbie and her colleagues, were given the "proper" rank of Lieutenant. Mary Munro was conscripted and arrived at Crookham on 21st August, 1943. She became a pathologist, working in Poona and later at the David Bruce laboratories 1957–60. She kept extending her Short Service Commissions until accepted for a Regular one.

Non-Medical officers began to come forwards in increasing numbers in the years after 1950. There had always been quartermaster officers, promoted from the ranks of the best of the Warrant Officers. There were also the officers who held appointments as hospital registrars (in no way to be confused with the trainee on the consultant National Health Service ladder) and those who were in the RAMC companies. Some, such as the Fords, father and son, had given a near century of service.[27]

22029526 George Poole was one such. He reported to the Depot on 6th May, 1948 — at that date still called Boyce

Barracks, as one of 120 National Service recruits to 'B' Reception Company. He remembered not his officers, but the R.S.M., "Lofty" Bryson, and the CDIs Bert Tennuci and "Taffy" Rowlands.

"After one month's training", he recalled, "we were finally allowed the privilege of leaving the barracks — if we passed the inspection of the Regimental Police at the Main Guardroom."

Two events stood out for Pte Poole: "On 23rd June I was right marker C Company, with 600 RAMC, for Her Majesty Queen Elizabeth, at the re-naming of Boyce Barracks to Queen Elizabeth Barracks." The other was on Corps Day 1948: "As a member of C Company Athletic Team we came in as runners up for the Cup. C.S.M. Brown knocked out a Naval heavyweight with one punch in an exhibition boxing match."

After the routine 12 weeks, he left the Depot as a Sanitary Assistant Grade III. His first posting was to Catterick Military Hospital where his duties comprised cleaning out the 16 grease traps around the hospital compound and running the contaminated linen service.

The subsequent years are typical of the career of those times. In January 1949 he went to 3 Hygiene Wing at H.Q. 2 British Infantry Division, Hilden; he played rugby for RAMC BAOR, was promoted to Corporal (still described as "War Substantive"), learned to ride and maintain a motor cycle and went to BMH Iserlohn as an instructor with the Field Ambulance Training Cadre serving the British Army of the Rhine Field Ambulances nos 7, 11, 28, 30 and 31. He married Fraulein Waltraud Liebig whom he met while playing water polo — his C.O., Colonel J.C. O'Connell, lending him his Humber 4x4 staff car for their wedding.

In November 1950 he was promoted Sergeant (still called "War Substantive") at Dortmund, went next to No 8 Coy at York, next again to Japan in 1953 and thence to Pusan to 10 Hygiene Section, co-located with 26 Field Ambulance; his O.C. was Captain J.E. Roberts, and the C.O. of 26 Fd Amb was Lieutenant Colonel J. Irvine.

An illness upset his career while in Singapore in 1955. He developed a duodenal ulcer, was downgraded to P7, and had to have a partial gastrectomy in Woodend Hospital Aberdeen in 1958. Happily, he was cured and his medical category restored to P2.[28]

Back to Malaya, he was promoted Staff-Sergeant and posted to H.Q.17 Gurkha Division's Hygiene and Malaria Control Unit at Seremban. His C.O. was Colonel G.R. Ritchie the ADAH and WO2 Bryn Francis, Chief Clerk. "Bryn and I played rugby for the headquarters and for Negri Sembilian State and during this time I carried out a complete anti-malarial survey of the Bukit Terendak Cantonment in Malacca."

From September 1961 to December 1962 he was in London District, where Colonel A.L. Mee was ADMS, and was in H.Q. Malta and Libya at the end of 1962; "Officer Cadet Bob Short had a short stay with us to learn the ropes."

In August 1966 George Poole went once more to Singapore, as R.S.M. of 32 Company RAMC. But no sooner had they settled in to the R.S.M.'s quarter, than he was posted to Hong Kong where Colonel J.E. Miller, M.C., (later Major General and DMS of United Kingdom Land Forces) was commanding. "The task here was to move the BMH Bowen Road/Mount Kellet to the new King's Park site. Major P.H. Webberley was Admin Officer, Major D.J. Blake Company officer, and Captain J Linde BEM the Q.M. The move was completed in ten days, with a slight hold-up due to strikes and riots by the local Chinese.... During this period the BMH water polo team became Hong Kong champions, the first team to beat the H.K. Regiment for many years. The team included Sgt Tony Neild (captain and trainer), Major Bruce McDermott, Captain Dave Margretts, Peter Poole (George's son), W.O.1 G. Poole, Des Robinson (Pathology), Sgt Pete Stevens and W.O.11 Terry Bowen. I completed the Hong Kong cross harbour swim in 1968–69, from Kowloon Railway Pier to the Island of Hong Kong."

Back to Germany in September 1969, he was R.S.M. of 28 Fd Amb in Hohne (at the site of Belsen); here Lieutenant Colonel Max Roberts took over as C.O. from Lieutenant Colonel A.J. Shaw.

In 1971 he was selected for a commission, and passed out with others who all had good service for their Corps: "Ken Henson, Roy Burton, John Baxter, George Godbold, Dave Bench, and Bob Booth." His first posting as a Lieutenant was as a Platoon Officer to the Recruits Training Wing, which was then commanded by Major Roy Eyeions (later Lieutenant Colonel Eyeions, OBE, Curator of the Corps Museum at Mytchett).

His final series of postings were "to 28 Fd Amb at Hohne where the first non-medical officer to command a field ambulance, Major J.H. Sharroch, was in charge, the first of many in later years, and to Munster in 1976 (C.O. Colonel Duncan Macphie), Iserlohn in 1979 (C.O. Colonel B. Gavourin), and the Cambridge Hospital in September 1980 (C.O. Colonel Swinhoe and Admin Officer Lieutenant Colonel Geoff Banks)...". This was my last posting as in August 1981 I retired at the age of 51, after some 33 years and 3 months' service."

Major George Poole in retirement continued to serve; he became Deputy Regional Housing Officer of the Royal British Legion at their West Midlands Office in Rugeley, Stafford.

His was a typical career. It spanned the years when overseas postings were the rule, back and forwards from Germany to the Far East, as it seemed. The non-medical officers of the RAMC were men of the greatest loyalty and ability, rising in rank, in fact, higher than the run of doctor MOs did. This account of his years of time in the Corps is as good a record of the sort of life the Regular element lived, and a more personal one, than a bare list of medical units could give. What the RAMC actually did in Germany, still the most important posting because of the continuing Cold War, will be seen next.

George Poole had two more postings. The first was in 1965–66, when he was R.S.M. of 157(Lowland) Fd Amb (TA) at Motherwell, and the second was in 1971–73 as Adjutant to 225(Highland) Fd Amb at Dundee. The TA had not the best of Regular "Permanent Staff", as they were quite erroneously described, not being permanent, in the 1950's, but its increasing importance in the B.A.O.R. and RAMCOrbat in the 1970s and 1980s meant that only the best were selected to serve with it. Its rôle will now also be examined and its part in this history recorded.

Notes and references

CHAPTER 11

[1]Personal communication, W.G.T. Bell FRCS Eng, a Trinity College Dublin graduate. He was a surgeon in Stockport, 1965–1991. His account is corroborated by Dr Robin Agnew, in Trinity Medical Newsletter of the TCD Medical Alumni Association, 6 July 1992, p. 5, "Mixed memoirs of VE Day 1945". It is highly revealing of the attitude of both the nationalist students and the Garda.

The so-called "Nationalist" areas in Belfast not infrequently showed lights during the War, even during air raids. Personal communication, Major J.R. Bell, FRCSEd., 352 FST, who was there as a child.

[2]It is interesting that more than one post-war officer, reading this part of the history in 1994, was somewhat dismissive of it. In particular, they were amused at the reference to Charlemagne. They clearly were unable to grasp that this was the perception of the time, as they were similarly unable to conceive the feelings of relief at the end of the 1939–45 War being dashed by the realisation of the danger in the new world order, and the subsequent fear of the atomic bomb.

[3]See the Reserve and Auxiliary Forces Act, 25th May 1939, 2&3 l 6: "WHEREAS a situation has arisen in which it is necessary that His Majesty should be empowered, whenever the service of His Reserve and auxiliary Forces is urgently required for ensuing preparedness for the defence of the realm against any external danger; to call out for service such of them as may be needed:

Now, therefore, be it enacted by the King's most Excellent Majesty, by and with the advice of the Lords Spiritual and Temporal, and Commons, in this present Parliament assembled, and by the authority of the same…"

[4]The debates in the early part of 1947 are worth reading. At first, the government had asked for only 18 months' service. But in response to objections from its own supporters, and from members of the Liberal Party, it tabled an amendment to reduce the period of National Service to 12 months. "This important development", said *The Times* parliamentary

correspondent on 5th April, "is a direct result of the opposition encountered during the second reading debate earlier in the week when 72 Labour M.P.s and 15 others, supported a motion for the rejection of the Bill...the strength of the hostile vote in Tuesday night's division, on the 2nd, was no doubt disturbing to the Government, if scarcely unexpected in view of the traditional beliefs of the Labour Party...Objection was taken on political and economic as well as on idealistic grounds. It can scarcely be doubted that dislike of the very principle of compulsory NS is the chief motive of the dissident Labour group."

Apart from those who opposed it, many Labour members who supported the Bill "made plain their view that the period of compulsory whole-time service should be restricted to one year." So the government decided to reduce by one-third the period " which they had previously defended as being essential to the scheme of continued National Service."

Not only were there Labour opponents of conscription. Mr Clement Davies of the Liberal Party said the Bill was unique — it infringed upon the personal liberty of people — should not be introduced unless there was a real need. He reminded the Labour Party of their taunts against Mr Chamberlain in 1938 when he introduced a conscription Bill. "They accused him of going back on his pledge to the people." How little do politicians change.

"But the Liberal Party", went on Mr Davies, "remained true to their convictions. No doubt that the measure would divide the country as well as the Labour Party. The real enemy was economic; if Britain had 40 million tons of coal to export, Mr Bevin's position at Moscow would be far away stronger."

"Would anyone at Moscow be influenced that our young men were being conscripted ? This is a challenge I will fight to the end."

Sir H.O'Neill, Antrim Ulster Unionist, expressed strong dissent to the omission of Northern Ireland from the scope of the Bill. They were perfectly prepared to play their part, he said.

At the division, 242 Labour members voted for the Bill, the 131 rump of Conservatives, 8 Liberal Nationalists, and 7 Independents. 72 Labour M.P.s, all 10 Liberals, 2 Independent Labour M.P.s, and the 1 Communist voted against. Mr Price White, a Welsh Conservative, voted against, saying the majority of his Welsh constituents were against conscription.

Two comments, from the debate of April 11th, (Hansard, Vol 434, p 1242) merit recording. One was from Mr James Callaghan, recently elected member for Cardiff South. He attacked the government for its attitude to the Armed Forces: "We cannot maintain these huge Forces that we have today. We cannot continue them for a second longer, and they should be drastically cut. There are greater risks in not reducing our Armed Forces than in reducing them."

The second was by Mr R.A. Butler of the Conservative opposition. He made the point that a core of life career medical officers was vital, "in view of the complexity of new weapons and the need to plan in the longer term."

[5]Rates of pay for NS soldiers were £1.8s.0d (£1.40p) per week. Regular soldiers got £2.9s.0d (£2.45p) per week. A Lieutenant medical officer NS on commissioning earned £1.5s.0d (£1.25p) per day, which equated to £547.50 in 1995 money. He was promoted to Captain after 1 year's service, but it was only after 18 months' service that he achieved Regular rates — being granted an increment of 4s.6d (23p) per day (£83.95p *per annum* to bring his salary up to £631.45p *per annum*. (Pay rates at 1st April, 1993 for Lieutenant medical officers (PRMP) were £55.10p per day which equates to £20,112 *per annum*).

[6]The PULHEEMS system came into general use in 1951. (24/ Gen/3625). Prior to that date the grading of physical fitness was A,B,C,D, and E — E being unfit for any duty. The new system, originating in Canada and being improved by the RAF Medical Branch, expressed fitness much more precisely, with gradings applicable to the tropics as well as to temperate areas, to general physique, upper and lower limbs, hearing, eyesight, and mental capacity and emotional stability. It was called the "P" Code number or profile. Each "box" had a number from 1 to 8 – 8 indicating unfitness for any form of military service. "P" was 1,2, or 3, with 4,5, or 6 the equivalent for those unable to serve in a hot or moist climate. "P0" indicated temporary unfitness for duty. These headings made up the letters PULHEEMS. The earlier method had been in use since 1916. MOs were taught its use during their basic training; it has continued since, with the inevitable modifications over the years.

[7]Donegan was greatly loved. "I have many clear recollections of QMS Donegan in 1953", remembered Captain Alastair Simmons in 1994: "I must have been one of the last in his drill squad before he became Depot R.S.M. He was a great little man — a round peg in a round hole!"

[8]Just as at Millbank, so at Redfields, were there staff of distinction. On 13th February, 1957, Mr William Mudge, who had been Mess Steward for 27 years, was presented on his retiral with a silver salver.

[9]In the NS Era the Corps had its quota of skilled sportsmen. All the billet orderlies at Crookham were, or seemed to be, professional footballers. Thus they were absent from Friday afternoons to play on Saturdays, and during the week on training. At least one rugby international spent his NS at the depot, so that he could play for the RAMC team.

From 1951 the Corps golf committee agreed that National Servicemen could play in Corps competitions- before that they had not been allowed! In 1952 Captain F.W.G. Deighton, a Walker Cup player, led the side beaten in the final of the Army Challenge Cup at Sunningdale. The others were Captain F.W.G. Trimble, Lieutenant Colonel A.P. Trimble, Captain S.A. Biggart and Mr J.L. Jones. Very quickly, the Golf team was full of NSM — in 1954 the RAMC team reached the final of the Army Golf Championships at Royal St George's, Sandwich. The team was Captains S.Alexander, A.N.B. Bradford, A. Webb, and J.S.G. Blair — all NS.

[10]One individual who did not do his National Service yet was fit enough, in post-NS days, to join the TA, was P. Edmond, an Edinburgh surgeon. (Personal communication, Mr R.J.M. McCormack, 1922–1981, Vice-President RCSEd.1977–1980). He was noteworthy as he became Commanding Officer of 205 (Scottish) General Hospital and also because he was chosen over the heads of Regular surgeons (as was more than one other) to operate upon a Services V.I.P. He was awarded the CBE.

[11]For an indication of just how little thought the NSM gave the Army after his two years were up, the story of Dr Norman Bradford, just mentioned as an RAMC team golfer, is a good one. In 1990, Lieutenant General Sir James Baird was at St Andrews for the Open. He had never been at the Open there before. Outside the R & A clubhouse, he was noticed by Dr Bradford, then President of the English Golf Union. "You're Jimmy Baird, aren't you?" he asked the former D.G. "I remember you", went on the cheerful Northern Irishman, "you played for the RAMC golf team." "Yes, I did", replied General Baird. "How have you been getting on, then" went on Dr Bradford: "did you stay in?"

[12]Captain David Bushby had been a NS officer in Royal Signals, then done his medical training, and gone back into the Army as a Short Service RAMC officer. He went to Borneo during the Indonesian confrontation, and after training at the School of Jungle warfare at Kotatingi in south Malaya, found himself a section commander in 19 Fd Amb (Airportable). The ADMS was Lieutenant Colonel A. (Sandy) Ferrie, later Major General Ferrie, his C.O. Lieutenant Colonel Gordon Miln, 2 i.c. John Edgington, and another officer, Major Shaw, later became D.G. Major Bob Scott, another officer who became a Major General, was at the base with the MRS(Medical Reception Station).

Captain Bushby (later Lieutenant Colonel Bushby, TD) was at Kota Belud in Sabah. "The hearts and minds operation", he recalled, "was particularly rewarding. For periods of not longer that two days sections were deployed by helicopter or occasionally on foot to remote villages bordering Kalimantan. The villagers were always most friendly and receptive, clammering for treatment for minor conditions. Gross pathology was occasionaly seen from old trauma, there was malaria and infestation but generally the health was good. They were happy and well nourished."

"Gurkha soldiers formed part of the team to provide military support. Accomodation was always provided in the long houses together with ample food and entertainment with song, dance, and the local brew of tapi. Rarely did the soldiers find the fare not to their liking though some did draw the line at roasted rat…what happened after we left may have posed problems as communities were suddenly thrust into the twentieth century and then equally returned to their old lives after we left."

[13]Lieutenant J.R. Munro's recollections were typical of this attitude. "The sight of the depot at Crookham on a the cold damp dismal day in November 1952 I joined the RAMC did not exude welcome" was his initial reaction. "I contemplated the next two years with equanimity but one or two in my intake were resentful." He had delayed his call-up to take the primary part of his higher qualification in anaesthetics, and was very recently married.

He found Crookham well organized. Soon after being fevered and delirious after his first TAB inoculation, a knee injury took him to the Cambridge Hospital where "I saw a middle aged Colonel with cherry tabs (something he had never seen before), who examined my knee, twisted it, and pronounced LIGAMENTOUS — MENISCUS OK… by contrast I was impressed by Lieutenant Colonel K.F. Stephens, the Adviser in Anaesthetics, whom I knew was well respected in higher civilian anaesthetic circles." Munro was graded "Clinical Officer in Anaesthetics."

"Millbank was comfortable and had the atmosphere of a sedate club", but the spell he enjoyed most was at Mytchett "Deep bore-hole latrines and truths I never forgot like hot dehydrating desert winds which sapped the body's salt…and how and where to set up a field ambulance, RAP, and how to cross a lake using a lorry framework and tarpaulin…the atmosphere was refreshing…we were no longer 'freshers'."

His first anaesthetic work was at Chester, where he respected the skill and judgement of the O.C. Surgical Division, Major Hartley, and the "3 NS juniors, one of whom was John Pendower, later Dean at Charing Cross and a barrister-at-law at the Inner Temple."

He was particularly impressed by the consultation and revision surgery on men with Korean abdominal wounds of "Major General Harsant, a small, compact and courteous man… all went smoothly and in record time…he thanked me profusely and apologised for dashing away, but had to go by Comet to the Far East."

While in Chester Munro's predecessor, Captain Leon Kaufman (later of U.C.H. and St Mark's) "advised me to go to Liverpool to see a young consultant called Jackson Rees at work."

The Middle East followed. He sailed on the R.M.S. *Empire Ken*, was angered at the arrogance of the NS Major M.O. i.c Troops "who pulled rank and shook the B.O.R. (British Other Ranks) out of their hammocks of an evening to do their FFI. (Free From Infection Inspection) to show who was boss."

The nothingness of El Balla and the Hospital at Ishmaelia (Ish) came next — "The O.C. Surgical Div. never left his office, but he was well served by his juniors... one of them was Bruce Bailey, later the plastic surgeon whose team undertook the re-sewing of the severed arm, and whom Lord Tebbit praised for his help after the Brighton Conference bomb...Bob Fleming was an equally nice chap — from St Mary's Medical School — no side about him despite the eminence of his father...the physician Major Duffy was held in high regard by us..."

The appearances of the DMS were highlights. Captain Munro's recollection of him is full of touches of interest and worth recording. "They were all terrified of him — especially the Regulars. He was dynamic, determined and could be rude and ruthless. He was the rising star...he made me two offers. One was to become his DADMS with a crown on my shoulders. This was tempting but my main object was to restore marital relations, and I told him so. I think, in view of subsequent posting that he took cogniscence" (Captain Munro finished his two years in Kenya, where his wife could join him).

"He also suggested that if I got down to the books and prepared myself for the Final FFARCS he would have me flown to london for the exam."(But the other side of the coin was that Munro take a Regular commission).

"I am sure he was sincere about that. But library facilities were non-existent. Had I stayed in Chester and had the guidance of Jack Rees in nearby Liverpool it might have been feasible. *When Lieutenant General Sir Alexander Drummond was DGAMS the prospects were better in terms of study leave sabbaticals and higher exams.*" (See below for the complement to this remark of Captain Munro's).

"On one occasion Major General Drummond came into the bar at Fayid with an ADMS. Aleck Drummond said: "Do you know what they call you, Johnstone"? "Yes, Sir — Flash Alf and I don't like it...Do you know what they call you, Sir"?

Answer from the DDMS : "Yes — SMART ALECK — and by God I AM."

[14]Cold Injury in Korea, Lieutenant Colonel J.C. Watts, MC, J R Army med Corps, 1952, Vol XCVIII, p 1–7.

[15]For details of the "layer system" of clothing, the "parka" outer garment, cold/wet, cold/dry variations, "mukluks" for cold/dry, etc, see J R Army med Corps, 1952, Vol XCVIII, p 60–65.

Colonel J. M. Adam, as he later became, was an excellent physiologist who investigated effects of cold in Korea. His picture appears in the companion picture book on p. 55 as a researcher and not an RMO.

Captain Morrison Dorward spent some time in the Seoul medical evacuation ward in 1953 and was also in the Commonwealth Base Hospital in Kure. He remembered, in 1953, the Coronation film being sent over for the troops to see. The C.O. then was Colonel Ambrose Meneces. "I can't say I liked all the Regular officers I met, but I'd have gone to the ends of the earth for Ambrose Meneces," said Morrison Dorward.

[16]POW in Korea were all from R.A.P. level; Cpls E. Bruton, D. Hansford, E. Marshall, C.J. Papworth, J.H. Taylor, C.C. Armstrong, E. Broome, H.W. Calder, H. Manning, F.E. Geary — all RAMC attached to the rifle companies. Sgt S.F. Baxter was the only SNCO. Medical officers were: Captains R.P. Hickey, D.R. Patchett and A.M. Ferrie. One RAMC private was missing — W.C. Webster. Neither M.O.s or other ranks were allowed by the Chinese to take care of their comrades. The march of 300 miles (500Km) north from the Yalu River was described as "grim."

"The Edge of the Sword", Captain A. Farrar-Hockley, Re-published by A. Sutton, 1993. ISBN 0750903791.

[17]Captain Griffiths became a consultant orthopaedic surgeon in Bristol, and a member of 219 General Hospital. Promotion being very much slower in the TA than in the Regular Army, he did not become C.O. till in his fifties. He was later given the honour of being Honorary Colonel to his old unit, and was awarded the CBE before retiral. It was only in 1984 that I learned that Harry Griffiths had been the officer who went to Korea in my place. We have been good friends since.

[18]A useful memorandum which has a full series of key post-1939–45 War references is: Projectile trauma — an enquiry into bullet wounds, by Lieutenant Colonel R. Scott, MD, FRCS, (later Major General Scott, CB) when Consultant Surgeon, Trauma Unit, Chemical Defence Establishment, Porton Down. It is not classified.

[19]I am grateful to Major General George Cowan OBE, FRCP Ed. and Lond, for this account.

[20]It was said after the War that "The Kitchen Front was the only one where Great Britain never lost a battle." Food rationing was introduced in stages from Monday 8th January, 1940. Sugar ration was 12 oz (350gm) per person per week, butter 4 oz (100gm), tea, margarine, and cooking fat 2 oz (50gm). Meat was about 1 lb (450gm) per week. In May 1941 the cheese ration was reduced to 1 oz per week — 25gm,

about one mouthful. In 1942 you were asked to use not more than 5 inches(12cm) in your bath, to save fuel: King George had a blue line painted around the bath in Buckingham Palace to make sure no-one used too much. For full details of War-time restrictions, see "How we lived then — a History of life during the Second World War" by Norman Longmate, especially chapter 13. London, Hutchison and Co, 1971, and Arrow Books, 1973; ISBN 0 09 908080 X.

[21]Brigadier Robert Bernard Price enlisted in 1912, served in both World Wars, and was known as a quiet gentleman with a kindly and amusing sense of humour. He was a graduate of St Bartholomew's Hospital of 1908.

[22]Lieutenant General Drummond trained at University College Dundee, in St Andrews University, but did not graduate there. He took the London Conjoint in 1924. He trained as an ENT specialist, taking the DLO in 1932 and the FRCS(England) in 1947. He had the distinction of being promoted from Colonel's rank directly to Major General on posting to Cairo as D.M.S. in June 1953.

His credits were many and variable. The most important was the links he made with the Colleges and with them the concept of approval for all RAMC by their Royal Colleges and Senior Associations before being accepted as of consultant status.

The RN and RAF followed this, with the setting up of the Armed Services Consultant Approval Board (ASCAB).

But he also gave nursing orderlies and others a much larger medical responsibility, produced new ideas for evacuation and treatment, developed the central sterile supply system for the Forces, encouraged first-aid training. He was devoted to the non-medical officer. In his lifetime his enormous dynamism made him a living legend.

[23]The "New Deal" announced by Mr Profumo had an 8-point plan of inducements:

1. Better pay and promotion. Doctors "could now practise medicine up to and including the rank of full Colonel. In the past promotion had often condemned officers to administrative work." (In fact, this ha been possible earlier).

2. Active careers were now to continue to 60 years.

3. Employment as retired officers to 65 with full pension as well as pay.

4. Guaranteed married quarters tied to unit appointments and for certain specialists. 5. Up to 7 years' seniority accounting for pay and promotion for civilian professional experience. (This had been allowed earlier — since 1954).

6. More Short Service Commissions.

7. Commissions for newly-qualified doctors in their pre-registration year.

8. The cadetship scheme: medical scholarships giving commissions with full pay and allowances and payment of matriculation and tuition fees to students in the final stages of their training. The cadetship scheme was promulgated on 26/4/62.

[24]There was a big response. About 900 enquiries came in between 1st May 1962 and 31st January 1963 — half and half from doctors and medical students. 172 fully registered practitioners applied in the same period, and 84 were accepted. 33 pre-registration doctors applied, and 17 were accepted. Prior to the "New Deal", there had been only 20 enquiries a month.

From the cadetships, it was expected 37 ex-cadets would be available for duty for 1964, 44 for 1965, and 22 for 1966. The first medical officer who went through from cadet 2/Lieut. to pre-registration to full registration was Captain Michael Brear from Yorkshire, in December 1963. The first medical cadets actually *commissioned* under the New Deal were 2/Lieuts F.K. Buckland, T.J.B. Bryan, M. Brear, P.D.V. Gwinner, C.M. Charbel, T.C. Dobie — all from London hospitals. By mid-1963, a total of 100 had been selected; the Universities with the largest numbers were Liverpool 8, St Andrews 7, and 6 each from Guy's Bart's St Thomas' and Durham. The writer, then an officer in the St Andrews OTC, was at the dinner in Keogh Officers' Mess to inaugurate the scheme. The senior officer in charge of proceedings was Major General J.P. Douglas.

[25]The Mitchiner Medal was awarded annually to a medical officer or late RAMC who had brought about an advance in any branch of medical science in its application to the Army, or contributed to an improvement in any matter affecting the health or living conditions of Army personnel. The Mitchiner Memorial Lecture was given to a distinguished member of the medical profession, and the Mitchiner Statuette was presented for him to touch at the end. Award holders were granted Honorary Membership of the Headquarter Mess during their lifetime.

The DGAMS Special award was to cover the entire rank range; it was a bronze medal and a purse of £100.

The Blewett Memorial Trophy was awarded to the Regular unit or individual who had done the most in the field of operational field support. It was a silver salver and medal, the trophy to be held for a year.

These were the premier awards. There were also the Leishman Memorial Prize, the Parkes Memorial Prize, the North Persian Forces Memorial Prize; the first was available to RADC officers as well as RAMC, and the others to MOs of other Services.

For Short Service officers there were the Montefiore Prize, the Knott Prize, the Consultants' Prize, the Parkes ATQ Prize and the

Syntex Prize for trainees in general practice. The John Fry Prize was for trained general practitioners.

All the above carried a cash award also, but the largest cash prize was the Alexander Memorial Prize, for professional work of outstanding merit, which carried a purse of £550 in addition to the gilt medal. There were Postgradute Prizes awarded annually — the Sidney Herbert, the Montefiore, the Parkes, the De Chaumont and the Ranald Martin Prizes. Leishman Prizes were also available for RAMC soldiers.

[26]The RAMC Charitable Funds, (Registered Charity No CR248219) and RAMC Association (Registered Charity No 1024102) managed these. The funds included the Corps Mess Fund, the Chattels Trust, the Corps Museum, the Journal, the AMS magazine, the Central Funds, the Sports Union. The RAMC Charitable Funds, the General Relief Fund, the Aldershot School Fund, the George Wilson Bequest, and the RAMC Officers' Benevolent Society, were amalgamated into the single Charitable Fund on 8th September, 1992.

[27]As in all Corps and more so in Regiments, there were many instances of son following father. One such which covered an extra long span of time was the Ford family. John Frederick Ford was attested in Burnley on 11th June, 1885, and was commissioned as a quartermaster in the 1914–18 War. His son, of the same name, enlisted as a bugler before the same War, was also commissioned as a Lieutenant Quartermaster in 1944, and subsequently promoted Major, He died in St Catherine's Nursing Home, East Grinstead, Sussex, on 29th December, 1994, aged 95 years.

[28]In the PULHEEMS classification, P7 was a "Home Only" posting. But a person who had recovered full health could be up-graded again to P2, when he could serve anywhere in the world.

Chapter 12

The century continues — The One Army Concept and the British Army of the Rhine in Europe during the Cold War. Small wars and terrorists.

Perspective.

The last 30 years of the century was a period of recession for Britain. Various elements at home and abroad contributed. During the government of Sir Alec Douglas-Home significant changes were made in the Reserve Army; the Territorial Army was abolished and replaced by the Territorial Army Volunteer Reserve. During the government of Mr Edward Heath the last British stations in Malaya were closed — after a short period of Commonwealth co-operation in the ANZUK Hospital (Australia, New Zealand, U.K.). Overseas embassies were closed and smaller properties built at larger expense, to accord with Britain's status as a second-level power. At home, the historic counties of Britain were replaced by a system of Regional Authorities with new and often unwelcome titles, and the National Health Service underwent the first of a succession of administrative changes, with loss of locally accountable Boards of Management and the disappearance of matrons under the insistence of the Salmon Report. Most of all, the country entered the European Common Market, believed by most who voted for it to be a trading association worth joining, but which soon appeared as an apparently inexorable progress towards a federal union with a continental bureaucracy on an infinite scale and the destruction of a thousand years of sovereignty. On the other hand, the enthusiasts insisted that the European Union was the panacea for all Britain's problems. It was not surprising that many honest citizens were confused.

On 4th October, 1957, the first artificial satellite, the Russian SPUTNIK I, was launched, and on July 20th, 1969, the US lunar capsule, with Neil Armstrong and Buzz Aldrin as crew, landed on the moon.

The decline of British industry was aided by inefficient and complacent managers and by the restrictive practices of certain Trades Unions; and the joke of the "Friday afternoon car" — badly built on the last day of the working week — was complemented in the 1960s and 1970s by the failure to design and develop better industrial products — a challenge taken up by others who subsequently captured our markets.

In the 1960s, again during a term of Conservative government, arose the "swinging sixties", where deference became mocked and there appeared the so-called "permissive society." Humour became malicious to an extent that had not been seen since the 18th century. There was widespread anti-military activity in universities; in a number of English ones, notably Birmingham, OTC members had to go to their Training Centre with their uniform covered by raincoats. The satirical BBC programme, "That Was the Week that Was", set the trend for the next 30 years. In later years the term "anti-culture of the sixties" was used to describe the decade.

The "Thatcher Era", when the first woman Prime Minister ruled with considerable support and obvious personal authority, was one of undoubted striking political achievement on the international scene, and honour to her for this was acknowledged. Her assessment that the British people needed to learn that the State was not the universal provider without any effort on the part of individuals was correct, and her first administration brought this truth home to them most sensibly. Her business instincts, however, remained all too often those of the shopkeeper; self enterprise and strict insistence upon financial return too readily turned into the "me first" syndrome and into cash return as the basis of all parts of society. It also produced the real concern that her administration "knew the cost of everything and the value of nothing." This last included Medicine and the National Health Service. The succeeding government of Mr John Major continued to tell the populace of their rights in "the consumer society" in various "charters", and perhaps failed to remind them of their responsibilities to others.

In this latter part of the century, too, arose a new tyrant. This was collectively called "the media" and comprised instant and critical reporting on television and the continuous shriek of the tabloid press. The media became a most feared element of world society, because of its immediacy and because of the type of reporting it developed. The investigative journalists were prepared to go to any lengths to secure their story and would hunt their prey with orc-like malice.[1] Also, the Australian Rupert Murdoch, whose personal agendas were well expressed, controlled a very large part of the press.

This résumé of the political and social background is deliberately over-simplified. But the elements chosen for inclusion were those which had particular and often precise effects upon the Army and its Medical Services.

The remaining Military Force was "Der Britischen Rheinarmee" (BAOR). By having an Army of 55,000 men permanently stationed on the mainland of Europe, the United Kingdom shared with NATO partners — particularly Holland, Belgium, and later Germany—the French having contracted out—the responsibility for a vital sector of NATO's Central Front.

The largest and by far the most powerful part of NATO was the United States Army and Air Force; by now the USA was the world super-power. The myth of a "special relationship" between Britain and the U.S. was continued. Americans toured everywhere — confident and assertive, visibly wealthy, — looking briefly at older cultures their dollars could not buy — and often annoying because of these qualities — just as the British had been a century before. But whereas their predecessors had learned foreign languages at their schools, U.S. children did not see the need to learn any other language than American English.

Developments in the N.A.T.O. rôle for the AMS.
"The Suez expedition was a near disaster because it was necessary to transport virtually all equipment by sea", said Major Bernard Leary. "The next years were spent in trying to develop air portability. RAMC units were included in these efforts but were at a disadvantage because all units behind the field ambulance were confined to the Reserve. This of course required legislation before it could be mobilized."

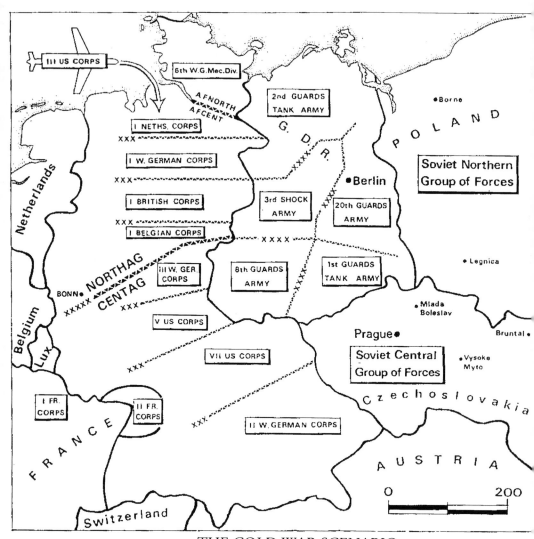

THE COLD WAR SCENARIO

Major B.D.J. Leary's words summarise for us the two parts of the field planners' responsibilities over the years 1962–1990. (He had just finished a year at Staff College in December 1961 before returning to an RAMC unit, so was well versed in the latest thinking). They had to plan for a possible major European War where the Regular Army had to rely upon a large percentage of the back-up medical support coming from the Territorial Army. The latter became progressively more important as the years went by, but their employment was constrained by the contract they had entered into: call-out was only by Queen's proclamation in the event of general mobilization.

The first responsibility for the whole-time RAMC was to keep abreast of changing military requirements and if possible anticipate them. At the Field Training Centre in 1961 when Major Leary was posted there, the Chief Instructor was Lieutenant Colonel Robert Mitchell (later Major General Mitchell, OBE, DMS BAOR). He had the task of carrying out a survey of all medical establishments with a view to conversion of at least some of them to airportable capability. In the decade of the 1960s there remained the continuous call for battalions to go here and there at a moment's notice. Such had been covered medically by sending with them a section of a Fd Ambs and an FST. But there was always the risk of something bigger coming along — requiring a unit of CCS size. At that time the AMS had nothing suitable. Further, numbers of men were reduced: "After 1961 we lost all the National Servicemen", Colonel John Edgington reminded us, "and yet we had the same commitments."

In 1962 Major Leary, now at a desk at AMD1 in the War office, was telephoned by the CIGS of the day (General Sir Richard Hull, GCB, DSO,) with the question: "Do you have an airportable CCS you could put on standby"? "I could only reply", answered Major Leary, "that the AMS did not have a CCS and if we *had* one it would not be airportable." The RAMC was in danger, he feared, of becoming unable to fulfil its war rôle.

In the meantime Lieutenant Colonel Mitchell had thought up the idea of a brick system of 50 bed sections which would be the basis of both field and static units. Cadre field units could then be reinforced by hospital teams whose members knew one another and were used to working together in the way the TA units did. The project was presented at the Director General's

Exercise in 1961. It was adopted as useful and remained in the system.

But the CIGS' request had to be met. Luckily, on Salisbury Plain was 22 Fd Amb which had become surplus to requirements. It was turned into 22 CCS. The shortfall was made up from the field ambulances in Malaya, still on its emergency war establishment. Thus was created the unit which as 22 Fd Hosp — the CCS as a unit having disappeared — would serve in later campaigns. The brick system would be used later also.

This task is an example of what was needed from the RAMC planners. In addition to the Field Training Centre was its Army Health opposite number, and two others of great importance — the Nuclear Biological and Chemical (NBC) School at Winterbourne Gunner near Salisbury, where selected personnel were taught the state of the art in those fields, and the Chemical Defence Establishment at Porton, where secret work was done.[2]

The cadre size of RAMC field units has been mentioned. It was true that in BAOR all too many of these were ill recruited. They were not units an ambitious young medical officer wanted to spend time in, especially if he wanted clinical advancement. But here it was the Territorial Army the planners looked to, to make up the Medical ORBAT. BAOR was made up of an Army Corps (1st Br(British) Corps). It was organized into four armoured divisions; an artillery division; corps troops and a non-mechanised field force (5 Field Force). 1Br Corps had over 600 Chieftain tanks and nearly 3,000 other armoured vehicles. The Regular AMS had not the man or woman power to provide the needed medical cover.[3]

"When we talk about the Army as a whole, it is a good thing to remind ourselves that despite our many different outward appearances we are one Army, Regular and Territorials." Field Marshal Sir Michael Carver, 1980.

The Territorials *were* territorial — they came from local parts of the United Kingdom. They had close local family and civic connections. In this they were more akin to the Infantry of the Line. In the TA as it stood, they were brigaded with their local tribe. Their close family relationship with the Regular Army was one the other Services did not understand. And they certainly were tribal; Londoners differing from the south-west, the south-west from the north-east (home of the great 50(Tyne Tees) Division). In Scotland there were tribal differences between Glasgow, Edinburgh, Aberdeen and Dundee. Their local loyalties were always keen, often fierce. It was not only Frank Seabrooke who discovered how "Welsh" 159 Fd Ambs could be.

107(Ulster) Fd Amb was formed as part of 107(Ulster) Independent Infantry Bde(TA) at Victoria barracks in 1947. Before the raising of the brigade there was no RAMC(TA) unit in Northern Ireland. What there had been was great loyalty; this was well known in two World Wars.

Numbers were small at first, around a nucleus of RAMC and other Ulster officers with war experience. From 1952, when Lieutenant Colonel George Gregg became C.O., there were only four other officers — Major J. Bleakly, 2IC, Major R.R. Baird, Major S. Stroud and Lieutenant J. Allen, a non-medical officer. Queen's University OTC had a thriving medical sub-unit by now (not all university OTCs had these) and it provided a steady source of medical officers. By 1961 there were over 200 on 107's books. In that year a second medical TA unit, No 4 GH(General Hospital, TA), was raised from a nucleus of 40 men from the field ambulance.

In 1962 the BMA held its Annual Representative Meeting in Belfast. Brigadier Sir Ian Fraser DSO, remembered as one of the early users of penicillin in the Middle East, was now Honorary Colonel of both TA medical units. A significant happening was the laying of the foundation stone of the new Military Wing in Musgrave Park Hospital, to be built as a replacement for the previous Nissen hutted hospital at Waringfield in use since 1942. It was opened in 1964 by Drummond's successor as D.G., General Harold Knott. Much more would be heard of Musgrave Park, though no one realised it at the time.

Training in the 1950s and 60s in 107 as in all TA field ambulances included casualty sweeps, first-aid training, some civil defence, and evacuation to a CCS. In 1954 at Stobs Camp in southern Scotland — kinship and religious ties with the Scots being real — the whole of 107 Bde trained together for Annual Camp, and 107 Fd Amb practised its war rôle.

At home, the unit training areas were the lead mines near Newtonards, the Cave Hill, Belfast, Cairn Castle on the County Antrim coast, the Antrim Bridging Camp, and Ballydemond.

The unit won the TA Challenge Shield, the major Reserve competition, on two occasions, establishing it as one of the best of the TA AMS

On the mainland of the United Kingdom, the major units were larger, being TA divisions. Each had its own TAADMS, a Regular officer as DADMS, and an appropriate staff within the divisional H.Q. But the training covered the same pattern.

In 1967 the TA was disbanded as an independent Army — it had been this since 1908, except during hostilities, when it was merged with the Regular Army and no distinction made. The changes of 1967 would lead to a somewhat similar concept occurring during the rest of the Cold War. 107 became renumbered 253 Fd Amb, and No 4 became 204 (NI)GH. It transferred from its base in Tyrone House to "Firmount" in Antrim Road, Belfast, and was to become a 600 bed hospital with all training — trade and other specialist — exactly as a war-time BGH would have. It was part of the progress towards the "One Army Concept." Like 253, 204 became a "NATO committed unit." The same applied to all the Medical TA ORBAT.

In the larger mainland areas, some medical units disappeared. An example was in Manchester, where the Fd Amb and div H.Q. were disbanded, leaving only 207 (Manchester) GH(V). "The doormat had 'Volunteers' on it", said the unit record, "but the unit remains in the same drill hall as designated and built for the RAMC and opened on 18th January, 1905, making it one of the oldest in the Corps."

"Today", the unit history went on, "we have a new 'One Army Concept' for the first time in our history. This means that an increasing professionalism and dedication is required for all ranks."

Towards this end, all TA units, including medical, were re-designated and given a new number system. The first line were category 1 — the only RAMC unit to come into this category was 144 Para Fd Amb, based in London. The majority were category 2 and were to be the best trained Reserve, with a minimum requirement of 12 weekends of training, a 14 day Annual Camp, and an Annual range course. Most if not all personnel did much more than this — for many the TAVR, as the new organization was styled, became a life career for both soldiers and officers. Moreover, it was possible for both medical and dental officers and soldiers to serve much longer than their comrades in the teeth arms. This was altogether sensible; the Regular AMS was looking to them (and nursing officers as much as medical and dental) as the reservoir of clinical experience and skill.[4]

To obtain his "bounty" — an annual tax-free award, the officer or soldier was to complete his training requirement, and in addition be given his Commanding Officer's approval that he was efficiently trained. It was an ideal way, from a Treasury point of view, of obtaining a useful Military Reserve at a minimum cost. For pay, though at Regular rates, did not include increments for length of service. When the "New Deal" with guaranteed progress through the ranks — especially for hospital consultants — was introduced, it did not apply to the TAVR.

In 1967 were also formed the 3rd line — the "sponsored units." The TAVR was in effect an amalgamation of the old TA and AER (Army Emergency Reserve) and the sponsored units were the successors of the latter. This new 3rd line was numbered 3; their members had only 2 weekends in a year, an Annual Camp and a range course fired during one of them if a field unit, as their training requirement. They were, as will be described, rather second class citizens when compared to the "Independent Units"; they were controlled from a central CVHQ (Central Volunteer HQ) in Keogh and were recruited on a nation-wide basis. Their rank structure was also limited.[5]

In total the Reserves more than made up for the shortfall in 1966 of 187 Regular RAMC medical officers against a requirement of 893. The Dentals were also short; of a requirement of 210 they had only 183 including 21 civilian practitioners.

From now till 1990, the TA units (the title TA was restored in 1980, to great rejoicing) had specific tasks in the whole AMS ORBAT. Each had a War Location (secret to all except the C.O., PSO (Permanent Staff Officer, an attached Regular, non-medical), Q.M., and R.S.M.). They were no longer related to a major local formation, but were dispersed throughout BAOR in forward and rear combat zones.[6]

Both the field and hospital units began to train much more specifically to carry out their task. Training became harder and more closely supervised by the staff of Regular HQs. The older generation of ex-wartime members faded away, and were replaced by ex-National Servicemen. In due course they, too, began to retire. As standards rose, as in the old TA of 1939 and later, some units were always better than others; there were *de facto* first and second rate units. The Annual TAVR Shield competition sorted out the levels; preliminary heats were held locally (253, for example, shared with 252 and 225 in Scotland or Northern Ireland, but after the "troubles" began in 1969, in Scotland) and the final at Mytchett. The Inspector of Training, AMS, a Major General, looked on closely and reported his observations both publicly and privately to the D.G.

Training followed a 3-year cycle. One year was unit training at home. The next concentrated on trade training, when individual medical members went to Keogh and other arms to their own Corps centre to up-grade their special-to-arm skill and knowledge, and Annual Camp, the high point of the Reservist's year, was smaller as a result. The third year was in Germany, where the unit, hopefully at best possible strength, went to BAOR by ship, sea, train, or by air, to train over the same area as it would serve in if an invasion by the Warsaw pact took place.[7]

General Reay, who was D.G. from 1981 to 1985, recalled the "battle it was to get realistic training for the medicals in the later 1970s." The Big Army was unwilling to provide the large numbers of soldiers for use as mock casualties to make medical exercises a true test. But with perseverance sufficient were provided; in a number of mobilization exercises such as "Crusader" ("Spearpoint") in September 1980, not only the Medical Reserves were tested but the Teeth Arms as well. The numbers involved were so large that the Director of Surgery, BAOR, Brigadier Kirby, designated one FST — 352 — to act as standby should the need arise for the treatment of genuine casualties, "No Duff" as they were coded.

Another necessity was for Reserve field units to train with a Regular equivalent. 31 Fd Amb, based in Münster, was an example of one which shared its summer exercise with 222, the East Midland Fd Amb. Lieutenant Colonel John Edgington, 31's C.O., was glad to have medical officers to boost his numbers and Lieutenant Colonel Alastair Fraser-Darling, 222's C.O., was equally glad to have his shortfall of other ranks made good with regulars of quality. Both sides enjoyed the social side of time off from training; Colonel Fraser-Darling tried hard to woo

Colonel Edgington to leave the Regular Army and join his practice!

An important method of learning for the Territorials was to serve with a Regular unit. The locum system served this purpose admirably. In the 1970s and 80s, a comprehensive list of locums in BMHs, for RMOs, and in other RAMC units, was published each spring. Territorials then applied for the unit and date which suited, and very many went back to a locum post on several occasions. Service in these had a double purpose. It gave Reservists experience with the full-time Army and it gave the full-time Army medicals the chance of leave from units where the lack of a locum would have produced troublesome shortages. The system worked very well, to the benefit of both sides.

From 1970 the British Military HQ was at UKLF (United Kingdom Land Forces) at Wilton near Salisbury. Details of organization were further tightened under the DsMS, first Major General Gray and then, notably, the fiery Major General Jimmy Miller MC. The introduction of "SOPs" (Standing Operating Procedures) ensured that a more uniform standard prevailed. But many real doubts remained unanswered.

As a result of queries about the process of mobilization, the whole TAVR undertook, in 1975, a Mobilization Exercise (MOBEX) called "Inside Right." For this, each Arm of the Reserves had a chosen unit put through the mobilization process as realistically as possible. A Scottish field ambulance, 225, was the AMS field unit selected. This unit had the unusual feature of having authority to wear the Tam-O'-Shanter.[8] Members had their friends from 253 attached, for this special exercise.

225 were "put through it" from the moment they left their TA Centre. Soldiers were encouraged to write their wills, to add realism to the event. They had to go through the entire mobilization process without leaving anything out. A real Rear Party, to deal with family and financial problems, remained behind. *En route*, they had to collect the equivalent weight and bulk of their ammunition, 50 additional vehicles at Derby, and their entire PUE (Pre-packed Unit Equipment). They passed through their war location in the time allowed, were harried by a Regular infantry platoon, carried out a specimen set-up, casualty collection, moved within a short time span, and returned,

exhausted, to Scotland. On the way back at a staging point, R.S.M. Bill Murray of 225 had an angry argument with Captain Maurice Cass RAMC after the R.S.M. told him "This field ambulance is as good and better than any regular one , and I should know." The RCT element, made up of Dundee Corporation bus drivers, and professionals to a man, had to slap their faces to keep awake as they drove. The C.O. asked the Dundonians: "Would you do it again?" and received the highest compliment of his life. "We'd go wi' ye tae Moscow", said the Jocks.

During "Inside Right", many of the mobilization procedures were shown to be unrealistic, and considerable changes made. Of these the most significant was that the vehicles and PUE were now stockpiled at the base TA centre — the exercise had shown that there was just insufficient time to break it open while on the way to war.[9]

Hospitals practised their war rôle also. For them, they had to set up, receive and treat casualties. These exercises became known as "Minimash" and continued till the end of the Cold War in 1990. They too practised their MOBEX annually, and were tested on its efficiency.

The Territorial Army was shown in the media over the 70s and 80s as being equivalent to their Regular colleagues. Newspaper advertisements declared: "Can you tell the difference?" showing two soldiers, one a Regular, the other a Territorial.

Could the Territorial Army AMS have done what was expected of them? The view of Directors of the period was that they could, but all had reservations about the shortfall particularly of other ranks in all sorts of units — there was never any doubt in the minds of successive Directors General of the calibre of the active members, most of all the clinical worth of the consultant staff. Inevitably, these had more weight of work, and a much larger experience of major surgery, than their often younger Regular colleagues.[10]

But it was a different story with the small sponsored units. Many who had been in an independent unit regarded it as the kiss of death to have to join one of these. The restricted rank structure, and the absurdity of having to actually lose rank on transfer, made several consultants of the highest ability leave after a very few years. The MOD in the 1970s made up numbers by filling FSTs with general practitioners, public health doctors, and even psychiatrists, entering the total number in the record, and then pretending that these units were well recruited with the correct surgical and anaesthetic consultants. They just did not reveal the status of those filling the vacancies. "The manning was widely inappropriate" as General Reay conceded. The training, too, was often poorly arranged by the sometimes unequal quality of those in charge of CVHQ.[11]

The TA (AMS) not unnaturally developed its own pride in its contribution. Most commanding officers tried hard to make their units mobilization-worthy; as in all things, some were more successful than others.

The TA (AMS) Honorary Colonels' Conference, held at the RAM College on the day of the Mitchiner lecture, increased in standing, discussed serious issues, and the senior officers present took note. This was particularly so from the time of Brigadier A.S.B. Dickson as Commander (his father had been Major John Matheson's C.O. in Edinburgh in 1938–9) and Brigadier H.S. Platt, the TA Adviser to the Director General. Brigadier Dickson was forward-looking and, perhaps because he had been a TA officer long enough to get the TD, was more aware of the feelings of Reserve personnel which some who had not his background lacked. TA Advisers with the local rank of brigadier returned in 1971 while General Talbot was D.G. Always former hospital commanding officers, and usually from the south of England, they were seen by the TA (AMS) as somewhat shadowy figures, but this did not apply to Brigadier Platt, who was noteworthy, as was Brigadier Hall-Davies, and later again Brig Rowe.

This, then, was the "One Army Concept" as it affected the RAMC. During the last 15 years of the Cold War the medical support for BAOR was 20 per cent Regular, 80 per cent Territorial. In 1991, there were, against a total establishment of 629 TA medical officers, (86 surgeons, 86 anaesthetists, 382 GDMOs, 75 physicians, radiologists, pathologists, psychiatrists) 428 in post (64 surgeons, 51 anaesthetists, 278 GDMOs, 35 others). But the *total* established strength of TA (AMS) was 9780 all ranks (7882 independent and 1898 sponsored in 1988), representing not only RAMC and RADC and QARANC but also RCT, RE, ACC, REME, RAPC, RAOC — and RAChD, from all over the United Kingdom of Great Britain and Northern Ireland.

This was the reason for D.G.s' concern: how many would on the day reach Germany, to form part of the Thin Red Line on the Teutoberger wald and be expendable with the rest of the British Army of the Rhine before the land battle was considered lost and the nuclear weapons used. For the Regulars were below strength too: GDMO levels in BAOR in 1991 were for example 62 against the establishment of 90, and 69 against 80 within U.K.; and consultants *in total* 115 against the required establishment of 148. The junior levels were fortunately excellent: 48 senior registrars against establishment of 60; 29 registrars against 2; 44 senior house officers against 40(10).

Home Events; a new Hospital. The terrorist campaign in Ireland.
A succession of events from 1967 have to be recorded. The new BMH in Hong Kong opened at King's Park (the old one had been in Bowen Road and Mount Kellett) in August 1967, and a new BMH in Berlin in May.

In 1967 Major E.H.P. Hills received the QA Medal for his nursing service between 1937 and 1967. He had started his career in the RAMC as a nursing orderly.

In 1968 Major General Eric Barnsley died. He had joined as a TA officer in 1912, remained by choice a "non-specialist" officer, and had looked after the archives and historical museum with the greatest care and authority.

In 1969 began a fresh outbreak of "troubles" in Northern Ireland.[12] After British troops were moved in to protect the population, casualties came by road or helicopter to the Military Wing of Musgrave Park Hospital in Belfast. It became the most active BMH the AMS had to support. The pace of activity increased from 1971; it was the Para Fd Amb which set in train the changes that put Musgrave Park on virtually a war footing. Quickly Corps members were casualties: Pte Dennis Porter was killed, Captain Bruce McKay, RMO of the Royal Regiment of Wales, was shot but recovered. The first ADMS of the new Era was Colonel Sandy Ferrie, his Chief Clerk S/Sgt A. Cameron. For the next 25 years, a succession of AMS personnel, including a few selected Territorials, learned by practical experience what casualty evacuation and military surgery meant.

In September 1971 there was an armed uprising in Jordan and British help was sought for medical cover. This was provided *via* Cyprus, where the BMH at Dhekelia was a firm base. Casualties arrived from the 20th. OPERATION SHOVELLER, as the operation was code-named, was under the command of Colonel Ferrie, and the medical "Ferrieforce" he led gained applause from the CGS himself. This was a unique operation; the troops had to wear civilian clothes though serving overseas in a civil war.

The RAMC was awarded the freedom of the borough of Aldershot on 27th June, 1973, its 75th Anniversary. A Commemorative First Day Cover, with stamp, was issued on 23rd June that year, and the Queen Mother visited Millbank on 6th July for the 75th Anniversary ceremony. The same year the Corps golf team won the Ordnance Cup at Muirfield. In 1974, the TAVR Shield was reorganized into 2 competitions — the Field Ambulance Challenge Shield, and the Hospitals Competition.

1966 saw the introduction of the commissioned RAMC Male Nursing Officers who were employed in the role of Training Officers in field ambulances to make up for the shortfall of medical officers. In 1970 due to the QARANC being unable to fill all of their established commissioned nursing posts, a total of 76 were allocated to the RAMC to be filled by Commissioned Male State Registered Nurses. Commissioning of these commenced on a quota basis in January 1971. In the mid 1970s Male Commissioned SRNs were used again to make up the deficiency of MOs by being used in the role of Regimental Medical Officer Assistants in Northern Ireland. In October 1992 all male commissioned Registered General Nurses were rebadged QARANC.[13]

And at midnight on 30th November, 1975, the U.K. Military Hospital in Singapore was finally closed, thus ending the British Military Era in Malaya. Tidworth Military Hospital was closed on 31st March, 1977, and the Royal Herbert in Woolwich on 25th June the same year. A new hospital in Catterick, to replace the old hutted one, was however opened on 6th October, 1976. The Duchess of Kent's Military Hospital (DKMH) was most pleasant in appearance and with an ambience many felt happier than Woolwich. It would endure longer than most, too, although no-one knew it at the time.

But these events were of less significance to the Corps as a whole than the closure of the Queen Alexandra Hospital at

Millbank and the building of its successor in a far-off site in Woolwich. This loss of the major RAMC Hospital in central London would prove decisive, in historical terms, in the reduction of the Corps at the end of the century.

For several years there had been talk of a re-build for the QA Hospital at Millbank. Some said a replacement had been suggested on the site behind the RAM College, but that English Heritage had refused the plan, claiming it would spoil the College as a listed building. Next a site was suggested in Regent's Park, but this proposal too fell through. Although the Royal Navy supported the AMS in its efforts to use the Regent's Park site, the RAF Medicals bitterly opposed it. They would regret their narrow, Single-Service attitude later.[14]

On July 8th, 1969, Mr Harold Wilson, the Prime Minister, announced in the House of Commons that "Her Majesty's Government had decided to transfer the site of the Queen Alexandra Military Hospital to the Trustees of the Tate Gallery and to build a new prestige Military Hospital at Woolwich. This would replace the Hospital at Millbank and the two already at Woolwich. Shrapnel Barracks was the site of the new hospital." It was said that Mr Wilson owed a favour to Mrs Jennie Lee, widow of Mr Aneurin Bevan, and it was her wish to expand the Tate at the expense of the Army Hospital next door. Whatever the background, the decision was a fateful one for the Army Medical Services.

The foundation stone was laid by the Colonel-in-Chief on Thursday 9th November, 1972.

In 1973 Lieutenant-General Sir Norman Talbot retired as Director General. His tour, the first D.G.'s to be done by a former obstetrician — he was the officer responsible for the development of Obstetrics and Gynaecology as a major specialty in the Army — was marked by one of the reviews the politicians were never tired of making as year succeeded year; The Defence Medical Services Enquiry Committee, as this one was called, was commented on by General Talbot when he retired: (The Committee) "has yet to report. We have endeavoured to define for them the problems as we see them and have made many proposals to improve conditions of service and professional job satisfaction...much has been put into this Committee — may much come out of it!"[15]

The last patients were transferred from QAMH on "a cold, windy, day", on 2nd April 1977 to the new Hospital at Woolwich. At the closure of QA, Brigadier K.P. Milne was C.O., and Lieutenant Colonel E.M. Elliot, Matron. "We must hope that one day the extension of the Tate Gallery to be built on the site", said Brigadier Milne sadly, "will do a fraction of the good work for humanity as the hospital has done so well over the years." There was clearly bitterness at the time, and with good reason.

The Royal Herbert Hospital at Woolwich closed at the beginning of 1977, and its patients transferred to QEMH. Colchester MH closed in late 1977, the Royal Victoria Hospital Netley in early 1978. So the new QEMH was to replace 5 military hospitals. It took outpatients from April 1977, inpatients from June, and opened fully on 25th June. The last patients to be transferred were the psychiatric from Netley, at the end of August, 1978. The Queen Elizabeth Military Hospital was opened officially and sympathetically by HM The Queen Mother two months later, on 1st November, 1978.

Notes and references

CHAPTER 12

[1]For "orcs" see "The Lord of the Rings", by J.R.R, Tolkien, George Allen and Unwin, London, 1954; twelfth impression 1980.

The "tabloids" were the professed pretended guardians of morality of the last part of the 20th Century. The "investigative journalists" and camera men were popularly known as the "rat pack."

As an instance of their attitude may be cited the assistant editor of the *News of the World*, who insisted on B.B.C. Radio 4 on 24th March, 1995, that his paper "had the highest moral standards in whom they gave money to, and how much, for a story in the public interest" — meaning in fact how much the *required* sum was to be. A further most revealing article is by Mr Kelvin MacKenzie, former editor of *The Sun*, in The Spectator, 19th July, 1997, 13–14.

Positive appreciation of the power of the media became a necessary part of military training. See, e.g, "Conflict, the Military and the Media, a New Optimism ?" by N.Gowing, ARRC Journal Sept 1997,Vol 1, no 1, p13–16.

[2]In 1994 the then Surgeon General, Vice-Admiral A. Revell, had to host his Russian opposite number. He asked his ministerial superior where he could take the Russian General. "Anywhere except Porton", was the reply.

[3]In peace time BAOR was divided into three main parts — the largest by far, 1st (British) Corps, the fighting element with its HQ at Bielefeld and troops in the States of North Rhine, Westphalia and Lower Saxony; the Rhine Area where the resupply units were stationed with its HQ at Dusseldorf; and the British Sector of Berlin.

The Corps was commanded by a Lieutenant General and organized into four armoured divisions. Each had an armoured reconnaissance regiment, two armoured regiments, motorised infantry battalions, artillery, engineers, signals, an army air corps regiment, other corps troops, and medical support. Medical field units followed the usual lines and were armoured when in support of armour. There were hospitals in Rinteln and Hannover in the Forward Combat Zone (FCZ which was the Corps Rear Boundary), Munster and Iserlohn in the Rear Combat Zone (RCZ extending back to Rheindalen), but no others. The Communication Zone (Com Z, behind Rheindalen) had no hospitals. The whole medical plan depended upon the support of the TA (AMS) if casualty evacuation and treatment were to succeed.

As the years passed, changes of strategic plan necessitated changes in the medical "Germany plan"; TA hospitals in particular had to be "bid for" by the commanders. The initiative for bids was with the planners in Germany, the medical being the DMS.

[4]The "upside" of the TA, General Cameron Moffat recalled, was that they knew their war location, were well trained, extremely highly motivated, with "extremely good people, knowledgeable and more adaptable than many Regulars. But for the short war scenario envisaged, their build-up would have been slow." The "downside" was the fear that "not enough would mobilize on the day." And one or two field ambulances were poorly officered, with too many Sergeants' mess and Junior Ranks Club members; equally, one or two hospitals were cosy clubs which excluded non-members.

But clinical skills were often high. An example was 225 Fd Amb, which on "Inside Right" had a C.O. consultant surgeon who had entered the merit award system in his thirties, the 2i/c later became Professor of Orthopaedic Surgery in the University of Edinburgh; two other officers who became consultants, two primary care doctors who had had signals training, one having seen regular active service and the other who became very senior in Academic general practice and later Medical Director of the Prescription Pricing Authority; non-medical officers included one who had had parachutist experience while doing NS and was senior technician in a university biochemistry department and another who had been a Regular R.S.M., a dental officer then on the staff of Guy's Hospital Dental Department, a house officer Lieutenant who spoke fluent German, and the Q.M., who did the same job in a 600 bed hospital in his civilian capacity.

The other example was 217 General Hospital which, at the same time, had six consultants on the staff of London Teaching Hospitals, all of whom were holders of merit awards, and a Commanding Officer merit holder in a non-teaching Hospital, among its officers; nursing officers who were matrons in civil life or senior members of the Department of Health; junior staff three of whom were also soon on the staff of London Teaching Hospitals.

Both these units, the field one from the north of the UK and the hospital one from the south, had senior NCOs, soldiers, and nursing staff of equivalent experience and ability.

But it has to be remembered also that many had no regard for the Reservists. Lieutenant Colonel Gauci, a member of the BMA's Armed Forces Committee, said "if any money becomes available, from government, it should go to us and not to the TA." Lieutenant Colonel Ken Millar, who later served as an AMS(TA) Commander, called the TA "a paper tiger", and was unsupportive. Lieutenant Colonel John Burgess, told in 1995 of new Reserve Forces Legislation to allow better support, said: "What happens to the Reserves is of no interest to the Regular RAMC". And the other Services, whose knowledge of the Reserves was all too often rudimentary, were even more uncomplimentary: the very confident Surgeon Commander Richard Dale RN said at Millbank in 1995: "The Reserves? They're a joke and always have been."

Some nursing staff of the AMS were also of the highest quality. Major Eileen White, RRC, TD, who had to lose rank after being Matron of 308 G.H. so that she could continue serving, met the Matron of QEMH on a training week-end and deferred to her. The next week, the Matron met Miss Eileen White, a Deputy Chief Nursing officer at the Department of Health — and she really *did* defer.

When any comparison with the Regular colleagues is made, it is important to remember that the number of Regular consultants was small and they did not have access to the pattern of work and large numbers of patients which the TA consultants had — the TA could call on members from throughout the U.K., some working in the highest grade of hospital unit. It was in no way derogatory to the Regulars if this was said. A number of Regular senior staff were of high clinical ability — Major Generals Morrison, Macfarlane and Cowan as physicians, Major General Simon Gavourin as a gynaecologist, Major General R.A. Stephen as surgeon (whose papers on testicular tumour were noteworthy), Brigadier Sam Janikoun, Colonel A.J. Watts, Major General J. T. Coull the orthopaedic surgeon. Major Generals Kirby and Pryn combined professional skill with organizing ability. In Army Health (this was split into Community Health and Occupational Medicine in 1976, following civilian changes), Major Generals R.A. Smart and T.W. Carrick were noteworthy. One who combined great clinical skill in physical medicine with military ability was Brigadier J.B.M. Milne. Of the pathologists, Major General Sachs was outstanding. A greatly loved and respected senior officer not a clinical consultant, was Brigadier Niven, who commanded the Depot.

[5]In 1967 they comprised: 380 Blood Supply Unit (BSU), 307 Fd Amb, 312 Fd Hyg Pln, 382 Fd Medical Coy, 381 Fd Med Eqpt Depot, Ambulance Staff Trains Nos 331, 332, 333; 308 (County of London) Evacuation Hospital and 304 GH (City of Glasgow, formerly City of Glasgow C.C.S.). 300, 301, 350, 352, 358 FSTs were important as they were to provide a back-up of highly trained surgical and anaesthetic specialists, plus theatre sisters and theatre orderlies; 370 neuro-surgical and 372 maxillo-facial Team, again to provide specialist skill the Regular RAMC did not possess.

372 MFT (maxillo-facial team) was commanded over many years by Lieutenant Colonel Peter Clarke, an Aberdeen consultant oral surgeon. In the NS era he did his two years in a mobile dental team in Kenya, where his RADC Sergeant was Sgt Greenslade and his chair assistant a young Kenyan, Ricardo. He was awarded the OBE for his long and excellent service.

[6]The teeth arms followed a similar pattern, but not all were assigned to BAOR. For the largest number, the Infantry, there were three rôles: 1) some individual companies were to become the 4th company of a Regular bn destined to go to Germany — rather like the sponsored medical units. There would then be two companies in a TA battalion with different establishments, which had the integral support arms they would need on mobilization; 2) battalions assigned to a particular rôle in Germany — manning a key point, for example; and 3) battalions assigned to home defence — these were somewhat poor relations.

By the mid-1980s, of a total complement of 217,481 in the British Army, the Regular Army provided 144,881 and the TA 72,600, i.e. 32 per cent of the TA, Independent Units made up 55,000 (75 per cent) and Sponsored 13,000 (18 per cent). Officer Training Corps, bands and some specialists made up 4,600 (6 per cent). The TA shortfall was 2,779. For all this, the bill was light: the TA cost 1.9 per cent of the Defence Vote and 4.5 per cent of the Army Vote. In the AMS(TA) the proportion of the BAOR support was 80 per cent — much higher than in other arms.

[7]The annual training cycle began in winter and spring, when units practised individual skills and minor exercises at platoon level, using small training areas near to their unit's barracks. During summer the individuals were moulded into larger combat teams and battle groups on the larger training areas and field firing ranges. These were at Sennelager, Haltern, Bergen-Hohne (the site of Belsen), Munster and Vogelsang. Finally, the major formation exercises were held in autumn after the harvest when the least damage would be done to the land.

During the training cycle, soldiers normally spent at least two weeks at a weapon training camp and about seven weeks on manoeuvre.

The strains on young families and especially on young wives did at times lead to difficulties; the Army had indeed become the post-NS "family army" which led General Drummond to ask for, and receive, paediatric and primary care support. From 1972 was established a training area large enough to allow practice with the increasingly complex and long-range weapons then arriving, at Suffield in Canada. (BATUS, the British Army Training Unit Suffield, where over 1,000 square miles (2,600 sqkm) of virgin prairie was available).

As well as the 50,000 Regulars who were in BAOR permanently, between 16,000 and 20,000 TA trained for their two weeks every year. They faced the prospect of attack by nearly 90 Warsaw Pact divisions.

[8]The story of the acquisition of the T.O.S. was an interesting one. The C.O., Adjutant, and R.S.M. thought long and hard of how the item could be acquired. It was the R.S.M., who had once been a storeman, R.S.M. Ray Walters, who had the idea of sending a message to the new computer he knew had just been installed in Bicester. Guessing the computer would read a command without question, they inserted the request: "From 225 (HIGHLAND) Fd Amb. Send T.O.S. as for Queen's Own Highlanders or Gordons, sizes ranges for 150 other ranks…". The computer, reading the word "HIGHLAND", did not query the request and 150 highland bonnets duly arrived. The headgear once on heads was quickly passed through the Dress Committee (with the help of the DDMS Scotland) and so became legally correct headgear. Worn proudly ever since, it was only questioned once, when Major General Beale, then DMS UKLF and on a visit, most foolishly did so. The General's aberration was a slight one. Different was the refusal of R.S.M. Graham Allard in the 1980s who in spite of repeated remonstrances from the Commanding Officer Lieutenant Colonel Bushby, refused to wear the T.O.S. This was an act of insensitivity and stupidity which the unit members did not forget.

[9]As a result of this MOBEX, all units had their PUE (pre-stocked unit equipment) stored on their premises and no longer in stores far off. It was a major change of policy. Various other changes were also carried out in the placing of vehicles, the provision of medical and military supplies. The changes were applied to all arms — the result of an RAMC finding that it was just not possible to mobilize in the way previously set out in the potential time available after the start of a European War.

[10]For these conclusions I am grateful for the advice and recollections of Generals Sir Richard Bradshaw, Sir Alan Reay, and Sir Cameron Moffat. I am also very grateful to Major P. Brown for obtaining General Talbot's private diary, written while he was D.G., whose

existence I heard of from General Moffat. It was particularly important to read.

[11] The highest rank possible for many years for the surgeon in an FST in the sponsored units was Major. Mr Myles Gibson, who was actually the Consultant Neuro-surgeon to the Army, held this rank for many years until as a favour he was promoted Lieutenant Colonel! In the 1970s, some officers were as a gesture allowed to keep a previous rank of Lieutenant Colonel and later still of Colonel, but those who had not served elsewhere than in a sponsored unit (later called specialist unit) had to remain Majors. It was clearly unfair and resulted in a number of experienced and highly able specialists leaving, sometimes with bad grace.

This anomaly, and the often very poor level of CVHQ support, (cf. p. 464) was the subject of discussion at the TA Honorary Colonels' Conference on 11th November 1987 — see p 3 paras 18–21. Brigadier Platt, the forward-looking TA Adviser, was the first to grasp this problem, and with the Commander AMS (TA), Brigadier A.S.B. Dickson, spoke about "bringing FST personnel 'in from the cold' which is where they are now." But in the event, though the proposals were agreed by a 2-star steering group, no worth-while progress was made.

[12] Northern Ireland was peopled by Ulstermen, protestants who wished to remain citizens of the U.K. The south was peopled by Roman Catholics who wished nothing to do with Britain. Sadly, there was considerable bitterness on both sides. But whereas the Ulstermen had no wish to trouble the Eire population, the Dublin Government and the southerners made no secret of their intention of taking over "The North." Fear of the south increased the Ulstermen's antipathy. The I.R.A. was supported, though not for political reasons publicly, by Dublin, and by many Irish in the USA. It was all too easy for the Dublin Government to keep alight the wrongs of previous centuries, especially as those wrongs had sometimes foundation in fact. There was support as well from the Roman Catholic church, sometimes covert, sometimes open.

[13] SRNs were: Lieuts. A.Lyne, D.J.F. Lang, E.E. Gruber (who in the 1990s became Director of Studies, Q.A., and worked at Millbank), M.G. Geer, T.G. McCabe, D.R.P. Morgan, D.G. Neaves, D. Thirwall, W. Malcolm, G.A. Watson, T. Murnaghan, M. Ingall, M.D. Devlin, J. Thomson, P.J. Nicklin. From the 1970s onwards, many units, especially in Northern Ireland, had male SRN Officers as RMOAs, (Regimental Medical Officer Assistants) but they should not be confused with those who became badged "QA."

[14] See below, chapter 14, reference 28, relating to the House of Lords' debates in February 1997. Marshal of the Royal Air Force, Lord

Craig was reminded by his Army opposite numbers of this refusal to agree to the new BMH being built in central London.

[15]The Compton Committee was set up in 1973 under the chairmanship of Sir Edmund Compton. He was moved sideways by Mr Heath into an investigation into the Civil Service, and the Committee then came under Mr Jarrett, reporting first in 1977. It later still became the Yellowlees Committee when Mr Jarrett took ill.

The main decision these succeeding Committees had to make concerned the central structure of the AMS — and whether to have a single Surgeon General or not. As well as central structure, it was asked to look at Tri-Service doctoring, Dental and Nursing, and Medical support, provision of technicians of various kinds, and so on. In the earlier stages, the Committee fudged the issue by setting up a Directorship of Medical Policy and Plans, a Tri-Service Director directly responsible to the Deputy Chief of the Defence Staff. Major General Jack Lapper was the first Director, followed by Air Vice Marshall David Hull. Sir James Baird recalled: "(Jarrett) came up with the Surgeon General concept among other demotions, eagerly seized up by civil servants and the Treasury in particular." (personal communication, 1996)

Chapter 13

The Falklands and Gulf Wars. Cold and Hot;
Traditional and most Modern Weapons. Regular and
TA AMS work together as shortages become apparent

Mr Charles Darwin had thought nothing of the Falklands when
the *Beagle* anchored at Berkley Sound in East Falkland in 1834.
Noting in his journal how the Buenos Aires Government has
sold them to an individual buyer but used them as a penal
settlement, and how Great Britain had confirmed her previous
right to them, he went on "The theatre is... an undulating land,
with a desolate and wretched aspect, everywhere covered by
peaty soil and wiry grass of monotonous brown colour."

On 19th March, 1982, Argentine soldiers posing as scrap
metal dealers raised their flag on South Georgia. 2 weeks later, an
Argentinian army landed on the Falkland Islands.

There was a quick and decisive response by Mrs Thatcher.
Britain had to mount the most ambitious amphibious operation
since the Second War — the Suez exploit in 1956 was nothing
in comparison. This time the journey was 8,000 miles and they
were English Miles, too. No Europeans would be involved.

The Task Force comprised the carriers H.M.S. *Invincible*, the
Flagship, and H.M.S. *Hermes*; the assault ship H.M.S. *Fearless*
(which, with H.M.S. *Intrepid* and the Antarctic Survey Ship
H.M.S. *Endurance* was due to be disposed of by the Conservative's
Defence Review prepared by Mr John Nott) from Portsmouth.
On the S.S. *Canberra* were 40 and 42 Commando, Royal
Marines, plus 3rd Bn, the Parachute Regiment, with Royal
Artillery, Royal Signals, and a few RAF technicians. There were
2,500 troops. Later followed the *QE2*, the North Sea ferry
Norland with 2 Para on board, and amongst others, the Parachute

Clearing Troop, (PCT) an element of 16 Fd Amb. Later again, further teeth arms units and their medical units in support, made the 8,000 British Mile journey to the South Atlantic.

The first leg was to Ascension Island. Hardly had the *Canberra* made her first connection with the Royal Fleet Auxiliary tanker *Plumleaf*, when a Russian intelligence aircraft of the Primori Class flew down to inspect. Easter Sunday passed, and was a subdued occasion.

"Whatever anyone else in the Task Force might have been thinking", said Lieutenant Colonel Bill McGregor, commanding the PCT, "no-one believed that it would end in fighting. Right up to the last few days there persisted a holiday mood, a deep inner feeling that the politicians would see sense..."

On the way south, there were echoes of the War which started this century for the RAMC. The bands playing "Rule Britannia" at Southampton, the settling in, the teaching of first-aid to officers and soldiers, the constant weapon training, practice firing and hard physical training for all ranks (which amazed the journalists, called "hacks" by the often suspicious marines and soldiers), the military lectures. But there were differences — apart from the aircraft, there was the collection of blood for transfusion. There was the constant flood of news and comment of every sort, from serious to superficial, which the troops could listen to all day long.[1]

On the *Canberra*, the hacks found the naval surgeons somewhat "standoffish", but the RAMC very much easier to speak to. Apart from the different attitude of the Senior Service to others, the RAMC were well practised in dealing with the press from their Northern Ireland training, where all units had increasingly careful public relations instruction, even including mock T.V. interviews. The RN knew little or nothing of this new reality.

The Task Force was under command of Rear Admiral Woodward. *En route*, Colonel McGregor remembered, "relations with the ship's crew were excellent throughout the entire campaign...the marines and paras, after an initial period of mistrust, soon realised that, apart from the beret colours, there was little difference in attitude, fitness or state of training, and settled down amicably. The few Royal Naval personnel present were superb and at that stage the RAF were few and far between."

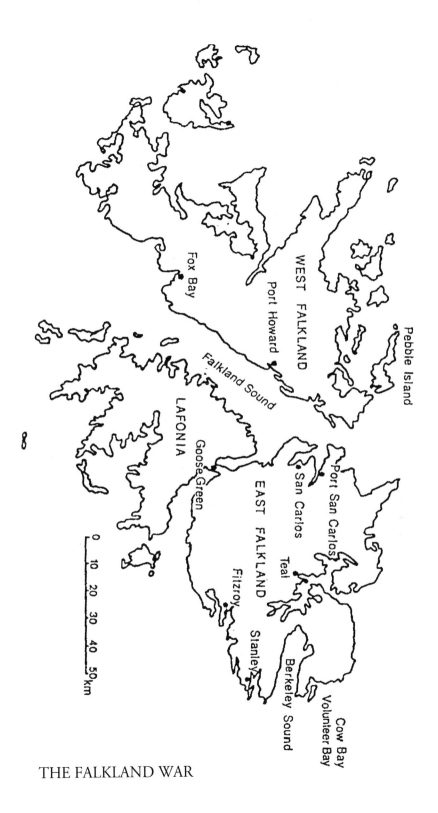

THE FALKLAND WAR

The first medical unit to land was the PCT. Its task in war was to clear battlefield casualties in airborne operations, and as these could not be evacuated immediately, it was provided with two integral FSTs — Nos 5 and 6. The whole unit comprised 36 officers and men. Each FST consisted of 1 surgeon, 1 anaesthetist, 1 resuscitation officer, 4 operating theatre technicians (OTTs), 1 transfusion technician and 1 clerk. There were 18 nursing orderlies under command of a male Captain SRN.

The RAMC teams had the great advantage that they knew one another and had worked together, both in Northern Ireland and also in Salalah in the Middle East. Anaesthetists Majors Dick Knight and Malcolm Jowitt McGregor knew well; the other surgeon, Major Charles Batty (who had been the writer's house surgeon and whose father we remember told the story of medical disease in the Middle East in 1941–43), he had not met. Other names to take us through the campaign were W.O.IIs, "Fritz" Sterba and "Phred" Newbound, very different, but both outstanding.

On the last days before the landing was to take place, Colonel McGregor had the experience his predecessors had suffered throughout the century. Because he had to decide when to bleed men to provide blood for the wounded, and wished 4 days for them to recover fully from their donor session, he went to the "O" (orders) group and asked the C.O. of 2 para, Lieutenant Colonel H. Jones, when the proposed assault date was. He was told this was secret and he could not be told! "It was beyond me how I was going to let this slip to the enemy", recalled Bill McGregor dryly. However his military training let him work out the day, and in the event he decided correctly.

W.O.2 Newbound takes up the story. "It was Fritz Sterba's FST (it was amusing, but true to form for W.O.'s thinking that he considered his opposite number to be the *real* man in charge) that was to set up in N.V. *Norland*. The other FST, mine, was to be helicopter landed into Ajax Bay…we were to go into a sheep slaughterhouse, though it was new and hadn't been used so far…on the morning of 21st May, we all stayed on board till called forward. As daylight came, all of 2 Para had disembarked and secured the high ground around Ajax Bay. Then the Argies started to bomb ships and continued all day. We had only GPMGs (general purpose machine guns) on tripods as anti-aircraft guns on board ship."

The plan was changed at midnight. Both FSTs had to disembark at the Bay by LSL. This meant the hurried unpacking and re-packing medicals are so used to. They got off, with all their equipment in its lacon boxes (which they had to squeeze through the narrow spaces of the ship) by 2345 hrs, just in time for the Captain of the *Norland* to cast off and leave the Bay.

"On the way to Ajax Bay, the coxswain told us we were sailing through a minefield. Then a message came that due to congestion at the quay, we had to sail around till a space could be found."

Once arrived, training took over; the unit was set up and began to function as do all trained FSTs. Phred Newbound considered that four points of special importance had to be made, and, as so often, these were logistic and personal rather than medical. As all of us who know the world of our Corps, logistic and personal items are those which cause difficulty and need recording for future reference.

First was the personal. Relations with the Royal Navy and Royal Marines were good — the Navy medicals and RAMC have always got on, and the inevitable differences between the two senior Services which produce difficulties are overcome with good sense. One incident only was unfortunate: "Some Naval officer poked his head into the refrigeration plant and said 'What's the Army doing in *my* hospital'. When Colonel McGregor had told him where to go, he had the good sense to go away and we never saw him again!" Phred Newbound otherwise had respect for the Naval Surgical Support Teams. "We knew at once that unlike us, they *hadn't worked together before* and had only been put together for the war…then they hadn't any *practical* experience as we had from Northern Ireland and Salalah… they were short of an anaesthetist and the other had no combat experience…Dick Knight and Jowitt showed him… Surgeon Commander Jolly was very sensible.[2] He realised that if the ASC was to work, he had to run it as the RAMC told him. So he split up the Marines with ourselves, and we got on splendidly from then on."

Second was the unusual site for the ASC — the refrigeration plant. Because of its "breeze blocks outside and inside and cork between", recalled Phred Newbound, "we had to warm it up the first day — then *it kept the heat in* and the warmth of the men inside kept it warm enough for operating."

Third was the electricity supply. "There were no windows. All light was artificial. We needed two generators on full time. When we got there first there was a great shortage of P.O.L. — all needed for the radar installation and it *drank fuel*. The rapier sights needed it too — they were a *great success*.[3] I had to go to the O.C. of the logistic cell at Ajax and say if you don't get us fuel in 2 hours, we will have to stop operating because the lights will go out. He came to see them, realised the problem, and had fuel diverted to them from then on."

Fourth was the initial lack of "dedicated" (i.e. specially assigned) helicopters. "But as soon as casualties came in", said both the Colonel and the WOs, "the dedicated hels appeared…we had 2 after Goose Green after the *Galahad* sank and after Fitzroy Cove, more than we could use…they were split up: some were with 2 FST (which was part of 22 Fd Hospital, the FST commanded by Major Jim Ryan, later Professor of Military Surgery at Millbank); he set up in a village hall…the Scots Guards then fighting on Tumbledown Hill."

The 2nd Bn Scots Guards had as their RMO Lieutenant Colonel A.J. Warsap, RAMC, later Brigadier and Director of General Practice for the Army. Being a Guards Regiment, their NCOs were guardsmen: C/Sgt Baird, a Sgt and 4 JNCOs, guardsmen, pipes and drums — all medically trained to MA (Medical Assistant) 2 level. Like the PCT, they stocked up with as many drugs and extra items not found in the standard lacon boxes and panniers they thought they would need. One mistake, the RMO considered, was to take with them an MFO box containing the entire Battalion's medical records; it should have been held centrally.

RMO Warsap's careful conclusions merit their place in this story. "Every unit in the British Army must consider itself a spearhead unit and be fully up-to-date with 'jabs' and routine medical examinations; the first-aid trg, especially the buddy system[4] was *very* effective. It prepared men to face injury in their comrades calmly; throughout this campaign we were lucky to have at the RAP and looking after the welfare and spiritual needs of the men Padre Angus Smith. Successful units pray together joyfully and unselfconsciously. We had the good factor of a unit of common ethnic background, volunteers, discipline and self-discipline. All ranks in close contact in which there is both a family atmosphere and respect for individuals."

The view of Captain John Lawson comes to mind when one reads these remarks.

His medical remarks too are important for the record. No paludrine was taken, and they failed to anticipate there would be a refuelling stop at Freetown (another echo of the Boer War). So Malaria prophylaxis was needed at very short notice, and had to be continued for 28 days after it started.

Clothing was a particular problem, because of the extra foul weather. The unique situation of the Falklands Campaign was that everything had to be manpacked; the loss of the Chinook helicopters when the ship carrying them all, the *Atlantic Conveyor*, was sunk in Ajax Ba, made this necessary. Tactical packing, so assiduously practised at the Field Training Centre a decade previously, had not been followed, and all but one large troop-carrying helicopter were lost. Constant revision of what was needed to be covered or worn was necessary — some soldiers did not cope and suffered both exhaustion and exposure, despite films and instruction *en route*. The drying out, the difficulties with the very new boot, of high ankle pattern, and with a hard heel piece which blistered the achilles tendon region, the trench foot, the water discipline, the urinary and gastro-intestinal infections, all were problems to cause worry and hardship. On the other side, the lack of battle shock was noteworthy.[5]

Following victory, all forms of illness, except trench foot and accidental injury, dropped dramatically. "The feeling of well-being and glow I likened to that after a parachute drop", said Lieutenant Colonel Warsap, "but more long-lasting." Captain John Burgess, RMO of 2 Para, had similar feelings. He praised the cooks, mess staff, RAPC personnel, who trained as extra SBs and "later did sterling work on the slopes of Mount Longdon...I never had any anger at the Argentinians, though they killed some of my friends."

2nd Scots Guards lost 9 killed and 43 wounded between 2nd June and 14th June; they were supported by a section of 16 Fd Amb under command of Major Ken Millar. 16 Fd Amb had an unhappy time, losing comrades when the Sir Galahad went on fire, and all their personal and unit kit. Major Roger Nutbeem, 2IC, was killed on the ship; his wife was awarded the MBE afterwards for her care of unit wives during and after the war.

W.O.II Newbound and his mates found themselves still busy. They had been moved forwards as the campaign progressed, with their kit — they found the RN Support Team equipment was far too heavy to be airportable and so had to be left behind. So the Naval personnel were split amongst them. The end of the fighting meant that they wanted a medical representation in Port Stanley, and after asking permission to take over the King Edward Memorial Hospital from the woman doctor and local plumber who were running it (the Argentines having transported all the British staff and local officials to the mainland, on the principle that this would remove the natural leaders who could incite resistance). Later came the HQ staff by sea from Ascension Island, and they took over its running. The military aspect of the hospital, now designated 2 Fd Hosp, was staffed by personnel drawn from U.K. and BAOR units on a 4 month posting and it is noteworthy that the second Commanding Officer after the conflict was Lieutenant Colonel Geoffrey Banks, the first non-medical officer ever to have commanded a BMH.

(Of historical interest is that also in 1982 Colonel Kathleen Clarke, a consultant anaesthetist, became the first woman C.O. of a BMH — commanding 201 GH (TA)).

The total casualties were 264 killed, 783 wounded, including 80 burned and 100 cold injury; most of them were treated on well established lines.[6] Some failures there were: the surgical element from 2 Fd Hospital, and the non-para part of 16 Fd Amb, were on land and set up, but re-embarked on the R.F.A. *Sir Galahad* and sailed round to Fitzroy Cove. Instead of landing troops, the *Sir Galahad* and a sister ship lay at anchor for several hours in daylight; the Argentine air attack was devastating. "I never heard the result of the Enquiry into the Fitzroy disaster", recalled Colonel Bill McGregor, "but through talking to many of those concerned it would seem that the RAMC were not completely blameless."

There were some problems too over the standard of documentation. The medical leadership, largely naval, and without practical experience like the RAMC, was criticised as "inept and aimless, and keeping us badly informed, with the exception of Rick Jolly, who was one of us." But Colonel McGregor, who received the OBE for his work, and who made this criticism, could sum up finally with the words "Even the Big

Army were pleased with us." And around the world, a surprising amount of credit went to Britain for its victory.[7]

The Gulf War.

The Falklands war lasted a total of 74 days and the land campaign 25 days from the landing at San Carlos to the capture of Stanley. By the standards of the large Wars, it was a skirmish or a 19th century action. The Gulf was also a short war, but very different. Its active fighting lasted some 100 hours, but the preparation for it lasted several months.

The Gulf war brought Britain back to her centuries old position of a minor partner, in numerical terms, supporting a multi-nation coalition against an aggressive foreign power. The coalition here would be set up against Iraq, whose dictator president's forcible annexation of Kuwait threatened both Middle East security and the supply of Western oil. While the actual land battle, code-named DESERT STORM, was very short and produced very few British casualties, the development of measures to counter the potentially devastating chemical and biological weapons such as Iraq might employ, lasted 20 years. Iraq had indeed used such weapons against her neighbour Iran, and British physicians in BAOR had seen the effects they produced. Further, this was an out-of-area conflict and involved medical problems very different from those of a European land battle.

The Defence Nuclear Biological and Chemical School at Winterbourne Gunner, Salisbury, Wiltshire and the Chemical Defence Establishment at Porton Down nearby, provided training and research against these new weapons. The provision of defence measures against nuclear attack, essential since the start of the Cold War, had given place to increasing active research against chemical and biological weapons. Provision had to be made for individual protection — the NBC or "Noddy" suit, and a variety of drugs given either by ingestion or injection to prevent or relieve the symptoms produced by the various nerve gases.[8] But provision had to be made also for protection of groups — good enough to allow surgical treatment of wounded to be given in a safe environment. This came to be called collective protection (COLPRO). Next, provision had to be made for the decontamination of soldiers affected by gases of the 1915–18 pattern or by newer volatile agents before they could be taken into collective protection from the contaminated area.

Great thought was given to the problem of casualty handling in a chemical environment under tactical conditions. In July 1975, Field Trial Report No 54 was issued by H. de V. Martin and Lieutenant Colonel A.S.B. (Derry) Dickson, RAMC. This followed a preliminary trial in 1972 to assess the ability of a field ambulance to function in a toxic environment.

The 1975 trial was set to enable the handling of casualties in a chemical warfare (CW) environment to be studied in as realistic a way as possible. Smoke canisters to simulate gas encouraged troops to "mask up" as fast as possible, blank rounds were fired, a Hunter aircraft flew over to spray a harmless agent whose decontamination could be monitored, detector paper was used to teach soldiers to look for colour change, and all involved had to take placebo tablets to simulate those they would take in actual warfare. Collection of casualties, transfer to RAP, decontamination with an absorptive called slurry, and the evacuation in a "casualty bag" impermeable to chemical agent, were all studied scientifically.

This Exercise, code-named HOT BOX, had observers attached. The writer was one, representing the TA field surgical teams. It was one example of the series of exercises which continued over the years, designed to make the care of British troops in such a CW environment as safe as possible.[9]

At the time of the Iraq war, the Chemical Defence Establishment at Porton Down staff worked hard to assess the threat, the characteristics of the Iraqi ballistic missiles which could deliver chemical or biological agents, the hazard distances which could arise from Allied conventional attacks on enemy facilities, those which could arise from interception of the Iraqi SCUD chemical carrying missiles by the U.S. Patriot missile, persistence of agent in the local climatic conditions, and many more.

All this background makes clear the "new" element in the war; the rapid development in technology of weaponry of many kinds. This war would be very different from the Falklands where basic weapons were employed. And as ever, the Royal Army Medical Corps had to be responsible for the health of the troops, for advising commanders on health matters, and for the collection, evacuation, and treatment of casualties. This time there were even more unknowns than usual.

This then was the important background to the provision of equipment suitable to protect against chemical weapons. As well as in England, it was tested in Germany in a number of exercises including PLAIN SAILING in the late summer of 1989.[10] Such equipment would be vital in the Gulf war if CW were to be used. Compared with 1916 and 1939, there was now the threat of biological war — a new dimension.

Another important background was the change in organization of the Medical Directorate at the highest level. Following the Jarrett Report, the later Yellowlees report proposed a major reduction. Instead of single Service Directors General, there was to be a single Surgeon-General, of 3-star rank (Lieutenant General or equivalent), with a Tri-Service directorate under his command. Lower rank single Service Directors were to remain. Other administrative branches were to become Tri-Service, but happily there was no intention of a combined Medical Service. This so-called "Purple" option had been introduced in Canada years before, but had not been strikingly successful. HM Government, thankfully, respected the deep loyalties of each Service to its own uniform. There seems little doubt that the changes were not to produce increased efficiency but to save money.

The first Surgeon General was Lieutenant General Sir Cameron Moffat. By votes cast, he was regarded as the best DGAMS since General Drummond. A big man in every way, he had been a surgeon before moving to administration and command. Major General A.C. Ticehurst summed up the feelings of many which cannot be denied: "We had one or two D.G.s who seemed to have 'to learn on the job' when the vacancy arose. But Cameron had schooled himself to learn widely, both about our own Corps matters, but also how the other Services' medicals functioned." And Captain John Wilson, a short-service physician and later an outstanding NHS consultant, said: "As a group we seemed to perceive ourselves in the person of our D.G. — we could have done with more men of vision. So he was the obvious choice for the first Surgeon-General, and was very good."

His successor and previous deputy, Vice-Admiral Sir Godfrey Milton-Thompson, had been a physician with an interest in gastro-enterology, and had spent virtually the whole of his service on shore. For this reason he was believed by several to be well versed in land matters.[11] He was the Surgeon General in post at the start of the build-up to the Gulf war, and his rôle will be examined in due course.

In this history, the accounts given have been those of RAMC officers and soldiers and units at intermediate and lower levels, apart from that of the visionary and realist Sir Alfred Keogh. The account of the Gulf war, code-named OPERATION GRANBY,[12] the British contribution to operation DESERT SHIELD and later DESERT STORM, will be that of the AMS officers who supervised and advised at the highest level, notably Major General J.T. Coull.

Not all Directors of major specialties, or senior administrators, were by any means of high ability as both clinicians *and* as planners. Directors of Army Surgery (DA.s Surgery) had several of high calibre — Generals Stephen, Kirby and Pryn were three such. The Corps had professors who spoke excellently, did good research, and taught well — R. Scott, and particularly I. Haywood, J. Ryan, and P. Roberts, were but four. Their teaching of battlefield trauma life support gained international reputation, and was highly respected by the US Military Surgical Service, who applied it to their own training courses.

General Jack Coull ranks in the opinion of the writer as the greatest full career Army surgeon and D.A. Surgery of the second half of the 20th century… He was *facile princeps*. The Corps was fortunate to have him in post before and during OP GRANBY.

Senior Medical Officers in any campaign, especially if they have a degree of vision, see things very differently from those at field or hospital level. From his thoughts after the Falklands Campaign while Consulting Surgeon BAOR, Coull recognised that the medical thinking was too stereotyped towards a European land battle alone. By 1987 he had proposed a revision of the BAOR medical plan using revised casualty rates, more realistic evacuation and treatment times, revised parameters for post-operative retention with greater dependence upon more modern forward resuscitation measures.[13] In his feeling that he had promoted farther forward life-saving surgery than envisaged previously he was wrong; Bowlby had anticipated him by 70 years.

With a forward-thinking training aid the major computer simulation, a programme for evacuation from a European land battle was developed. It was designed to evaluate existing plans and to train units and commanders. This was being modified and extended to cover other possible areas of battle, including OUT-OF-AREA deployments, and was nearing completion in 1990.[14]

And so, when on 2nd August 1990 Iraqi forces under the command of the Presidential dictator Saddam Hussein attacked Kuwait, there was already in place a plan which could be applied to the British involvement certain to take place.

The command problem of the build-up, called Transition-to-War (TTW), was the changing order of battle (ORBAT). The medical commander saw it increase from the initial AMS support of 2 RAF squadrons in an OUT-OF-AREA commitment where new chemical and biological weapons could be used, through steadily increasing provision as DESERT SHIELD (the U.S. code name) became DESERT STORM, and full support had to be found for a British light division.[15]

It is worth recalling at this point the precedent set in this campaign of close involvement of medical staff officers from the Surgeon General's headquarters from early on in the deliberations of the Defence Operations Executive (DOE) in the Ministry of Defence. Brigadier (later Major General) Ticehurst, who was Director of Medical Operations and Plans since February 1990, recalled: "This Committee, chaired usually by the Deputy Chief of Defence Staff (Commitments) or sometimes by the Chief of the Defence Staff himself, was concerned with the very highest military political decision making, and comprised very senior officers from all three Services, together with scientific, legal, and intelligence advisers as well as representatives of the Cabinet Office. The Surgeon General was permanently represented on it by the Director of Medical Operations and Plans. This arrangement, compared to previous campaigns where the medical advice was passed on to the senior officer who included medical as part of his wider brief, was of course a recognition of the very perplexing medical military political issues which were foreseen. As events unfolded, this presence proved to be an invaluable conduit on the one hand for providing medical input for decision making and on the other for providing intelligence which enabled medical staff to engage in forward planning." He believed that this level of medical input was entirely new, but General John Matheson remembered its happening before the Battle of El Alamein, and that it continued later within the 1939–45 War.

"Among the decisions taken by the DOE involving medical advice were: the complex issues of prophylactic programmes, the interpretation of available intelligence on the chemical and biological threat, numbers of beds needed in theatre and at home, evacuation policy, co-operation with the Department of Health, medical health intelligence especially when it required co-ordination with the Americans, medical care of prisoners and refugees. In addition the initial decisions on the use of the TA Medical Services were taken by this Executive Committee...it was fortuitous that both the Directors of Medical Operations and Plans involved in the Transition to War were AMS brigadiers who had undergone formal staff training."

General Coull had several key elements to keep in his mind as the months passed. The first was that the increase in size of the British force to be employed demanded medical units proportionately larger and more complex, with essential and up-to-date equipment to go with them.

(The overall direction of this medical contribution from the U.K base was taken over by a senior RAF officer Air Vice Marshal Johnston, based in an underground bunker at High Wycombe. It was a somewhat odd arrangement in view of his lack of knowledge of land warfare).

The next was how to provide this equipment and what to provide with the constant uncertainty of whether the Iraqi High Command would use chemical or biological weapons. These were not an entirely unknown quantity as some had been used by the Iraqis against Iranian soldiers in their recent local war over several years. Brigadier Chris Garrett, Consulting Physician BAOR, had shown most explicit photographs of affected Iranians to medical and nursing staff on PLAIN SAILING and on many other occasions. But their effect when used in anger against the personal and collective protection of British troops — their respirators, clothing, boots, antidotes, decontamination — this was not known. There could well have been difficulty in

convincing any Force Commander just how much medical support the medicals believed had to be provided.

This had to be achieved with the constant uncertainty of how the press would behave, bearing in mind the intense media coverage in modern war and realising well the high expectations of these individuals who had no responsibly for actually *doing* anything, but only a great aptitude for enjoying asking questions and looking for things to go wrong. As General Coull said on one occasion, "Any surgeon going to the Gulf will not only have to be able to stand on his own — he will have to be able to operate with Kate Adie[16] looking over his shoulder." He knew the appetite of the press and did not want to have the RAMC on the menu.

The planners had to work in the knowledge that the Head of Government, Mr John Major, was a further unknown quantity. His predecessor Mrs Thatcher had been forthright and supportive to the Forces when they had to pull the Falklands chestnuts out the fire; would it be the same this time? On the political side, too, was the fact that Britain was a small player within a large multinational United States led alliance, and that the home support for it might not be as uniform as eight years before. Even in the USA, the Senate had only voted by a small majority to send US troops to the Middle East. And how would the Arab host nations respond?

In the event, the build-up was progressive. The certainty of AMS involvement, once the decision to deploy British air assets was made, was due to the long-standing arrangement that the RAF was dependent on the AMS for field and hospital support (so-called 2nd and 3rd line) in OUT-OF-AREA operations. On 14th August the first request was for three medical units to move — a medical support troop (MST) made up of an FST with supporting elements from a field ambulance section, a chemical decontamination centre (CDC), to provide 25 beds; and the 50 bed element of 22 Fd Hospital with elements of 84 Field Medical Equipment Depot (FMED). Very soon a second MST was added, and, from 16 Fd Amb, a further CDC and ambulance support for 22 Fd Hospital.

Enhancement, the term applied to increase in deployment of ground and air forces, proceeded steadily.[17] There was a coalition of many nations: Kuwait itself and the Gulf Emirates; Saudi Arabia; and the USA, Britain, France, and Canada. In addition came in train a mixture of European nations, from Norway, a loyal NATO member from the north-west, to Romania, a former Iron Curtain Country from the East. Early came the opening of a base surgical hospital in old RAF hospital quarters at Muharraq in Bahrein by 22 as a full unit commanded by Lieutenant Colonel Chris Town. It deployed with 200 beds, half of them plus part of the operating complex within COLPRO. Next came 33 Fd Hospital (in effect the Cambridge Military Hospital, CMH) as a general hospital at Al Jubayl on the east coast of Saudi Arabia. Its COLPRO was larger than that of 22; it was put in a huge Firestone tyre factory, the supporting pillars of which made the placement of the COLPRO liners difficult. 33 was commanded by Colonel I.S. Creamer MC, and his senior surgeon Colonel Mike Payne put in an immense amount of effort in the planning of this COLPRO deployment as well as being responsible to the Medical Commander as the Force Surgical Adviser. "Colonel Payne was my link man", General Coull recalled.

The factory owner was said to have charged £1M for its use and a local sheikh allegedly demanded payment for the use of his sand to fill sandbags. This sort of demand, in the tradition of the greed of the Crimean war, was made by home firms also; with all too evident determination by businessmen to force as much money out of the Ministry of Defence as possible, knowing the Army had no choice but to pay.

Most of the U.K. based Regular hospital staff were now overseas, and in Aldershot, civilian patients had to be treated elsewhere as the CMH was virtually closed. The state of affairs was uncomfortably like that of the Boer War a hundred years before, and would have unjust political repercussions later. The Defence Medical Equipment Depot, Ludgershall, was fully involved, as was the Army Blood Supply Depot. In the Middle East, units were now training and practising their war rôles.

By December it was decided by Government that "a Force enhancement to light division size be made." D.A. Surgery, General Coull, was sent to the Middle East to inspect and appraise existing sites and advise on the size of the medical enhancement to support it.

While in Saudi Arabia, he met, amongst others, the Commander of 7 Armd Bde, Brigadier Pat Cordingly ("with his staff officers and all our four bodyguards in a small hotel bedroom", Jack Coull recalled, "we discussed items of the highest importance"). He met the US surgical controller, Colonel Tsoulos. Most important of all, he met the Force Commander, Lieutenant General Sir Peter de la Billière and with the Commander Medical, British Forces Gulf, Colonel J. Tinsley, gave his opinion on the number of beds required and surgical teams, based on the new Force size and on casualty estimates. "It was a fairly tense meeting. But our proposals were approved by the Commander — 1750 beds and 71 surgeons. Had the previous scales been adopted (those before General Coull's re-write) the number of surgeons would have been only 28. This proportion of medical in a force was to be the highest ever taken to give medical cover — 12.5 per cent. The surgical numbers were as estimated for BAOR. But it was not possible to predict chemical or biological. Also, considering the degree of dispersion of troops, it was clear casualties could be slow to treat.... I estimated it would take 10 hours to bring a casualty back."....[18]

On 1st October the new Surgeon General took over from Sir Godfrey. He was Air Marshal Sir Nigel Mills, after the war shown to be gravely ill. It seemed "it was the RAF's turn"; not the best of systems. Coull found him "a real gentleman — but somewhat lacking the decisiveness of his predecessor in decision making. He would, however, listen to his advisers — somewhat more than Sir Godfrey."

Following his visit to the Middle East, the D.A. Surgery moved back to the Operations Branch from Millbank "to where the previous S.G.(Milton-Thompson) had banished him and the other Army Directors." He had been appointed Adviser in Defence Surgery to the new Surgeon General. He occupied therefore a similar position to that of his fellow Aberdeen graduate in the Peninsula. He had something else, however; he had Tri-Service authority. "It made all subsequent personnel management much simpler."

Time went by. Because the Service hospitals were so reduced in staff — the Duchess of Kent's at Catterick was now closed, as was indeed RAF Hospital Ely. CMH had only 50 beds for low care (except for maternity which the local Regional Health Authority insisted must remain); QEMH had lost much of its expertise as its plastic surgery unit had moved to the Gulf. In contrast, the RN Hospital at Haslar was hardly affected. As soon as it was decided that 1 Armoured Division was to move from Germany, BMH Hanover was closed to become 32 Fd Hospital, its war rôle number. It was commanded by Colonel Peter Lynch. Shortfall was made up by doctors, nurses, and other personnel from other Army units, Royal Navy and RAF, and by TA volunteer reservists and some Regular reservists. *Total* surgical capacity for all other British servicemen was reduced by more than half and a total of 21 wards in Service hospitals closed. "But 32 became a truly Tri-Service hospital", recalled General Coull; "I could post in from all Services. Also, an amazing number of different units made up the total — it must have been 50."

Following the Force Commander's agreement for beds and personnel for the Gulf (equipment will be considered later), it was manifest that many more medicals were essential. The options were two: one, to close *all* Service Hospitals, and the second, to use the Territorial Army in substantial numbers. It did not take ministers long to decide that further reductions in Service provision for returning casualties could not be accepted.[19]

Unfortunately there was no statutory provision to embody the TA unless in the event of major war, when call-out is on the Queen's signature. This is the contract TA officers and men sign; had a major war in Europe broken out, their commitment was clear and unequivocal. The use of NHS facilities for reception of casualties in such a War was equally clear and unequivocal.

But this was not a major threat to the Realm. It was not general war.

At this point the politicians seemed somewhat at a loss. First they called for volunteers only — although the decision to use the TA was made in October, it was not till 25th November that 3000 ex-RAMC personnel were sent letters by post and TA units sent a "signal" asking for volunteers. Both groups responded, but the numbers were small. At this time, *no job or salary protection was offered.* Some Conservative Government sources, unfairly, publicly suggested that the TA were behaving badly. This provoked a degree of bad feeling on the part of some Regulars, which persisted, and on the part of the Reservists whose employers were unhelpful.

There remained no doubt of the need for another hospital, and it was to be a Territorial one. There was no shortage of units keen to volunteer; in the event it was 205(Scottish) GH who were told on 16th December, after a telephone call on the 14th from the Chief of Staff, Headquarters Scotland that if they could find at least 250 volunteers from within the unit they would be given the task. *This time volunteers would be assured job protection.* A briefing at their HQ in Glasgow and their centre in Edinburgh (and telephone calls to their outstations at Inverness and Dunoon) by their capable and articulate C.O., Colonel Glynne Jones, was held on the 16th when personnel were formally asked to volunteer but were given 24 hours to consider. By 1800 hrs on the 17th, 83 officers and 159 other ranks had done so. The unit had its formal selection confirmed on the 18th and on the 19th had its formal orders to mobilize. One of the annual training exercises for all TA was its MOBEX; on 27–28th December 205 did so "for real." Nevertheless, it was not the whole unit which mobilized, but those who did formed the focus and infrastructure for the other Territorials and individual reservists who followed.

Mobilization commenced at 0900 hrs on the 27th and all volunteers were processed by 1530hrs. 245 all ranks were "embodied", the official term for TA mobilization. After insisting upon being given a break for Hogmanay, the unit moved to Saighton Camp at Chester on January 2nd where they were joined by its Regular, TA, and individual reinforcements. They were complete by 5th January, and all began intensive training.[20]

Saighton Camp was the brain-child of a remarkable officer, Brigadier Bryn Francis. He had held every rank from boy soldier upwards and was the first soldier to achieve brigadier's rank in the AMS. The camp was ideal for RAMC training, especially hospital training, having huts of the right size and arrangement to simulate a field hospital. TA Reserve units had trained over some 4 years when the Gulf war began, and in that time the camp had been improved and its facilities extended under Brigadier Francis' combination of tenacity, professional and business skill, and military knowledge. Saighton Camp became the training camp for the whole AMS during the Gulf; all units, Regular and Reserve, had the use of it. It must have its place in this narrative. After the Gulf war was over, a commemorative statue in a sand pit was unveiled by Major General A.C. Ticehurst, DMS at HQ U.K. Land Forces, the second last two-star officer of distinction to hold that post. Sadly, Brigadier Francis died suddenly at the age of 61 in 1994.

On 17th December the Secretary of State, Mr Tom King, invoked section 10 of the Reserve Forces Act and individuals were again contacted, advised of enhanced pay and of job security arrangements, and warned of compulsory mobilization if insufficient numbers came forward. Those who would now volunteer went to a Temporary Mobilization Centre at Aldershot on 27th December. A total of 499 individual reservists and Territorials reported but because there was still a shortfall of 233, 410 individual reservists were issued *compulsory* mobilization notices. 312 reported, and the target was reached. In all 1011 TA and individual reserve personnel, almost all TA volunteers, came forward to make up the numbers required for the medical cover in the Middle East.

All this was a worry. But there was the added worry of the numbers of specialists within the ORBAT. For the first time, strict specifications were laid down for the *minimum* clinical grade of surgeon and anaesthetist. One of the two general hospitals was to specialise in head and neck surgery and the other in burns. Here, as General Coull recalled, "neurological expertise in particular depends heavily on Reservists as the Regular cadre has none or few in its ranks." He had little time for certain civilian plastic surgeons and was not afraid to say so: "Much unwarranted criticism was levelled by the civilian plastic surgery hierarchy regarding our burns expertise, but not one volunteered to forgo his lucrative private practice and preferred to sound off to the media and Ministers from the safety of the sidelines."

Furthermore, fewer civilian surgeons now had any experience in the care of conventional war wounds. It was essential to keep the NHS aware of the needs of returning casualties, especially with the perceived prospect of chemical and biological warfare. A "touring circus" of lectures was given to hospitals throughout England, Scotland, and Wales by the Professor of Military Surgery (Colonel Jim Ryan), the D.A. Surg, and particularly, by a TA consultant from Belfast, Rodney Peyton, whose considerable Northern Ireland experience and lecturing flair was greatly appreciated. They spoke to several thousand staff in the run-up phase over a period of some six weeks. Audiences were receptive and unaware of what to expect in the way of military casualties, with many misconceptions, especially regarding chemical contamination.

The final problem of personnel was called by Colonel C. Town in his detailed report on the Gulf war "the straw that nearly broke the camel's back".[21] The extra load was that of injured and wounded prisoners of war. "After lengthy discussion", General Coull remembered, "Government finally heeded our expressed concern about them and appreciated that the medical deployment was geared to the allied casualty estimates and did not include this additional load. We proposed another TA General Hospital — 202 Birmingham or 257 North London — to carry this out, but we were forestalled and Ministers insisted that the Foreign office would recruit assistance from other nations "ONMA" or Other Nations' Medical Assistance. The problems were predictable: TA disenchantment (their morale went down like a stone — this is what they had trained for), poor or no understanding of English or any common language, non-standard and incompatible equipment, unfamiliarity with our equipment and drugs, *no experience of chemical protection*, no knowledge of our carefully worked out Casualty Treatment

Régimes, and, in the case of especially the Romanians, alcoholism." Canadians were the exception ("they were kindred spirits who fitted easily into the medical chain but the rapid end to hostilities precluded their full participation" said Colonel Town). The Norwegians, too, were good and likeable.

The decision to use outside assistance was political, not military or medical. As always, the Government insisted it knew best, and seemed content to have this collection of nations looking after the British wounded and sick. "There were TA personnel who could have been used had they been allowed to deploy as formed units", recalled Colonel Town.

But this was only a part of the Medical Commander's worries. The other major worry was provision of equipment and the way the medical task was to be carried out in the war the Generals who commanded generally wanted to wage. Here too he was aware that expectations were such that only the best available would do. Not only had new equipment to be used, but all had to be trained in its most efficient use. The fact that unhelpful civil servants insisted on every bid being argued for, often in multiple bureaucratic letters, did not make things easier. The supply Directorate, headed by Colonel Frank Davis, toiled to deal with new bids, contracts, and re-supply.

The range was large — self-retaining surgical retractors, improved lighting by battery operated headlamps, pulsed lavage and suction equipment, cell-saver technology to re-transfuse collected blood, oxygen concentrators, "noisy, bulky and heavy but very efficient"; power supply generators which "were always adequate, taking into account the vastly increased electrical demands by the new equipment and the multiple Air Filtration Units to inflate the Porton Liner complexes"; special penicillin autoject syringes for use through NBC suits, modified operating tables (the McVicar table being the prototype), and many more. Coull's external fixation apparatus for fractures, its worth already known, continued to be used.

Training, much done at Saighton Camp, involved total intravenous anaesthesia, an alternative for the operations done in the restricted atmosphere of the Porton Liners for the Collective Protection, new style bowel anastomosis by skin staples, cricothyrotomy instead of tracheostomy, chest drainage. British Army Trauma Life Support (BATLS) courses, developed so enthusiastically by Colonel Ian Haywood, and continued by Colonel Jim Ryan, were given to teach all ranks the necessary skills so that they could "act up" if needed.

New protocols had to be written for the care of the chemical casualty and the handling of contaminated waste and dressings in the event of such occurring. These were a combined effort by the D.A. Surgery, the staff at the NBC School, and Porton. Milton was proven to be the most efficient and safe agent for wounds where contamination was possible.

All this work involved negotiation with suppliers, anxious meetings, difficulties with production and price. But "procurement" as the term for the obtaining of supplies was called, "was actually very good and quick." Thus individual surgeon's demands for special items or favours had to be resisted; the Commander issued strict instructions that local purchases in Arabia were not to be made.

The actual delivery of care had to be worked out. The concept of independent surgical teams was done away with for this campaign, and all FSTs were allocated to hospitals. A new scale of operating tables was introduced. Resuscitation became even more important.

The departments were staged into three areas — "crash, maintenance, and pre-op." Casualty triage was on usual lines but resuscitative measures were now more sophisticated and nursing sisters trained in intensive care to the highest standard were available. Because anaesthetic care was so vital, anaesthetic assistants were trained to maintain anaesthesia under supervision and free the doctor anaesthetist to resuscitate the most seriously ill patients. Dentists were used as such assistants, but they "were not universally satisfactory."

There were disappointments. The Commanders Medical British Forces Middle East made some mistakes. The Commanding Officer of 205, Colonel Glynne Jones, was not wholly experienced in military staff detail — a not uncommon failing of TA officers who had never served full-time with the Army. A/Colonel L.P. Lillywhite, who was Commander Med 1 Armd Div, and became Commander at Force Maintenance Area, (and who had once been Colonel Glynne Jones' house physician) "took decisions if it suited him, even if it went against home policy — this caused bad feeling." There was sympathy towards Brigadier Hardie, who was posted in relatively late: "he had a difficult time." Of the local Regular medical commanders it was Colonel Town whom the Territorials respected and liked. The D.A. Surgery was disappointed most of all when a casualty arrived in England with a wound primarily sutured.

The war was soon over. The casualties were so light as to be negligible by major war standards.[21] At ground level, far below the Commander's, the usual happenings occurred.

32 Fd Hosp were carried in by a Kuwaiti jumbo jet. Via Blackadder and Baldrick camps they made their way to the desert. Rain and early morning frost surprised everyone, for was not this the Arabian desert? They found their desert kit "inappropriate"; soon learned to use burn pits for solid excrement (RN and RAF they found had no idea about Army Health), and to use "desert roses" as urinals. They found that decontamination teams could work for only one hour at 100°F (37°C). There were constant false alarms — "nerve agent on site"! — three or four times daily. Canaries were used to detect gas as in past wars. 80 operations were done, including those by the ever-popular and kindly Canadians, but only 150 patients passed through in total. There were many mine injuries; some vascular repairs, delayed primary sutures, and 35 external fracture fixations. This was the story of the now Tri-Service hospital.

205, now by Major General Shaw's decree re-named 205 GH(V), had their recce done for them by others, and so did not have their own so-often tried arrangement of departments. 50 beds were put up by the advance party on January 14th plus the resusication area. The main party arrived 2 days later, and by the 30th, they had 600 beds open and 10 theatre tables. First casualties arrived on February 2nd. "Although we had been mixed in small platoons at Saighton", said the C.O., "where the IRs, all ex-Regulars, began to realise we knew what we were doing, it was they who caused some trouble; *none* of the ex-regulars knew how a field hospital worked in the field." If this is thought to be TA boasting, we should recall that Pte Craik said exactly the same thing in September 1939.

But the C.O. had his difficulties; he felt he should have been firmer on occasion, and perhaps did not delegate enough. The constant need to bid through the correct military channels was a worry.

So was the rear party, whose problems were passed on; here too, the IRs had not been used to being away from home for sometimes many years, with the inevitable results. And he remembered some left behind. One we have met before was Lieutenant Colonel David Bushby, who told us about his "hearts and minds" work in Borneo. He stood in the Glasgow HQ waiting to hear if his G.P. locum would materialise; she did not. Now the Colonel remembered the look on his face when he realised he could not go with the others.

At regimental level, the experience of 40 Regiment RA, the Artillery regiment of 7Armd Bde, showed how history repeats itself and also brings out realities of the mobilization, of setting up in the Middle East, and the contribution of the RMO.

B.S.M. (W.O.II) D. Mowat, of HQ Battery, recalled being taken off his fitness test in Hohne on the 12th of September and hurried to a conference; the C.O. had heard they were to be warned for a move to the Middle East. "Almost overnight the regiment doubled in size", he said. "We had to make up our numbers from other units which were not going...we were chosen because the bde had done the BATUS course recently...we were rushed into training the next day... chaos...."

At once, each battery got an RAMC Sergeant borrowed from local field ambulances put on its strength for the duration of the war. Various "experts came to talk but tried to do too much." At once, "jabs" and "docs" (documentation) had to be brought up to date; it was soon found that there were shortages of the required inoculation material.

In Iraq, they noticed the appearance of new kit and were impressed that some was brand new — special NBC field dressings had been made only two weeks before at Ethicon's factory in Edinburgh.

The NBC suits they found good: "It was the Americans who would have killed for one of our suits."

Their RMO was Lieutenant Colonel Ghosh. "He put great effort into the training, including that of the CMTs (fully trained combatant medical technicians) in the batteries...in time he built up a big RAP... it ended up more like a surgical centre. He was given a gunner W.O.II to run the RAP and the Assistant Chief Clerk to assist with documentation."

In the desert, their location, with the RAP and ammunition in the centre, was as that of Captain J.D.P. Graham 50 years earlier. This time the RMO insisted a red light be kept on at nights at the door of his RAP "until an armoured vehicle ran into it!" He fell out with the Technical Q.M., who felt he was too much a doctor and too little a regimental officer. "But he was right for his job", W.O.II Mowat was sure.

As in Colonel John Matheson's day, one soldier whose request to return home to Germany was refused (most of the wives who gave trouble by demanding return of husbands were Germans) became mentally upset and fired several shots at his battery commander; the police and RMO dealt with him.

Of note was the fact that the excellence of medical cover was made well known to everyone over the early stages of the campaign. The gunners knew where the medical units were, and what was in place if they were wounded or sick. Perhaps the most striking recollection of B.S.M. Mowat and his regiment were the words used by their C.O. on his final briefing on Saturday, 23rd February: "We will likely have casualties. But the best doctors in Britain have come out here and will take care of you." As always over the century, the soldiers *wanted* the medicals on hand and in adequate numbers. This fact, for fact it is, ought to be remembered by senior commanders after battles are over.

The second striking recollection of the B.S.M.'s was the course of relaxation he was ordered to take part in when he went to 32 Fd Hospital to have a filling replaced in a tooth. He and others who were in the hospital were put into army beds and given "therapy", because, he was told, there were too many imaginary ailments being produced, and relaxation was believed to be the way to combat this. He wasn't very impressed!

Major General Coull's own summary is quoted:

"Overall, an interesting episode and although the threat of B and C warfare, the medical problems associated with a subtropical desert climate and the eventual awareness by the planners of the importance of disease and of non-battle casualties enhanced the place of the general physician more than ever before, it still remained the province of the surgical disciplines. Future surgical training with its narrow confines preventing the acquisition of a broad based experience combined with increasing medico-legal pressures and the ever-present eye of the media renders the concept of the 'generalist' military surgeon anachronistic."

"While it was possible in the Gulf with the numbers of Regulars and the enormous contribution by the TA to provide at each hospital a correct spread of clinical expertise and still make available senior surgeons with multi-disciplinary knowledge as officers commanding divisions, future surgical deployments will need more staff as the individual's field narrows. This limitation will apply more particularly in the Reserves than in what is left of the Regular Service contribution."

"The Gulf war involved only some 15 per cent of the teeth arms but 50 per cent of the medical support arm. Considering how stretched were the medical resources to provide for a single light Division it will be appreciated how great would have been the task in Germany had Russia ever invaded where we would have deployed four full Divisions."

"It was a pity that the impression was given in some quarters that the TA did not do well. When we saw the large numbers mobilizing at Aldershot, it was the TA who were far the most enthusiastic…their training for war was their strength; they did it all the time."[22]

The General agreed with Frederick Forsyth's summary in his novel "The Fist of God": "The fact that germ warfare, poison gas, or the nuclear possibility were never employed was, like the outcome of the Battle of Waterloo, 'a damn close-run thing'." He was also clear that "for certain tasks in certain places there is still no substitute for the oldest information-gathering device on earth: the Human Eyeball, Mark One."

But the summing-up of B.S.M. Mowat is equally deserving of record: "All that stuff we heard on the media was nonsense…we did not believe Mr Major when he was reported as saying we would stay there for 2 years. *We knew the Army had been stripped bare to produce one division.*" It would not be long before Conservative politicians and some senior officers ignored that conclusion.

Notes and references

CHAPTER 13

[1]While some pressmen's accounts of the Falklands Campaign gave the impression that they expected prime treatment at all times, the press overall behaved responsibly. There were the inevitable occasions when security problems arose, but these were contained. The sinking of the *Belgrano* by H.M.S. *Conqueror*, given the largest headlines by some of the tabloid papers, resulted in political anger by two Members of Parliament, Mr Tam Dayell and the Marxist Mr Anthony Wedgewood (Tony) Benn, (whose public school accents they could not hide) both of whom were fiercely against the war from the beginning. Mr Benn's "tearaway leftism" angered even his own party (cf Sunday Standard, June 13th 1982, as the last battle on the Falkland was being fought). One reporter on the BBC Radio 4 programme, where every nuance of the pre-war and war events was ground into the news by the commentators secure in their safety from responsibility for decision, told how "I tried to shake him (a Royal Marine marching over the wet of the island) by keeping asking him what he was doing here, but I could not get him to say anything ... he kept saying he was doing his duty for his Queen and Country." Baffled, the hack gave up. The patriotism of the man with a military responsibility and the aims of the hack seemed very different !

[2]Surgeon Commander Richard Tadeusz Jolly, OBE, was a graduate of St Bartholomew's Hospital of 1969, and was generally believed to hold a surgical fellowship, which he did not. He held the Diploma in Aviation Medicine. He had formerly been Surgeon Lieut-Commander RNR but was presently on full-time duty. Commander Jolly styled himself "Officer Commanding Ajax Bay Field Hospital, S. Atlantic" in *The Medical Directory*, and wrote a successful book on the Campaign, "The Red and Green Life Machine." He was applauded by his RAMC colleagues because he took the trouble to learn the Army methods of casualty evacuation, and for his good sense in conceding that the battle was a land one once he got on shore.

[3]The Rapier air defence missile system was electrically controlled. For the running of the system, a generator powered by petrol was

required; at this date the system did not function during the hours of darkness. Because of the efficiency of the Argentine Air Force, there was no doubt that the Rapiers were top priority for fuel.

[4]The "buddy system" was for two men to work together and watch each other for signs of fatigue or any other upset. If one became a casualty, the other cared for him. The system suited two friends, and demanded discipline and comradeship. If need be, each kept up his buddy's morale.

The system did not apply only to soldiers or marines. Officers, too, consciously made themselves "buddies" for colleagues. The writer did many consultant reliefs world-wide and had responsibility for one major equipment trial, and my "oppo" (as another term had it) was Colonel John Heber L/RAMC. As an anaesthetist, he was totally unflappable, whether in Germany, Hong Kong, or Nepal, and we formed a friendship which endured for the rest of our lives.

[5]Psychiatric casualties were light in this Campaign. This was considered strange by a US Medical Corps psychiatrist, Captain H.H. Price, in his article in the Corps Journal 1984, **130**, 109–113, because "there were not psychiatric personnel in the units and psychiatric screening of all evacuees." What psychiatric casualties there were were evacuated to the hospital ship *Uganda*, and to the *Canberra*. The 2 per cent rate Captain Price attributed to the high quality of the troops taking part. His article is of interest, coming from an objective assessment by a US officer.

[6]Lieutenant Colonel McGregor's comments:

"Were there any lessons to be learned ? One was certainly the benefit of Marine and Para physical training (he was himself a parachutist) in producing soldiers who functioned superbly in atrocious climatic and operational conditions. Another was the advantage of Surgical Teams who had worked and trained together over hastily assembled teams from static hospital environments. The episode confirmed that forward surgery is feasible in highly adverse conditions provided the equipment was light, portable, tested and familiar."

The results: Total casualties — killed — 294, wounded — 783 (80 burns). Cold injury — 100.

For F.S.T.s 5 and 6: Total cases — 144.

Head and Neck — 28 — (7 brain — 3 tracheotomies).

Upper Limb — 42. Lower Limb — 70 (18 amputations).

Chest — 16 — (8 intercostal drains).

Abdomen — 18 — (11 laparotomy).

Comments: "Only twice did I face the decision to delay operating on serious cases until others had been dealt with. Both were penetrating wounds of head and both survived. Apart from these I found the decisions on Priority could be left to the Resuscitation Officers. Indeed the best of these at arranging a list was a Naval Dental Surgeon.

In dealing with GSWs of head the minimum of skin excision was required, together with scraping of bone. Irrigation along missile tracks with saline usually clears débris, including bullets, from the brain tissue." (At this point, it is of interest to re-read the surgical accounts of the Boer War).

"Cases of penetrating wounds of the chest should survive with no more than soft tissue excision and intercostal drainage, if they have survived as far as initial surgery.

It is my impression that cases with abdominal wounds will travel safely for short distances by air, provided they have not been subject to laparotomy. It is only once the belly has been opened that they become unstable. After operation, they travel well by helicopter and presumably by pressurised aircraft. There is no doubt that helicopter is the ideal transport medium for wounded, and that dedicated units must be provided for the Medical Services of the future."

[7]There was remarkable praise from many in the USA. Mr James Michener told the writer: "Your country has won a real victory. We had a failure…" On the other hand, there was sarcastic criticism from some French: (Difficulties in Britain) "qui n'a pas empêché les troupes de Sa Graceuse Majesté de se lancer à la reconquête des iles Falklands" (L'Express); Dr Joyce Galbraith was saddened at the jibes at "imperialism" in Australian papers. Even 11 years later, Brian O'Keefe, an Irish journalist, ran a series of anti-British articles in Argentine magazines "Malvinas una Fortaleza" etc.

For a full account of 2 Fd Hosp in the Falklands see AMS Magazine, Vol XXXVII, 1983, p 2–35.

I am also grateful for background information given at the Symposium organized by the United Services Section of the Royal Society of Medicine which I attended on 17–18th February, 1983.

[8]Noddy and Big-ears were two happy gnomes in a series of children's books in the 1960s. They were very popular. The "noddy suit" was so called because its shape was similar to Noddy's. Big-ears was censored in the 1990s — or perhaps proscribed is a suitable term, because it was thought politically wrong to refer slightingly to someone's ear size. But it is doubtful if Big-ears would have been in the least upset !

The respirator was developed and was comfortable to wear and easy to put on. The suit was hot to wear, and gave of course problems with micturition and defaecation, as well as with drinking or eating. In the heat of the Middle East, drinking was a serious need if the soldier was not to become dehydrated.

[9]In discussion with Colonel Dickson, overboots, gloves for medical personnel, contaminated wounds, a dart gun for administering atropine, a drug antidote to nerve agent, were included. He replied to the writer's queries on boots: "Because of the one-size-left-to-right concept of design, the complex lacing system is necessary to ensure a snug fit for all sizes of boots.

As for slipperiness, the overboots in mob stores all have rubber studs in the soles which offer a very reasonable grip on all types of surfaces." And on gloves: "It would be ideal to have light-weight gloves enabling medical assistants to work with dexterity on chemically contaminated casualties. Porton are currently investigating NBC gloves because, of course, it is not just the RAMC that require a specialist design. Surgical gloves have not been tested, but I believe liquid agent will penetrate them within 30 minutes."

Contaminated wounds were regarded as being fatal, but "Bob Scott, however, could probably bring you up to date with current research in this field." Colonel Scott, later Major General Scott, was working at Porton at the time. And of a dart gun: "An intriguing idea which I'm sure nobody has ever thought of ! but it could bring difficulties..." These discussions were taking place in August 1975, and of course are only one series of very many.

[10]For the simulated field hospital for this exercise, the Porton liners — blow-up tents and corridors of material impervious to nerve agent, kept blown up by pressure and with internal and external flaps as safety doors and air locks with areas large enough to serve as an operating theatre and recovery areas — were set up in a large warehouse. The medical personnel came from 22 Fd Hospital (the surgical staff of QEMH Woolwich, and the back-up ward medical and nursing staff from 308 GH TA (sponsored)).

[11]General Moffat had as his deputy Surgeon Rear-Admiral Milton-Thompson: "I was amazed", he recalled, "just how little idea he had of BAOR and a major war in Europe. And he had not the slightest idea about the TA. So I sent him to Germany to find out, and sent him to the TA units at annual camp" (personal communication). (The same applied to the next S.G. from the Royal Navy, Admiral Revell, who told the writer in 1994, on his appointment: "I have to confess I know nothing whatever about the TA."

The fact that the next S.G, was a naval officer was because the appointment had become "Buggins' turn" — it went through each Service in turn. This, one of the surest ways of ensuring mediocrity, was not, on General Moffat's recollection when the concept of the Surgeon General was put to him by the Minister, the original proposition. The original proposition was that the post would go strictly on merit, and be weighted towards the Army as it had by far the largest medical requirement and the most complex needs. "It was presented to me at first", he remembered, "but then got lost."

The RAF Medical Branch, whose insistence that it had an equal share in spite of having significantly less of a war rôle, would demand that the next S.G. after the naval one *must* be an airman. For a telling analysis of how the principle stifled ability and fresh thinking, see "On the Psychology of Military Incompetence" by Dr Norman F. Dixon, op cit, chapter 14, "The Intellectual Ability of Senior Military Commanders."

This devastating dissection, by a former sapper officer of distinguished service, of the bullying tactics employed to suppress any hint of criticism, no matter how constructive and how necessary, makes essential reading.

As examples of this, Lieutenant-Colonel D. Dineley, a member of the Mytchett HQ, explained to officers of the Haywood Club, a club for junior RAMC officers, when the writer was lecturing to them on 29th May 1999: "We do not censor. But we do not tell the whole story." This euphemism indicated the same attitude. And Colonel Donald Stewart, former C.O. of 308 County of London Evacuation Hospital (V), recalled how he had written a history of the hospital including comment on the level of CVHQ staff. He submitted it to the Mytchett HQ for comment: "They returned it to me with every single word of criticism removed" (personal communication, 6th April 1999). Another example was given by Mr Henry Keown–Boyd's experience of being asked to write a regimental history, and finding, a day or two before printing, that "a retired senior officer of that regiment had been summoned to the MoD and ordered to remove certain passages... it was clear to me at the time," wrote the writer to the *Daily Telegraph* of 17th March 2000, that "'political correctness' was the MoD's only concern."

[12]Code names on the British system were chosen on a random method from an MOD list; this accounts why they often had no apparent relevance to the campaign. The US system was surely more apt.

[13]General Coull believed his predecessor, Norman Kirby's, figures not entirely realistic: "they were too optimistic for the time envisaged for their evacuation." He held to the standard BAOR figure of 5 per cent per day of the field Force as requiring admission — but this figure was for *conventional* injury. In the event, "the low casualties (in the Gulf) will be extrapolated for a future war and will be said to indicate 'no need for medical resources'."

[14]"Guide to Medical Support for Out of Area Operations" and "The Joint Medical Support Plan for the UK base in War" were the contingency planning pamphlets just completed by AMD from General Coull's revision before the Gulf war began.

[15]From the initial 3 units the Medical ORBAT became:

a. RFA (Royal Fleet Auxiliary) *Argus*, described by General Coull as "quite superb", where a 100 bed hospital with operating facilities had been constructed in a pressurised environment in part of the air-frame holds.

b. 28 Gurkha Ambulance Group.

c. 205 GH (V). 6 Surgical teams, 2 surgical support teams, 600 beds.

d. 22, 32, Fd Hosps, each 8 STs, (surgical teams) 200 beds.

e. 33 Fd Hosp, as 205.

f. 1, 5, Armd Fd Ambs, 24 (Airmobile Fd Amb).

g. 84 FMED (forward medical equipment depot).

h. 60,61, Field Psychiatric Teams.

i. No 1 Fd Laboratory.

j. MSTs A and B.

k. RAF War Hosp, Muharraq, 2 STs, 100 beds.

l. 1 Air Evac Sqn RAF.

m. 4626 Air Evac Sqn R Aux AF.

n. Other Nations Medical Assistance, Canadian, Norwegian, Swedish, Danish, Romanian, Singapore ST, Dutch, and New Zealand.

[16]Miss Kate Adie was a war correspondent who became noteworthy for the sharpness of her reports and also for her great courage in going to dangerous areas. She was awarded the OBE for her work.

The war evoked frenzied activity by press. James Naughtie, on the BBC Radio 4 programme on 15th January 1991 reported that 67 per cent of press wished to keep journalists in Baghdad, even though the war was in progress; they are "desperate for a scoop", he said. In Saudi Arabia, a good feature of General Schwarzkopf was his patience in answering daily questions ranging from naïveté to insolence, from an army of newsmen. General de la Billière commented in his book on the campaign of the pressure put on the Commander "both to disclose his own plan...or to consider others being dreamt up by amateur strategists in the Pentagon. As if he did not have enough ideas of his own to develop, wild possibilities kept being thrown at him" (Storm Command, p 103). It was said that if the Iraqi Foreign Minister blew his nose, commentators immediately anguished over its possible significance !

[17]General Sir Peter de la Billière's Account, "Storm Command, a personal account of the Gulf War", London, Harper Collins, 1992, is of interest and worth reading. Also, in a different way, is "The Fist of God", by Frederick Forsyth, Corgi Press, 1994.

"For the first time helicopters, though not dedicated to the casevac rôle as the US had come to accept, were primarily tasked to this end (Chinook and Puma), each with an RAMC para-medic, a combatant medical technician, aboard replacing a normal crew member. Nevertheless, even with this technology, the average time from wounding to hospital was 10 hours—so much for the 6-hour rule" (General Coull, personal communication). The "6-hour rule" is the time generally held to be the longest safe time between wounding and surgical treatment.

[18]For general war, the evacuation plan to the U.K. base had always been dependent on the use of NHS facilities. The plan was modified to meet the special circumstances of OP GRANBY and provided for 3 phases to meet rising casualty numbers:

a. Phase 1 was limited to the use of Service hospitals, three designated as "Acute Care Hospitals"—RN Hospital Haslar, QEMH Woolwich and RAF Hospital Wroughton, and three for non acute— RN Hospital Plymouth, CMH Aldershot and RAF Hospital Halton. RAF Brize Norton was the primary receiving airfield but other RAF or civilian airfields could be used.

Reception and transport arrangements were to come from Service sources.

b. Phase 2 extended the catchment area to nearby NHS hospitals and provided reception teams and transport from NHS resources.

c. Phase 3, which would only be used when casualty numbers exceeded estimates, provided for beds within all NHS regions.

[19]It was believed that the command of a mixed unit of Regulars and Territorials by a Territorial had not happened since the 1939–45 War—this was said to Colonel Glynne Jones by the senior officer who met him on his return to England. But the TA was in fact dissolved at the start of that War, and so there was no distinction between the groups (cf above, chapters 5,8).

The choice lay between 205, 202, and 257. Jones believed 205 was chosen because they had won the Hospitals Cup the previous year and had an extra good report on their camp exercise FOLDING BED at Krefeld in 1989. 205 was also well recruited in all branches, nursing and other ranks as well as medical officers.

Perhaps the reasons given by Colonel Jones, who was most percipient, for the choice are important enough to be applicable to the phase where Reserves, in the post-Cold War period, are likely to remain essential. They must be remembered for future reference:

Behind the mobilizing TA was the current TA Adviser, Brigadier Johnman. He had recently given up command of 205, and worked extremely hard in encouraging volunteer Reservists to prepare for enlistment and anticipating requirements.

In Scotland, 205 drew its members from a range of hospital areas, and so when mobilized, did not seriously denude any one NHS region. Here it contrasted with Birmingham, where the specialists all came virtually from two hospital groups; their removal would have resulted in serious local shortfall. Also, 205 were from an area of Britain where *initial* casualties would not be sent from overseas at an early stage in the war.

The real value of the TA system, in having a ready-made cadre whose training was war-based, was evident at the time of the Gulf war. For when it became likely that the TA was going to be required, even before the D.G., Major General A.J.Shaw, told Mr Tom King that he did not have the command or the infrastructure to put 600 beds on the ground and the Secretary of State was forced to call it out, those thinking TA(AMS) units at once switched their week-night training and weekends to meet the possibility, i.e. to N.B.C. and survival in hot environment. They had the time, the equipment and the facilities to do this.

As far as "getting off" was concrned, Dr Jones recalled he had "no difficulty with the Ayrshire Board — the CAMO (chief administrative medical officer) said at once: 'we'll soon get a locum for you'"; this indicated a supportive atttiude perhaps not to be found in some other parts of the UK. And at the day of mobilization, when 270 members turned up and 246 were taken, those not were excluded on account of being recruits, including some officers. "Only 10 had important interviews or such and very very few did not go for family reasons... in fact, financial problems were much more serious" remembered Glynne Jones. At the MOBEX for real the pay desk, usually a nominal desk on training exercises, became highly important. Colonel David Bunney, L/RAPC, (Royal Army Pay Corps) sent especially from MOD, tried to solve some problems without success such as the Corporal who worked in civil life on an oil rig in the North Sea and who made £35,000 a year. The difference was not made up !

By contrast, the mobilization at Aldershot, for individual reservists (ex-regulars) and for individuals from non-205 Territorial units — was irregular and full of problems. Regulars from Germany had identity discs but had no documents. Many who had been out of the Army for some years were unfit and certainly untrained in new procedures; had not even put on a respirator. Many had insufficient kit; the TA had full or nearly full kit.

"The fact that by the law all the individual reservists had to be called out before the TA in this sort of situation", Colonel Jones believed, "meant that there was in fact a delay — it would have been satisfactory to call out the TA before."

As Colonel Town in his formal report recalled (below, 20), 205 was not in fact mobilized *as such*. Colonel Glynne Jones was told he "was not allowed to shut down 205, so it had to be left running to let training carry on." It was, as decided at high level, to form the nucleus about which many others, Regulars and Reservists, were to gel.

Finally, the importance of the Rear Party became apparent at once, for reasons from genuine money problems to those where the TA soldier had made the mobilization an excuse to flit and leave his family in difficulties of a different moral sort.

[20]"The Army Medical Services On Operation Granby" was written by Colonel C. Town (previously Lieutenant Colonel Town, commanding 22 Fd Hospital) and the writer thanks Colonel Banks for allowing him access to it. The report is a definitive one, and much of this account has been taken from it. The report was however never published, as a minute from the Ministry, written by Mrs D.S. Cox, stated: "The tone of the article is very critical and refers to several sensitive issues." The letter, six pages long, contained re-written paragraphs which played down failures the original report recorded, especially as regards the shortages which all too plainly came to light — the reduction in Regular Service hospitals, the need for so many

parts of the system to be raided to make up deficiencies in manpower or equipment. References to the political difficulties in calling out the Reserves were similarly toned down. The advice given to Winston Smith comes to mind.

On the other hand, some comments by Colonel Town were incorrect, including those regarding procurement; General Coull agreed with the amendments made in this particular respect, having the benefit of his higher position in the administrative and command structure, from where he could see things differently.

These comments are included not to criticise the civil servant involved, but to emphasise the difficulty the historian has in attempting to reach a fair conclusion, even concerning events and interpretations of those events in the most recent past.

[21]Casualty numbers in 32 Fd Hospital were 107, of whom 44 were Allied and 63 prisoners of war. Of the latter, one died. In total from 20th January till 20th March, 1991, 1252 patients were treated; 381 evacuated, and 871 returned to units. 105 operations were done, and 360 dental procedures. The other medical units admitted only 84 battle casualties, evacuated 32 elsewhere in the theatre and 50 to U.K. Disease and non-battle cases amounted to 3,739; 1 died in a medical unit. The short surgical report from 32 Fd Hospital, "Penetrating Missile Injuries in the Gulf War, 1991", describing 63 patients, was by Surgeon Lieutenant Commander T.J.W. Spalding, Major M.P.M. Stewart, Surgeon Commander D.N. Tulloch and Colonel K.M. Stephens L/RAMC, *Br. J Surg* 1991; **78** : 1102–1104.

[22]General Sir Michael Wilkes wrote in October 1997: "given the over-stretch which has been a consistent bugbear throughout the medical services over the past 7 or 8 years, the TA medical element has provided a vital and immediately reassuring back up to what was in essence a thin red line operation. This was most in evidence during the Gulf War when the TA response to the call to arms was quite remarkable. In hindsight I am sure we over ensured in providing so much medical support for an operation that predictions suggested would cause huge numbers of casualties. In the event, and happily, the war was to produce very few casualties and many of our medical resources were completely under utilised. I know that this caused problems in the Gulf for those TA officers who had rallied to the colours and then found their civilian practices at home had suffered. However, the spirit of the reserve soldier in active service conditions has always been remarkable and I believe that these difficulties were eventually amicably settled. Whether it will colour the attitude of those called out to future adventures remains to be seen.

The expertise and flexibility of mind which is so obvious during a TA deployment has to be seen to be believed. To the eye of the Regular a TA deployment can appear a complete shambles but invariably the nett result is highly professional. I believe that increasingly the TA medical services must under-pin their Regular counterparts if we are to meet the sort of requirements which the post cold war is placing upon us across the spectrum of operations." (personal communication, 9th October 1997).

I am grateful to General J.T. Coull, Colonel G. Banks, and Major General A.C. Ticehurst, for considerable help and guidance in writing this chapter.

Chapter 14

In Arduis Fidelis. The battle for the RAMC.

Perspective.
"In all wars the final victory must be won on land. However
irresistible the armed forces of a country may show themselves by
sea or in the air, the naval and aerial arms can never strike the
decisive blow. They can guard and protect on the one hand,
devastate, cow, and paralyse on the other, but they cannot break
through the last line of defence. That task must be left to the
tanks and their supporting infantry.... The British Army, by
traditional usage, always seems to be compelled to start a war
from small beginnings...this is due partly to the fact that though
we have usually been prepared to maintain a Navy second to
none, and came recently to a similar conclusion upon the subject
of an Air Force, we have systematically starved our Army
throughout its history, both in numbers, equipment, and adequate
means of training."
(Ian Hay, The Battle of Flanders 1940, HMSO 1940).

"In all great systems and agencies of any kind, there are
certain accessories, absolutely necessary for their efficiency,
yet hardly included in their essential idea.... And such in
military matters are the commissariat, transport, and
medical departments, which are jealously suppressed in
time of peace, and hastily and grudgingly restored on the
commencement of hostilities." (Cardinal Newman,
"Who's to Blame", 1856, pp 358–359).

In 1888, the British Medical Association analysed the opinions
of 1200 medicals in the Army and the Royal Navy. During a
recent war in the Middle East there had been a large provision of

medical support, much larger than hitherto. Casualty numbers had been slight, and those occurring were well treated. The Government had thereupon decided to reduce the Army Medical Service numbers by 50 per cent. The British Medical Association noted the consequent discontent among medical officers, and wrote to the Secretary of State to ask what action he proposed to take. His reply was: "These opinions must have been obtained and expressed in a manner altogether in contradiction of military discipline. Medical officers, like other officers, have a proper channel through which they can be heard, and I am not prepared to accept any Civilian Association as their mouthpiece."

Nevertheless, BMA in 1897 wrote very fairly but very critically about the state of affairs within the Forces Medical branches, now worse than ever. "It is no wonder that the British Army Medical Service is on its way to extinction. It is imposssible for anyone acquainted with this state of things to regard with equanimity the prospect of a war. If such a calamity were to overtake us, it is difficult to see how we could avoid the utter collapse of the medical arrangements. A spectacle of misery and mortality to equal which we must look back to the horrors of the Crimea would not be a matter of astonishment."

This warning was laughed to scorn by senior officers at Horse Guards. But the BMA went to the major medical schools of the day, and to senior medical figures, (Lord Lister had been one of those who had made earlier comment — he was one of the "ignorant civilians" the War Office had dismissed) and took a further initiative. A deputation, which included senior BMA office bearers and senior academics, met Lord Lansdowne, the Secretary of State for War, on January 22nd, 1898. At this key meeting, Lord Lansdowne ignored the antagonism of senior generals and heeded the advice of the Association. In doing so, he agreed to take the first step which led to the government's requesting Queen Victoria to sanction the formation of the Royal Army Medical Corps[1] in June that year. Unfortunately for everyone the Boer War broke out the next year, but the BMA had suceeded in its support for its fellow doctors serving in the army, and the BMA had undoubtedly the major hand in bringing about the birth of the new Corps.

One hundred years later, in September 1995, the British Medical Association tried to arrange a day conference to hear of developments during major changes in the RAMC and other Service Medical Branches. This was because of the large number of anxious medical officers who had contacted them, as in 1888, because of their fears for their and their Services' future. The reply from Surgeon Commodore M.P.W.H. Paine, QHS,[2] Assistant Chief of Staff, Medical and Dental, in the C-in-C Fleet's office at Northwood, mirrored that of a century earlier: it showed the same tone and attitude.

Secretary of the Armed Forces Committee,
British Medical Association 3 July 1995.

Dear Sir
BMA Conference for Armed Forces Doctors — 19 September 1995.
Reference etc
1. I am unwilling to address or attend your proposed conference; the implication that medical officers in the Armed Forces have not been kept informed is refuted: their concerns are best expressed through the established channels.

yours sincerely, M. Paine

The background in the 1990s.
That the Gulf war took place the way it did was due not to the local events and the setting up of the coalition, but to the fact that the Cold War had ended the previous year. The political details do not concern this history, but the military fact of immediacy was that large conventional military forces were thought to be no longer required. The fact that the disappearance of a monolithic enemy would result in local instability was actively played down by politicians wrestling with economic recession throughout the world. Their anxiety to reduce military spending was entirely understandable.

The prospect became evident at once. The removal of the Eastern Bloc had resulted in a reappraisal of the defence need, and with this a reduction of the size of the Armed Forces. The political background was clearly stated: "a fundamental reassessment of the structure of the Armed Forces."[3] The Regular Army and the TA were to reduce, as was the Royal Navy, by one-third. The Royal Air Force was to reduce to a greater degree. The Services were to become a "capability based organisation" and the ORBAT chosen for the Army was option WHISKEY.[4]

A series of Corps of distinction — including the medicals' friends, the Royal Corps of Transport, successors of the RASC — were merged into two "large Corps" — the Adjutant General's Corps and the Royal Logistic Corps. Would our Corps survive? No particular optimism was felt. Ministers of Defence in the recent past — Mr Michael Heseltine and Mr Tom King — had not earned high respect from those serving, including the country-spread Territorials, and their political wing, the Territorial and Auxiliary Voluntary Reserve Associations. The Minister now at Defence, in 1992, was Mr Malcolm Rifkind, an Edinburgh advocate. He was the first with this particular Edinburgh legal background to occupy the post since the man remembered throughout the century for his military foresight — Lord Haldane. The two were very different.[5]

From 1992 till 1994, a series of Treasury driven papers, some 30 in all, were produced by civil servants, covering all sections of the Armed Forces; that concerned with the reductions of the Medical branches was DCS(Defence Cost Study)15.[6] The civil servant who chaired the study and working party was Mr Norman Hale, a former Under-Secretary of State at the Ministry of Health. He was earlier responsible for the papers on "care in the community" which so exercised the anxieties of doctors, nurses, social workers, WRVS and others, as they tried to make the new system function in practice. The Defence working party was known to contain no doctors.

But prior to the final formulation of the study, the chance was given to the individual D.G.s — and of course the Surgeon General — to plead the medicals' case. The officer to whose lot this fell was Lieutenant General Sir Peter Beale.

General Beale was Commander Medical United Kingdom Land Forces (UKLF) till December 1990. He was therefore involved in U.K. planning for the Gulf war. He became DGAMS in January 1991 and Surgeon General in October 1991. Initially, he was concerned with the earlier proposals for reductions, but was also deeply involved in the later Defence Cost Study. He would have to act now as General Drummond had done before him thirty years previously, when serious difficulties arose at the end of the National Service era, and negotiate with the highest level of Defence Chiefs. As S.G, however, he would have to argue for all three Medical Services — a wider task. The relationship of the General Staff at highest level to the army medicals, as so often before in the century, could have far-reaching results. This varying relationship, so often dependent upon personalities, was one of the major five factors which determined the effectiveness of the RAMC as a professional body, set to deliver medical and health care to the army, and noted in the prologue to this history.

On 26th February, 1993, the Ministry announced the outcome of its own major review into future needs for hospital care (now called "secondary care" as in the NHS changed terminology) in the Forces. This review declared that "the primary purpose in peacetime of Service hospitals in the UK was to train medical military personnel to perform their rôles in war".[7] The review clearly stated that 1500 beds were necessary *to provide the level of training essential for the numbers of medical personnel needed by the Armed Forces in wartime.* In written evidence to the Defence Committee of the House of Commons in March 1993, the MoD stated there would be a reduction "of up to 20 per cent overall" in the 1992 manpower levels of 9,100, suggesting a future Defence Medical Service (DMS) of around 7,300. The review proposed the closure of QEMH Woolwich (and RAF Halton near Aylesbury), leaving 1,200 of the 1,500 beds to be provided by 3 "core" hospitals, RAF Wroughton, the Cambridge (CMH) at Aldershot, and the Royal Naval Hospital on the Gosport peninsula. This was regarded as "the safe level of reductions."

And then in late 1993, Mr Rifkind set the whole arrangement on its head by announcing that a further review was to take place. The decision of Lord Haldane's successor was the basis for DCS15. He wished £500M savings in 10 years, using the evocative slogan "Front Line First"(FLF).

What came out of DCS15, published by the Secretary of State for Defence on 14th July 1994, was the reduction of Service hospitals to one only. It appeared that an option had been to close all of them. The hospital left, the so-called "core hospital", was RN Hospital Haslar beside Portsmouth. Amongst other reasons for its choice, it was said to have the "case mix" required for clinical training in peacetime which the two others did not.

RAF Wroughton, whose accessibility to airheads made it the choice many thinking RAMC supported (such as Lieutenant General Beale and Major General A.C. Ticehurst, immediate-past Commander Medical United Kingdom Land Forces), was dismissed as it had no casualty department, and was "too far from a teaching hospital." There were not enough troops near to the Queen Elizabeth Military Hospital in Woolwich for it to be chosen. Further, the local Woolwich NHS authorities were looking to buy and use it for civilian patients.[8] CMH was too expensive to renovate. The Cambridge Hospital in Aldershot, much more so than Woolwich, had been emptied of staff during the Gulf war, and in doing so had lost its NHS patient load built up over a period of years. Those NHS patients were now treated nearby at Frimley Park, and were bringing Frimley added income. (By contrast, the Royal Naval Hospital at Haslar had hardly been affected during the Gulf.) In Yorkshire, The Duchess of Kent's Hospital at Catterick would be retained but "under review."

To produce the extra clinical load requirement for hospital training, a new concept, the MDHU (Military District Hospital Unit, later re-named Ministry of Defence Hospital Unit so as not to offend susceptibilities of some RN and RAF in a sadly 'politically correct' time) was to be set up on the pattern of one such in Derriford Hospital in Plymouth. The RN Medical Service — *very* much smaller than the Army's — had had an arrangement in Derriford for some years. Serving hospital doctors were already on the establishment of that District Hospital, as a small number within the total large NHS staff complement. If they were sent to war from an MDHU, the parent NHS hospital was prepared to let them go. The NHS hospital, in the new business-first orientation of the Thatcher ideal, had the advantage of obtaining a source of staff whose wages its Trust did not have to pay.

Two other such new units were chosen, without academic advice; one at Frimley Park by Aldershot and the other in Peterborough, presumably for Army and RAF respectively, though all were to be staffed on a "Tri-Service" basis. The principle of placing military doctors and military nurses within a district hospital, and as a minor element there, was untried elsewhere than in Derriford. The imposition of such an untested form of medical organisation mirrored that being imposed by the Conservative Government, again without consultation, in the wider world of the NHS. Also following Conservative political thinking, a number of civilian-run "Agencies" were to be introduced in due course to take over hospital care, the dental service, and provision of medical equipment and blood supply from the military. Serving medical and dental officers would be employed by those "Agencies" and not by their various Directors General.

In addition, the health services for British Forces in Germany were to be subjected to a market testing process by which the primary, community, and acute health services for British servicemen and women, their families and attached civilian staff, a risk population of 70,000, were put out to competitive tender. The 1993 current "provider", the Army Medical Services, was to be one "tenderer" for the new contract. A purchaser/provider split, as in the new Thatcher NHS, was to be instituted. This was to proceed from 1993 onwards; it did in fact continue until 1995.[9]

To many outside observers, including Members of Parliament, it seemed strange that it had now been discovered, only a few months after the first review whose conclusions were so firmly expressed, that the requirement for Service hospital beds had suddenly fallen to only 7–800.

The chairman of the Cost Studies committee was Lieutenant General The Hon. Sir Thomas Boyd-Carpenter, who was then Deputy Chief of Defence Staff, (Programmes and Plans). He was responsible for implementation of many of the personnel-related defence cost studies and so was the person the various Directors had to face, as the plan which affected their particular Arm or Service was presented, along with his other committee members. It should be emphasised again that the medical plan was only one of some 30 Cost Studies. The DCS proposals went next to the PPOs (Principal Personnel Officers, in the case of the Army the Adjutant-General, Sir Michael Wilkes) before being sent back to Government. Sir Peter Beale recalled: "We were told by General Wilkes 'You over-egged it in the Gulf' (i.e. you had far too many medicals (medical personnel) there). But *he* had added medical people himself as he was Commander UKLF — he was part of the planning process. Did the high medical provision and low casualty rate in the Gulf war act against the RAMC? My answer is, 'yes, it did'."

"The planning assumptions were that we would only need an army of one division, with one other division, ever again. It was also assumed that U.K. would *always* be neutral from now on. All planning assumptions related to 'how many surgeons and anaesthetists were required'. This concerned secondary (hospital care) — it was the costliest, so ideal to cut in order to save money."

"I asked that Wroughton be the core hospital. I argued for retaining three, as at present.. Eventually they said that because of the small total numbers, there would be *one big hospital of 400 beds*, and that would be Haslar."

"Our only chance was to convince the PPOs. Whatever arguments I made, they listened but were not prepared to agree to. And the Members of Parliament were not interested either — they had to listen to 2 or 3 Defence Studies in an afternoon. The medical study was given no priority."

"Primary care — that of the regimental medical officer — was largely tied to the regiments. So it escaped reduction on such a scale. I purposely did not draw attention to it or to Army health and our second-line units, the field ambulances. And I did not mention Catterick. I did not want to make these four hostages to fortune. So they were not included in the argument. But had we been supported by our military seniors we would have been all right."

"From the start I argued for the retention of our College at Millbank. But as technician training was progressively being moved elsewhere, and the pathology department was closed, it became all too clear that the College could not be sustained where it was in London." (Technician training however was still going on in Millbank in the Spring of 1997).

"I argued against the Agency concept — the privatisation of services. The government thought 'Agencies would be transparent i.e. you could see what they were doing.' I was against the market testing in Germany. We lost the Army Blood Transfusion Service — it deserves great credit. But Agencies suited Conservative Government policy. I argued against the size of the training base — there was no question of putting training at the top of the agenda."

General Beale's *forte,* first as D.G. and then as S.G., was not, from his own account, to argue a case forcefully. He was well aware that his reputation then and afterwards was not high with his own Corps officers. Although it was said by Major General George Kennedy CB, CBE, of the General Staff (the Director General, Territorial Army, and later of the Defence College Directing Staff) that the medical case could have been put better, especially when compared to the submissions made by Directors of other Arms, General Sir Peter Beale worked hard for his Corps, and in the wide span of history merits thanks and a special place. He wrote letters to the Chief of the Defence Staff and to individual Chiefs of Staff which show clearly his accurate analysis of the DCS15 proposals. He complained without success to the Deputy Chief of the Defence Staff, Lieutenant General The Hon. Sir Thomas Boyd-Carpenter, about the way the Naval officer acting on that General's behalf, Commodore Harris, was proceeding, and he deserves considerable sympathy from the RAMC that his efforts came to nothing.[10] General Wilkes felt, as General Kennedy did, that the Army medicals' case could have been put better. General Wilkes, however, of the Senior Army officers, was aware of the independence of attitude the doctors possessed, and was, perhaps, more sympathetic that they realised. And his doctor critics also, perhaps, forgot the fact that he too had orders from the Minister of Defence, to obey and to see were carried out.[11]

General Boyd-Carpenter was clear in his own mind that the changes in Mr Rifkind's Front Line First paper were complex and not purely resource driven. Other factors, such as the developments in the purchaser/provider relationship following the NHS changes, and contemplated changes in medical education, and the reduction in overseas garrisons with loss of overseas hospitals, would in any event have necessitated a radically different approach by the DMS to the peace time structure for secondary medical care needed as springboard for its war rôle. The General made the point that, for the senior medical officers, "change on this scale was not something that all of them were very comfortable with, and whether this affected their ability to market it is a question that you might care to put to them."

Mr Rifkind (later Sir Malcolm Rifkind, KCMG) recalled: "I certainly recollect that there was considerable controversy as to whether the reductions were going too far and I know there are those today (personal communication January 30th 1998) who believe that that is indeed what happened. From a Ministerial point of view, we were anxious to endorse any organisational change or change in provision that would improve efficiency and the use of resources without reducing the quality of service provided. Accordingly we were very much guided by the professional advice of the Army itself as to what would be appropriate."

"Questions such as the number of military hospital beds were determined on perceived needs and not on purely financial considerations. The whole point of the Front Line First review was to make economies that could be justified in terms of efficiency but that would not damage the operational effectiveness of the Armed Forces."

Notwithstanding the view as seen from the Senior Chiefs' side of the table, the conclusion has to be reached that the Cost Study decisions had been made before the medical representatives were allowed the opportunity to give their own side of the story. Brigadier W.R. Short, assisting General Beale, was entirely certain on this point. He recalled: "Harris and the team did all the presentations — we (i.e. the individual Service Medical Directors) had to argue against *what had been decided*." He was not afraid to comment further: "Harris played one (D.G.) off against another." Brigadier Short remembered vividly how exhausted General Beale was at the end of the final session, and how distressed he was when they were together after they had left the meeting with the Chiefs and he realised he had failed in his aim.[11] In the writer's opinion, while the medical case could have undoubtedly been argued better, the warning General Beale gave, that DCS15 "would not work", was certainly made to the Chiefs. The attitude of those same Chiefs would be remembered in years to come, when there was frank admission of the gravest mistakes being made in their 1994 decisions.

General Beale's reply to General Boyd-Carpenter's question asked above was also clear. "As for selling DCS15, we did our utmost to adhere to the party line once the decisions had been made. That was our job. Having argued all along for less stringent cuts and alternative solutions we abided by the collective decision and tried to sell it appropriately. Sometimes, it is not possible to pull the wool over the eyes of others able to think clearly. Doctors in particular are notable in being able to think for themselves and to reach balanced judgements."(11)

A further reason for the College at Millbank to be closed was the pretext that "it did not have beds for teaching" and was "too far from the core hospital" in the highly inaccessible Gosport peninsula. A new Tri-Service College was to be put into HMS *Dolphin,* the Submarine Depot and Museum, or one of its adjacent buildings.

There were other factors. One was the Conservative Government's insistence on turning hospitals into Trusts, to be run independently on business principles and for profit. Managers appointed were not from the world of medical knowledge but from the world of business, and in the event, the new executives, all over the country, quickly asserted themselves and their primacy over the hospital doctors. Some NHS senior staff were very ready to join these managers; the same applied to some Service medical officers. What was to be imposed upon the Service ethos were the NHS changes writ small.

The next was the choice of the layman who was appointed by General Boyd-Carpenter to ensure the reductions went through. The man ordered to implement the plan of DCS15 was a Naval officer called Harris, a long-serving Captain who had been specially promoted to the rank of Commodore for the task. General Boyd-Carpenter had a high regard for him. "He had earlier been selected by the Royal Navy as a military member of the original study team, and therefore understood the issues; he was of the right seniority for such a task and was available; and I knew him from past working with him that he had a good, incisive mind, capable of grasping the issues. I believe he tackled a difficult and demanding task with efficiency and integrity. There was certainly no question of any political involvement in his appointment." (personal communication, 11th February, 1998).

Commodore Harris was entirely open in stating that the reductions were primarily to save money and the provision of a Medical Service secondarily. His ignorance of the implications of things medical, his refusal to listen to sensible argument, his anger if his rigid opinion was questioned or if an outside body criticised, his floundering over medical issues he could not understand, made the implementation an unhappy confrontation for all concerned.[12]

The threatened loss of Millbank was a source of deep unhappiness to the RAMC. Although a distinction was made between the HQ Mess and the College, everyone realised that the loss of the one would mean the loss of the other. But the Naval officers who were now in charge of all the changes showed no concern. From early in his new term of office, the new Surgeon General, Surgeon Vice Admiral A. Revell, appeared all too often flanked by two more Naval officers, Commodore Harris and Surgeon Commodore Robert Harland, at his public appearances. Observers were at once suspicious of too great a Naval control. In the later summer of 1994, Surgeon Commodore Harland was in the ante-room of the Headquarter Mess. He said to the writer: "Of course, all this will go. It will close." When asked what the RAMC would do, he replied: "Oh, I suppose they'll have to find somewhere. It'll be up to them to find somewhere. Keogh, perhaps." He did not seem to understand or care just how serious a loss this would be to the RAMC. Nor did the Surgeon General.[13]

At this date there was real doubt about the effectiveness of the leadership at highest AMS level over the past two years, and the new DGAMS, Major General F.B. Mayes, was as yet untried. The British Medical Association, with its long tradition of strong support for the Armed Forces Medical Services, sought in vain to obtain information about what exactly government had in mind. It had to respond to anxious calls from its Service members, and these were arriving in significant numbers. It was evident that a serious reduction was about to take place, and that their comment and possible help might be needed. The refusal of the Conservative Government to give any information whatever to British Medical Association in early 1994 had unfortunate repercussions later. When in later 1994 evidence was still sought, BMA were then told that because "things had reached such a sensitive stage, it was not proper to give any information to them." Recognising that they were the only forum Service fellow-doctors could use to obtain redress, the BMA decided to take active steps just as it had done a century earlier. As in the 1890s, the Battle for the RAMC was waged to a large extent by the British Medical Association. History was set to repeat itself, though very few had ever read the exchanges of the earlier encounters of 1898, 1921–1933, 1951, 1956, 1961, and 1967.[14]

After the full text of the proposed changes was made public, BMA called a Tri-Service conference on 21st September. It was attended by nearly 100 participants, Regular and Reserve. Two presentations were given by each Service, describing the rôle of its Regular and also its Reserve elements.

The Surgeon General, Vice Admiral Revell, still recently in post, answered questions at the end of the meeting. He did this for nearly an hour, and was warmly congratulated afterwards by the Armed Forces Committee chairman, Colonel J.S.G. Blair, for his excellent handling of what was not infrequently hostile questioning from serving medical officers. Questions came from *them* — there was no BMA input at this meeting.

Yet the impression remained of loss of morale as anxiety surfaced over career prospects within the Regular Services. Medical officers from all three Services wrote, telephoned, or actually went in to the BMA offices with their increasing disillusionment. Visits by Commodore Harris to military hospitals made this feeling worse.[15] At the end of the year, the AFC chairman went so far as to arrange an evening meeting for officers at QEMH Woolwich who wished to leave but were being prevented from doing so because the D.G. insisted they must remain in post. Legal advice and other help was offered. In this, BMA was doing no more than carrying out its duty of supporting its members.

On 24th January, 1995, the chairman, Colonel Blair, the vice-chairman, Air Vice Marshal R. A. Riseley-Prichard, and the secretary, Mrs Finlan, went to meet Vice Admiral Revell at his office. They had previously travelled to Portsmouth to talk to him in 1994 after his appointment was announced. The purpose of their visit at the 1995 date was to seek information about future career prospects for doctors in the Armed Forces, with a view to deciding upon the advice the Association should give to those considering such a career and to those presently serving. Again they stressed that the BMA should have been consulted at the earliest possible stage.

The S.G. told them: "These changes *are the best thing that has ever happened to the Armed Forces Medical Services. For the first time their work will equate precisely to the civilian NHS.* " "Haslar", he continued, "is to be expanded from 200 beds to 400, and would provide very good training." The MDHUs were to be chosen for their size and training potential — hospitals of 1,000 beds were mentioned — and would provide *more* recognised training than ever before. It was intended that there would be military wards, although they would not be *exclusively* so. Only a very small proportion of the total medical staff would be military. He was less forthcoming about health and hygiene training and its availability and seemed ignorant of the vital necessity of Army Health measures.

"On the general practitioner side", he said, "it was inevitable that there would be a reduced requirement for medical staff. Further, it was becoming more difficult to organise hospital training to meet the RCGP's requirements."

When BMA suggested there would be an insufficient number of beds to give each consultant adequate clinical work, Admiral Revell replied: "Calculations have been based upon 10 beds per consultant which was acceptable to the College. Increased patient throughput meant that beds were not the measure they once were".[16] The fact that soldiers could not go home at once after operation did not seem to have been addressed.

Soon after, on 27th February, the two AFC office-bearers met Commodore Harris supported by the medically qualified members of his Defence Medical Services Implementation Team (DMSIT) — Surgeon Commodore R. Harland, the S.G.'s representative on the Armed Forces Committee, Colonel L. Lillywhite (remembered by Territorials who met him in the Gulf), Group Captain W. Pike and Surgeon Captain J. Soul.

Harris was very enthusiastic about the changes. He gave an optimistic forecast and answered most questions confidently except when asked about Army (community) Health. His doctor members were however more cautious. But unlike the S.G., Commodore Harris told his audience that the reductions as being carried out to save money. Tapping his cheque-book, he told the AFC pair, "This is what it's all about."

The BMA representatives remained somewhat sceptical about his confidence that the future was bright; the evidence of depression and disenchantmant amongst medical officers from the whole rank range, and the doubts they had heard being expressed by Warrant officers and senior NCOs, did not accord with the Commodore's opinion. They also noted his need to consult his medically qualified supporters on straightforward points of medical knowledge, especially about provision of community health. But the chairman and vice-chairman told Commodore Harris that the British Medical Association, with its long history of campaigning — frequently against the government of the day — for the best Defence Medical Service, and though having serious reservations which they felt bound to express, would monitor the reductions responsibly and give their general support to the Senior officers in what all agreed was a most difficult task.

Each single Service Director General was later consulted by BMA. Air Vice Marshal Baird was happy to come to London and discuss his RAF problems. Rear Admiral Craig was seen by the chairman in Portsmouth. He had no comment to make; the chairman was left with the impression that for Craig, as "everything was going to Haslar, there was nothing more to discuss." But the DGAMS, General Mayes, when seen on 26th January, was very frank about his worries. He said plainly: "Please do not criticise too openly. If you do, they will all leave." He telephoned the chairman at his home on 3rd March with the same plea. Criticism was certainly made in the BMA News Review, since the flow of letters of complaint from those wanting to leave grew faster. In the background, the AFC chairman actively discouraged certain BMA doctors who urged more severe action, and he insisted when he reported to the Council that they support their Service colleagues. He and the AFC undoubtedly wanted to help.

And so in May of 1995, he wrote to Vice Admiral Revell prior to the BMA's Annual Representative Meeting in Harrogate. He and his Committee, backed by the BMA Council, were anxious to set up another day seminar, on September 19th, with up-to-date presentations by senior officers giving notice of progress, and with a keynote speech by Admiral Revell himself.

Letters were sent out in May to the various D.Gs. General Mayes accepted gladly.[17] The others demurred. Then the news broke. The S.G. had forbidden the senior medical officers of all Services to speak and take part in the seminar. Major General Mayes suddenly found he now had another important engagement and apologised that he must withdraw. The meeting was postponed. The S.G. wrote to BMA to confirm his refusal.

The chairman replied at some length. "I am sorry that you are not able to come to the symposium which BMA is arranging later this year. I do understand why you do not feel it would be useful, and I do really know how hard you have all been trying to explain the necessary reductions which are taking place to serving medicals. What we from our part want to do is to try to put together something forward looking, and I would hope we can have these meetings become an annual event.

"I very much take your point that any meeting should be positive rather than negative, and have spoken to our Secretariat and asked them to seek speakers as we had in the afternoon at the Royal Society of Medicine the other week, to describe new advances from their own Service, and to provide a shorter and optimistic title. This is being done with the aim of helping from our side, and I hope you would agree with such an approach."

"You have had a good deal of background support. I have stated to BMA Council that they must support their AF colleagues, and have rejected the possibility of black boxing.[18] But there do remain elements which could be made better, and even if I had not had your letter, I had intended to speak positively at the Representative Body (the ARM) next month and make positive suggestions. If there is any point you would like me to make, please write in confidence — equally, I would be happy to let you have the text of what I plan to say." The chairman wrote again after the ARM to report that he had supported the concept of MDHUs and the efforts of the most senior officers. Neither letter had a reply.

One of the motions passed at the Harrogate Conference was that a Tri-Service Royal College be retained on the Millbank site. Once confirmed by Council, this became official BMA policy. As a result, the AFC chairman wrote to Mr Portillo, now Minister of Defence, asking that the College remain. The letter in reply was full of detail about Millbank, and gave full arguments about the reasons, not yet finalised but as ever "subject to consultation", over the threatened move to H.M.S. *Dolphin*. On 8th November, a major European Defence Meeting was held at Millbank. Major General Cowan, who as Commandant was by established protocol to sit beside the Minister at the formal dinner and who intended to speak his mind, found to his surprise the day before that he had been given a seat some distance away. But at the end of the dinner, as he was leaving, Mr Portillo spoke to General Cowan and thanked him for his hospitality. He said: *"I didn't know this place existed."*.[19]

Another motion passed at Harrogate asked that NHS trusts give adequate time off for training to their TA medical and dental (and nursing) personnel. Again in the background, the AFC chairman had been in contact with the senior staff at TAVRA's HQ in London to seek their help. "We have watched with sadness and incredulity", said Brigadier Tom Sneyd, "how the Medical Services have failed to put their case and are being reduced."

The TA(AMS) was not mentioned in DCS15 except insofar as it was to support one Division and one detached brigade. But of course the TA was also involved in the current reductions and re-deployments. Brigadier Lewis Johnman, whose contribution at the time of the Gulf war had been enormous, when his popular personality had been ideal both in liason with General Beale and the TA overall, left in October 1992. His contribution deserves the highest praise. Brigadier Bernard Rowe, who had been in the Regular RAMC, and had served in the Gulf as a pathologist, was the new TA Adviser to the DGAMS. General Beale commented: "Bernard had not the easy manner of Johnman. But Johnman was a G.P. Rowe in civil life was a very senior doctor as a Director of the Public Health Laboratory at Colindale. He had the great advantage of much experience in dealing with senior civil servants."

Brigadier Rowe found himself with a totally different job from his predecessor. For him there was none of the excitement of planning for war with the sense of importance that went with it. He now had to face the prospect of fighting for the TA medicals in a hostile situation. His DMS was initially Major General A.C. Ticehurst. Next and soon he had a new Director in the U.K. Land Forces HQ in Major General Peter Craig[20] who in turn was uncertain of the new TA Adviser's competence. Brigadier Rowe regarded Craig well from the outset, as he "would listen and was helpful with advice."

He recalled: "Johnman wrote me a pessimistic letter which more or less said it would all be wrapped up in a few months. I did not agree. But the prospects were not good."

"In early 1993", Rowe remembered, "the first establishment committee began to sit. At that time we were working without an operational requirement. They were talking about only four big hospitals, Glasgow, Newcastle, Bristol, and London. AMD did not get its operational plan until the middle of 1993. By February 1994 there was agreement for four field ambulances for the Rapid Reaction Force (ARRC) — there were now no hospitals. There was a plan for the remaining nine field ambulances to be turned into 'Independent Hospital Squadrons', but this was turned down by the Army.

"Slowly the concept of four field hospitals each with 4 FSTs, to be provided by the TA, appeared. The D.G., General Mayes, said the Regulars could produce 4 field hospitals, each with 8 FSTs. We were looking at a total of say 3,000 beds, plus FSTs plus independent FSTs and TA FSTs. This was responding to capability plans coming from the S.G.'s office.

"By now, as far as the AMS went, there were 6 Regular fd ambs, 3 for each division, 1 para fd amb, 1 for the airportable bde, and 1 to support CSSG UK (Combat Service Support Group), making a total of 9 in all. General Mayes still said there would be *four* Regular field hospitals, though I could not see where he would get them. It was this insistence which brought about the reduction from two TA hospitals in London to one…it was suggested that 257 (the north London TA hospital) amalgamate with Bristol…ridiculous!…I had to point out to the D.G. that his plan had no TA unit in Wales. So that was put right. In the end, they settled on 3 Regular hospitals. There were the same number of Regular fd ambs. In no way can they (the Regular RAMC) find enough FSTs.

"Finally, there are 4 ARRC TA front-line fd ambs — Dundee, Belfast, Sunderland, and Hull. They were told their peace establishment was 240, the same as war. Then, when they had worked like mad to reach their new establishent, they were told they must cut — caderise — to 160. You can imagine the effect on morale.

"Then, there are 3 additional TA fd ambs for home defence and ARC of 120 peace and war establishment — Leicester, Cambridge, and Maidstone. The hospital number rose to 11. The specialist teams remained at 12 and there are still the ambulance train group and the medical equipment depot."

As TA spokesman he also had to fight for the appropriate status he knew the often senior members of the profession would merit. "The Regulars wished to downgrade ranks of commanding officers of TA hospitals and field ambulances. I wrote to Mayes saying 'if you do that, they will all leave.' He replied: 'We are just testing the water!' So when the TA ranks remained colonel and lieutenant colonel, the Regular RAMC found they were granted the same ranks. I believe we did them a good turn!"

Bernard Rowe's contribution was real and important. He had the huge asset of the semi-independence of outlook and refusal to be over-awed by seniors when necessary which has been the great asset of TA throughout the century. He appreciated the warm help received from Colonel David Jolliffe, Chief of Staff to the Director General, as soon as he arrived in post, and was himself warm in his praise of General Short for all the help and understanding which he gave also. He argued well for his vital portion of the whole RAMC, and deserves to be remembered with distinction in this history.[21]

16th June 1995 saw the closure of BMH Hong Kong. There was a Beating of Retreat and lowering of the three AMS flags. There had been a hospital presence there since September 1841, when the 98th Foot, the North Staffordshire Regiment, arrived on the island. Previous hospitals had been in Bowen Road (1906), Mount Kellet (1930), and the present hospital, at King's Park, opened in 1967.

Now it was winter 1995. The QEMH in Woolwich had ceased clinical work on 28th September, and was running down to complete closure on the 25th of January the next year. The AFC chairman, who was aware of the continuing letters to BMA complaining of how the reductions were being implemented, decided he would have to ask BMA to take a more active rôle. He had heard what RAMC officers whose integrity he respected were saying. His committee was solid in backing him. He therefore went to the BMA Secretary, Dr Mac Armstrong (who had once been a TA officer) on Tuesday 7th November to ask if the Association would approach the Royal College Presidents to make a strong representation to the Government.

Dr Armstrong was unhelpful. He insisted the doctors were arguing "special pleading" and said that the chairman was seeing things wrongly. No action was needed, argued Dr Armstrong. The Service career was "all right."

Faced with this, the AFC chairman was at something of a loss. But Major General Cowan, aware that he was near his retiral, asked him if he could come to see Dr Sandy Macara, the Chairman of Council of BMA. This he did, and aired his serious misgivings. In later discussion with Dr Macara, the AFC chairman suggested that the Presidents of the Royal Colleges be approached and asked if they would put their signatures to a letter of concern and worry about the way the Armed Forces medical branches were being run down, and make positive suggestions. Dr Macara agreed, and there is little doubt that the sincerity and anxiety of General Cowan was the catalyst which affected his decision.

In parallel, the AFC Chairman had decided to go ahead with a day conference on February 8th, 1996. As it happened, this was the day before the IRA exploded a large bomb in London. Speakers chosen were those over whom the S.G.'s writ did not run — individuals of independent mind and with knowledge of their subject. One was Dr John Cule, who had been mentioned in despatches in Italy in 1944, and later, as a psychiatrist, had experience of military stress. Dr Cule was the President of the International Society for the History of Medicine: the conference was fortunate in having a speaker of his calibre taking part. His paper, on the reaction of military to stress, included sobering examples of how senior officers were happy to suppress unwelcome comment and implied criticism, even by removing the officer concerned, when it did not suit their intention of forcing their policy through. The new Chief Executive of the Defence Secondary Care Agency, Mr R.G. Smith, was asked to take part and agreed, but was advised not to by the S.G.[22]

The meeting took place and over 120 doctors, mainly Regular but with many Reserves, attended. A bigger room had to be found to accommodate them. The chairman of the meeting, Dr John Ferguson, who had commanded a TA field ambulance and was an experienced BMA negotiator, promised that any comments would *not* be recorded, that any expressing views would *not* be reported by name, and that the Association would use opinions expressed to help the major communication about to be made to the Prime Minister.

The response to this seminar was remarkable. Many Service doctors told their grievances there and then or wrote notes at once; they spoke particularly to Dr Jane Richards, the new Chairman of the Representative Body of BMA. Complaints were often to the effect that the doctors involved could not get their senior to tell them what was to happen, or refused to help with what was seen as a real personal problem. The "established channels through which their concerns were best expressed" had been found wanting. There was certainly no suggestion that the powerful, more able leaders had left their Service and that quiet acceptors would now be ready to accept what was happening. Afterwards, a woman MO wrote to BMA: "Interviewed by Chief of Staff after attending the AF day and I do not wish this issue to further brand me as a 'troublemaker.'"

These personal pleas from the Conference strengthened the hand of the Chairman of Council and of the AFC. A letter did go to the Prime Minister, signed by the most important and apposite of the Royal College Presidents. His reply went over the same familiar ground about the changes. The letter, however, was not without conciliation in places.[23]

Commodore Harris met the BMA representatives on 22nd April. He had kept them waiting since February. He began by telling them that "he was the architect of the assumptions" and had in fact *"planned much of the substance of DCS15."* "My plan", he said, "does not envisage the need for Reserves. I know this is a departure from previous thinking this century, but the Defence Medical Services is to be an all-Regular body. This is a departure." Of the RNR (he did not mention TA at this point) he said: "the Navy has washed its hands of the RNR."

Of RNH Haslar, he said: "We have not yet worked out the usage of say day surgery there." He still spoke of Haslar's having "375 to 400 beds", adding that "we have access to 800 patients at Frimley Park and we have enough patients at Haslar." He went on to say that "we have too many surgeons there (Haslar) for the number of patients involved...we will have nine theatres working" implying that they would then be able to employ them all. Of standards, he said: "the Surgeon General is responsible for the standard of consultant employed."

Of Germany, he said he "had not looked in at Iserlohn, but we will use civilians as required".

"Training in the MDHUs is enhanced on what they are now being trained in (sic). Trainees go to small district hospitals for the mix…the training is *the best ever* ".

Of the Tri-Service College in London, he was totally dismissive. "It was put there I suppose when the only medical schools that were any good were the London ones. *But* now *we have Southampton, which is first-class…we will build you a bigger and better Millbank in HMS Dolphin.*" The other and, in BMA eyes, prudent point of view, that the move should be delayed until the Gosport hospital had been shown viable and successful, was dismissed at once by the Commodore. In the same vein he continued: "The royal college presidents were misled by the BMA, but the Surgeon General has put them right", and he insisted that the BMA were "just interfering."

He was however sensibly concerned about over-specialisation. Over-specialisation raised difficulties for training for the military, because the National Health Service was now producing young surgeons knowing narrower and narrower fields.

When pressed about the Volunteer Reserves, he was most inconsistent. He began by saying "we could not rely on the Reserves to make good." He later went on to say "there was a place for Reserves to play — a deployable part", and ended by further contradicting his earlier insistence about there being no need for Reserves by telling his listeners "of course we need a TA neuro-surgical team as that is not done in the Regulars."

The Commodore was quick to listen when he heard the doctors' information that medical students had complained about inadequate or misleading information when they were applying for cadetships or after they had been accepted, and he undertook to make enquiries and remedy any errors found.

BMA were of course not the only body which criticised the way the cuts were being implemented and were desperately worried that they were being rushed through too quickly. The all-party Committee of the House of Commons' Fifth Report[24] was highly critical, much more so than the BMA had ever been in public. Its criticism was, naturally, all denied in the Government's reply. Once more Government, with its Medical Directorate, answered that fears were ill-founded and the numbers were exactly right: "the resultant medical field force levels are sufficient for all realistic planning scenarios." It was confidently asserted that the plan was good in all respects.

Admiral Revell, after the public criticism made by the AFPRB in its Second Report, now found it necessary to ask to meet the BMA. At first he tried to see only the Chairman of Council with Dr Mac Armstrong, and a secretary, for a "cosy chat." Dr Macara, who like Dr Jane Richards, the Chairwoman of the Representative Body had by now met the Admiral personally, refused. The Admiral, he said, must meet representatives of the AFC, which represented BMA service members.

On 11th June Admiral Revell met the AFC representatives, the chairman and Dr John Ferguson, and the Council Chairman and BMA Secretary, along with a senior lady BMA staff member.

He held the floor for nearly an hour, going over the same ground he had gone over in 1994, and yet again insisting that the cuts imposed by political decision were *the best thing that had ever happened, as far as training prospects were concerned, to Armed Forces Medical Branches.* He appeared to dismiss any difficulty (and he admitted some existed) as "not my problem."

Criticism by BMA was again, he insisted, wrong and misjudged. The facts and decisions of DCS15 were incontrovertible. He stated that Commodore Harris *had* in fact been instrumental in the planning of the reductions and the new arrangements.

Asked why the Reserves were not mentioned in his Organisation Chart which he produced for the meeting, he replied: "The Reserves are not my problem. I am not concerned with the Reserves. There is the RNR, of course, but they are only fill-ins. I know the Army has a special arrangement with the TA, but I am not concerned with the Reserves."

He was, like Commodore Harris, very dismissive of Millbank. "Professors would no longer sit around in Millbank doing nothing — or reading — they will now *work* at Haslar on the wards, in outpatients, in the theatre — *they will work.*" Asked about teaching: "Teaching? they will be able to do that on the side."[25] The BMA suggestion that a trial period to assess the worth of the Gosport site should be given before the transfer of the College — as BMA had similarly argued for over the proposed changes in the big outside world of the NHS — was summarily rejected by the Admiral.

He answered questions well. MDHUs, he said, could not be set up in other parts of the Kingdom "because we just don't have the people to man them". He went on: "And if more were set up, *it would harm Haslar*". He supported individual Service identity. He admitted morale was as low as could be imagined. The listening doctors could not but feel sympathetic.

The Bosnian war.

The very next day, June 19th, there appeared an account in *The Times.* "Protest at conditions for British troops in Bosnia." All eleven members of the Defence Committee had visited the Implementation Force in Bosnia. They had met British units serving in the Multinational Division (SW), including 4th UK Armoured Bde, 2nd Light Infantry, The Queen's Royal Hussars, and 32 Engineer Regiment. They had also seen US units in Multinational Division (N) based at Tuzla. It was a critical report. The coincidence of this account reminds us that there was a war in progress, and that our Medical Services were involved. The arguments and political pressures over the future of the DMS were not being carried on in a time of total peace. And a fact of the highest importance has to be realised: *the DCS15 plan made no provision whatever for medical support in a peacekeeping or humanitarian requirement.*[26]

"The MPs were shocked by the conditions, although morale was still high…'we were told that lavatory conditions were so inadequate that troops wait till they leave camp on patrol and then make use of appropriate cover in a mine-infested countryside…while the Americans shipped air-conditioned mobile operating theatres to treat injured soldiers, the British wounded had to be operated on in tents with no air-filtering system'."

There was also a shortage of surgeons. The report said that the number of deployable Army surgeons had dropped from 33 to 22 in the past two years. "The Army needs nine medical officers and four surgeons in Bosnia and is having to rely on doctors from other Services and other countries."

"The MoD needs to show a faster response to meeting unforseen needs for supporting soldiers in the field."

The war in Bosnia was a civil war. The removal of the major external threat at the end of the Cold War quickly produced the feared destabilisation. One symptom of this was the demand by political activists for independence at the expense of their neighbours. Freedom would, they claimed, result in instant happiness, and after vengeful replacement of street names with little local heroes' ones, deliver continuing prosperity for their small tribal group. The threat existed in countries other than Bosnia.

In Yugoslavia, where President Tito had since 1945 built a successful nation with a flourishing tourist industry, such a civil war had begun later in 1991. Fighting between Bosnians, Serbs and Croats became so vicious, with the spiteful removal of "foreign elements" from each tribal area — ethnic cleansing — and large scale murder to achieve it, that the UN sent a peace-keeping force along the Croatian-Bosnian border in 1992. The first British units in this early force included 24 Airportable Field Ambulance under command of Lieutenant Colonel Lois Lodge. She was the first Regular female C.O. in the RAMC. Next came 4 Armoured Field Ambulance from Minden in Germany. The first Force Medical Adviser was Colonel David Wright, who was awarded the CBE for his outstanding contributions.

In later 1992 the Muslim population in Tuzla was so threatened that the operation had to be enlarged. OPERATION GRAPPLE involved the deployment of a battalion of armoured infantry to assist UN by escorting food and humanitarian relief convoys. The battalion, to be changed every six months, had in additional to its regimental medical support a medical support troop (MST). This unit, said to have been conceived in the Gulf war but in historical terms was very much as an ASC (advanced surgical centre) had been in the later 1939–45 War, was an FST with a laboratory, X-ray, plus 25 beds and nursing care.

Captain Mark Weir (once a member of the Armed Forces Committee of BMA) was RMO of the first British infantry battalion sent, 1st Bn The Cheshire Regiment. At the pre-reconnaisance meeting at Sennelager, he advised those present of the need for the MST. Captain Weir had been in the Gulf, where he had been asked by Ms Kate Adie: "Are you a proper doctor?" and had replied: "Yes I am — are you a proper journalist?" Amusingly, the same lady saw him in Bosnia and asked: "Are you still in the Army?" He recalled the initial lack of information, the need to obtain drugs and supplies suitable for civilians of all ages from Médecins Sans Frontières, the change from suspicion to warm co-operation by the local Bosnian hospital staff, the various influxes of refugees, the wounds suffered by soldiers of both sides, and the difficulties his C.O. had with the Muslim photographer-journalists who were determined to make a story.

Lieutenant Colonel Michael Staunton went to Bosnia in early 1994, as Senior Medical Officer in the British Area. Returning after his initial reconnaissance, his conclusion that "things were not good" caused a furore. He considered that the aim of having a "logistics battalion" including medicals was wrong. Also, medical training needed to be modified. "BATLS was most valuable but was given to those who could not use it."

Colonel Staunton therefore set up a BATLS course within Bosnia, to ensure that all combat medical technicians, including those from the TA whose contribution he valued, were fully trained. By now the RAMC had some 120 all ranks in Bosnia, including 30 nurses. Casualties went back directly to Woolwich.

Difficulties with the military laymen continued as they had over the century. Refusal of the brigade staff over helicopter provision had echoes of the Falklands war. They made standard excuses: the helicopters for medical evacuation "were out of the direct line of command. They could not be used in winter", and so on. "Their notion of the six hour rule (that wounded must not be delayed longer than six hours before definitive surgery, if infection was to be avoided) they seemed to have picked up wrongly at Sandhurst", Colonel Staunton recalled.[27] He wrote to Brigadier Ridgeway, but it was only when a helicopter carry saved the lives of nine soldiers after a bad crash that things changed. "He was then very grateful and complimentary."

Staunton's other success was to induce the whole UN medicals to work together. "When we had standing operating procedures (SOPs) for all, all the other nations co-operated. It was wonderful! We worked together. Flew the surgeons around. This was helpful, as the problem of repeated tours for surgical staff, owing to shortage, was a burden."

Captain Steve Emmerton took a BSc in nursing with honours at Surrey University and enlisted as a nursing officer in the RAMC in 1990. He went to Bosnia from April to October 1995, on the sixth rotation or "roulement" of OPERATION GRAPPLE. He was sent to Zepca in what was called the "Maglaj

Finger", a wedge of countryside for which the Household Cavalry and later the 9/12 Lancers were responsible. "We had to set up the MST", he explained. "It was MST 1 and I was senior nursing officer. We had eqpt from U.K., were in a portakabin with 8 beds. We had a trauma area with 2 beds, and a small operating theatre. Lieutenant Colonel Peter Guy was the surgeon; he was on his way out.(of the RAMC). The anaesthetist was Lieutenant Colonel Jowett, formerly a Regular but now TA. The medical centre was adjacent. We had no problems with re-supply except when the roads were closed. We had a busy and useful time."

The cavalry were very good. He admired especially the officers whom he saw as professional and smart. Their commanding officer saw the medicals daily, and the local brigadier was a regular visitor also. The medicals appreciated this greatly.

The chain of evacuation was provided by General Staff (G3) officers working in liaison with Medical Commanders. It was first to Gorni Vakuf, by bad road or helicopter, then to Split, and lastly to U.K. by air. "All the roads were terrible."

They had a busy time. Shelling by the Serbs on 1st May produced no casualties as the Maglaj school nearby, used as soldier accommodation, was hit but the shell did not explode. In was different on May 3rd, when they had several casualties: "a sapper lost his leg, another had a retroperitoneal haemorrhage and had to be evacuated…Col Guy saved the man's leg but it had to be amputated when he got home to U.K. later."

Captain Emmerton was a shrewd observer and clearly a highly competent nursing officer. He summarised his time: "We were providers of health care, available to a small population…because of the geography, we had to have an inordinately (sic) large amount of medical support relative to the total number of troops on the ground. We were a peace-time deployment and to get patients to surgical care in the shortest possible time, had to have medical units dotted all over the place."

He did not find care for the local inhabitants easy. "They did not expect sophisticated medical treatment — many said they had not seen a doctor for years — but they became most manipulative. I took medical supplies (all civilian supplies came from civilian charity sources) to a civilian store and found by chance they had rooms full of medical drugs, dressings and so on hidden away, after telling me they had nothing. I suspected they passed them on to their army."

Corporal John Caithness, from the other side of the country, was a combat medical technician in his TA field ambulance in Dundee. He was due to start a full-time nursing course in February of 1995, but that January thought he would delay it and volunteered through his unit for full-time service in Bosnia. So with another corporal from his unit, Corporal Barr, he went to the mobilisation centre for all TA going to Bosnia, which was in Vimy Barracks in Catterick. He was like Captain Emmerton a shrewd and capable man, and he was certainly not afraid to criticise when he saw things he thought wrong.

"They did not treat the TA well in Vimy", Corporal Caithness recalled vividly. "At that time the schedule was very tight — it was only 8 days. It was a bit like a sausage factory. The Regular storemen thought the worst of us…they called us 'thick and had gone there as we had nothing else to do.' Some seemed to think we were just a joke — this was the garrison staff (mixed cap-badges). They were unaware of our ability and training. We had no actual explanation by an officer. Some of the officers had been TA but were now regulars. But later it got very much better for the TA."(28).

The volunteer reservists were put into the groups they would serve with while in Bosnia. Cpl Caithness was posted to a group of 25, including two TA officers, to serve with HQ ARRC in Sarajevo. They joined their unit at Rheindalen before being air lifted there.

He enjoyed his time. "We were an RAP for over 1000 people. We had an RMO, a Captain David Houston from Aberdeen — he was *really good*— one of those MO s you could work with. We had a Regular sergeant and corporal and the two of us. There were a lot of TA about — doing tradesman tasks. A couple of days after we arrived, the squadron sergeant-major called us over and said: 'You are as good as regular soldiers…we can't fault you — in two days we found you knew your stuff."

" I gained valuable experience there which was of use to the unit (225). And we got our medals and certificates from the brigade commander 1 Signal Brigade — he came for a beer after."

Returned to his home unit and reverting to his part-time status, Corporal Caithness found that it was not only Regulars who did not treat him kindly. "I was never even interviewed by my C.O. when I got back", he complained. "I thought I'd have my name at least in Part 1 Orders. But it never was." Yet, like many another who has had no thanks for what he had done in serving the RAMC, Corporal Caithness did not lose his loyalty. His summing up was: "If they hadn't had the TA in Bosnia, they'd have been bust."

By the autumn of 1995 the international community, frustrated by the continuing problems of the civil war, set up a larger and more warlike force. It was called IFOR (Implementation Force) and included aircraft which by their strikes finally obliged the factions to accept negotiation. The Dayton Agreement followed. In August of 1995, 24 Airmobile Brigade, including 19 Airmobile Field Ambulance, was mobilised but not in the event deployed in the field. However 19 Field Regiment RA saw active duty, when their RMO, Major Ross Walker, was praised for his part in casualty care and evacuation.

The Headquarters of 3rd (U.K.) Division was sent to command the Multinational Division South-west with Colonel Creamer as Commander Medical. This was styled OPERATION RESOLUTE. After six months, it was suceeded by HQ 1st (U.K.) Armoured Division, whose Commander Medical was Colonel A. Macmillan. He considered the new expectation of the civil population for high quality medical care, the reality of multi-national co-operation, and the new model of the medical cover needed for a peace-keeping task, with transverse evacuation — differing in many respects from the traditional linear one — as significant and novel.

Dental colleagues were there as well. Major N.E. Maris, RADC, enjoyed her tour in 1996 because of the satisfaction she got from treating refugees needing often the most basic dental care. She spent the greater part of her time doing this humanitarian work. The peasants were always grateful for help offered, but some of the higher level dentists and officials less so.

By 1997, the system was indeed much smoother. There was less active warfare. More facilities were in place. The early difficulties of service pay being delayed for the volunteer reservists had been overcome, and their essential contribution had been admitted. One who performed a slightly different rôle was 2/Lieutenant Mark Foster. Mark had formerly been a laboratory technician RAMC, been made redundant under DCS15, and to his credit gone on to qualify for entry to medical school. Now a young and confident TA medical officer, his move to Bosnia in June was smooth. He gave his time that summer not as a medical but as an adventure training instructor at the all-arms adventure training camp at Povija, where the whole range of outdoor activities was available for everybody during rest periods for those serving a tour in Bosnia. The 4–5 day "package" included sailing, diving, windsurfing, water ski-ing and walking.[28]

Later again, by August of 1997, a British Medical Association journalist, Mr Lindsay Clark, with no previous knowledge of the world of military medicine, visited 19 Airmobile Field Ambulance in Sipvo, Western Bosnia. He found the doctors he met had had tours in Bosnia before, were capable and energetic, and were actively re-furbishing the local infrastructure. Major Kevin Beaton and an RMO with a Gunner Regiment, Captain Sandeep Dhillon, were reported by Clark with obvious interest and respect. The journalist was surprised to find "four or five TA medical officers there, and TA soldiers and TA nurses...they all worked together as if they were all the same." This unsolicited testimonial from a young person with no military background is, perhaps, the best note on which to end this account of the Corps' Bosnia contribution, and is worth reading in full.[29]

Behind the difficulties of the Regular Army changes, however, was another and happier process. This first bright light was the smooth progress of the Reserve Forces Act (RFA) through Parliament. It was the exact opposite of the progress of the DCS15 plan. From the beginning, the Government showed a very different face, as far as the discussions leading to the formulation and preparation of the RFA were concerned, from the secret and arbitrary behaviour of those who set up the changes for the Regulars. Its handling was a model of consultation.

As far back as September 1993, a conference was held in the Duke of York's Headquarters in Chelsea. (This great and historic building too was to be sold for a sum of money by the Conservative Government, but happily the campaign to save it succeeded). The new proposals for altering the terms of the whole Reserve

Army — and RAF and RN Reserves in their smaller numbers — enlistment, training, and especially call-out in conditions short of general war, were put to a large gathering of employers, experienced Reserve people, office-bearers from TAVRAs, and from National Employers' Liason Committee (NELC), from all over the United Kingdom, plus a few serving Regular officers.

From then onwards the important elements, especially TAVRAs and NELC, made their points. The BMA made its points on behalf of doctors, dentists, and nurses, especially about its fears that they would not be given time off to train by the aggressive new NHS trust managers now coming into command as the NHS was being transformed into a mainly profit-conscious organisation. Liason with helpful and interested MP s was excellent. It was a model of good-will on all sides. Again this was largely due to the personalities involved, and again, it was a lesson to those forcing though the DCS reductions and changes.[30]

The second bright light was the attitude of the new DGAMS as soon as he had taken office in April 1996. Major General Robin Short, QHP, MB, ChB, was not by his own admission an academic. In fact, he was dismissed as a "boots and gaiters man" by some when his appointment was announced. This was not out of jealousy, but from a fear that he might be out-manoeuvred by the College presidents and others.[31]

The day after he demitted office, Major General Brian Mayes told the Colonels Commandant "The last two years have been a disaster." The very next day, General Short said (rather like Brigadier Rowe) "I do not agree that this is a total disaster." And then he began to do something which had not been done for many months: he set about his task with great confidence and enthusiasm: he began to give people *hope.* One of the very first things he did was to ask the AFC chairman to meet him. The AFC chairman had already asked the new D.G. to come to the Brighton ARM of the BMA. In his reply and acceptance, the General in turn invited the AFC chairman to Millbank, when in discussion he showed both his worry and his realism. His action marked the beginning of a new relationship. He quickly set to his task with diligence and enthusiasm.

General Mayes had indeed had an unhappy tour in post. He deserves much sympathy, and did more than many gave him credit for. He was entirely aware that the Treasury had simply demanded a sum to be saved, and the cuts were dependent upon finding the necesssary money for the Government and not upon military requirements as the S.G. had stated. The establishments were all that could be afforded; the pretence that the Single Directors had been *given what they had demanded* was actively misleading. He was shattered by the sudden change of plan by Mr Rifkind. "I believe that at the second (DCS15) stage we lost control — it was taken out of our hands", was his most significant statement. He loyally tried to think in Tri-Service terms, whilst his opposite numbers did not. He realised that the training base was too small. He gave Commodore Harris much time and advice: "I spent literally hours on the 'phone with him", he recalled, "and tried to explain what the Army needed. Unfortunately he too often got the wrong end of the stick and carried out something different." He kept as optimistic a spirit as possible, but finally admitted that things were indeed serious, and perhaps lost heart. "I attempted to preserve sufficient dedicated people to keep the AMS going. We lost a whole generation of doctors", General Mayes said openly, "something which never happened before." Again, he deserves credit and sympathy, in this history. General Sir Michael Wilkes praised him as being "very clear sighted."

He saw no difficulty in the Royal Defence Medical College's moving to Portsmouth. It had to be protected at all costs but not in its present location. He had a much more realistic reason for this belief than the Surgeon General: it was not shortage of beds that was the problem, it was shortage of senior staff. "Of course hospital staff are short", he said. "Mr Norman Hale, the DCS15 civil servant, used the option of reducing secondary care, because they could save more money that way." General Mayes believed that he had been misquoted. In his opinion, the RAMC could not afford to have the previous numbers at the old College — they would have to do clinical work and teach together. Therefore they must go to Haslar. And so he agreed to the move of Millbank to the Gosport peninsula. Further, it was because the senior advisers could not be allowed to waste time in London, in his opinion, that he moved them to Keogh Barracks.[32]

General Mayes knew that General George Cowan took a different view. But General Cowan was right and the D.G. was wrong. An academic Royal College of distinction *had* to have its own allocated staff. Their function was a different one from that of the "working" consultant, just as in a professorial academic department in a university. If the RAMC was to retain the very best academic input, it *had* to have such persons.[33]

During 1996, the BMA had been quietly making contacts with Members of Parliament and senior members of the profession, and perhaps partly because of that, and partly because of the efforts former RAMC activists like Lieutenant Colonel Bill Maclay had been making by letter, lobbying of retired senior officers, and individual approaches to M.P.s, the Defence Committee of the House of Commons decided to "undertake a short inquiry into Defence Medical Services as a follow-up to its Fifth Report of Session 1994–95." The clerk to the Committee, Mr Andrew Kennon, wrote to Dr Macara on 24th October: "I am writing to invite you to submit written evidence to the Committee for this inquiry. Your letter to the Prime Minister of 15th March has been drawn to my attention. I expect the Committee will wish to focus on defence medical services as they are now.... Although the future of the RDMC is relevant it will not be the central focus of the inquiry..." he then listed 7 issues to be addressed: 1) recruitment and retention of Service doctors, 2) operation of MoD hospital units, 3) size and organisation of field hospitals, 4) availability of Regular Army surgical teams, 5) effectiveness of Haslar as the sole core hospital, 6) availability of reservists, 7) adequacy of facilities for war time hospital care. Written evidence, and on any other issue the BMA wished, was asked for by 20th November.

The new DGAMS had not been idle. He had sought, and obtained, a meeting with the Chiefs of Staff on Mitchiner Day, November 5th. The day was also that when President Yeltsin had his heart by-pass operation. The meeting was described as "acrimonious". But the Chiefs agreed to a review.

On Friday, 8th November, the AFC chairman had a long discussion in Scotland with an M.P. of strong RAF connections with whom he had kept in touch.(Mr Bill Walker (Con); he lost his North Tayside seat to a Mr J.Swinney, (SNP), in the 1997 General Election). The M.P. confirmed that the decision to close Millbank had been taken by Mr Soames before the consultation document had been made public.[34]

On Tuesday, 19th November, 1996, a meeting of the greatest potential importance took place in the House of Commons between the AFC chairman, Mrs Finlan his secretary, and Miss Sue Marks, Head of the BMA parliamentary division, and Mr Paul Murphy, MP for Torfaen in Gwent. Mr Murphy was the Labour Shadow Secretary of State for Defence. A meeting with a Labour spokesman had been the aim for the AFC chairman for some months, but only now had the Labour Party agreed to hold one. Mr Paul Murphy accepted the worries told him by the BMA representatives, and undertook to reply quickly.

The BMA's evidence had been put together with great care by the chairman and his staff. They used statements made directly to them by officers serving in Germany, and from Cyprus for the RAF, as well as U.K. It was passed to the Chairman of Council for his comment, and then went to Mr Andrew Kennon, the secretary of the House of Commons Defence Committee (HC DC), as ordered, on 20th November. Because of its importance, it was signed by Dr Macara himself. It reiterated the BMA's criticisms of each point at issue, and restated its continuing strong disagreement with the closure of the RDMC in London.

December 1996 was certainly a month of high importance in the unfolding drama. This was the month the Defence Committee visited Haslar Hospital. The C.O., Brigadier Guy Ratcliffe, and his matrons, gave them a list of failings, and junior officers spoke freely. The Parliamentary Committee listened carefully

In the first week of December also, another meeting of prime importance had been held, for the Select Committee for Defence's hearing of oral evidence from the Surgeon General and from the newly appointed Deputy Chief of Defence Staff, Air Marshal Peter Squires. Major General Peter Craig, now working within the BMA building, reported on the hearing to BMA on the 17th. He was unimpressed with the obfuscatory replies given. "The impression was that all difficult statistics would be fed back out of the glare of the press and would therefore lose interest", recalled General Craig.[35]

On 9th December, Mr Paul Murphy was as good as his word. He sent a letter to BMA confirming his anxiety expressed when he had met them in the House the previous month. He confirmed his Party's support: "Treasury-driven cuts have had very serious consequences for the Armed Forces Medical Services, resulting in hospital closures and an overall reduction in the service provided to the three armed services.

Labour will, within the overall strategic concept of our defence review, ensure that there will be appropriate Defence Medical and Dental Services which will form an integral part of our armed forces, will have a sensible training base, and which has its own clear identity."

Another Labour Defence spokesman's views were reported in a Scottish paper, the *Courier and Advertiser*, earlier, on November 8th. Dr John Reid had visited the Black Watch at Fort George near Inverness. "Morale in the Forces is at an all-time low", he told the reporter, "because of Tory incompetence. Labour will begin to shape a new, positive role for our Armed Forces, making a positive contribution to maintaining peace in the 21st century. The election of a Labour government will be a welcome boost for the Armed Forces." As Mr Murphy recommended, the AFC Chairman wrote Mr Reid, PhD, on 6th December, and asked to see him in his west Scotland constituency. This he did on December 20th, and Dr Reid invited him back for a second discussion. The chairman felt he had made progress in making the fears of the Service medicals known to an M.P. likely to become a Minister in the near future.

On January 29th, 1997, the new Defence Secondary Care Agency announced, in a Ministry of Defence News flash 010/97, that a special arrangement was being made: "to reduce the waiting time at Military Hospitals. This one-off arrangement is designed to reduce the time that military personnel have to wait for treatment by allowing those presently on the waiting list to be treated by two NHS Trusts, at Portsmouth and Oswestry. It will have no detrimental effect on the length of time that civilian patients have to wait at those hospitals.

Up to 1300, mainly orthopaedic, military patients (author's italics) will be treated between now and the end of March, enabling them to be restored more quickly to operational fitness. This is a further example of the close co-operation between the Defence Secondary Care Agency and the National Health Service."

The BMA Armed Forces Conference was arranged for 25th March. It was hoped that the next S.G, Air Marshal John Baird, would agree to attend. The location chosen was the RDMC at Millbank, to emphasise the BMA's support for the College in London.

The main presentation was to be the results of a confidential survey which younger members of the AFC had requested. This had been agreed at the AFC meeting on Thursday, 26th September, 1996, when Admiral Revell attended. All Regular serving medical officers were to be surveyed. The questions were devised to allow respondents anonymity. It was interesting, and perhaps significant, that Admiral Revell asked that searching questions be included. "They are always telling us they don't like things", he said. "Perhaps this survey will let us know why, and what it is they don't like." The results, he agreed, would be valuable, and he added that he hoped they would be sent to the senior officers in all three Services.

It was not until November 1996, however, that the final list of questions was complete. A special department of the Association, experienced in setting up such surveys, was responsible. The AFC chairman did not see the final questions until they had been completed.

Admiral Tony Revell received the CB in the New Year Honours List, prior to his hand-over in February 1997. He was the second officer in the 20th century at his level to fail to be knighted. The other was S.G. Jamieson.[36] The end of his career in post had been unhappy, with increasing criticisms, notably those concerned with the so-called Gulf war syndrome but also with his implementing of the DCS15 reductions.[37]

The reports of the HC DC and debates in the House of Lords, following their visits to Haslar and Frimley Park, and their questioning of Air Marshall Peter Squire and Admiral Revell were presented at the AFC Conference in Millbank on the 25th of March. In the House of Lords' debates retired Royal Air Force and Army officers of highest rank had spoken out anxiously against the medical reductions. No naval Lords did so. And when the House of Commons Committee was about to make its report public in December, Mr Julian Brazier TD, MP, who had been in touch several times with the AFC Chairman by telephone, made it very clear that the Conservative Party wished the conclusions deferred until after the forthcoming General Election. "From our Party point of view", he said, "we want the report held up. We certainly do not want its findings made public now." This was on 10th December, 1996. The intervention of Mr Brazier was of interest; in the summer of 1995, he had told the AFC chairman "The Navy is the favourite Service of this (Conservative) Government[38] and will carry out its policies."

The AFC Conference had as its theme "The relationship between the Defence Medical Services and the National Health Service." All the speakers were Army and included the TA Adviser to the DGAMS, Brigadier Glynne Jones. Two civilian speakers took part. The fact that the RAMC provided most speakers was because of its major part in any military, or in this instance, peace-keeping, exercise.

There were about 100 at the Conference. The opening speaker was the Commandant, Surgeon Commodore Ian Jenkins, who had gone to visit the Chairman of the BMA Council on a number of occasions, insisting to Dr Macara that his AFC was wrong and that his own agenda was correct. Commodore Jenkins, although General Cowan's successor, did not live in the College. He commuted from Portsmouth, and was clearly anxious, as were one or possibly two AMS officers, to move the College to Gosport as soon as possible. The BMA secretary, Dr Mac Armstrong, also visited the RN Institute at Alverstoke on naval invitation, following which visit he added his voice to the same naval argument, that the changes had to be acceded to and "accepted phlegmatically." It was characteristic of his sincerity and good endeavour that he wrote as he did.[39] But Dr Macara was not swayed. Nor was Dr Jane Richards, chairman of BMA's Representative Body, when she visited in May of 1998.

The paper on the programme awaited with most expectancy was the result of the confidential survey. This was given with great clarity by Dr John Ferguson, who could present it "without fear or favour." The results were devastating; much more severe than BMA had believed likely. Over 90 per cent of MO s stated that conditions were deteriorating. Of those before the 16-year point, when early pension could be taken, 59 per cent were very likely or likely to leave. Only 39 per cent saw themselves still in the Services in 5 years' time. Only half would recommend a medical cadetship to a medical student. Worse were the written comments; they showed an intense dissatisfaction, with near-total loss of morale. The patience and perseverance of BMA had been successful. These replies had vindicated all they had been saying, and when passed to the Minister in due course, would form a valuable piece of evidence for the new Surgeon General to make use of. The reductions had been flawed in concept and calamitous in execution, and the Association had helped to make this public knowledge.

While Dr Ferguson was presenting the viewpoints of the House of Lords debates, Major-General Chris Callow jumped to his feet and in an angry outburst called out loudly: "This must not be allowed to go on. It must stop." The General apparently did not wish the truth to be heard (details in BMA archive). One of the speakers informed the AFC chairman, in alarm before the meeting, that General Callow had threatened him over the telephone. The general himself telephoned the chairman before the meeting and harangued him, saying that the questions in the survey were slanted and biased. The chairman told him firmly that his allegations were false and insulting to the BMA and to the professional firm which had set the questions.

On April 29th, Dr Macara authorised the AFC chairman to put together a "New Deal" for the DMS, with three points. First was the necessity to return the RDMC to Millbank and to secure the HQ Mess. Second was the proposed new "Big British Military Hospital." Swindon was a PFI hospital (Private Finance Initiative) but was "on hold" because of lack of support from banks. They discussed the pressing need to broaden the training base and the range of specialty available to Service hospital staff. The AFC chairman suggested that 400 beds of the proposed 1000 at Swindon be allocated to the military. Dr Macara said: "Make good facilities available and you will get good people applying." The two men recognised that the move would involve down-grading of Haslar to an MDHU. The third major point was that the unpopular and expensive Agencies should be reduced or abolished, and their functions restored to the serving officers.[40]

The General Election result of 1st May, 1997 was not unexpected. What was unexpected was the huge New Labour majority. Parties were now Labour 417, Conservative 162, and Liberal Democrats 40. The Labour majority was larger than the total rump of Conservatives. Many Ministers, including Mr Rifkind and Mr Portillo, lost their seats. Throughout the country the aim of the electorate had been "to get the Tories out", and in several instances this was done by tactical voting. Labour had captured the so-called "Middle Ground", and much of their policy promise was conservative in outlook and in nature.

A letter had gone from BMA to Air Marshal Baird, the new Surgeon General, asking for a meeting with him. It was the Royal Air Force's turn to hold the post of Surgeon General. But Air Marshal Baird's appointment was not a matter of form; there were arguments and discussion before the Ministry, and the RAF, confirmed his appointment. An Edinburgh graduate of 1961, he had had the excellent staff training given by the RAF to its senior medical officers. Now he had the large task of attempting to restore morale and save the Defence Medical Services.

The AFC chairman and Mrs Gail Norcliffe, a BMA staff officer, met him in his room in the MoD Main Building in Whitehall on 22nd May. From the moment they entered the Surgeon General's room, they were aware of a totally different atmosphere to what they had experienced previously.

AM Baird was accompanied by Mr David Reynolds, a civil servant who as Head of Medical Finance and Services, was very supportive of DCS15. He had answered letters written to Mr Nicholas Soames in the past. The staff officer present was the Director of Medical Policy, Surgeon Commodore Charles Evans. The discussion was, however, between the new S.G. and the chairman. Air Marshall Baird was more forthright than Major General Short had been, and did not shrink from admitting the extent of the problems resulting from the now discredited DCS15 plan. Far from finding the BMA losing credibility, as the naval agenda had claimed, he looked to it for help, and was especially grateful for the survey, which he said would strengthen his hand when speaking to Ministers. "Things are so bad", he told the BMA representatives, "that the smallest thing could bring the whole thing down... I have visted all the MDHUs, Haslar, and Catterick;...and I know what people are thinking and feeling. It now hangs by a thread...we will have to tell the Chiefs of Staff that a Force could not leave this country as medical support could not be provided."

The new S.G. made plain his support for the RDMC's being in London. "We lost that battle", he said. "It was a Ministerial decision so we have had to carry it out. It will need a policy reversal to restore the College to London. But I will do the very best I can to save the Mess." They discussed the problems, and the AFC chairman put forward the BMA idea for a Joint Service hospital independent and large enough to restore status and pride to the Defence Medical Services.

His next suggestion, that the Secondary Care Agency be closed and its functions restored to the serving Regular medical officers, came as something of a surprise. The idea of a large new hospital was of interest to Air Marshal Baird. However, Surgeon Commodore Evans said: "We must not take this too far — *it would harm Haslar.* There are Naval medical officers there who are of an age that their service would not be helped by a move to a new hospital — we would have to be very careful." In reply, the AFC chairman pointed out that BMA was concerned with the Defence Medical Services' survival and not with a single Service agenda.

Lastly, they discussed the question of a single Medical Service concept, the so-called "purple option." They agreed strongly that they disapproved of this. Overall the meeting was pleasant, productive, and friendly. The chairman undertook to look for ways BMA could help, in general and in detail. A further possible meeting was anticipated; both parties, the military and the BMA, were now awaiting a formal meeting with Dr Reid, Mr Soames' successor.

However, Air Marshal Baird suggested they meet again on the 17th of June to discuss problems of the Reserves. He said: "People say that the shortfall can be made good by Reserves. But are there actually Reserves so readily available?"

At the June meeting, they discussed first the proposals of the recently issued Armed Forces Pay Review Body(AFPRB). The BMA gave written and oral evidence every year to this body. BMA is the only trade union allowed to give evidence to the AFPRB, and this was a means of giving the greatest help to serving officers, mainly Regular but also Territorial . Many serving officers had surprisingly little knowledge of this substantial and powerful function the British Medical Association performed. As a rule, BMA worked hand in hand with Regular colleagues who by the nature of their contract could not put forward more radical requests. MoD would "arrange" for BMA to put forward such requests; they could do this was because their AFC members were either retired and so no longer under military constraints, or were experienced negotiators who were not afraid of the senior officer sitting across the table from them. The close and useful relationship had disappeared in the years 1995 and 1996, but now in 1997, been rehabilitated. The latest AFPRB decisions included a better pay prospect for Regular consultants than their civilian counterparts, but also offered the hope of a definite improvement in pension levels. The latter could at last, after many years of negotiation, include total pay (including consultant pay) and not only military basic pay. The possible changes suggested in the Bett Report[41] were also discussed, although it had been shelved by the previous government.

But for most of the time, they discussed the problems of the TA(AMS). The S.G. was frank; he asked for advice and information from the AFC chairman. There was now a "sea-change." The TA was now regarded as having reinforcement of the Regulars as a "core activity !" But there were shortfalls, especially in physicians. Here the BMA suggested the S.G. try field ambulances for senior G.P. doctors, many of whom were in fact hospital specialists, and some were very senior G.Ps, *with Service experience*. These last, the chairman suggested, could well be used as "physicians" for seeing Service sick. Their knowledge of Army life would be invaluable.

The BMA raised the problem of TA personnel being treated badly by Regulars often ignorant or antipathetic, before or after arrival in Bosnia. The Regular seniors could not have it both ways; they could not ask for TA personnel to make good their shortfall and then attack and disparage those same persons. Corporal Caithness was not alone in having had difficulties.

At these meetings, when the Vice Chief of the Defence Staff, Admiral Sir Peter Abbott, was present, the BMA representatives were surprised just how little he understood the problems of staffing reserve hospitals, and had to explain carefully. They found the senior civil servants somewhat fixed in their views, but the military were prepared to listen.

The third meeting was with Dr John Reid, PhD, Minister of State, on Tuesday 19th August, 1997, at his office in the Ministry of Defence.

The S.G. and Mr Reynolds were present; they had been with the Minister for a few minutes before the visitors were invited in.

The "New Deal", approved by Dr Macara, was spoken to by the AFC chariman. Dr Reid said he had the greatest sympathy for the case to retain the College in Millbank, but the move had gone too far. "If it had been a year ago", he said, "we could have done something." He had caused enquiries to be made, but no satisfactory use of the College in London could be made now.

The suggestion about a big new hospital was agreed in principle by Dr Reid, and he said a site other than that suggested (Swindon) was possible. The chairman proposed using St Bartholomew's Hospital as a site. The Minister agreed to look at the possibility, but no more.

The suggestion to abolish the Secondary care Agencies he said "as a Labour man he was in agreement with in principle", but he would have to look at it and see if the new Agencies did save costs. But he had in mind to reduce them in number, perhaps to a single one.

The chairman was then asked about the Reserves, in effect the Territorial Army. Dr Reid was anxious to learn how easily time off from civilian employment could arranged for volunteer Reservists wishing to serve with a peace-keeping Force. Difficulties with trust managers and of locum provision were discussed in detail. As the visitors were leaving, AM John Baird said to the AFC chairman: "We must show the Minister that we now work together."

August 1997 saw the closure of the Royal Defence Medical College at Millbank. Its library, teaching and technology equipment, had been cleared away over the previous weeks and days. Surgeon Commodore Jenkins caused all the photographs of previous commandants to be removed to Gosport, but they were recovered in December and returned to Mytchett. The last PGMO's course was an RAMC one, of almost equal numbers of young men and women.

Now began a period of waiting. The "New Labour" Government had stated it would, on taking office, carry out a Strategic Defence Review — as already seen. Over the weeks leading up to the Commons' debate and the formal announcement the RAMC were making their bid to save the Headquarter Mess. And preparations for the centenary celebrations the next year were going ahead with increasing speed. For the event, a committee of the Director General was meeting regularly to finalise plans.

A number of newspaper reports appeared during September suggesting that the Territorial Army was to be radically downgraded. That in the Sunday Times on 28th September reported that elements in the MoD, unamed senior civil servants being quoted, would result in the TA becoming, "like the Army Cadet Force, with only limited funding and little contact with regular units." A measure styled 'R 8', the Reduced Readiness Measure", placed the TA at a six month readiness, so that, it was argued, its members did not require as much training time and money. The name of General Sir Charles Guthrie was associated with this measure. While it seemed unlikely that the policy could refer to medicals in clinical terms, since the TA doctors carried out their specialty on a daily basis, it did of course have implications for medical unit field training. With the normal avoidance of direct reporting by MoD, it was not revealed that R 8 was a mechanism for saving money by effectively funding the TA to 54,000 members rather than to its existing establishment of 59,000, and by cutting its equipment by up to 40 per cent. It was clearly difficult for the Regular spokesmen to be entirely open, because of the good reputation the TA had in the country. Certain Members of Parliament commented that it was curious how senior Generals stated in public their warm regard for the volunteer Reservist, yet within the Ministry, along with civil servants, appeared to take a different view. Some Members, and some members of TAVRAs, believed there was a move to reduce TA units to little more than individuals for making good Regular Army shortages.

At the beginning of 1997, the TA had indeed been reduced to 54,000 all ranks. 600 Regulars were to be discharged, to achieve a saving of £15M. But on February 18th, it was announced that the bill for Army advertising for 1996–97 was £21.590M, almost twice that of the RN and RAF put together. Accepting that in a technological age future manpower needs are difficult to assess, interested persons found it hard to understand why trained men were to be dispensed with, and others re-allocated, when it was claimed that 17,000 recruits were required, especially for infantry.

On 8th October, 1997, Major General Short sent a letter to "All Regular, Reserve and Retired Officers of the RAMC." In it he told of the likeliehood of the Mess being sold, mentioned the possibility of his entering into a business contract with a firm which would take over and develop the site, and asked for opinions of those written to about fighting to retain the Mess on its site, or moving it to another site. He also asked for financial support, the minimum figure being suggested being £250 as an individual contribution. It was unfortunate that the marketing of this important letter was poorly done; individuals who should surely have been on its distribution list were left out — such as General John Matheson. Further, those who pledged a sum as high as £1K did not receive the courtesy of an acknowledgement. Perhaps for these reasons, the opinions returned varied. The British Medical Association at once contacted the D.G.'s Directorate, with the offer of its good offices and access to wide publishing of his appeal through its Journal and News Review. But the offer was not accepted by his office.

In mid-November, President Saddam Hussein raised tension by refusing to allow US inspectors into Iraq. He also threatened to shoot down U2 observation aeroplanes flying over his country's airspace. While many Arab individuals from a range of Islamic countries were antagonistic to Hussein, a significant number pointed out that while the US and the West were happy to allow the State of Israel to carry out policies harmful to fellow-Arabs especially in Palestine, the same leaders were harsh towards Arab countries, including Iraq. The US was accused of double standards; its President Clinton had lost a deal of sympathy as a result.

Most fortunately, the threat faded, but had it not, the possibility of there being inadequate medical support for any U.K. Force existed. The background intervention by the Russian Foreign Minister Yevgeni Primakov, which helped to cause the United States to agree to take no military action, could be an indication of the very first sign of decline in that Superpower's hegemony. The threats of military action by US and Britain would return in the new year.

On December 17th, 1997, Air Commodore W. Pike, who had been one of Commodore Harris' assistants, came to BMA to ask their views about what had to be done to repair the damage. Assisting him came Surgeon Commander R. Dale, who was representing the clinical side and who described himself as equating to a trust director. It became clear that Air Commodore Pike and the Commander now acknowledged the failure of both the Secondary Care Agency, and also of Haslar Hospital as the core hospital, but were unwilling to say so in as many words. Pike told the BMA office-bearers: "we are near your point of view now," and went on to suggest that the secondary care agency return to military control, and have the medical training agency amalgamated with it. He also talked in terms of several military wings being set up over a wider spread of the country, in agreement with the suggestion made by the AFC chairman to Admiral Revell almost two years before. Haslar would revert to a wing or "MDHU" within the Portsmouth NHS. Finally, he agreed that the new wings could usefully be associated with TA units of good standing, to provide military training at no extra cost. Commander Dale had changed his attitude to the TA; he now said he appreciated its usefulness.

The RAMC had always insisted that, in contrast to the secondary care or hospital element, morale in so-called primary care, which was the current term for General Practice and included work done by RMOs and with families, was high. It was also said that the high pass rate in the Royal College of General Practice examination was proof of such a high standard. But in December, general practice MOs in Germany told BMA that they had difficulty in obtaining time to complete their RCGP accreditation requirements. As a result, the chairman and Lieutenant Colonel John Ferguson, the Armed Forces Committee's expert in General Practice, made a visit to British Forces Germany on January 27th and 28th 1998. They were instructed to do so by their BMA superiors.

Visits were made to Rheindalen, Osnabrück, Sennelager, and Hohne, on bitterly cold days. The medical officers in all these places talked freely about their frustrations to the two BMA office bearers, recognising that they were there to help and did not belong to the Army hierarchy. They told of their anger at constant deployments, over stretch, and of the failure of the conditions in Germany to give them long enough periods of training to complete the RCGP accreditation requirements timeously. The GP trainers, from the other side, complained that as soon as a trainee was trained, he disappeared elsewhere, and they did not have use of his services. Saddest of all, they stated that they "did not trust their most senior officers, Short and Callow, to support them." Difficulties with the Alliance Trust which ran the German hospital service were on the whole improving, but ridiculous anomalies angered them; outpatient notes in German had to be returned to U.K., there translated at a central office, and subsequently sent back to Germany. This process could take many weeks. The fault for this they blamed on the officers who had set up the trust initially. Finally, they complained that civilian medical practitioners had a much higher rate of pay, and many perquisites, which they did not. Whereas formally such posts had been held by retired medical officers, now they were occupied by civilian practitioners in their thirties.

The experience of the German visit was used when the annual meeting with the Armed Forces Pay Review Body and BMA took place on Wednesday 11th February. The two BMA representatives were able to quote exactly what they had just been told — excepting, of course, anything critical of the AMD — of frustrations felt by primary care officers, so that they could press their case for significant improvements in salary and conditions. The AFC chairman also expressed in the strongest terms BMA's support for the RAMC Headquarter Mess. At the end of the meeting Sir Gordon Thurston, the AFPRB chairman, spoke privately to them and thanked them for their helpful contribution to what he agreed was a major problem.

But another problem appeared. On 6th February 1998, Dr Macara called the AFC chairman into his office. "I know you have been most loyal to the new DGAMS," he said. "You commended him to us as someone who would give us all hope." This was true. The AFC chairman had made a point of strongly supporting the general, and indeed had proposed him for promotion in the Order of St John, where he held a junior position. "But I do not consider General Short is someone we can have as an ally." Dr Macara went on. He explained he had listened to the D.G. at a special lunch at Millbank, when "the more he tried to persuade, the more his important guests became unconvinced." He had also carefully interviewed General Short over lunch at BMA.[42]

Dr Macara was firm in his opinion. The AFC chairman wrote that night in his diary: "This decision of Sandy Macara's is a serious one for the RAMC, as far as BMA is concerned. We agree, in fact, just not to bother any more with Robin Short and pass him over. People will be advised accordingly." He passed the BMA decision to the SG. Air Marshal Baird did not disagree.

The centenary year continued. While events particular to the RAMC were proceeding, the background fears of the entire Defence Medical Services (DMS) could not be disregarded. These were interwoven to a degree in some respects; entirely separate in others.

Preparation of the centenary history continued. General Coull, who had been closely involved in the background in the early part of the year,[43] was kind enough to read the final chapter and agree its content. He had advised the author on certain items, and modifications were readily agreed. His provision of so much material for the previous chapter was helpful, and Major-General Ticehurst had given invaluable background for it also.

The Annual BMA Armed Forces Symposium took place as usual. A choice of speakers was made by BMA to display the present and future excellence of the Corps. Dr Macara spoke only briefly and did not attend the dinner. He warned the audience: "Do not take BMA for granted." BMA had arranged for Dr John Reid to attend the dinner, when he spoke warmly of the Corps and of his hopes to preserve Millbank as its HQ mess. A piper from Dundee had come down to play, and Dr Reid commented humorously on his "Gaelic with a Dundee accent!"

Events for the Centenary began in Scotland on 21st March, when the new Medical Reception Station was opened, after EX SCOTTISH STARLIGHT on 25/26th April. On 6th May, the author gave the Haldane Tait Memorial Lecture organised by the Scottish Society of the History of Medicine in Craigiehall, Edinburgh, followed by a dinner attended by 90 enthusiasts. On 29th and 30th May there was a meeting of the Military Surgical Society at RCS Edinburgh, followed again by a dinner. Events in Glasgow were the Open Day for 205 Field Hospital on 30th May, a church parade on 31st, and a reception by the Lord Provost of Glasgow and Beating of Retreat on 27th June. 225(H) Field Ambulance had a charity event on 5th July, and the Edinburgh Military Tattoo had an AMS day during the International Festival.

On 15th June, a golf match was held over the King James course in Perth, followed by a dinner in the Royal Perth Golf Club, the oldest Royal Golf Club in the world. On 16th June, a special centenary golf match was held against the Royal and Ancient Golf Club at St Andrews, both organised by Dr Blair, Captain of Royal Perth and secretary of the RAMC (Scotland) Golfing Society. The first was won, the second lost by three matches to two. Sadly, only two southern members could attend, owing to the total failure of Major Paul Mannering, the RAMC golf secretary, to pass on the information given him in February by the Scottish golf secretary to the new secretary, Major Gareth Thomas, on handing over. Corps golfing members were not pleased.

In the south, the AMS athletics meeting at Aldershot was held on 13th June, the DGAMS Study Period and reception on 17th and 18th June, the RAMC "At Home" in Millbank on 19th June, the soldiers' function on 20th, followed by the Drumhead service the next day. And around the country, at TA medical centres, celebratory events took place.

Everything culminated on Corps Day, Tuesday, 23rd June, at the Westminster Abbey Service, followed by the Corps Dinner in the New Connaught Rooms in the evening. An eye-witness recalled: "Got to London by 9.20 a.m., then by tube to Waterloo. Bus to the Abbey — it was full of RAMC — we found ourselves in the south stalls beside the choir. We saw the Queen Mother arrive — she is *marvellous* — on sticks — she is marvellous for 98. The packed Abbey was excellent for the RAMC centenary service. We got a taxi back to Millbank for the reception there...."

The service began at 11.30 a.m. The first event was the dedication of the Book of Remembrance. The Dean and Chapter, together with Her Majesty, moved to the Third Book of Remembrance, which lay under guard of four Pennant Bearers in front of the RAMC memorial window. General Coull, the Representative Colonel Commandant, asked the Dean, the Very Reverend Dr Wesley Carr, to make the dedication, which he then did. It was a moving act.

After the National Anthem, Dr Carr gave the Bidding:

"We have gathered to thank God for a centenary of service by the Royal Army Medical Corps; to commemorate past achievement; and to dedicate our future to the ideals of the Corps' motto: *In Arduis Fidelis — Faithful in Adversity.*

During one hundred years of peace and war, God has enabled the Royal Army Medical Corps to sustain its ministry of compassion, care and healing. Many, throughout the world know that they live today because of the skill of its members.

This devotion has not been without cost. Therefore we also commemorate the valour of those who risked and especially those who lost their lives in the service of their comrades. In thanking God for them, let us also pray that the world may be spared the horrors of war and learn to live in peace.

Inspired by this history and by the example of those who created our tradition of selfless service, let us now dedicate ourselves to compassion for the sick and wounded, praying that God may abundantly bless all that the Royal Army Medical Corps undertakes in its second century."

The service followed. The Director General read the first lesson, and WOI (RSM) J. P. Best, RAMC, the second. Included was John Bunyan's splendid hymn — perhaps a Providential choice: "He'll with a Giant fight". The sermon was preached by the Chaplain General to the Armed Forces, The Reverend V. C. Dobbin, MBE, QHC.

After the service, the Corps Band, from the Territorial Army (WOI M. Feehily, Bandmaster), played Elgar's march Pomp and Circumstances No. 4, and The Spitfire Prelude by Sir William Walton. When the service was over, invited guests were taken to the Headquarter Mess for the reception. They filled the Mess; it was a most enjoyable occasion.

A notable absentee from the invitation list was Major General George Cowan. The D.G. had failed to invite him. But this officer was not to be denied; in his own words, he "just turned up at Millbank for the lunch reception after paying for his ticket." He remained in the non-V.I.P. lounge.[44]

The evening banquet, at the Connaught Rooms, was memorable. Everyone seemed to be there. The D.G. spoke with confidence. The Chief of the General Staff, General Sir Roger Wheeler, was perhaps more cautious in his outlook. But all agreed it was an occasion not to be missed. Our Corps was having its hundredth birthday, and we had been there to share it with our comrades and friends.

Yet background fears for the future of the Medical Services had not gone away. Worries were very real, as much of the conversation outside the Abbey and later in the Connaught Rooms testified. The AFC chairman broke his day, in fact, by hurrying to the Territorial Headquarters in Chelsea in the afternoon to relate his most urgent concerns to General Evans and Brigadier Sneyd. These utterly trustworthy friends promised full support. For on the previous Friday, 19th June, the chairman and Lieut.-Colonel John Ferguson had had a long and very frank talk with the Surgeon General. They had heard first of needless attacks by a medical journal, and of media attacks when use of pigs for training military surgeons in Denmark had been made public, and promised full support.

The main discussion was about the polarisation of the DMS between the RN and the others. Some RN medical officers were set to coerce the Surgeon General by threatening to take away his remaining secondary care staff, and so destroy the DMS if Haslar was closed. The three men talked about the likelihood that the whole Service would collapse. They also discussed primary care, which was causing the SG great concern. Air Marshal Baird spoke of the "Sponsored Reserves", an idea of Mr George Robertson, the Secretary of State for Defence, and of how few consultants in the TA would actually be willing and even able to provide help on request, in spite of their assurances. They even spoke of the possibility of an all-Reserve Medical Service. They discussed the hope of new possible sites for a "core" hospital and for new military wings. They talked for three and a half hours in what was perhaps the most significant background exchange of views between BMA and the Medical Services. While undoubtedly others at senior level had equal fears and discussions, this session is recorded here, as it was personally experienced, and is relevant to the fortunes of the RAMC.

In all this, during the centenary year and until his final retiral — after his period of office being extended until AD 2000, Air Marshal Sir John Baird came over without doubt the most able and distinguished Surgeon General of the late twentieth century. As Brigadier Ronald Brown put it, "his arrival saw a sea change in the SG's approach to DCS15 and our general situation — cessation of flannel and denial, and acceptance of problems with a clear effort to work to correct them" (personal communication, 15th June 1999). And as we in the Armed Forces Committee discovered, he alone was prepared to admit that things were badly wrong. Not for him the pretence that all was well — or "turning the corner" to use Colonel A. Macmillan's expression — for fear of compromising his career. He gained not only the high respect, but also the real affection, of those representing the big outside world of British doctors, the British Medical Association. Sir Alexander Macara kept in friendly touch with him. His courage in telling politicians that their Defence Medical Services had problems so serious that safe cover for a major enterprise abroad could not be provided, continued until the end of his time in post.

Two days after the centenary celebrations of the RAMC, on 25th June, the AFC chairman had a working lunch with Mr Jim Johnson, chairman of the Central Consultants and soon to become the chairman of the Joint Consultants Committee, and Dr Jane Richards, chairman of the Representative Body of BMA. The AFC chairman and Dr Richards recounted their visit to Royal Hospital Haslar and the new adjacent Defence Medical Centre in HMS Dolphin, the shore establishment, on 13th May.

At that visit, where Commodore Jenkins and Captain Ray Radford had strongly pressed the case to retain Haslar, the naval doctors gave the BMA office-bearers the strongest possible evidence of their agenda. They were taken to HMS Dolphin, shown the multitude of offices, some looking unoccupied, and told in no uncertain terms that it must all continue — as it was so good — and that various "bad influences" were querying its continuance, including the S.G. and other unspecified officers. In February, when from the 17th onwards doubts had begun to arise about Haslar's long-term viability, Captain Radford had had repeated telephone conversations with the AFC chairman; that month, however, reports by Sir Myles Irving and later Sir Duncan Nicoll had advised that Haslar was not suitable and that other sites had to be sought. At the May visit, the RN officers dismissed the reports as "antagonistic" and "had been commissioned by the S.G. on his own". The BMA office-bearers left unimpressed. It is fair to comment, however, that the naval officers were doing no more than the army ones were doing over Millbank; they were pressing for their own centre. But the great difference was that Millbank had its years of prestige, was in the capital, and had been placed there for the very good reason that it was not far-off as Portsmouth now was. The Navy were striving to retain what they felt they had recently won.

The senior BMA officers were enthusiastic following the AFC chairman's briefing, and had several useful offers to make. Mr Johnson wished a meeting with Air Marshal Baird before the coming BMA Annual Representative Meeting, but as the Air Marshal was not available, suggested one in the Athenaeum Club in July.

July was another eventful month, with two meetings of the highest importance. On the 21st, the AFC chairman and his staff officers met the three "shadow" Ministers of Defence in the Tory opposition in London, at their request. They wished to hear BMA opinion on the medical reductions. They were Mr John Marples, Mr Simpson and Mr Kee. The group had an hour and twenty minutes of strong talk. Mr Marples admitted frankly "we over-did DCS15" and confessed "we made a mess of it". The routine BMA points were made and all serious worries declared openly. The MPs listened well. They were totally dismissive of the choice of Haslar as the central site.

The next evening, another useful meeting took place in the Athenaeum, with the most senior BMA figures present, plus the Surgeon General. Decisions were made how best to help the Air Marshal, and Mr Johnson offered to let him address the Joint Consultants' Committee — a rare honour. "We went over the main points of the DMS problem," the AFC chairman recorded, "we are near each other's point of view."[45] The TA had during these months been anxious also. On Monday, 16th March, the AFC chairman had had a long telephone conversation with the S.G., when the latter reported his relatively smooth passage with the AFPRB — ideas between them were now "joint" — and they talked about the leak from MoD about large reductions in the Reserves. The AFC chairman had written to *The Times* on the subject, expressing fears.

The letter sent to Territorial medical personnel from Headquarters, Land, demanding agreement to a new style of contract, showed a lack of understanding of the reservists' minds, and was counter-productive. A small number of Regular RAMC officers were given command of TA field and hospital units at this time. Overall, they were unconvincing to the Territorials they commanded: notable exceptions were Lieut.-Colonel P. B. Baker (222 Fd Amb Leicester), and Lieut.Colonel John McGory (224 Fd Amb East Midlands). And throughout 2000, TA members became increasingly dissatisfied with what they saw as the "diffusion" of their units into sections of larger "regiments", lacking the essential local loyalty (Colonel Harry Griffiths, personal communication).

The centenary year saw a "first" — the Matron of 256 London Field Hospital, Mrs Sylvia Quayle, was the first

QARANC TA officer to assume command of a TA hospital. Supported greatly during her command by the DGAMS, Colonel Quayle was guided within the unit on medical matters by her consultant physician second-in-command, Lieutenant-Colonel Mary Heber. Dr Heber would later become commanding officer in succession, and establish another historical "first" — it would be the first time a daughter had succeeded her father in TA hospital command. Her father, Colonel John Heber, commanded 217 Volunteer Hospital, 256's predecessor, in the 1970s.

On the positive side, the RAMC were fortunate in having Colonel Chris Best, in charge of TA(AMS) HQ in Chester and later in York. This officer — non-medical — was exactly what the Territorial officers and soldiers looked for — someone who understood them, liked them, and whom they trusted. The Reserve RAMC owes a great debt of gratitude to this first-class man. His name and contribution must be remembered in this history.[46]

Within the "Big Army", a significant series of changes helpful to the Corps followed the removal of the Directorate of Medical Operations and Plans from the control of the Surgeon General's office, to come under the Assistant Chief of Defence Staff for Logistics (as medical matters had been designated "supporting" staff and so in the "logistics field" since the early part of the century). This allowed an "operational view" to be voiced strongly *outside* the S.G.'s orbit by general staff officers well aware of medical needs and sympathetic of them. It was almost a throw back to the days of the Esher committees (p. 104).

A year later, this move was reviewed and Medical Operations and Plans came back to the Surgeon General. Air Marshal Baird would then have a major battle to keep the Medical Supply Agency within the DMS and *out* of Logistics. He won the battle, and also had the philosophy accepted that the Medical Services were *not* part of the new Defence Logistics Organisation Unit, but were a part of Front Line Service *in their own right*. This was a notable victory, and restored the DMS back to where it had formerly belonged, returning it to the position which had been lost in the now openly acknowledged, Field Marshal Lord Wolseley style, disaster of DCS15. The S.G.'s next victory was to have this British DMS status and position approved by NATO, against some very strong German resistance (personal communication, 6th December 2000). A medical cell reviewed the Permanent Joint Headquarters (U.K.) at Northwood and was responsible to the Commander Joint Operations (CJO) for operational medical matters — but with direct links also to the Surgeon General.

From 1997, an "Operational Medical Study" had begun. Its original terms of reference were issued by the Assistant Chief of the Defence Staff, Major General G. A. Ewer, CBE, a former RCT (now Royal Logistics Corps) officer. It was "to address the shortfall in operational medical capability consequent upon DCS15".

Against a background of hostile, perceptive and realistic House of Commons Defence Committee reports, the Director of Operational Capability, Brigadier Andrew Ridgeway, carried out the audit and easily confirmed that the Medical Services were incapable of giving the level of support needed for fighting troops. As a result, the Operational Medical Study Team (OMT), whose terms of reference were drafted by Brigadier J. R. Brown of the Army Medical Services, brought the Army Medicine "right to the forefront of the General Staff Agenda" (Personal communication, 15th June 1999). "It was considered vital to have a Medical Services officer on the Team", as its requirement amusingly stated! (This insistence was from the Surgeon General). Eighty recommendations were made by General Ewer's team, and all were accepted by the Chiefs of Staff. As in post-Boer War days, these same-style General Staff officers were being obliged to take notice. The subsequent Lawrence Report,[47] set up by the Labour Government, was also a source of enthusiasm. It backed the Operational Medical Study Team's findings and the fact that subsequently the DMS continued to slip away was certainly not its fault.

The Mitchiner Lecture, the premier academic event of the Army Medical Services year, took place at the Headquarters Mess on Tuesday, 3rd November. Numbers attending were less than of late.

The proceedings began by Major Mannering, the D.G.'s Military Assistant, making various announcements and telling an inappropriate "manly joke". The Ukranian General Olexy Tanchin, chief neurosurgeon of their military Medical Services, then gave the lecture.

After the lecture, General Short welcomed the distinguished audience, stressing the historical importance of the century and the need for its appreciation. To this end he concluded his remarks, surprisingly, by flourishing and commending a paper copy of a short pre-war history of the Corps.

Dr John Cule, the immediate past President of the International Society of the History of Medicine, and an important guest, later remarked to me that he was "astonished to see and hear a Director General of the Royal Army Medical Corps make such a calculated substitution, by recommending a much older and smaller volume, while omitting any reference whatsoever to the much larger and definitive history". He was not the only person to pass comment. I was also present and was extremely disappointed, as I had wished so well for the General.[48]

Finally, the D.G. gave a spirited imitation of a cockney soldier being carried off on a stretcher, to end the Mitchiner Lecture of the centenary year of the RAMC.

For Major General Jolliffe, who became DGAMS in 2000, General Short was his hero of heroes. "I was very indignant that he was not made Surgeon General," he told the writer on 5th February the next year. "He was far and away the best choice. He was pugnacious, I know, and he upset some people, but he was *just what we needed*. If we had not had him, they would have walked over us. He may have bullied a few people, but it was all needed. He should have been promoted S.G." Holding this view, not unsurprisingly, he was harshly critical of Air Marshal Sir John Baird.

This was not the majority view. Criticism of General Short was widespread. His early hoped-for promise did not materialise. His pugnaciousness, often insensitive, was widely commented upon: "he antagonised the dentists, he antagonised the nurses, he antagonised everybody". His attempts to bully even his superiors was described with disfavour by the Surgeon General (Sir John Baird, personal communication, 20th June 1998).

He lost the goodwill of the British Medical Association — the only DGAMS of the century to do this. No commendation of the Corps appeared in the Journal; the offer of a memorial centenary bench, made early in 1998, was withdrawn. His statement to General Coull, when he attempted to reason with him over the history book, that "he didn't care if it was published or not", was dismissive of all those earlier Directors General, who with so many others had so willingly given time and care to its preparation over seven years; indeed, to the Corps itself. (General J. Coull, personal communication, 15th March 1998)[49]

Like Admiral Revell, he received an additional medical qualification. The Royal College of Physicians and Surgeons of Glasgow made him a Fellow in 1998. Like Admiral Revell, he was awarded the CB, as was Major General Callow — all three received the same decoration, in spite of holding very different levels of posts.[50] His successor, General Menzies, would re-establish the post and would be quickly promoted Surgeon General — in fact, within a year. Air Marshal Sir John Baird was enthusiastic: "I am delighted to leave things in the very capable hands of my successor, Lieutenant General Bob Menzies" (personal communication 1st February 2000). And Lieutenant General Sir James Baird, pointing the contrast, said: "I had the highest regard for Bob Menzies" (personal communication 6th November 2000).

Aftermath

In 1999, the BMA found complaints from serving officers continued. Newspaper headlines and fears expressed by Members of Parliament continued: "Alarm bells sounded over medics" (*The Herald*, 14th April). Concerns were also found among medical TA reservists, now essential for providing service abroad, that the new NHS internal market-made trust managers had become reluctant to release TA specialists. Their need for financial profit had produced a different attitude from that accepted in the past.

The summer AFC report was critical and mentioned low morale. Several medical officers had written to BMA, complaining of their prospects. On 10th July, Brigadier Jolliffe wrote to thank BMA for help over the Armed Forces Pay Report, but criticised them for a public report which he saw as "the sort of journalism (which) is a stab in the back to those BMA Armed Forces members who have their work cut out in fighting off other resource-hungry elements within the Ministry of Defence". The BMA report was a pugnacious one, and it seemed strange that Brigadier Jolliffe did not agree with pugnacity. His complaint was that the words, "BMA warns that more doctors will leave armed services", had been heightened to "crisis in defence medical services". His letter was entirely understandable, having regard to the background tensions of the moment, but was spoiled by his charge: "I even wonder if the timing of its publication to coincide with the letter from Air Marshal Sir John Baird might not have been deliberate."

But the real reason for the BMA's hard line was that the current year's pay award to Service general practitioners of 4.5%, hailed a 1% increase over their civilian counterparts, *was in fact less than the 7.3% awarded to GPs in the civilian world.* BMA were doing no more than making their point in terms which a century of experience had taught them was essential, if any notice was to be taken by government to an anomaly. Once again, the truth had to be made clear, and on this occasion, in strong words.

In late 1999, what was described as a "Re-launch" of the Defence Medical Services took place at the Royal Hospital, Chelsea. General Cowan attended as a representative of the National Health Service. He recalled: "It was in an upstairs room. The Surgeon General spoke, followed by three GP officers, one from each Service, and then three female nurses, also one from each Service."

The Re-launch was supported by Messrs Saatchi and Saatchi. It lasted only some two hours. Unfortunately, it did not produce any results.

Early 2000 saw continuing complaints. In *The Times* of 24th January, the headline "Admiral slams state of Forces healthcare" was front page news. Admiral Sir John Brigstocke, a former Second Sea Lord, had "taken the highly unusual step of putting his concern about the 'parlous state' of the Forces medical service". With 5,400 personnel — the equivalent of 12 battalions — off sick, the Admiral noted that the budget for the Surgeon General's Department had been cut by £1.5 million. He noted in particular the shortage in orthopaedic surgeons. Noting too the servicemen's worry about the deteriorating state of medical cover, he went on: "I share those concerns and I can confirm that the Defence Medical Service also shares them."

"The parlous state into which our medical services have been allowed to slip, through lack of medical resources and funding and a clearly defined future, has now been recognised at the very highest level." The Admiral's letter contradicted the statement to

Parliament just the week before by Mr John Speller, a Defence Minister, that there were no spending cuts.

The hundredth birthday celebrations of Her Majesty Queen Elizabeth the Queen Mother made up a series of wonderful events, and RAMC were present to share their pride in their Colonel-in-Chief with many thousands of others from all walks of life. The 4th August, her birthday, was marked by parades in London and good wishes throughout the world.

Later in 2000, in August, the RAMC Headquarters Mess at Millbank finally closed. During the past year, its standards had fallen — the tap water became described as "unfit for human consumption", bedrooms were left dirty and some staff were less helpful. Mr Dooley complained about what he saw as lack of interest on the part of the then PMC. A final mess dinner, when Mr Dooley and Mrs Kerslake were guests, was held; the closure following was a discouraging end to a century of greatness. The sad, shuttered windows now emphasise Millbank's desolation. The balance has not been redressed.

On 13th October 2000, the following letter was sent from the Army Medical Directorate at Keogh Barracks:

	Reference D/DGAMS/7/5/00
See Distribution	Date 13 Oct 00

USE OF CORPS BADGES AND ABBREVIATIONS

1. The inappropriate use of the RAMC badge on official letter headings of AMS units is widespread. In addition the return of the incorrect use of "RAMC" in unit titles has been noted. These abuses are inconsistent with the corporate image this Directorate seeks AMS units to portray. It was directed post 'Options for Change' that use of "RAMC" in unit titles should cease as it neither reflected the AMS image at unit level nor was necessary to identify the function of the unit concerned.

2. AMS units should be aware that work is in progress to introduce an AMS badge/logo for use at unit level. This would seem the best way to define AMS identity. Once developed it would be incorporated as the AMS logo in letter headings and used to replace other unit emblems, for example, unit signs and badges on unit PT/sweat shirts.

This concept is in its infancy and it will be some time before it is available for unit use.

3.   Units are directed, with immediate effect, to cease using the abbreviation "RAMC" as part of a unit title and to cease using individual Corps badges on official letter headings.

PF JOHN
Maj for DGAMS.

Does this mark the end of the RAMC? Does its tone show a determined disloyalty to a famous Corps and its badge? Was it not odd that the DGAMS in question, Major General David Jolliffe, did not sign this historic document? If it was, our centenary history ends not with a bang but with a politically correct whimper.[52] When asked by the writer on 5th February 2001 if he was aware that some RAMC Associations were upset at the possibility of losing their loved badge, the DGAMS replied: "Tell them to bang their heads against the wall. It won't happen." Their fear was realised, however, in an article in the *Sunday Mail* on 18th March. While two former RAMC colonels who had served in active theatres made their anger clear, Lieutenant Colonel Dineley strongly commended and justified the new formula. It was perhaps not known to the men involved now speaking well of the "AMS" title that this was exactly what the ill-fated predecessor of the RAMC had been called a century before, and only when it was removed and the RAMC badge substituted, did pride appear. The men involved were perhaps also unaware of the widespread anger amongst RAMC, especially Territorials, past and present, all over the country, at the denial of the Corps title and badge. It was highly significant how at once they — especially former sergeants and soldiers — saw the order as an insult to their dearly loved Colonel-in-Chief. The full circle had turned.[51]

In retrospect, in the year 2000, some later facts confirmed what has been recorded already. In that year Sir Malcolm Rifkind, in correspondence with the author, admitted responsibility for the decisions made while his government was in post. This was very greatly to his credit — few politicians would have been so honest and fair. On the other hand, Mr Jonathan Aitken, who as

Minister for Procurement had Defence responsibilities at the same date as Sir Malcolm, confirmed the earlier criticism of how the DMS case had been made.[52] Lastly, Lieutenant-General Sir Thomas Boyd-Carpenter confirmed, by his failure to answer my pertinent questions in 2000, that he was less than sympathetic towards the Medical cause, and his place in this history has to be so recorded. And by late AD 2000, *all the things BMA had long ago warned would happen, did happen.* The full circle had turned back to the last decade of the nineteenth century.

The writer, notwithstanding his difficulties in 1998, made a generous offer to the new DGAMS, by way of General Coull, to give copies of the new edition at a very competitive price, and so allow the RAMC museum to make a considerable profit on their sale. General Jolliffe stated that "he had no problems with that". But when told that a new edition would include new content and comment, his attitude changed. He was therefore invited to lunch at the British Medical Association on 5th February 2001.

General Jolliffe had only just obtained a copy of the first edition, but made no comment upon it. At lunch, he told his host: "My friends won't bother about what an old buffer like you writes." He continued: "If you don't write right, I'll send two of my boys to (do) you... we do not want anything written which puts off people from joining." He strongly supported General Short's opinion that "he did not care if the history was published or not" as, in his view, seven years of hard work should undoubtedly be ignored and "binned" if the writer did not agree at once to write as the Directorate demanded. He added, "If you want your book on our shelves..."

While it may be argued that this sort of personal detail should not be included in a major history, it is equally arguable that, as with critical comments made by soldiers after the South African war, historical accuracy and balance require its inclusion. It is thus necessary to record the sadly common attitude of many senior regular officers wishing to make everything sound excellent and without fault; and to ignore the truth especially when it is critical of the quality of the senior persons in post at the time. To quote General Jolliffe again: "Nothing must be put in which will put people off joining the Corps." This determination to disguise unwelcome events or suppress other facts recalls the quotation: "The social importance of history can be seen in the way dictators of every colour immediately try to control and direct its practice."

Such generals are late twentieth century examples of a tradition inherited from the suppression of Larrey's Russian campaign despatches by French senior civil servants, the clear accounts of refusal by seniors to admit errors in the Crimean War — including the efforts to block Miss Florence Nightingale's reforms and their later efforts to discredit her for telling the truth. It continued with the spiteful destruction of Lieutenant Colonel I. M. Carter's career for revealing what actually *did* happen to evacuated casualties in Mesopotamia in 1915, and in 1944 to "the removal of the Intelligence officer" who reported large German troop concentrations before the Battle of Arnhem "on health grounds as being under stress and requiring to be evacuated" (personal communication: St John Armytage, Esq, Foreign Office, 25th April 2001).

If members of the RAMC of the 20th century as we all knew it die out, this is their record for posterity. But army medicine has shown its ability to survive since the Crimea, and if that ability continues, this record is its hope for the future.

The personal last word may be left to Dr John Reid, the Minister of State. He met the BMA AFC chairman with Brigadier Mike Newell, his opposite number in the British Dental Association, in his office on Thursday, March 26th, 1998. It was a critical meeting, from the doctors' and dentists' point of view. Dr John Reid, for whom they both had by now the highest respect and trust, said simply: "We are grateful to you for all your advice. While I cannot promise to do all you have asked, I can say we recognise that correction of shortfall in the Medical Services is one of our highest priorities, and that we will enhance those Medical Services to bring them to a suitable level once more."

What else he said will have to await the publication of the Strategic Defence Review.

It may be asserted further that this account of recent events, and in such detail, is seriously slanted against officers then at the higher level and no more than evidence of pique from a Corps feeling threatened and deprived. But members of the RAMC of the time knew well that the Conservative Government Treasury had imposed an arbitrary figure of savings which had to be made. They saw the sudden appearance of a second plan — the Rifkind plan — as evidence of this. They knew that the reductions had to satisfy financial demand and were not made primarily to suit medical needs. The establishment figures, repeatedly insisted by Admiral Revell to be "the choice of the individual Directors", were indeed so, but were all that the financial limits would allow. They were not related to true operational requirements. The speed at which the cuts were to take place was another source of disquiet. While Major General Duncan McPhie, a most able and sagacious officer, noted, from his experience as Director of Medical Services in Germany, that while the Medical Services had to win their case on merit and not expect easy favour just because they were doctors, he still believed a less than equitable policy had been forced on them. As doctors, the bulk of RAMC medical officers had every reason to be alarmed. And the intervention of the British Medical Association, far from being "interfering civilians" to be dismissed by a number of senior officers, (General Jolliffe was one in 2001 who was dismissive of the BMA's role) did no more than express the fears of the profession in the country at large. It could act when those serving were unable to do so, as it had done when it had forced the government of the last decade of the nineteenth century to behave responsibly. It had supported the medical Armed Forces vigorously, with only a very few exceptions, ever since the formation of the RAMC in 1898.

To the RAMC, and to their allies in the British Medical Association with their traditional warmth for the Service doctor, the continued pretence that "the present changes are the best thing that had ever happened, as far as training was concerned", was a source of real and deep anger and resentment. Medical officers would have responded differently, there can be little doubt, had a more honest admission of the true state of affairs been made. Commodore Harris, to his credit, was entirely open in his admission to BMA, as he tapped his cheque book. Admiral Revell was not; his insistence that all was well, and his actions against anyone who demurred, echoing the often angry ripostes of Mr Soames, continued till the end of 1996. And this account reflects the feeling amongst RAMC of those years. Many felt bewildered at what was happening to their beloved Corps. The admissions of those Chiefs of Staff in late 1997, that they had "made a mess of the medical planning of DCS15" did no more than increase resentment.

Loss of morale showed in many ways other than by resignation. For those still serving, friendships were strained as individuals held opposing views. As ever, some attempted to play down criticism, others fostered it. To the historian it is therefore entirely relevant, and justified, so to record in this chapter, and the method of Thucydides has been deliberately used. Had the story not been not written as it has, it would have been lost for ever. This was a rarely found opportunity to record facts and detail events denied to colleagues of a hundred years before. This was what happened; this is what was said. The revisionist historian of fifty years hence, write what he will, was not there then. And the names of those involved will not, indeed must not, be forgotten in the history of the Royal Army Medical Corps. But once more, to the historian, it is the sweep of the whole hundred years of high achievement over the first century of our Corps which is important, not a short five years at its end.

This centenary history of the Royal Army Medical Corps ends with the exact words of Thucydides. "And with regard to my factual reporting of events of the last few years I have made it a principle not to write down the first story that came my way, and not even be guided by my own general impressions; either I was present myself at those events which I have described or else I have heard them from eye-witnesses whose reports I have checked with as much thoroughness as possible. Not that even so the truth was easy to discover: different eye-witnesses gave different accounts of the same events, speaking out of partiality for one side or else from imperfect memories."

"And it may well be that my history will seem less easy to read because it describes events so particularly. It will be enough for me, however, if this history of mine is judged useful by those professional historians who know by study how past happenings took place, and how difficult it is to record them. The happenings of the recent bad times and the almost standard reactions to them will, at some time or other and in much the same ways, be repeated in the future."[53] My work is "not designed to meet the desires of an immediate public", but has been done to last as long as the Royal Army Medical Corps exists.

No army of any size can take the field or undertake a peace-keeping requirement without well trained and well equipped medical support.

The Royal Army Medical Corps must be capable of fulfilling this rôle.

IN ARDUIS FIDELIS.

Notes and references

CHAPTER 14

[1]For the considerable background to this period, debates, questions, etc, on Army questions, in both Houses of Parliament, the reprint from "Hansard's Parliamentary Debates, 1883–1898", is necessary reading. Also "BMA, Parliamentary Bills Committee, Report of the Sub-Committee applied to the Question of Advancing Army Medical Reform", 11th May, 1898. Details of the membership of the deputation which met Lord Lansdowne, and other relevant items, are in *BMJ* 1898, **1**, pp 39, 236, 319, 329–332. Comments of senior officers are also found in the same journal, p 416. The deputation of 20th January was led by Dr Saunby, President of Council of BMA; Dr Macnamara, Vice-President of BMA; Sir Thomas Grainger Stewart, of Edinburgh University, BMA President-Elect; Surgeon General Sir James Mouat, V.C., Sir William Thomson, RCS Ireland; Professor C. B. Ball, University of Dublin; the deputation was introduced to the Minister by Dr Farquharson, M.P. Key reference is *BMJ* leader, p 319. A total of 19 academics and BMA officers made up the delegation.

Lord Wolseley's address to the North London Rifle Club, reported in *BMJ* 1898, **1**, 321 is of interest as showing how this Commander-in-Chief pretended that all was well. "He would stake his honour that if the Government decided to go to war, and to send an army *abroad,* we could put on board ship at the quays on the coast of England, and in out(sic) ports, *TWO full army corps,* complete down to the very last possible stores that would be required, *complete in every way,* and that could be done before the Navy could have the necessary ships to carry them from these shores." The BMA attacked this manifest falsehood as far as the army medical service was concerned.

[2]Michael Paine graduated MB, BS, from the London Hospital in 1963 and achieved the FRCS of England 14 years later, in 1977. For some time he did orthopaedic surgery. He became Medical Director General of the RN Medical Service in April. 1997.

[3]For general background to military thinking at this post-Cold War period, see the Army Doctrine publication of December 1993, Vol 1, "Operations". Later the "Army Doctrine and Training News" was published, introducing terms such as "Manoeuvre Warfare" —

which did not sound like anything very new — "Tactical Doctrine Retrieval Cell", "Biological Radiological and Chemical Information Systems" (BRACIS) 1996. It was the period of "chosen words." Scholarly papers came from the Strategic and Combat Studies Institute, Royal Millitary Academy. See, e.g., "Intermediate Deployments: The Strategy and Doctrine of Peace-keeping-type Operations", by Christopher Lord, No.25, 1996.

For the contrast with the immediate period, see "Design for Military Operations — the British Military Doctrine", Army Code 71451 Ref D/CGS/50/8, 1989.

[4]The "Statement on the Defence Estimates 1995", Cm 2800, HMSO April 1995. The Regular Army was to consist of 7 brigades within a muiti-national corps HQ and corps troops, 2 divisions, 2 combat service support groups (CSSG), and a U.K. contribution to a multi-national airmobile division. As usual TA units made good the gaps. "The remainder of the Army is now organised for national defence or reconstitution and regeneration in time of crisis", said the statement. In the most general terms, the Regular Army was reduced by some 26 per cent, the TA as a whole by 21 per cent, the AMS Regular by 23 per cent, and the AMS(TA) by 51 per cent from 10,000 to 5,000.

[5]Mr Rifkind never looked or sounded very impressive during the relatively short time he was Minister of Defence. A photograph showing him about to put a mortar bomb down its tube the wrong way round, and another of him walking awkwardly on the walkways at Faslane, were most unfortunate and created a bad impression in military eyes.

At the Haldane memorial dinner in Edinburgh on 17th February, 1996, he was severely criticised by Lord Edwards. He was by then Foreign Secretary. He lost his Edinburgh seat at the 1997 General Election, and again four years later.

[6]DCS 15 was published on 14th July, 1994, in the Document called "Front Line First". There was an oral statement in the House by Mr Rifkind. The seven paragraphs gave the results very broadly, and the detailed justification for the cuts and the choice of RNH Haslar as the core hospital was only given later in December, 1994, in reply to criticism by the Defence Committee in September (House of Commons 655 of Session 1993–94, paras 27–30). The all-party Committee commented: "It would have been more helpful if the original Consultation Document published in July 1994 had included the supporting justification subsequently provided to us in December 1994.... We are concerned at the scale of the reductions in the defence medical services, hitherto concealed — whether deliberately or

inadvertantly — from public and parliamentary scrutiny." The full Defence Committee Report is worth studying as well as DCS15. The Government, as would be expected — the official statement following the same pattern as those of the Crimean War and Boer War — denied all the criticisms made by the M.P.s in "The Government Reply to the Fifth Report from the Defence Committee Session 1994–95"(q.v. HMSO, 5th July 1995).

[7]Lieutenant Colonel George, Deputy Matron, Royal Hospital Haslar, said: "We have been told that what we used to think we had to do, look after serving men and their dependents, is no longer true. We are supposed to be down here training for what we would do in war."(personal communication 10th June, 1996).

[8]The reasons why QEMH was not considered for retention is given in a formal editorial by Colonel A.H.H. MacMillan, J R Army med.Corps,1996, Vol 142, 1, p 3–8.

Because there was confusion about the non-acceptance of the Queen Elizabeth Hospital, the following comment is of interest. "The editorial stipulated, virtually word for word, what DCS15 had said regarding the exclusion of QEMH as a core hospital, because of the negotiatons to sell that hospital to Greenwich Health Trust (GHT) were considered too advanced. This statement is a fallacy.

The original study of 1992 recommended one core hospital for each Service, (as already detailed above), including a completely rebuilt Cambridge Hospital for the Army. On this premise that the Cambridge was rebuilt then the MoD would consider selling the CMH site, and on this premise negotiations with GHT began in 1993 to site share the QEMH until March 1998 when the proposed rebuild of the Cambridge would be complete. These negotiations predominantly concerned shared service contracts and, whilst the ultimate aim for GHT was to buy the site, specific negotiations for this purpose had not progressed very far.

DCS15 was published in July 1994 recommending Haslar as the Tri-Service core hospital. The plans with GHT, therefore, had to be rapidly reorganised but it was not until Christmas 1994 that a specific date for closure (Sept 1995) was confirmed. Negotiations with GHT were slow, predominantly due to their prevarication over certain issues, and they finally signed the contract to purchase in August 1995. Presumably, therefore, it would have been perfectly straightforward to stop negotiations up to that point, and clearly the statement regarding the QEMH as the potential core hospital in DCS15 and the Corps Journal was at best premature. I hope this explains some or part of clear misconceptions on behalf of some people." I am grateful to Brigadier G.E. Ratcliffe for this information and point of view. He was the last

C.O. of QEMH and the first of the new RH Haslar when it became Tri-Service. In this difficult post he proved himself a most loyal and competent officer, who held the Tri-Service ethos well.

On the other hand, General Mayes argued well for the opposite point of view — that there were not enough troops nearby to sustain the QE. His preference was for a bigger and modernised Cambridge Hospital in Aldershot, as had been General Beale's. In General Beale's time, the glorious Royal Artillery Headquarters at Woolwich was itself under threat, allegedly because there were no soldiers stationed locally. Later, however, it was saved when the R.A. had a regiment restored to the barracks.

[9]The Conservative Government's policy of introducing "purchasers and providers", as it turned the NHS into a business-oriented organisation, had an impact for the single Service hospitals. The DMS Implementation Team's pamphlet of March 1995 alluded to this: "The NHS purchasers were not prepared to see NHS hospitals becoming non viable owing to competition from a large adjacent military hospital, especially one that might close in the event of another Gulf. As purchasers mainly decide where patients go, the planned large service hospitals would have been non viable." (DCS15, The Army Medical Services; The Changes – some questions and answers). It was estimated that local NHS services in the Frimley Park — Aldershot — Guildford area made financial gains of about £23M on the closure of the CMH. For details of the Conservative Government's original white paper on the internal NHS market, see Department of Health. *Working for patients*. HMSO, London:1989:26. The full package is ISBN 011 321219 4.

The Directorate of Medical Services, the Surgeon General's Department, had refused to allow the three Post-Graduate Deans to take part in choosing which District General Hospitals were to be selected as MDHUs. They were told medical input was not needed, as the question was "commercial in confidence." But other serving officers were in the MDHU selection team.

For a military and non-critical assessment of market testing in Germany, see: "Health Services Market Testing — the Experience of the Community Services Review Team in British Forces Germany", Lieutenant Colonel A.J. Leach et al, J R Army Med Corps 1996; **142**: 76–70.

[10]See, e.g., General Beale's letter to Air Marshall Sir John Willis, SG/10/23 (19/94) of 13th January, 1994, where he wrote: "I am of the opinion that we have already reached a minimal level of resource, or 'critical mass', as the result of our reorganisational programme…further reductions would, I consider, leave us even further short of providing the right level of medical support just when it was needed. I ask

whether Ministers would truly accept and be answerable to an inferior level of medical support for the Serviceman." He wrote a similar letter to the other Service Chiefs. See also his "Haul-Down Report" of August, 1994 on leaving his post. I am very grateful to Sir Peter for his information and his comments, and for agreeing to the format used.

Major-General A.I.G. Kennedy, CB, CBE, who was Director of the TA and later at the Royal College of Defence Studies, Belgrave Square, in London, gives a view from without the Medical Services. He believed that the earlier "Options for Change" made a disproportionately large reduction in logistic services "in order to retain a sharp end focus", as he put it. "Options set the pattern", he remembered; "it placed the Army's medical cover squarely on the TA (here he referred to the Gulf war) but the TA was not given enough corresponding financial support to function. So there was an erosion of capability." General Kennedy, speaking from the point of view of the General Staff, agreed that had there been serious casualties in the Gulf things would have been different: "logistic needs were stretched but not medical."

He was critical of the presentation of the medical case by the Regular Headquarters staff, certainly in the 1995–6 period, and recalled: "I can't say I was influenced by the TA Medical Advisers — I got the message from high quality C.O.s in the TA (senior consultants) that what was left of the Regulars was not enough to make a good service. In fact, I sought them out for advice." (personal communications, 1996, 1997).

[11]The opinion of General Sir Michael Wilkes, KCB, CBE, was similar to that of Major General Kennedy. "As Adjutant General I dealt very closely with the DGAMS of the day, Major General Mayes. He was very clear sighted and absolutely certain that some degree of re-organisation was necessary, quite apart from the wider requirements of the Study. However, the cards which we were dealt in the game against both the Defence Costs Study Team and the other Services' medical arms were very poor indeed…a long series of conference meetings first to decide what the Army Medical Services actually wanted and then, secondly, to present this in a way to the DCS team that our requirements were properly taken into account." General Wilkes went on to indicate the fragmentation of medical opinion between Commander Medical BAOR and Commander Medical Land HQ at Wilton, which meant that "it was extremely difficult for both the DGAMS and myself as Adjutant General to prevent individual Commanders-in-Chief taking the line which their medical advisers were proposing. As you would expect wily civil servants were quick to divide and rule in the interests of gaining their objective of a combined medical service."(personal

communications, 9th October and 19th December, 1997). I am extremely grateful to Sir Michael for his careful letters of comments and for his most valuable overview. Sir Michael retired early from his post as Adjutant General, and became Governor General of Jersey.

General Sir Thomas Boyd-Carpenter gave me useful material from his point of view. He asked if I would let him see what I would write from his personal communications (9th December, 1997, 14th January 1998 and 12th March, 1998), and I was happy to do so.

Mr Nicholas Soames, Minister of State for the Armed Forces, was written and asked for his views and opinion on similar points raised with Sir Michael Wilkes on 9th October, 1997, but did not reply to the letter. Mr Soames was a grandson of Sir Winston Churchill. He held office during the time of the implementation of DCS15.

I am grateful, finally, to Major General Short for his opinion (personal communication, 4th December, 1997) in the reporting of this 1994–95 period.

General Beale's answer to General Boyd-Carpenter's query was in a personal communication, 26th February, 1998.

[12]Lieutenant General Sir Peter Beale; Major Generals B.S. Mayes, J. T. Coull, G.O. Cowan, W.R. Short; Brigadier G. Ratcliffe, AMS; General Sir Martin Farndale, Master Gunner, 1995; AVM R.A. Riseley-Prichard; Group Captain A.J. Batchelor, RAF; Mrs C. Finlan and Miss A. Powell, BMA — personal communications.

See also the "Loose Minute" D/DMSIT/2/10/3 dated 21st March 1996, written by Commodore Harris to the Chief of Staff to the Adjutant General, with 14 copies. In this he argues characteristically and with obvious determination for the move of the Royal Defence Medical College "to Dolphin at the earliest opportunity compatible with the training requirements and arrangements necessary to effect the move." (in BMA AFC file, 1996).

[13]At the Armed Forces meeting on December 1996, the AFC chairman asked Admiral Revell, who unexpectedly had asked to attend, if he would see to it that the HQ Mess be continued, especially for the RAMC centenary. "Nothing to do with me", he answered. "You had better ask the Director General of the Army Medical Services."

[14]As well as in 1898 and 1904, when BMA argued and protested on behalf of the Army Medical Services, it was involved for over a decade during the prolonged arguments of the Warren Fisher Era ("Committee on the Medical Branches of the Defence Services Report, chairman Sir N.F. Warren Fisher, HMSO, Comd. 4394, 1933). During this period, BMA refused to advertise in its journal on behalf of the Defence Medical Services. In the 1950's BMA were involved with Sir

John Maude's "Report on the Shortages of medical officers in the Forces", in Lord Waverley's similar report, HMSO 1956. In the immediate post- National Service period, BMA strongly supported General Drummond's "New Deal." In 1967, BMA again refused to advertise on behalf of the DMS — see below, reference 18. All are reported in *BMJs* of the times.

[15]Brigadier Guy Ratcliffe's personal account of Commodore Harris' meeting at QEMH Woolwich to the staff of his plans for cuts and closures. AVM Riseley-Prichard and Group Captain A.J. Batchelor reported in the same vein about the equivalent meeting of the Commodore at RAF Wroughton (personal communications, 1996, 1997).

[16]See Defence Committee's Fifth Report, para 7. "The driving element behind the reductions in beds and personnel numbers from 169 to 112 in the assessed military requirement for 'bed-generating consultants': those consultant posts, primarily in surgery and in general medicine, required to train junior doctors to provide medical services in wartime, and which require patient throughput, measured as beds, to maintain their skills and those of the medical staff working with them. Some of that reduction is attributable to the desision taken in the DCS review that there was no *military* requirement for a number of specialties, such as paediatrics, obstetrics and gynaecology, dermatology, renal medicine (which the RAF had developed in an excellent unit) and nuclear medicine. In the distant event of an operational requirement for such specialties being a requirement,(sic) it is assessed that it could be met by Reservists. The requirement for other specialties such as psychiatry and ophthalmology has also been drastically reduced. (Major General Mayes thought that a maxillo-facial specialty was not necessary, but eventually realised his mistake and tried to reinstate it). "The new requirement is by contrast concentrated almost exclusively on surgery and general medicine." There was a proportionate fall in all medical, nursing, and technician numbers. Cuts in technicians fell most severely upon the laboratory and pharmacy grades. The medical pathologist virtually disappeared.

[17]DGAMS/7/2/D of 5 June 1995: "DGAMS is delighted to accept the invitation to address the Conference on the future of the Defence Medical Medical Services."

[18]In 1966, the 7th Report by the Kindersley Committee recommended pay increases for G.P.s in the NHS — as the pay of RAMC was related to that of NHS G.P.s, it was expected theirs would follow. But the Government refused to accept the analogue and made an arbitrary award. The rest of the Army was given a pay rise almost double that proposed for medical officers, and M.O.s were then subjected to a pay

freeze for 6 months. When they ultimately received it it was 15 months after the rest of the Army, even though backdated for 9 months.

It was this which led BMA to decide, in March 1967, to "black box" the RAMC and the smaller RAF and RN Medical Branches. By "black boxing" was meant that any job advertisement for the Service MOs, of all three Services, had a heavy black line of print around it in the *British Medical Journal*, with a warning notice that anyone wishing to apply for the job must first contact the BMA. Applicants were thus effectively warned against applying. The effect was considerable, and entrant numbers fell almost to zero.

[19] Mr Portillo's remark was a strange one. He had been briefed by the Surgeon General's staff (Admiral Revell's) in writing, *countering any arguments Cowan might advance.* (Major General G.O. Cowan, personal communication.)

[20] Major General Peter Craig, a Durham graduate who had been Director of Army Surgery before being promoted to DMS of Land Forces, was the only senior officer who had the courage to resign when he reached the opinion that DCS15 would cause very serious damage to the DMS. He was clear that he could not "try to sell these changes to my colleagues", as he wrote to Mr Keith Mans, M.P., chairman of the all-party Defence Committee, on 6th December 1996. He argued cogently against the changes.(letter in BMA file). Craig was angrily attacked by the unsympathetic Mr Soames and spitefully by fellow senior officers for his honesty and principle. He was "cut" by the DGAMS at the centenary dinner at the Connaught Rooms.

[21] Brigadier Bernard Rowe kept a full account of every meeting he attended, those present, the agenda and the conclusions. Its detail is of high value as history of his time as Adviser. I am grateful to him for allowing me to see it and for his detailed help.

The Revised TA(AMS) Orbat had 10 independent hospitals, now called "field", 7 field ambulances, 9 specialist field surgical teams, an airmobile surgical team, a burns team, and a head and neck surgical team. In addition, there was a "sponsored" field hospital, an ambulance train group, a field medical equipment depot, and a parachute squadron. All were volunteeer reservists, i.e. traditional territorials.

201(Northern) FH(V), 202(Midlands) FH(V), 203(Welsh) FH(V), 204(Northern Ireland) FH(V), 205(Scottish) FH(V), 207(Manchester) FH(V), 208(Liverpool) FH(V), 212(Yorkshire) FH(V), 243(The Wessex) FH(V), 256(London) FH(V) were Independent, and 306 FH was sponsored, having a lower training commitment.

The field ambulances, as noted in the text, were of higher and lower categories. 200(1st Home Counties), 222(East Midlands), 225(Highland), 251(Hull), 253(North Irish) and 254(City of Cambridge), were the territorial regions.

[22]"The Defence Agencies" were a form of privatisation of military medicine. Their launch was announced on 30th April, 1996, when the "Defence Secondary Care Agency" was formed. Secondary medical care, which meant in effect hospital care, had always been provided on a single Service basis, but would now be "provided by a Joint Service Agency under the control of a Chief Excecutive." Agencies would inevitably erect a barrier of so-called "ring-fencing" hospital staff and thus remove them from their respective Director General's control. This in turn weakened his influence over his own hospital doctors; the Chief Executive would employ them and not he. The civilian appointed was a Mr Ronald Smith, a former Chief Exectuve of a trust in Linconshire who had just resigned. Salaries of these Chiefs were of the order of £75,000 and Mr Smith's staff numbered 40 in total. There were also to be a Defence Dental Agency and a Medical Supplies Agency. The latter smacked of Crimea days. "Fundamental to the formation of all three Agencies is the continued provision of high quality medical support to the front line, in the most cost effective way, in both peace and war", said the MoD press release. And Admiral Revell stated, at the launch of the Agency, "These changes will fully meet our future needs, and contribute to the operational effectiveness, morale and well-being of the Armed Forces, and provide wider training opportunities for Service personnel."

The Agency staff establishment was very large. It consisted of the Chief Executive's Department, of Mr Smith, his personal secretary and a clerical assistant; the Directorate of Plans and personnel, whose initial Director was Air Commodore I.A. McCoubrey, his personal secretary, with staff officers for Establishment, Contingency planning, and Personnel, a military personnel administrator plus three civilian assistants; a Medical Director, Brigadier P. Lynch, with personal secretary, a staff officer clinical and a staff officer medical co-ordination, with a clinical administrator.

There was a Director of Nursing Services, with personal secretary; a Deputy for Nursing Services with a Nursing staff officer.

Next was a Directorate of Corporate Development. It had a Director, secretary, assistant (a grade 7 civil servant), plus 3 hospital managers, a strategic planner, and two others. The Directorate of Finance and Market Intelligence was headed by a grade 5 civil servant Director, a deputy Director and four market Intelligence officers, with 2 information technology consultants. It had also a Director of Finance with six assistants and 22 secretaries.

Lastly there was a Registry, with three assistant officers.

"Each Service will continue to recruit to its own medical branch and will be responsible for issuing appointments and posting orders for personnel of their particular Service into, within and out of the Agency after agreement with the Chief Executive and for agreed duration. It is expected that uniformed staff will spend the major part of their career working within the Agency." (Hon Nicholas Soames, Minister of State, in a Parliamentary written answer, 30th April, 1996.)

Finally, the three large glossy booklets, DSCA Corporate Plan 1996, Framework Document 1996 and Launch Document, each with a forward by Mr Soames, are necessary reading. Of interest also is the large glossy 1996–97 Annual report of the Health Alliance, the German equivalent, styled "Care with Quality", published on 14th December, 1997. Its civilian chief executive, Mr Bob Wilcox, described his trust as "an excitingly new project that is at the leading edge of health care co-operation in Europe — and we have just begun! As well as delivering the non-operational health services required of us, we have, without exception, met the demands made for operational deployments of our uniformed health care professional staff." It was a novel way of describing the Corps.

For a strong opinion praising the new Defence agency, see letter by Brigdier P. Lynch, its Medical Director, in J R Army Med Corps, 1996; **142**: 86: "Now that we are here, it is clearer where we were, and I for one welcome the changes they bring. Consultants are going home late and tired, but fulfilled. What they need now, more than anything, is peace and stability."

Mr Smith resigned in the first week of April 1998. At the same time, the Review of DSCA, by Professors Sir Miles Irving and Sir Duncan Nichol, both of Manchester, and dated 25 February 1998, was made public. (In BMA file.)

[23]In BMA files. Dr Macara's letter: HOSP/AWM/CF/CB of 15 March 1996. It was also signed by Sir Norman Browse, Chairman Joint Consultants' Committee, Professor Sir Leslie Turnberg, President Royal College of Physicians of London, Dr L. Newman, President Royal College of General Practitioners, Sir Rodney Sweetnam, President Royal College of Surgeons of England, and Professor Sir Robert Shields President Royal College of Surgeons of Edinburgh. The Prime Minister's reply is dated 22 April 1996. "The Ministry of Defence are aware of your concerns ... and will ensure that your views are taken fully into account." See also the letter to BMA from Mr P.G. Schulte, Head of Defence Medical Services (Finance and Secretariat) D/SG(F&S2)4/106/14 (PGS 203/95).

[24]The House of Commons Defence Committee Report No 5 indicated problems in the payment of requisitioning NHS hospital facilities in the event of a war of any size and extent, such as the recent Gulf campaign. The cost of loss of medical care given previously by

CMH was very considerable. The Front Line First budget for the expansion of Haslar was stated in the original DCS paper to be £5.8M. But a written reply from MoD to Field Marshal Lord Bramhall in the House of Lords on 3rd May, 1995, revealed that even then the estimate had risen to £12M. This did not include the cost of 85 married quarters for which Commodore Harris and his fellow planners had failed to make allowance, or perhaps had not thought about.

[25]The RAMC departments were, in the old RAMC College establishment:

Military Surgery, Military Medicine, Military Psychiatry, Military Pathology and Military General Practice — all joint chairs with the appropriate Royal College, the Parkes Chair of Preventive Medicine, and Entomology, Dental Science, Medical Illustration, and finally, the library. All had rôles within the College for teaching to serving officers, Regular and Territorial, specialist and non-specialist, and to civilians on military topics. Research, often in association with Porton, was carried out. Those in the departments of medicine and psychiatry and dentistry had clinical duties, and the pathology department its own specialist laboratory work. Latterly military surgery had no clinical commitment, but with 20 BATLS (Battlefield Trauma Life Support) week-end courses in a year, was well occupied. It shared the capacity to undertake research. There was a Research Exectuve which vetted projects on ethical, financial, and military grounds. Supervision was by the College Council which met quarterly, and was chaired by the Commandant, a Major General.

Millbank College was closed on authority of Mr Nicholas Soames, in D/Min(AF)\MS\211 dated 18 October 1996, and the letter to staff signed by Lieutenant Colonel F.S. Tredgett, the then Administrative Commandant. Closure was completed by August 1997. The last PGMO course for RAMC took place in July 1997. While RAF officers had done their initial professional training at Millbank, no RN entrants had done so. These remained at Portsmouth, and the Millbank staff had to travel there to lecture to them.

[26]I am grateful to General Sir Peter Beale for emphasising this fact in discussion.

It has to be remembered that Bosnia was not the only site of bitter civil war. "Rwanda 1994: A Study of Medical Support in Military Humanitarian Operations" by Lieutenant Colonel A. Hawley OBE, MB, RAMC, in J R Army Med Corps 1997; **143**: 75–82, describes the deployment of the British contingent there. The same edition has an article on mental health problems in Bosnia: D.A. Winfield, Squadron Leader RAF and Sgt P. Lafferty, mental nurse, ibid, p 103–106.

[27]In Spring 1955 a Major Royal Artillery did the commanding officers' course for Regulars and TA at Larkhill, and when asked by the

writer if his course had had a period of instruction on the Medical Services, replied that it had not. This fact was stressed at a symposium in the Royal Society of Medicine in the sumer that year, and the remark directed carefully by the speaker toward the S.G, Admiral Revell, who was present. In 1996, a TA female medical officer consultant cardiologist, attending a similar commanding officers' course, when asked the same question by the writer, gave the same reply. *There had not been a single period of instruction on the Medical Service.*

[28]Major training centres were used throughout the country as assembly points for TA *en route* to Bosnia — after Catterick came Winchester, Pirbright, Grantham, Brecon, Bovington (not in that order): mobilisation proceeded against a set programme. TA were demobilised at different centres from those they had left from, and this led to problems at times. Even by early 1998, although it had been agreed that a fixed Moblisation Centre was essential, especially to meeet the new rôles and tasks the TA would be doing in the future, the site had not been finally decided.

[29]I am grateful to Major Weir, Colonel Staunton, Captain Emmerton, Corporal Caithness, and 2/Lieutenant Foster, for their help when I spoke to them. They corrected Colonel Macmillan's account, which did not admit difficulties — a very typical "club history". I thanked Colonel Macmillan for his written summary. The article by Mr Clark appeared in the BMA "News Review" of September and October, 1997, pp 42–43 and 28–29 respectively.

[30]Reserve Forces Bill 112, 51/4 March 1996: "An Act to make provision with respect to the reserve forces of the Crown and persons liable to be recalled from permanent service"…received from the Lords 23rd April, 1996." The Standing Committee A debates in the House of Lords on 16th and 23rd April, and the New Clause 1 debate in the House of Commons on 20th May, are of particular interest. They introduce certain M.P.s who took an important part in the debates of January 1997. Of especial interest also is the report of the Reserve Forces Bill team, "Safeguards for reservists and their employers: a consultation document on schemes for exempting reservists from call-out and recall and for financial assistance for reservists and their employers", October 1996, the consultation document. BMA were closely associated; see letter from Sir Alexander Graham, NELC Chairman to chairman BMA AFC, of 25th October 1996(BMA AFC file). The House of Lords debate of 22 April 1998, "Strategic Defence Review and The Reserve Forces" is important reading at a later date, as is the House of Commons debate of 18 May. Both contain strong criticism of DCS 15.

[31]There were a number of instances of officers who turned down the prospect of becoming Director General over the years; there were two in this last part of the century.

[32]I am grateful to Major General Brian Mayes, CB, QHS, FRCS, for his full and frank discussion, and for his information, during his term of office as Director General.

[33]It has to be recorded that outside civilian academics at the highest level were also critical of the failure of certain senior DMS officers to understand the position of academic medicine. Dr W. McRae, President of the Association of Anaesthetists, consultant to the RAF, and later President of the Royal College, was extremely so. In his view, certain senior medical officers "were totally ignorant of the nature of an academic department's working." (personal communications, 1996).

[34]On 1st August 1996, a Consultation Document, "The Future Use of the Defence Estate at HMS Dolphin" was issued, *not by the Medical Services, but by Director of Naval Plans.* The arguments for closing Millbank and transferring the Royal Medical Defence College were hidden within this document. Detailed costings and alternatives were in annexes. Of interest are the minute D/RP (Navy) 721/6, copy to 724/1/15 of 15 March 1995, and D/SG(F&S) 4/106/14/1 of 20 March 1995, which weight the RDMC costs to strengthen the argument for closure. On Mr Walker's information the decision to close the College had already been taken when the discussion document was issued(Mr W. Walker M.P., personal communications). See also Mr Soames' letter to Mr Walker D/MIN (AF) NS/2/1/1 dated 18 October 1996, sent after representations by the AFC chairman. The letter gave the impression that the decision had only been taken after the consultation period was over and "no new evidence had emerged." (In BMA AFC file). Also the letter D/MIN (AF) /NS/2/1 from Mr Ben Palmer, assistant PPS to Mr Soames to General Cowan of 11 February 1997. Many of the contentions advanced in that letter were weak, and were proved so with the passage of time.

[35]Defence Committee Third Report, Defence Medical Services, together with Proceedings of the Committee relating to the Report, Minutes of Evidence and Memoranda, ordered by the House of Commons to be printed 19 February 1997. This is essential reading, in particular the questioning (minutes of Evidence) of Admiral Revell the Surgeon General, Air Marshal Peter Squire, DFC, the Deputy Chief of the Defence Staff, and Mr David Reynolds, civil servant, by Mr Keith Mans and other Members of Parliament on Wednesday 4 December, 1996. The reader will reach his or her own conclusions. Of even greater interest in many respects are the details of the debate in the House of Lords "Defence Medical Services" on Thursday 6 February 1997 pages1760–1762, and "Armed Forces: Medical Provision" on 5 March 1997, pages 1938–1960. BMA evidence was

freely quoted. Answers by Government Ministers were standard: "I do not believe the situation is quite as serious as my noble friend makes out."... by Lord Henley. For questions relating to the Defence Secondary Care Agency, see the written answer to Baroness Park on 24 February 1996. The cost of putting the structure in place was, for the financial year 1995–96, £3.36M. Of this total, £2.84M was spent on setting up the computer systems necessary for the running of the Agency and and in particular for the production of agency accounts on a commercial basis, and on establishing and equipping the agency headquarters. The balance of £0.52M covered staff costs.

Key paragraphs are 51: "We can, however, only report to the House our firm view that the state of morale at all levels of the Defence Medical Services is lower than we have ever encountered in the armed forces. This is in contrast to our impression that morale was high among the staff of the Territorial Army Field Hospital (256 London) we visited." Also 53: "We conclude that staff shortages in the DMS are so serious that it is not clear whether it will recover. It is possible that the scaling down of the DMS has been effected by MoD in such a way as to allow a major and potentially critical staff shortage to develop."

For an example of the general alarm felt in the Army, see "The Officer", July/August 1996: "Fears grow over hospital closures" and the reply by the S.G., "Medical services will continue to be first-class."

[36]Admiral Revell was awarded an Honorary MD degree from his own university, Birmingham, in the summer of 1996. In the oration, he was warmly praised: "...he defines his duty as protecting the people who protect us, from fear, in an age when wars are no longer global, but civil. See how he deals with problems. Anyone who saw Admiral Revell on television, interviewing a Commons' Select Committee on the so-called Gulf War Syndrome, may ask where he acquired such skills, not just forensic, but of public debate?...he has plenty to do in retirement: to start with, he is road manager for Winchester Cathedral Choir." Dr Ben Davis wrote: "I knew him very well when he was a student, as I was at the time Assistant Dean and Senior Tutor to the Faculty of Medcine. A most charming man I have a great regard for him. He graduated here in 1957."

[37]After the Gulf campaign, service persons began to complain of symptoms which they claimed were the result of immunisations, various prophylactic measures against chemical agents, exposure to pesticides, pollution from oil well fires, and others. At first these were regarded with doubt, but in the USA, where litigation was the universal rule after the slightest mishap, a scientific investigation was begun. On 20th February, 1996, the BMJ reported that the British MoD had agreed to fund research into complaints by members of its

Forces. (Vol 312, 332–333). The investigations continued, with the DMS Directorate declining to accept the severity of the complaints. In a leader on 25th January, 1997, BMA went over the information to date, after specific articles the previous two weeks, that on the 11th about research projects, and that on the 18th on main research findings. On May 13th, 1997, *The Times* carried a full-page feature: "Ex-soldiers insist military chiefs lied over Gulf War chemical blitz.... Minister (Mr Soames) promises fresh start in effort to uncover the truth."

After allegations that the Surgeon General had done nothing in the hope that the problem would go away, and there was criticism by Sir Richard Mottram, one of the departmental officials, the tabloid newspapers ran headlines such as "Top Forces Doc escapes Gulf syndrome row" in *News of the World*, 2nd March, 1997.

The question of the syndrome remains under examination at the date of publication.

[38]Personal communications, 1995–96.

[39]Dr Armstrong wrote on 21 March 1997 to his Chairman with copy to the AFC applauding the facilities at Haslar. "Those who cling to the belief that Service doctors would be best served by retaining Millbank cannot I believe have visited HMS *Dolphin*. The accommodation is extensive and modern, support facilities first-class, and the teaching facilities when fully taken over from the Submarine Training School will be very extensive.... I believe that if we do not change our attitude we run a very severe risk of losing all credibility among senior staff and possibly of losing the very real privilege of being the only trade union recognised within the armed services." He had become the mouthpiece of the Naval lobby.

[40]"A New Deal for the Defence Medical Services" BMA AFC file, July 1997.

[41]"Independent Review of the Armed Forces' Manpower, Career and Remuneration Structures, Managing People in Tomorrow's Armed Forces", (Sir) Michael Bett, CBE, HMSO, 31st March 1995.

[42]In BMA archive.

[43]Full details of BMA/AFC/DGAMS personal assistant's correspondence, and of AFC chairman's with Major-General J. T. Coull, in BMA Archive.

[44]Major General G. O. Cowan had been asked, when a more junior officer, if he was willing to transfer to the administration stream, with a view to promotion to highest rank. He had refused, as he wished to continue to practise medicine. He was asked by Major General Mayes, in 1996, if he would accept nomination to succeed him as DGAMS. After careful thought he again refused; in his own words, "because he was unhappy with the outcomes likely from DCS15, particularly in

respect of the College and secondly because he felt that at that particular juncture a colleague with more field and command experience would be more appropriate in the post". Brigadier Short was then appointed *en dépis d'un autre*.

At the beginning of the centenary year, the events scheduled to take place were, as always, in the "Blue book" which all subscribers to the Corps Mess Fund receive. General Cowan telephoned the Regimental Secretary, Colonel Banks, requesting a ticket for the centenary reception in Millbank that summer. To his surprise, he was told "Sorry, this invitation is in the gift of the DGAMS." *He never received an invitation.* This omission was a strange one for the most recent Commandant at Millbank, and the most outstanding physician of the period, respected amongst medical academia at the highest level, and known as a gentleman of complete integrity. After he retired he became Postgraduate Dean North East Thames, and later again, was appointed to the prestigious position of Chairman and Medical Director of the Joint Committee on the Higher Medical Training of the Federation of Royal Colleges of Physicians of the United Kingdom (personal communications; other details in BMA archive).

[45]Details in BMA archive.

[46]For proposed TA alterations, see Defence Medical Services: A Strategy for the Future. "Modern and effective medical support is a fundamental part of Britain's military capabilities. Our Armed Forces must have the best medical support we can provide. This was an important theme of the Strategic Defence Review... But providing the right medical support is not simply a matter of extra equipment. Since July, a great deal of work has been undertaken on the personnel and organisational problems which have bedevilled the Defence Medical Services (DMS) in recent years." George Robertson, Ministry of Defence, December 1998.

For details of proposed new units, see e.g. LAND/G3 Res 445/46/ 4 (G3 TA) dated 16 November 1998, Ministry of Defence Army Medical Directorate 1b, D/AMD/22/91 dated 10 December 1998.

[47]Full 12-page booklet includes Mr Robertson's introduction given above. It covered changes for medical personnel, and "in the medical contribution to operations". Changes in "structure and management" (p. 6–7) included a series of "new" organisational structures, as new High Level Management Board, a stronger role for the single Service Medical Directors, giving them greater budgetary authority — to restore some of what had certainly been lost following DCS15, and the statement that "the Medical Directors Generals will report to the Surgeon General, giving him for the *first time an oversight of all the Defence Medical Services*" (author's italics). This

last seemed a surprising inclusion, since it was widely believed to have always happened before!

[48]In September 1999, *The British Society for the History of Medicine Newsletter* recorded: "Of unusual interest is the fact that Major-General W. R. Short, the previous Director General of the Army Medical Services, peremptorily informed the author in September 1997, through his clerk (in fact, his personal assistant, Major Mannering; letters in BMA archive) that he must conform in style and content to a trio of his nominees. In early 1998, the General, again through his clerk, and without the courtesy of a personal communication, threatened that unless the author agreed to write the history as he directed, no money would be forthcoming from RAMC sources.

"This insult to one of the well known British medical historians caused him to seek help elsewhere. Wide support was gladly given, from all the most senior medical historians, and the final production was undoubtedly of much higher quality than had the military been responsible for its production and printing."

"General Short's Army Medical Directorate have refused to stock or to sell this major work. It has been pointedly ignored by the *RAMC Journal* or by the *AMS magazine.* In editorials by Generals Shaw and Short in the January edition of the Corps Journal celebrating the Corps' centenary, it was ignored. Dr Blair has not received a word of thanks from the AMS, nor have he and his colleague in the preparation of the companion picture book, received any word of thanks for that important work either." (I am grateful for permission of Dr John Ford, then president of the BSHM, to include this comment of the British Society.)

[49]For this assessment, I am grateful to views from Sir Alexander Macara, Dr J. A. R. Lawson, OBE, PPRCGP, Professor J. Forfar MC; Admiral Sir Godfrey Milton-Thompson, Air Marshal Sir John Baird; Major Generals J. Matheson, D. Macphie, G. O. Cowan, P. Craig, A. C. Ticehurst; Brigadiers M. Newell and J. R. Brown; Group Captain J. Amy, Colonels R. Anderson, H. Griffiths, T. C. Dow, J. Hamilton, R. L. Steele (Erskine Hospital); Lieutenant Colonel E. W. White RRC, TD, Major G. Poole, Captain H. Wilson, TD, Dr Campbell Mackenzie RD, Dr Michael Allen, Dr J. A. Wilson; members of the Haywood Club met in May, 1999; Mr R. Arnott, BSHM. I am also grateful for correspondence made available by Douglas Grant, Scottish Academic Press, detailing the General's refusal to make the history available to newly commissioned officers and cadets.

[50]Major General Short was given the Fellowship of the RCPS of Glasgow *ad eundem* on 24th November 1998. He was a Glasgow medical graduate of 1967. His recommendation by Dr R. D. Stevenson,

Professor W. Stewart Hillis, Dr R. G. Jones (brigadier and TA adviser to the general), and Mr R. Quinn, referred to his career as "being mainly involved in instruction and operational planning", and continued: "As Director General of the Army Medical Services he has highlighted the significant and unacceptable deficiencies in Defence Medical Services available to Operations which resulted from the Defence spending cuts in 1993. Following the House of Lords debate on the Defence Medical Services in January 1997 the Secretary of State ordered a complete reappraisal of medical support to Operations, which is nearing completion, and which is expected to redress the balance."

"Under his Directorship and leadership, recruiting and morale within the Army Medical Services have improved dramatically. He is dedicated to ensuring that the current political requirements to provide peacetime standards of medical care in the field for servicemen is achieved, even under conditions of war."

"He would deem it an honour to be elected to the Fellowship qua Physician *ad eundem* of the College, in this centenary year of the Royal Army Medical Corps."

(I am grateful to Mr Colin MacKay, President, Royal College of Physicians and Surgeons of Glasgow, for permission to quote this recommendation, and for his most useful comments.)

[51]Air Marshal Sir John Baird confirmed that the denial of the title and badge had never been discussed or ordered at Surgeon General level. He surmised that "it must have been a decision taken within the DGAMS structure" (personal communication, 1st June 2001).

Subsequent correspondence with Sir Malcolm Rifkind and Mr Jonathan Aitken, and with Lieutenant General Sir Thomas Boyd-Carpenter, in 2000, amplified previous accounts. Sir Malcolm "entirely accepted responsibility for the decisions taken in early 1990" in a personal letter of 25th July 2000. That he was prepared to do so willingly and frankly is to his enormous credit: few politicians show such courage and honesty. His further comment deserves inclusion: "As I recollect it, however, the advice I received from the Chiefs of Staff was that while the Defence Medical Services were unhappy with the proposed restructuring of their service, the Chiefs were satisfied that this could be done in an acceptable way, without damage to the operational needs of the Armed Forces… As the Chiefs of Staff were very willing to advise against reductions of resources in many areas, there was little need or expectation that Ministers would seek to second-guess them in this particular sector, unless there was some over-riding consideration that had not been made available to them." But Sir Malcolm, sadly, remained unwilling to answer the question "why were there no doctors on the Hale Committee?" — the committee which had decided what reductions were to be made (personal communication, 4th January 2001).

The account of Mr Aitken, who was then Mr Rifkind's Secretary of State, confirms the previous opinion all too well. It, like Sir Malcolm's letter above, and General Boyd-Carpenter's below, are essential inclusions. Mr Aitken, in answer to my question how well the medical case was made, wrote as follows: "In answer to your specific question I think it is fair to say that I was unimpressed and underbewhelmed, (sic) as the responsible Minister, by the second rate nature of the papers and presentations put forward by those responsible for fighting the Defence Medical Services corner in this review... the medical case had been poorly put forward. Indeed Defence Medical Services were almost the only part of the Ministry of Defence not to engage wholeheartedly in the cut and thrust of debate over 'Front Line First'. Had the medical case been better put I have little doubt that the Ministerial Team would have listened and acted more sympathetically than we did" (personal communication 5th August 2000).

There was however another point of view, and I have to thank Sir John Baird for pointing out that Mr Aitken's view did not take notice of the effect the Hale Report had had upon the senior medical staff. "The Hale Report (DCS15)" recalled Sir John, "was devastating to us — and we (the senior Medical Service officers) did not agree with most of it. I was Principal Medical Officer at Headquarters Strike Command at the time, and none of my views was taken."

"It should be remembered that there was not a single medical person on the Hale team — and he himself was a retired civil service man who had worked most of his life in the NHS. The Report itself was hailed by civil servants and politicians as the perfect DCS paper — and should be the benchmark for other DCS studies. It was therefore probably not given much debate by (Service) Chiefs and Ministers. In fact, as we all knew, it was seriously flawed, and the subsequent implementation of its proposals led to the damage to the Defence Medical Services — as we had predicted" (personal communication, 6th December 2000). The British Medical Association agreed entirely with this view; their pleas were also totally ignored at the time, as their predecessors pleas had been ignored a century earlier.

Thus while the politicians and the most senior General Staff were critical of the doctors, the doctors in turn felt that they could have had more sympathy from these very critics. Past history had shown that such complaints had good reason to be true. General Boyd-Carpenter, asked if he felt sympathetic to the Surgeon General and his assistants, did not reply directly but stated that "because of changes in the NHS, with the introduction of the internal market 'and its lineal descendants', and in the accreditation arrangements sponsored by the Royal Colleges, and partly by the reduction in overseas garrisons, the DMS had to be re-structured". The response to his point about the accreditation changes is that the arrangements then in place were as good as could be made; further, the three Service post-graduate deans were not consulted. The other points have been noted already. I asked him, in my reply, if he had any knowledge of the BMA's activity and attempts to influence the effects of DCS15 and said that BMA were certainly sure that the near extinction of the specialist pool by the summer of AD 2000 was a direct result of the changes made in his period of office. He did *not answer.* Asked again if he had sympathy for the SG of the day and his medical supporting team, and whether there had not been a case for trying to look into their case farther, *he did not reply* (correspondence in August 2000 in BMA file). The refusal of Mr Soames to answer questions had already been recorded: he was regarded by senior medicals as unsympathetic also. Nor did Sir Malcolm Rifkind, when asked directly by me if he did not think it odd that there was no doctor in the Hale Committee, *make any reply* (correspondence in August 2000). In total contrast, a letter received on 21/12/00 from Mr Iain Duncan-Smith, then Shadow Minister of Defence, insisted upon a future Conservative Government's commitment to listen closely to advice from BMA (personal communication).

[52]Political Correctness was the new righteousness of post-Protestant modernism. The guardians of PC — perhaps better called Pernicious Corruption — held that nothing should be written or even spoken which could be construed as offending the susceptibilities of someone else somewhere, indeed, of offending their every passing whim. "Whatever suits me must be allowed." These guardians were sometimes referred to as the "Liberal Elite". They were allowed and encouraged by New Labour to order speech and thought in a society where élitism was otherwise considered disgraceful and to be removed as soon as possible — in fact, Politically Incorrect. See e.g., *The Daily Telegraph*, 21st December 2000, with the result of five years' research on snowmen by Ms Tricia Cusack at Birmingham, reported in the cultural history periodical *New Formations*. See also, *Politically Correct phrase book* by Nigel Rees, Bloomsbury Publishing, 1993, and even more relentless but entertaining, *The Official Politically Correct Dictionary and Handbook* by Henry Beard and Christopher Cerf, Grafton (Harper Collins Press), 1992, ISBN 0 586 21726 6.

[53]For present No. 47 (Thucydides). *History of the Peloponnesian War*, translation by Rex Warner, Penguin Books, London, 1954, revised introduction 1972, 1, 22, pp. 11, 10 of introduction.

Abbreviations

ADMS	Assistant Director of Medical Services
ADS	Advanced Dressing Station
AER	Army Emergency Reserve
AFPRB	Armed Forces Pay Review Body
AFV	Armoured Fighting Vehicle
amb	ambulance
AMD	Army Medical Department
AMED	Advanced Medical Equipment Depot
AMTU	Advanced Malarial Treatment Unit
AMU	Anti-malarial unit
APC	Armoured Personnel Carrier
ARRC	Allied Command Europe Rapid Reaction Corps
ASC	Advanced Surgical Centre
BAOR	British Army of the Rhine
BC	Bearer Company
BGH	British General Hospital
BMA	British Medical Association
BMH	British Military Hospital
BMJ	British Medical Journal
BRCS	British Red Cross Society
BSM	Battery Sergeant Major
BTU	Base/Blood Transfusion Unit
BW	Biological Warfare
CCP	Casualty Collecting Post
CCS	Casualty Clearing Station

CH ....Clearing Hospital

C.I.G.S. .... Chief of the Imperial General Staff

CMP.. Civilian Medical Practitioner

Comd Med .... Commander Medical

COLPRO .... Collective Protection

CP .... Collecting Point/Command Post

CSSG .... Combat Service Support Group

D(A)DAH .... Deputy (Assistant) Director of Army Health

D(A)DMS ... Deputy (Assistant) Director of Medical Services

DAH ....Director Army Health

D.A.H. .... Disordered Action of the Heart

DGAMS, (D.G.) .... Director General Army Medical Services

DMS .... Director of Medical Services

DMSIT ...... Defence Medical Services Implementation Team

DS .... Dressing Station/Directing Staff

DSCA .... Defence Secondary Care Agency

DZ ....Dropping Zone

en .... Enemy

evac... Evacuation, Evacuate

Fd Amb .... Field Ambulance

FDS ....Field Dressing Station

FH .... Field Hospital

FMA .... Forward Maintenance Area

FMED .... Field Medical Equipment Depot

FMTU .... Forward Malarial Treatment Unit

FRIC .... Fellow of the Royal Institute of Chemistry

FRS .... Fellow of the Royal Society

FST .... Field Surgical Team

FSU ....Field Surgical Unit

FTU .... Field Transfusion Unit

GD ....General Duties

GDMO .... General Duties Medical Officer

G.O.C. .... General Officer Commanding

GSW .... Gunshot Wound
hel .... Helicopter
hosp .... Hospital
IMFTU .... Indian Malarial Forward Treatment Unit
IMS .... Indian Medical Service
KSLI .... King's Shropshire Light Infantry
LCI .... Landing Craft Infantry
LCT .... Landing Craft Tank
LofC .... Lines of Communication
LSI .... Landing Ship Infantry
LST .... Landing Ship Tank
MAC .... Motor Ambulance Company
MDHU .... Ministry of Defence Hospital Unit
MDS .... Main Dressing Station
MRC .... Medical Research Council
MST .... Medical Support Troop
NBC .... Nuclear Biological & Chemical
NSDO, NSMO ..... National Service Dental, Medical Officer
NSM .... National Service Man
NST .... Neurosurgical Team
NYD(N) .... Not Yet Diagnosed (Nervous)
OMO .... Orderly Medical Officer
ORBAT .... Order of Battle
OTC... Officers Training Corps
PFA .... Parachute Field Ambulance
PMO .... Principal Medical Officer
POP .... Plaster of Paris
QM .... Quartermaster
Q.M.G. .... Quartermaster General
QAIMNS .... Queen Alexandra's Imperial Military Nursing Service
QARANC..... Queen Alexandra's Royal Army Nursing Corps
QHP, QHS .... Queen's Honorary Physician, Surgeon

RAMC .... Royal Army Medical Corps

RAP .... Regimental Aid Post

RASC .... Royal Army Service Corps

RCGP .... Royal College of General Practitioners

RCT .... Royal Corps of Transport

RDMC .... Royal Defence Medical College

RE .... Royal Engineers

REME .... Royal Electrical and Mechanical Engineers

RFC... Royal Flying Corps

RLC.. Royal Logistic Corps

RMO .... Regimental Medical Officer

RMP .... Royal Military Police

RNR .... Royal Naval Reserve

Surg-gen .... Surgeon General (early)

S.G. .... Surgeon General (recent)

TA (AMS) .... Territorial Army (Army Medical Service)

TAVR...................... Territorial and Army Volunteer Reserve

TAVRA .... Territorial Auxiliary and Volunteer Reserve Association

TF .... Territorial Force

TE .... Training Establishment (Depot and)

WOI .... Warrant Officer (class 1) (R.S.M.)

Index

Refs

A

B